12

13

14

16

15

17

THE FIRESIDE BOOK OF C♣A♦R♥D♠S

EDITED BY
OSWALD JACOBY
AND
ALBERT MOREHEAD

SIMON AND SCHUSTER, NEW YORK, 1957

PUBLISHED BY SIMON AND SCHUSTER, INC.
ROCKEFELLER CENTER, 630 FIFTH AVENUE, NEW YORK 20, N. Y.

FIRST PRINTING

LIBRARY OF CONGRESS CATALOG CARD NUMBER: 57-12410
MANUFACTURED IN THE UNITED STATES OF AMERICA
BY H. WOLFF BOOK MFG. CO., INC., NEW YORK

ACKNOWLEDGMENTS

THE EDITORS gratefully acknowledge the copyrights of the following material reprinted in this book and thank the copyright owners for their permission to reprint.

"Bee" design and brand playing cards, a ® registered trademark of the United States Playing Card Company. Old playing cards on the end pages from the Card Museum of the United States Playing Card Company, Cincinnati, Ohio; Catherine Perry Hargrave, curator emeritus.

"The Origin of Gaming and Cards," by Catherine Perry Hargrave, © 1930, 1957 by the United States Playing Card Company.

"How Playing Cards are Made," © 1945 by The New York Times Company, from *The New York Times Magazine.*

"Coffeehousing," by Samuel Fry, Jr. and "Kibitzers Do Not Live Long," by Lee Hazen, © 1949 by The Hearst Corp., and "I'm Not Superstitious—But," by Richard L. Frey, © 1950 by The Hearst Corp., courtesy of *Cosmopolitan* and the authors.

"The Tarot," by Geoffrey Mott-Smith, © 1952 by Albert H. Morehead, and "Faro Bank," by R. F. Foster, © 1937 by Albert H. Morehead.

Excerpts from WAR AND PEACE, by Leo Tolstoy, and from THE BROTHERS KARAMAZOV, by Feodor Dostoevski, translations © 1949 by Alexandra Kropotkin.

"It Beats the Devil," by Sidney S. Lenz, from *Liberty* Magazine, 1925, © 1953 (renewal) by Sidney S. Lenz.

Excerpts from THE STRANGE LIVES OF ONE MAN, by Ely Culbertson, © 1940 by The John C. Winston Company, reprinted by permission of the Estate of Ely Culbertson.

"On Certain Fine Points of the Game," by George S. Kaufman; "The Bennett Murder Case," by Thomas O'Neil, Ely Culbertson, and Sidney S. Lenz; "Character," by Stephen White; "Jackie's Legal Joist," by A. Moyse, Jr.; "Introducing Aunt Mathilda" and "How to Build Card Houses," by Geoffrey Mott-Smith; "Bridge Tournament," by W. B. France; "Why I Gave Up Bridge," by Ethel Jacobson; all from *The Bridge World and Games Digest magazines,* © 1933-1947 by Alphonse Moyse, Jr. Reprinted by permission.

"Peeking Through the Screen," by Robert Neville, © 1933 by The New York *Herald Tribune.* By permission of the author and copyright owner.

"Sims Team Saved by von Zedtwitz," by Walter Lister, © 1932 by The New York *Post.* By permission of the author and copyright owner.

"The Case of Mr. X," by William E. McKenney, © 1938 by William E. McKenney. By permission of Marguerite McKenney.

"The Case Ace," by Octavus Roy Cohen, from *The Saturday Evening Post,* © 1926 by the Curtis Publishing Co., 1954 by Octavus Roy Cohen.

Excerpts from THE BRIDGE FIEND, by Frank Crowninshield, © 1909, 1937 by Frank Crowninshield. Courtesy of Mrs. Francis Thayer.

Excerpt from NIGHTMARE ALLEY, by William Lindsay Gresham, © 1946, 1948 by William Lindsay Gresham. Reprinted with permission of Rinehart & Company, Inc., and The New American Library of World Literature, Inc. (Signet Books).

"Adventure of the Empty House," by Sir Arthur Conan Doyle. Reprinted by permission of the Estate of Sir Arthur Conan Doyle.

"The Portrait of a Gentleman," from COSMOPOLITANS by W. Somerset Maugham, © 1925 by W. Somerset Maugham. Reprinted by permission of Doubleday & Company, Inc., New York, and of A. P. Watt & Son, London.

"My Lady Love, My Dove," by Roald Dahl, © 1952, 1953 by Roald Dahl. Originally published in *The New Yorker.* Reprinted from SOMEONE LIKE YOU by permission of Alfred A. Knopf, Inc.

"Some Kinds of Bad Luck," by C. S. Forester, © 1943 by The Curtis Publishing Company. Reprinted by permis-

To

JACK GOODMAN

whose love of card games was exceeded only by his genius as an editor and writer.

ACKNOWLEDGMENTS (continued)

sion of Harold Matson Company.

Excerpt from SUCKER'S PROGRESS, by Herbert Asbury, © 1938 by Dodd, Mead & Company. Reprinted by permission of Dodd, Mead & Company.

Excerpt from FROM HERE TO ETERNITY, by James Jones, © 1951 by James Jones. Reprinted by permission of Charles Scribner's Sons.

"Contract," by Ring Lardner, © 1929, 1957 by Ellis A. Lardner. Reprinted from ROUND UP, by Ring Lardner, with permission of Charles Scribner's Sons.

"Your Lead, Partner," by Ogden Nash, © 1956 by Ogden Nash. Reprinted from YOU CAN'T GET THERE FROM HERE, by Ogden Nash, with permission of Little, Brown & Co.

Excerpt from THE MAN WITH THE GOLDEN ARM, by Nelson Algren, © 1949 by Nelson Algren. Reprinted by permission of Doubleday & Company, Inc.

"The Mug's Game," from THE HAPPY HIGHWAYMAN, by Leslie Charteris, © 1939 by Leslie Charteris. Reprinted by permission of Doubleday & Company, Inc.

Excerpt from WILD BILL HICKOK, by Frank Jennings Wilbach, © 1952. Reprinted by permission of Doubleday & Co.

"Dummy, Dummy! Who's Dummy?" by E. J. Kahn, Jr., © 1941 by The New Yorker Magazine, Inc. Reprinted by permission of the author, E. J. Kahn, Jr.

Excerpt from THE VICIOUS CIRCLE: The Story of the Algonquin Round Table, by Margaret Case Harriman, © 1951 by Margaret Case Harriman. Reprinted by permission of Rinehart & Company, Inc.

"Cosmic Card Game," by Thomas Kyd, © 1951 by *The American Scholar.*

"The One-Hundred-Dollar Bill," from THE FASCINATING STRANGER AND OTHER STORIES, by Booth Tarkington, © 1923 by Booth Tarkington; 1951 by Susannah K. Tarkington. Reprinted with permission of Doubleday & Company, Inc.

Excerpt from THE AGE OF HATE, by George Fort Milton, © 1930 by Coward-McCann, Inc. Reprinted by permission of Coward-McCann, Inc.

Excerpt from THE GENTLEMAN, by Edison Marshall, © 1956 by Edison Marshall. Reprinted with permission of Farrar, Straus & Cudahy, Inc.

Excerpt from IN THE REIGN OF ROTHSTEIN, by Donald Henderson Clarke, © 1929 by The Vanguard Press, Inc. Reprinted with permission of The Vanguard Press, Inc.

Excerpts from THE PLEASURE WAS ALL MINE by Fred Schwed, Jr., © 1950, 1951 by Fred Schwed, Jr. Reprinted by permission of Simon and Schuster, Inc.

Excerpt from CARDANO, THE GAMBLING SCHOLAR, translated by Sydney Henry Gould, edited by Oystein Ore, © 1953 by Princeton University Press.

"High Bridge," by Sam Hellman, from *The Saturday Evening Post,* © (renewal) by Selma S. Hellman.

Excerpt from FORTUNE POKER, by George S. Coffin, © 1947 by David McKay Co., Inc., by permission of the author and publishers.

"Adventure of the Fallen Angels," by Percival Wilde. Reprinted with permission of Roger Wilde.

Excerpt from "How Truman Played Poker," by Merriman Smith, © 1945 by United Press, Inc. By permission of the author.

"Ballade" and "The Kibitzer," by Edgar A. Guest, © 1928, 1956 by Edgar A. Guest.

"Dealer's Choice," by Phyllis McGinley, from A SHORT WALK TO THE STATION, originally from The New Yorker, © 1946. By permission of Viking Press.

"Mr. Ely Culbertson" by E. V. Knox, from *Punch,* 1933. Reproduced by permission of *Punch.*

Excerpt from GAMESMANSHIP, by Stephen Potter, reprinted by permission of the author.

Use of the name "Mark Twain" by permission of Harper & Brothers.

Excerpt from PSYCHIC BIDDING by Dorothy Rice Sims, © 1932, by permission of The Vanguard Press, Inc.

Editors' Preface and Acknowledgments

OUR FIRST THANKS *must go to Charles Einstein, who so ably edited the FIRESIDE BOOK OF BASEBALL, one of our worthy predecessors in this series of anthologies, and who quite unselfishly suggested card games as another worthy subject.*

We have received the utmost co-operation from publishers, authors and copyright owners on both sides of the Atlantic, whom collectively we thank for the permissions detailed on earlier pages.

In making our selections we have given almost exclusive attention to English-language writings that have proved their appeal to American readers and to such foreign writings as have been translated, published and widely read in the United States and Canada. We do not doubt that other countries and languages provide an equally eligible literature of card games, but in too many cases both the games and the literature are unfamiliar to us. We have not found it necessary to omit anything we consider essential to the reading experience of the well-read American card-player.

Preceding each selection there is a commentary or explanation preamble, invariably printed in italics. This preamble expresses the joint opinion of the editors unless any part of it is set off and initialed (O.J. or A.H.M. as the case may be).

Every footnote is the comment of the editors jointly unless it is signed by someone else's name or initials.

OSWALD JACOBY
ALBERT MOREHEAD

Introduction

BY HOWARD DIETZ

THE ANTHOLOGY *is a form of cannibalism in which writers feed on other writers. When poets are not writing poetry they are preparing golden treasuries of verse. Mystery-story writers compress their favorite detective stories into one binding. Professional jesters edit volumes of jokes and anecdotes which are first aid to after-dinner speakers. There are omnibuses (or is it omnibi?) of novels, annual issues of the best plays, anthologies of everything. One day there may even be an anthology of anthologies, which will solve the problem of what books to take on a desert isle along with Marilyn Monroe.*

This book is about cards and not about how to play them. It is a potpourri of opinions, a collection of appreciations culled from many sources, primarily the masters of belles lettres, and from the occasional articles written by card experts whose lettres are not quite so belles. If you wish to read what Mark Twain, Bret Harte, Thackeray, and other heirs to posterity have said about Cribbage, Old Sledge, Écarté, and all the games of luck, there are pages to turn to.

Fortunately for Bridge addicts like me, games of the Whist family are served as a main course (Poker fanatics will find a comparable number of enticing dishes, it is only fair to point out). From the introductory to the "Murders in the Rue Morgue" you will be reminded that Edgar Allan Poe ranked Whist above chess in "its influence on what is termed the calculating power" and added that "beyond doubt there is nothing of a similar nature so tasking the faculty of analysis."

In Poe's day Whist was less "tasking" than the modern evolution of Whist into Contract Bridge, the invention of Harold Vanderbilt. Here at last, at least as far as I am concerned, is the perfect card game, limitless in its combinations, provocative in the problems to be solved by inferences of logic. Thousands of people all over the world are being diverted by the potentialities inherent in almost every deal. It is a habit-forming game, more difficult to give up than cigarettes. Marriages have been built with Bridge as a common bond. Divorces have resulted from partnership incompatibility, and murders have been committed in suburban homes far from the Rue Morgue but still close to the Fireside.

Bridge is, in fact, a way of life. No one who has studied the game, read the standard books on it, treats it with indifference. Most of us are hampered by our built-in temperament, which affects our judgment and makes us repeat our errors. We realize that Bridge is a scientific pastime that is concerned with making the most of our allotment of cards and not altogether with winning or losing. There are the life masters who place well in tournaments year after year. And there are the life slaves who invest their spare time in the game but never achieve greatness.

Is there such a thing as a born Bridge player? Let the question remain unanswered—but there are those who were born not *to be Bridge players. One time I attempted to instruct Moss Hart, the playwright. My rôle was similar to that of a golf pro who couldn't break ninety. I told Moss, in defending against a no-trump contract, it was common practice to lead the fourth from the longest suit. Moss was on lead against a contract of six no trump. He held the ace, king and two small clubs. Obediently he led the fourth best. I would venture to say he was not a born card-player.*

Experts invite the suspicion that card sense is a sixth sense. If that is so, then they are born. One can learn all the recognized safety plays, be conversant with all the systems, but still lack that instinct which makes for the right guess the right number of times. An expert player is one who can logically explain his mistakes, which he does in the post-mortems after the right play has had the wrong result. But, in the long run, the right play mathematically will be the winning one. Thus an expert card-player, like a ranking tennis player, is one who makes few errors. Proficiency is demanding, and Bridge players think Bridge and talk Bridge. Their reticence on other subjects is only exceeded by those who have retired from the world of reality, such as the silent Trappist monks. But, of course, Bridge experts can be made to talk. Play with one as a partner, slip up on a defense, and you will see what I mean.

In card circles it is considered a faux pas *to ask an expert whom he considers the best player: you should ask him who is the second best. If you are addressing your question to Oswald Jacoby you are not merely being tactful. Spanning a long career through the reigns of Ely Culbertson, Sidney Lenz and Hal Sims, Jacoby still holds his ground as the experts' expert—though younger players have emerged for consideration. By profession an insurance actuary, devoted to the continual study of the odds on life and death, he uses his actuarial equations in the field of cards, figuring the odds on life and death in the matter of squeeze plays, finesses and other gambits in every game of chance you can mention. He has minimized the element of chance in card games.*

Jacoby was born in Brooklyn in 1902 but is now settled in Dallas. His books on Poker, Gin Rummy, and Canasta, as well as on Bridge, are in popular demand. He conducts a daily column in the Scripps-Howard newspapers. A characteristic of his play is the speed with which he solves the key problem in a hand. His tempo gives his opponents little time to organize their defense in a situation that requires thought. His general demeanor at the table could be called untidy. He fingers his cards carelessly as if he were going to use them as a liniment. He does not arrange his cards into suits, but the position of each one is clearly in his mind. One time I saw him put the cards in his pocket and draw them out in turn without a glance and without an error. There is method in his sloppiness.

His partner in this anthology, Albert Morehead, has devoted more time to the literature of cards than to actual play. He abandoned tournaments some years ago, when he was one of the leading players. This was before master points or life masters had been thought of. He is best known as the Bridge Editor of The New York Times. *He also conducts the Master Solvers' Department for the* Bridge World, *a small but effective magazine that is read by advanced students of the game. Morehead has been described as the modern Hoyle and is considered the most reliable arbiter of technical disagreements between unhappy partners, of which you doubtless have a complete set. He was born in 1909 and an early choo-choo headed him north from Chattanooga. His career embraces more than sixty books on the subject of cards. This hearthside companion is his sixty-fourth.*

Playing as rarely as he does, but watching card games as often as he does, qualifies Morehead as a master kibitzer, one of that ubiquitous tribe discussed in this book by Lee Hazen. If you are stranded in a wilderness or lost in the Arctic waste, can't find a living soul, pull out your pack of cards (standard equipment for the explorer), start playing Solitaire, and hear someone whisper over your shoulder "Put the black jack on the red queen," you will be particularly pleased if the card-watcher turns out to be Al Morehead. He will enrich the hours with a history of great plays in that world of escape known as Contract Bridge.

If you have a passion for card games but are not disinterested in money, I would not advise your taking that slow boat to China in company with the compilers of this volume. You might find yourself a little short for the long journey home when the dawn comes up like thunder. In your desperate attempt to get even a dire fate may befall you, trapped in a port of difficult return, a derelict beachcomber combing the beach for a fourth.

Better off to curl up with a good book. This one.

HOWARD DIETZ

Montecatini Terme
Italy
1957

Contents

GIN RUMMY

THE GAMBLERS' GAMES

FARO

THE GREAT AMERICAN GAMES

SOLITAIRE

SIDELIGHTS ON CARDPLAYING

POEMS ABOUT CARD GAMES

CARDSHARPERS

CARD TRICKS

Illustrations

ENDPAPERS

KEY TO PLAYING CARDS SHOWN ON FRONT ENDPAPERS

[1, 2, 3, 4] Kwan p'ai, or Chinese money cards. These cards are from the suit of coins. The designs are derived from Chinese paper money and have remained substantially unchanged since the 10th century.

[5, 6, 7] Chinese domino cards, decorated with characters from an old legend, "The Story of the River's Banks."

[8, 9, 10, 11] Hindu playing cards. These are relatively modern, probably 18th century. They are the ace (10), king (8), queen (9) and knight (11) of the spade suit.

[12] Hand-colored card from a French pack of about the year 1500. This is one of the four knaves, which showed figures in chivalry: Lancelot, Hogier, Roland, Valéry.

[13, 14] Tarots from a French pack, very much reduced in size (see No. 16). Such cards may have been made at any time in the 14th to 17th centuries.

[15] A French card of about 1500. The suit sign of the sword was the precursor of spades in modern packs.

[16] One of a celebrated set of tarots hand-painted for Charles VI of France in 1392, shown in actual size.

[17] A French card of the same era as No. 15

KEY TO PLAYING CARDS SHOWN ON BACK ENDPAPERS

[18, 19] Italian tarots of the 15th century.

[20] German, about 1500. The acorn suit, *Eicheln,* is still used in many modern German packs.

[21] The Duchesse d'Étampes in a decorative French pack printed in 1856. She was a favorite of Francis I, a contemporary of Henry VIII.

[22] A circular card of the U.S., 1874.

[23, 24] The knight and bishop from a pack of chess cards. They were used for card games based on but not identical with chess.

[25] A joker from a U.S. pack in times when Euchre was the favored game.

[26, 27] Tarots from Austria, used in the game Tarok, catalogued "about 1867." These show the then young Kaiser, Franz Josef, and one of his Hungarian hussars.

[28] Playing-card back design of 1877, U.S.

[29] Card made in the U.S. to commorate the Golden Jubilee of Queen Victoria in 1887.

[30] George and Martha Washington on the ace of spades, about 1850. This is the face of the card, not the back.

[31] An ace of spades of the 1870s, U.S. The fanciness of the ace of spades dates back to the time when it constituted the tax stamp.

[32] Ace of spades from an 1895 U.S. pack.

[33, 34] Early indexed cards, U.S., about 1881.

PAINTINGS SECTION

[*begins opposite*]

DRAWINGS THROUGHOUT THE TEXT

The Renaissance coincided with the centuries when playing cards were introduced into Italy and spread rapidly through Europe. Great artists from the fifteenth century on have found in card-playing a subject for the portrayal of action and emotion. This should have helped students to reconstruct obsolete card games, but unfortunately the contribution of art to knowledge has been almost as meager as that of the incunabular literature of games. Just as illustrators today consider it rather unsporting to read the works they illustrate, painters have been notoriously careless about the technical details of the games they portray. The selection of paintings that follows has been made purposefully: to trace the history of our present games through their ancestor-games; to give representation to some of the most famous painters and most famous works relating to card games; and for general interest, provided the painting also serves both of the first two purposes. This is not an art book, and noteworthy paintings by such masters as Murillo, Leonardo and dozens of others have been omitted for one reason or another while the commercial painting of a Faro game (No. 9 in this section) was considered by us to be an essential choice.

1. PRIMERO

"Lord Burleigh Playing Primero." This painting has often been attributed to Federigo Zuccaro (1543-1609), an Italian painter who spent the years 1574-80 at the court of Elizabeth I; but today, the best opinion would make the artist John Bettes (c. 1530-80) and the date about 1560, long before Zuccaro could have done it. Lord Burleigh (the one who was "more burly than Lord Leicester, but created less stir") is the man at the left. In 1560 he was forty years old and was Elizabeth's chief minister, the most powerful man in England. The game is described on pages 20-21.

1. *Country Life*, London

2. National Gallery of Art, Washington, D.C.: Samuel H. Kress Collection, loan

2. POKER

❡ "The Card Players," painted about 1525 by Lucas Van Leyden (1494-1533). The players, like the artist, were Dutch. The game was undoubtedly one of several French games, ancestors of Poker, played with three-card hands. Considering the date of the painting, it was probably the game that Rabelais called pair et sequence (which reached England later as Post and Pair; see page 21). Such games developed from Primero but introduced the pair and three of a kind (pair-royal in England, brelan in France) as ranking hands. Players bet after seeing their cards, and each player had to meet the bet or drop, so bluffing was possible as in the Poker of today. This painting is also significant as a portrayal of early kibitzing practices.

3. ÉCARTÉ

❡ "Card Players," painted about 1652 by Nicolas Maes (1632-93), Dutch artist. This is one of the most famous paintings of card-players but throws no reliable light on card-playing of its times. The players are engaged in one of the many five-card games of the Triomphe family, perhaps Écarté; but the undealt portion of the pack should be shown on the table. There has never been a game played with a ten-card pack. Ecarté is described on page 214.

3. Reproduced by courtesy of the Trustees, The National Gallery, Lo

4. Courtesy of the Fogg Art Museum, Harvard University

5. Worcester Art Museum

4. TRIOMPHE

"The Cardsharper," about 1660: A painting variously attributed to Michelangelo da Caravaggio (1569-1609) and to certain of his followers. It is distinctly not the same as a Caravaggio original, which differed in having a spectator—probably an acccomplice of the cheater—advising the victim; but the most recent opinion is that Caravaggio made this copy himself. The game is Écarté or another form of Triomphe, as in the preceding Maes painting, but this time the artist did not overlook the undealt cards. The thick pack with unrounded corners and unprinted backs was typical of the early centuries of card manufacturing in Europe (see page 23).

5. POKER

"The Young Card Players," by Mathieu Le Nain (c. 1607-1677). There were three Le Nains and each was responsible for at least one painting on this theme; it is impossible now to guess which copied which. The game is a form of Primero or Primiera, an ancestor of Poker—it may be the same game as the women are playing in the Van Leyden painting (No. 2).

5. From the Buckingham Palace collection. Copyright reserved

6. PIQUET

("*Interior with Cardplayers,*" 1658, by Pieter de Hoogh, Dutch artist. Card games were a preoccupation of de Hoogh's, but he was unusual in devoting his attention more to the composition than to the emotion revealed by the players' faces and actions. The game here is probably Piquet, a French two-hand game that was popular in Holland at that time. Piquet has survived with little change and still has its following in New York and London clubs as well as on the Continent.

7. Reproduced by courtesy of the Trustees of the Tate Gallery, London

7. BRIDGE

("*Hearts are Trumps,*" 1871, by John Everett Millais (1829-96). This detail from a "conversation piece" shows the earliest form of the game we now call Bridge. The beautiful daughters of Sir William Armstrong are playing Dummy Whist, in those days often called simply Dummy. It was a game for three players and was never played when a fourth was available; but there were a few (very few) enlightened souls among Victorian Whist players and they observed that exposure of the dummy added greatly to the opportunity for skillful play. A few years later, no later than 1886 and probably earlier, the first primitive form of Bridge appeared.

8. Stephen C. Clark Collection, Museum of Modern Art, New York; courtesy Stephen C. Clark

8. UNIDENTIFIED

❡ "The Cardplayers," 1890-92, by Paul Cézanne (1839-1906). In the years from 1890 to 1892 Cézanne made five paintings of card-players. In three paintings they were playing a two-hand game; in the other two the game was three-handed. The two-hand game might be assumed to be Belotte, on the grounds of mathematical probability (that being the game most often played in France). Cézanne did not supply enough technical detail to permit positive identification of the game. It may be Bézique or Tarok or Belotte (which may be played by three).

9. FARO

❡ "Bucking the Tiger," 1887, artist not known. A lithographed poster of this painting is well known to all who enter bars in the Pacific Coast region. It is distributed by the proud makers of Cyrus Noble whisky, whose "old goods" were so prominently advertised. The setting is Tony Down's Famous Arizona Saloon in Tombstone. Faro antiquarians will observe that the layout is unusual; it displays the diamond suit instead of the spade suit. They will observe also that, considering the few players, the action was big. In the picture, the dealer has just completed a turn and is paying off. The game of Faro is described on pages 236-239.

Moulin Studios, San Francisco; courtesy Haas Brothers

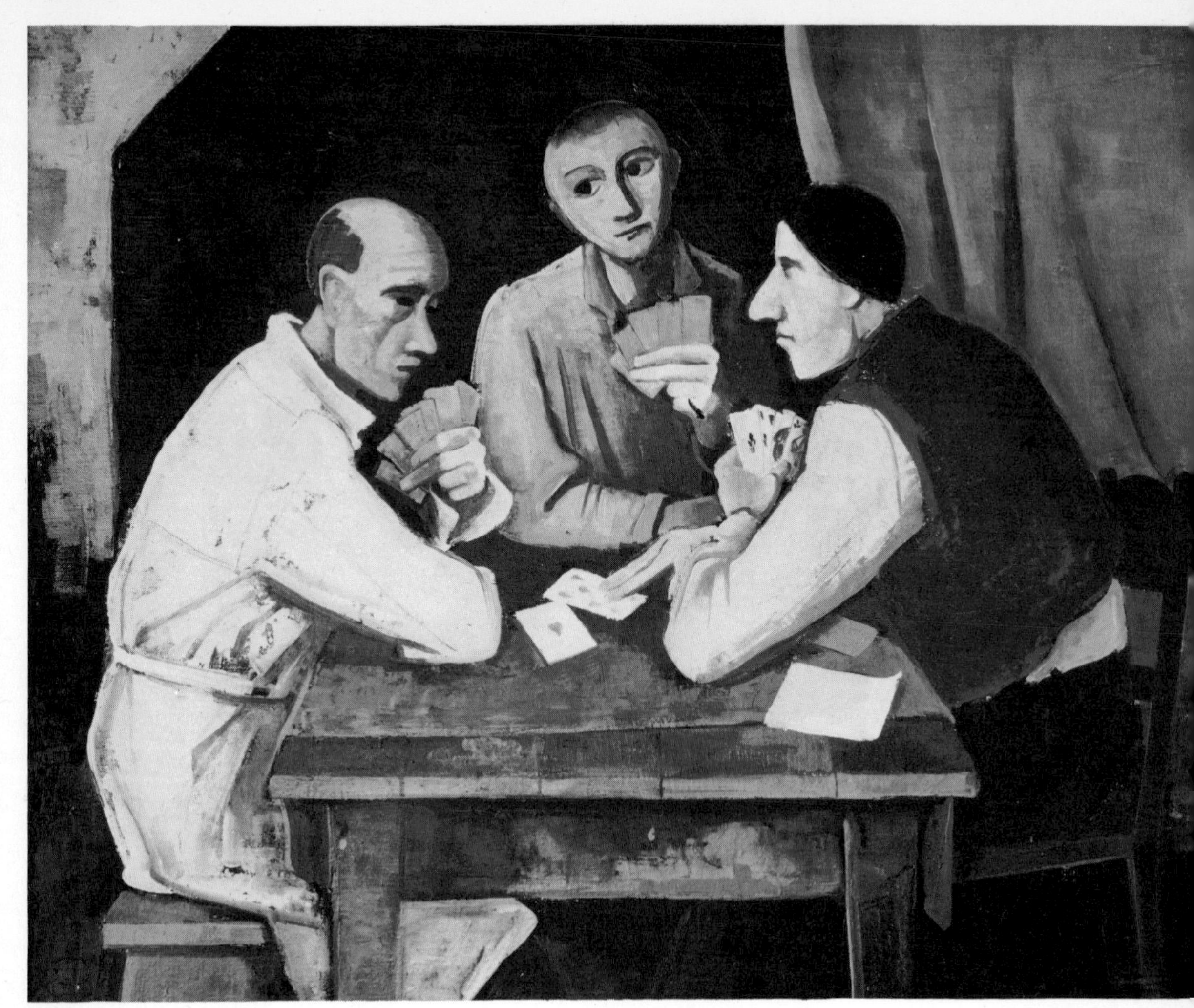

10. San Francisco Museum of Art, Albert M. Bender Collection

10. SKAT

[*"Card Players," 1936, by Karl Hofer (1878-1955), German artist. The painting has been much admired, but it does not illustrate the game very well. The players do not have enough cards and the table does not show where the completed tricks have been put—unless the player at the right has won them all and the pile of cards under his left arm is thicker than it seems. But one thing is evident: it is up to the player at the left to play a card.*

ORIGIN AND ODDITIES OF CARDS

❡There are too many legends connected with playing cards and card games to list them all. The most fascinating (but, alas, the least reliable) legends relate playing cards to concubines. A Chinese encyclopedia of 1678 says they* were invented A.D. 1120 to amuse the concubines of a Chinese emperor; since the emperor had so many women that even on a milkman's route he could not have covered the whole ground in less than two years, it is not surprising that they were deemed to require other recreations. The French perhaps had the same idea when they attributed the invention to a courtesan, a favorite of Charles V of France, in 1377. But against all this Professor Thomas F. Carter of the University of California has produced an indisputable Chinese reference to playing cards dated A.D. 969. ❡There is little doubt that printing originated in China in the Tang Dynasty, A.D. 618-906. The first printed items were either money or playing cards. Does it matter which? If it was money, the Chinese used it for playing games; if it was playing cards, they signed names and amounts on them and used them as money. The known fact is that for hundreds of years Chinese money and cards were almost identical in design and size. ❡What games did the Chinese play with these primeval money-cards? We can only conjecture, but knowing the conservatism, the resistance to change, of the Chinese, we can suppose that one of their games was the one we call mah-jongg, which blossomed into our games of Rummy, Canasta, Gin, and so on, more than a thousand years later; and that one of them was like Poker, and another was like Whist or Bridge, and so on, for the themes of card games are fixed, stable, and variable only in detail. ❡Catherine Perry Hargrave, author of the fascinating article that follows, is the foremost authority on the history of playing cards in the Western Hemisphere. She is author of the monumental A History of Playing Cards and is the curator emeritus of the United States Playing Card Company's museum, in Cincinnati, of historical playing cards. We may believe that Mrs. Hargrave went slightly overboard in placing the first Chinese paper money in the sixth century

* Playing cards, not concubines. Concubines were invented much earlier.

instead of the seventh, and perhaps in one or two other minor respects, but this does not in the least lessen our respect and admiration for her scholarship or our recommendation of her article.

The Origin of Gaming and Cards

by CATHERINE PERRY HARGRAVE

So much has been written in this world of ours about men's work, and so little about their play! Yet the former is not often a matter of choice, while the latter is a spontaneous thing and so, perhaps, as true a mirror of their lives and times as their more forced pursuits.

Chatto, an Englishman, writing* of these things in the middle of the nineteenth century, says, "Man has been distinctively termed 'a cooking animal'; and Dr. Franklin has defined him to be a 'tool-making animal.' He may also, with equal truth, be defined to be a 'gambling animal'; since to venture, on chance or judgment, his own property, with the hope of winning the property of another, is as peculiar to him in distinction from other animals, as his broiling a fish after he has caught it with his hands, or making for himself a stone hatchet to enable him to fell a tree.

"Other animals, in common with man, will fight for meat, drink, and lodging; and will do battle for love as fiercely as the ancient knights of chivalry, whose great incitements to heroic deeds—in plain English, killing and wounding—were ladye-love and the honour of the peacock. There is, however, no well-authenticated account of any of the lower orders of animals ever having been seen risking their property at 'odd or even,' or drawing lots for choice of pasturage. Even the learned pig, that tells people their fortune by the cards, is never able to learn what is trumps."

Dr. Stewart Culin of the Brooklyn Museum, who has made a life-long study of the games of primitive peoples, says that all of our modern games, including chess and cards, are survivals of the ancient rites of divination of primitive man. To draw a circle on the ground, divided into the Four Directions, was an important part of these magical processes. And upon the casting of an arrow into this ring depended the future. Many of the gaming sticks of the American Indians are marked with the feathered shaftment of an arrow, and the Korean playing cards, to this day, invariably bear a pictured arrow upon their backs.

It is an answer to Mr. Chatto's open question. It gives you a great deal to think about. It casts a glamour over parchesi and chess and cards like the breathtaking wonder and beauty of the northern lights when you watch them from the bottom of a canoe on a lake in the Maine woods. Even Bridge never again seems quite the same.

Marco Polo, returning to Venice late in the thirteenth century from his travels in strange countries and on unknown seas, told among other wonders how the Great Cham in far Cathay caused paper money to be made from the bark of the mulberry tree, "some of the value of a small penny, tournois; and others of the value of a Venetian silver groat; others of the value of two groats, others of five."

The Chinese had been making this paper money since the sixth century. At first a game was played with the little paper bank notes themselves. Later, cards in the form of the paper money were made, using the old money symbols, a coin, a string of coins, myriad strings of coins, and tens of myriads of strings of coins, which are the names of the suits today [in Chinese playing cards]. A complete pack consists of four sets of thirty cards each for Kwan P'ai, "stock cards," or Ma Tseuk, "sparrows," in which there are three suits of ten cards each, nine numerals and one honor card. This honor card in the suit of coins is called the Red Flower, in the suit of strings of coins White Flower, and in the suit of myriads Old Thousand. The Red Flower and Old Thousand, and all the cards of the suit of myriads, show pictures of the celestial generals from the old legend, "The Story of the River's Banks." The White Flower is a picture of a mountain, rising from the mists, while below is a deer in the forest, or a little white flower, which are used interchangeably, the symbolism being the same. These little cards are long and narrow, copying their Korean neighbors on the north, while in the four-suit game called Lut Chi, "waste paper," and used in the south of China, they are broader and shorter and more the shape of ours. Perhaps centuries ago they more nearly approximated the size of ours than they do today, for it was undoubtedly some of these Chinese cards which found their way into fourteenth-century Italy and suggested the

* William Andrew Chatto: *Facts and Speculations on the Origin and History of Playing Cards,* London, 1848.

PERSIAN PLAYING CARDS PAINTED ON IVORY

cards that were known in every country in Europe before the century was past.

Dice is one of the oldest games of chance, and dominoes are, of course, only a different arrangement of the dice markings. Both games very probably originated in China [or Korea] and the Chinese seem to have been playing the domino game, either with "tablets" made of ivory or bone or with "slips" made of parchment or early paper, at the time when the paper money was also being used to play a card game. Today dominoes and the domino cards are used interchangeably to play the same games.

The packs of domino cards are made up of a suit of twenty-one cards with the plain markings of red and black dots, and from one to four additional suits with fanciful decorations in addition to the domino marks.

Sometimes there are suits bearing charming snatches of chrysanthemum blossoms and plum and bamboo. Sometimes the markings are butterflies and fiddler crabs and bats in the gayest of colors, the last always an emblem of the best of fortune. Sometimes there are coins and scrolls and characters; and always there is a series bearing the portraits of the celestial generals of "The Story of the River's Banks." Quite often they are the loveliest little color prints imaginable.

There is a theory that these domino cards also found their way into Europe in the thirteenth century, and that these little people from the old Chinese folk tale became the strange persons on the twenty-one *atouts* or high cards of the tarot series, which was the game that found favor on the continent in the fourteenth century.

In the British Museum is a manuscript, *"De Moribus et Disciplina Humane Conservationis,"* written by one Johannes, a brother in the monastery at Brefeld, who says, "Hence it is that a certain game, called the game of cards (*Ludas cartarum*), has come to us in this year 1377, but at what time it was invented, or by whom, I am ignorant. But this I say, that it is of advantage to noblemen and to others, especially if they practise it courteously and without money." The first chapter treats *"de materia ludi et de diversitate instrumentorum"** and explains how "in the game which men call the game at cards, they paint the cards in different manners, and play with them in one way and another." Which would seem to show that [playing cards] were well known and that they had been in use sufficiently long for more than one kind of game to be played with them.

He goes on, "As the game came to us there are four kings depicted on four cards, and each one holds a certain sign in his hand and sits upon a royal throne, and under the king are two

* "Concerning the substance of games and the kinds of gaming implements."

'marechali' the first of whom holds the sign upright in his hand, and the other holds the sign downward in his hand." The two marshals, in the packs of the fifteenth century and later, become the queen and valet or the two valets or knaves, and it is interesting to see that in the hands of all single-head jacks, even those being made in Belgium today, the staves of two of them are still held upward and in the other two down.

Venice was the great seaport of Europe in the fourteenth century and many strange craft from faraway lands made her port, laden with cargo. It seems more than probable that Chinese playing cards were brought into Italy in this way. Whether they came with merchants from the east, or in the luggage of adventurous Venetians, returning in the footsteps of the Polos, or even with the Polos themselves, no one knows. In his *Istoria della città de Veterbo* Covelluzo writes that in 1379 "there were encamped about Viterbo paid troops of the opposing factions of Clement VII and Urbain VI, who did commit depredations of all kinds, and robberies in the Roman states. In this year of such great tribulation the game of cards was introduced into Viterbo, which came from the Saracens and was called Naib."

The cards of western China today are considerably wider than those of Canton, and perhaps in the thirteenth and fourteenth centuries they may have been even more like ours in shape and size. The Chinese coins are very like those of the old Italian cards, their strings resemble very closely the Italian or Spanish swords and batons, and the Chinese hieroglyph for *Kwan,* or ten thousand, makes the familiar cups of the cards of the Latin countries. The Red Flower of the Chinese pack becomes the valet of the European game, the White Flower with its stag the cavalier or horseman, and Old Thousand, the king.

In connection with Covelluzo's remark about the card game which came from the Saracens and was called Naib, it is interesting to know that the Hebrew word for sorcery is *naibi,* which brings us to the most curious of all cards, the tarots.

The tarots were curious pictorial cards very evidently embodying an eastern symbolism in their strange designs. Tradition says that they were brought into Italy by wandering fortune-telling gypsies who had journeyed from India across Persia and Arabia into Egypt and from there into Italy. There do not seem to have been any numeral cards with these for a while. In a modified form they became a children's game, picturing the arts and sciences, the muses and virtues and myths. Combined with the numeral cards from China, they became "cards for playing," and as such are mentioned in a manuscript of the fifteenth century in our library. The author concerns himself principally with the morality of cards and card games and arrives at the conclusion that those games are commendable which do not keep the people from mass, and which encourage the heart to good works.

The earliest playing cards of Europe that we know are some tarot cards that were painted for the King of France, late in the fourteenth century. In the register of the Chambre des Comptes of Charles VI of France, in the year 1392, is the entry of the royal treasurer for moneys paid one Jacquemin Grigonneur, painter, for three games [packs] of cards "in gold and diverse colors, ornamented with many devices for the diversion of our Lord, the King." Seventeen of these strange old painted cards survive in the Bibliothèque Nationale at Paris. They are very large, each one is seven and a half inches long and four inches wide, and the backgrounds are in gold, intricately stippled. There is a valet of swords; le mat, or joker; and fifteen atouts [trumps], or high cards, La Temperance, La Force, La Justice, La Lune, Le Soleil, Le Chariot, L'Ermite, Le Pendu, Death, La Mason Dieu, Le Jugement, Le Pape, L'Empereur, Les Amoureux and La Roux de Fortune. Some of these show curious deviations from the usual tarot designs.

There are records of playing cards in France long before the time of these cards of the King. In the *Roman de Renard le Contrefait,* which is supposed to have been written not later than 1341, is the line "Jouent aux Des [dice], aux Cartes, aux Tables [backgammon]!"

By 1397 cards were so plentiful that a Paris decree forbade working people to play at "tennis, bowls, dice, cards or nine-pins on working days."

The tarot cards that were painted for Charles VI so long ago had Italian suit signs, cups, swords, coins and batons, just as do the tarot packs that are made in France today. But early in the fifteenth century other games were played with other cards, bearing the familiar suit marks of hearts, spades, clubs and diamonds.

The French suit signs were supposed to typify the four classes of society: hearts or *coeurs,* standing for the church; spades or *piques,* which were the points of lances, standing for the knights; clubs or *trefles,* which were clover leaves, for the husbandmen; and diamonds or *carreaux,* which were the arrowheads, for the peasantry from whom the archers and bowmen were drawn.

In Germany cards seem to have been brought into the country by the *Landsknecht,* or foot soldiers, who were in the army of Henry VII returning from the fighting in Italy. They wandered all over Europe and took with them not only the cards but the very simple game which they delighted in and which was called, because of its origin, "Lansquenet." It is still a common card game in Germany.

Many old writers were of the opinion that playing cards had found their way into Europe through Spain, having been brought there by the Moors. There doesn't seem to be any proof of this, however, though it has been pointed out many times that the earliest of Spanish card games, Hombre, is very like the card game Ganjifa which is played in India.

The Flemish monk, Pascasius Justus, however, traveling through Spain in 1540, says that he traveled many leagues throughout the kingdom of Spain without being able to procure the necessities of life—even bread or wine—yet in every miserable village playing cards might be found.

Our English cards, which are nothing but copies of the French ones, were brought into England early in the fifteenth century by soldiers returning from the fighting in Anjou and Poitou, and while François Villon was playing at "Gleeke" in Paris, the English court was delighting in the same game.

In 1484, playing cards had become the most important part of English Christmas festivities and with the passing of the years were more and more commonly used, so that Richard Seymour seems justified in writing, in his preface to the *Court Gamester* of 1734,* "Gaming is become so much the fashion amongst the Beau-Monde that he who in company should appear ignorant of the games in vogue would be counted lowbred and hardly fit for conversation."

¶*Whatever it may take for a rich man to enter the kingdom of Heaven, it is easier to get a camel through the eye of a needle than to change the designs on the faces of playing cards. Let any card-player have two or three losing sessions with an unfamiliar deck and he will swear the cards are unlucky for him—and go back to the old familiar faces. So our card designs have endured for nearly four hundred years and seem likely to go on indefinitely without essential change. Here Robert Hutchings, writing for the Association of American Playing Card Manufacturers, tells how our modern cards came to have their characteristic faces.*

* Also in earlier editions (1720).

Designs of the Face Cards

by ROBERT HUTCHINGS

OUR CARDS [in the United States] actually had their origin in France and came here via England. The designs still have a close resemblance to the medieval French originals. But each succeeding generation of artists has effected some slight change in the basic design. Sometimes the change was due to carelessness, sometimes to an artistic impulse. On several occasions, in the early days, an effort was made to flatter the reigning monarch by altering the design to make it resemble him.

But during the period [1642-58] of Cromwell the appearance of the king on the cards became more austere. For instance, the [English] king of hearts prior to 1642 is said to have borne a marked resemblance to Charles I, the tragic Stuart ruler who was executed in 1649. With the ascendancy of Cromwell to power, a vague likeness of Charles was retained, but he was given a more somber expression. While the battle-ax had gone into disuse in 1642, the pasteboard King Charles was shown holding one. In still later designs, a sword was substituted for the battle-ax.

At various times the king of hearts has represented Adam, Julius Caesar, Constantine, and Alexander. In some [French] decks of the late nineteenth century some kings of hearts had the contemporary hero General Boulanger, or Victor Hugo, as their models. But in today's deck the king of hearts is essentially the Charlemagne of fifteenth-century French decks.

The queen of hearts has had a colorful history. Never once has she represented the real-life consort of Adam, Constantine, Alexander, or the other kings of hearts. In the earliest pack it is believed that the queen of hearts represented Helen of Troy, a belief supported by the theory that the knave of hearts was Helen's lover, Paris. But in the ensuing years the queen of hearts is reputed to have represented various people in fact and fiction—Roxane, Rachel, Queen Elizabeth of England, Juno, Joan of Arc, and Isabella of Bavaria. Most commonly she has been identified with Judith of Bavaria, the beautiful daughter-in-law of Charlemagne. Thus the representations of the king and queen of hearts with which we are most familiar today go back to two famous figures of the ninth century.

Probably the most impressive figure in pasteboard royalty is the king of spades. His appearance—regal, austere, and strong—has been retained from French playing cards of the sixteenth century.

In the early decks his majesty held a mighty saber. It is obvious that he was not the kind of man to be satisfied with the miserable sword shown in today's design, which may account for the slight frown now appearing on his forehead.

Contemporary French card-makers still include a golden harp in the background of the king of spades. It is reported that in some earlier French decks the name of David appeared on the king of spades, suggesting the Biblical King David. But that regal figure hardly conjures up an image of the little David who in the Negro spiritual is urged to play on his harp!

The queen of spades goes back to Greek mythology for her origin. She is reputed to resemble Pallas Athene [or Minerva], the goddess who sprang fully armed from the head of Zeus and who played the oddly inconsistent roles of goddess of war and goddess of wisdom. Down through the years the designers have occasionally changed the queen of spades in the belief that a pagan goddess was not a suitable consort for David. They substituted Bathsheba at one time and on another occasion substituted Joan of Arc. But today's queen of spades is still more like Pallas Athene, or Minerva, than the others.

Eventually, if you were to trace the history of all the court cards, you would find that despite innumerable mutations the ancient designs rooted in history and religion or mythology have persevered.

While the design of the face-card has remained true to tradition, the over-all design of the card itself has undergone many basic changes.

Certainly the original cards, hand-lettered and -colored, would not be practical for use today. They were works of art, to be sure, and as you examine them you can not help but marvel at the patience and skill that went into their creation; but for the fast, hard use to which cards are subjected today such cards would be highly impractical. The little imperfections which are unavoidable in handmade cards would have made them somewhat less than satisfactory today.

From time to time their breadth was reduced and their length extended. Sporadic efforts to evolve a card easy to handle have been made, and probably the most unsuccessful of these was the creation of circular cards. While these completely round playing cards introduced a brand-new opportunity for designers, they must have left a great deal to be desired in the matter of handling. Imagine trying to rack up a thirteen-card Bridge hand made up entirely of round pasteboards!*

The first playing cards made in this country [the United States] were made at the time of the earliest settlers, years before printing presses arrived in America. Those early cards were made from leaves and from the skin of sheep and deer. They were designed and painted by hand, of course.

The first American paper mills were erected in the seventeenth century, and apparently the enterprising printers of that day produced small cards with religious verses and playing cards simultaneously. This same association is revealed in some old merchandise invoices which show that Bibles and playing cards were frequently bought by the same customers.

Benjamin Franklin was one of the leading card manufacturers in the eighteenth century, and it is an interesting footnote to history that some of his own playing cards were used as insulation in the electrical friction machine which he built in 1731.

Another famous personage who put cards to unusual use was Lord Jeffrey Amherst. He used playing cards with plain backs for handwritten invitations to some of his more lavish parties. Still another unusual use for playing cards was found at the University of Pennsylvania. In 1765 admission to classes at the university was gained through the presentation of playing cards, properly inscribed.

During the Spanish-American war the faces of our national heroes—Dewey, Schley, and others—appeared on the face-cards of American manufacture, and in the First World War doughboys and Red Cross nurses were introduced by some card companies in lieu of the traditional queens and kings.

* Not true. Circular playing cards (known in India more than six hundred years ago) are unusually easy to handle. Recent attempts to reintroduce them have failed for two other reasons: superstition, mentioned before; and the fact that they are harder to separate into conspicuous tricks than rectangular cards are.

❡*And here, in an article first published in* The New York Times Magazine, *one of the editors reveals some of the trade secrets of playing-card manufacture—something he knows from personal experience, being a former playing-card manufacturer himself.*

The Unique Playing-card Industry

by ALBERT MOREHEAD

ALTHOUGH card games are the world's most general form of recreation, and playing cards can be found in nearly nine out of ten American homes—more than have radios—there are only five manufacturers of playing cards in the United States. Furthermore, the largest manufacturer makes more than two-thirds of all the cards sold.

This situation exists because the production of playing cards is deceptively difficult. To a skilled printer a pack of cards looks like nothing more than a printing job. Nevertheless hundreds of fine printers have tried to make cards and have eventually given up in despair.

The fundamental principles of playing-card manufacture have changed little over the course of the centuries.

The stock on which the cards are printed must consist of thin sheets of paper pasted together with a black paste. A single sheet of heavy paper would not do; if a card player sat with a lamp at his back, the light could shine through his cards and show what he held in his hand. The black paste makes the cards properly opaque.

The pasteboard is then aged for long periods to dry it out. Like wood, paper will warp if it contains moisture, and playing cards must lie flat and not curl up. The manufacturers of the best cards age their "stock" for at least two years. At today's prices for paper, this takes capital, for vast quantities of paper must lie idle at all times—perhaps a million dollars' worth at a time.

One or two full packs of cards are printed at a time on large sheets of this pasteboard. The individual cards are then stamped out, one at a time, with a sharp die that works on the same mechanical principle as the housewife's biscuit cutter, but so fast that it cuts out several thousand cards per hour. Simultaneously—and synchronized to that infinitesimal fraction of a second in which the die descends—a hammer-like steel block pounds down upon an anvil-like steel base and the edges of the cards are pressed into a "knife edge."

This knife edge is invisible to the naked eye, but it is of vast importance to the quality of the cards. If you had to play cards with mere cut-out pieces of pasteboard you could not shuffle them —the edges would fray. The knife edge on playing cards permits each card to slip in between two other cards as you shuffle, retarding the fraying process so that the pack may be used many times.

Delicate operations like this—on which first-class printers have broken their hearts and their purses—require special machinery. Modern refinements on traditional playing-card processes have never been disclosed in patents. They are among the world's most jealously guarded trade secrets.

Twice in recent years the big playing-card manufacturers have shut down branch factories, one in New Jersey and one on Long Island. In each case they sent in demolition gangs to break up the costly machinery with sledge hammers. The owners preferred to turn it into scrap metal rather than sell it for high prices and let the secret designs become known.

It used to be said that all the playing-card manufacturers employed spies who were disguised as workmen and sent into their competitors' plants. In recent years the competing manufacturers have become friendly and have formed an association; its purpose, however, is solely to promote the playing of games, and not to get together on trade secrets or prices. Every now and then the industry breaks out into a price-cutting war and the public actually buys cards below cost.

The retail prices of playing cards never give a true picture of what the manufacturers and stores get for them, because, like cigarettes, they are subject to a Federal tax stamp. The present tax on playing cards is thirteen cents a pack. Before the war the lowest-priced cards (twenty cents) were actually sold by the manufacturers for five and a fraction cents a pack. But we Americans never really taxed playing cards heavily; in England, for nearly a hundred years, the tax was half a crown (sixty cents) a pack. Then Parliament suddenly had a change of heart and cut it to threepence (six cents).

The demand for playing cards is never likely to go begging, despite the paucity of manufacturers. Even after closing some of their factories and breaking up the machinery, the manu-

Early American playing cards (1856) made without the traditional markings to appease the Bible Belt.

facturers could easily double their present output. It has even been said that the largest playing-card plant (the United States Playing Card Company, in Cincinnati) could effortlessly supply the playing-card wants of the entire world. Other playing-card factories are in Racine, Wisconsin, Poughkeepsie, Chicago, St. Paul, and Rochester, New York.

Besides the manufacturers of paper cards, there are three firms that manufacture playing cards made of a plastic material, and a dozen or so others who put out games (such as "Authors") which follow the form of standard playing cards but do not have the aces, kings, and other conventional designs.

There once was a great demand for card games that do not require standard playing cards, especially in the "Bible Belt" and in New England with its Puritan heritage. It was the Puritans, back around 1600, who first called playing cards "the Devil's picture book" and ruled that it is sinful even to have them in the house. Until the present century most Protestant churches followed this dictum. However, card games of other types were deemed permissible even in devout homes. "Authors" was the first of these games; it was produced in Salem, Massachusetts, in 1843. Now, of course, the copyright has run out and any manufacturer has the right to make an Authors set. With "Rook" cards, which have four suits of consecutively numbered cards, almost any game can be played. Dozens of other proprietary card games have since emerged, and they sell in the millions. Salem is still a center of their manufacture.

Until the present century, playing cards were used mostly for gambling games. Faro and Poker were the leading gambling-house games. Now dice and slot machines have replaced cards in the gambling houses and the greatest use of playing cards is for simple home pastimes without stakes. Church opposition to cards has therefore relaxed.

Partly because of gamblers' superstition, playing cards have changed very slowly over the course of the centuries. Until after 1850 it was not customary for playing cards to have "back designs," because gamblers believed that a plain white back could not so easily be marked. Several years ago the United States Playing Card Company put out a series of cards in which the back of an ace had a hairline imperfection where one of the plates used in printing had been slightly scratched. The company called in the entire production—300,000 packs—and threw them away.

Card players today are accustomed to the "double-head" card which can be read from either end, and to the "index" in each corner which permits one to recognize the card without seeing its entire face. However, cards of this type did not become standard until the late 1870's. Until then a player had to look at the full face of the card—and sometimes hold it right side up—to know what it was.

Either superstition or habit still prevents any change in playing-card design. Attempts have been made during the last [1931-40] decade to make the four suits more easily distinguishable by printing the clubs in blue and the diamonds in orange, but the cards were a failure. Equally unsuccessful were efforts to redesign the pips and to clothe the kings, queens and jacks in modern dress. Circular cards, though they are easy to handle and to read, met a very unenthusiastic reception; yet circular cards are nothing new and were very popular 300 years ago. A brief flurry was caused in 1938 when cards with a fifth suit appeared, but these too got a thumbs down from card players and were soon withdrawn from the market.

PLAYING CARDS IN EARLY ENGLISH LITERATURE

¶*The earliest references to playing cards in European literature came surprisingly close together—in France in 1341, Germany and Italy in 1377, Spain in 1387. But the first known English reference is nearly a hundred years later, and not until the 1500s did card games begin to receive attention in respectable English literature.* ¶*The first mention is in a sermon by Hugh Latimer, Bishop of Worcester, in 1529. Latimer was a favorite of Henry VIII because he sided with Henry against the Pope. When Mary I came to the throne in 1553 Latimer was irrevocably doomed to disfavor and death; and one of the most famous quotations of English history is his dying utterance, made to his fellow-Protestant, Nicholas Ridley, with whom he was burned at the stake in 1555: "Be of good comfort, Master Ridley, and play the man. We shall this day light such a candle, by God's grace, in England, as I trust shall never be put out." Here, modernized in spelling, is what he had to say about cards in a 1529 sermon. The "Triumph" he spoke about came later to be known as Whist and grew into Contract Bridge.*

"AND where you are wont to celebrate Christmas in playing at cards, I intend, by God's grace, to deal unto you Christ's Cards, wherein you shall perceive Christ's Rule. The game that we play at shall be called the Triumph, which, if it be well played at, he that dealeth shall win; the Players shall likewise win; and the standers and lookers upon shall do the same. . . .

"You must mark also that the Triumph must apply to fetch home unto him all the other cards, whatever suit they be of. . . .

"Then further, we must say to ourselves, What requirest Christ of a Christian man? Now turn up your Trump, your Heart (Hearts is Trump, as I said before), and cast your Trump, your Heart, on this card."

—HUGH LATIMER, 1529.

¶*One cannot study high-school English and not know* GAMMER GURTON'S NEEDLE, *first published in 1551. Here Dame Chat invites some friends to play a game of Trump (Whist):*

"WHAT, Diccon? Come nere, ye be no stranger:
We be fast set at trump, man, hard by the fyre;
Thou shalt set on the king if thou come a little nyer.
Come hither Dol. Dol, sit down and play this game. . . ."

¶*John Lyly, the Euphues man, got into the* GOLDEN TREASURY *with a song from Alexander and Campaspe (1589): "Cupid and my Campaspe played / at cards for kisses; Cupid paid . . ." Elsewhere he was guilty of an anachronism when he had Roman soldiers playing cards at the Crucifixion; cards were unknown to Rome then and the soldiers cast dice made of sheep's knucklebones. Most enlightening was a 1621 poem by John Taylor, the "Water[front] Poet," mentioning a host of archaic games:*

THE prodigall's estate, like to a flux,
The mercer, draper, and the silkman suckes;
The tailor, millainer, dogs, drabs, and dice,
Trey-trip, or passage, or the most at thrice.
At irish, tick-tacke, doublets, draughts, or chesse,
He flings his money free with carelessnesse.
At novum, mumchance, mischance (chuse ye which),
At one-and-thirty, or at poor-and-rich,
Ruffe, slam, trump, noddy, whisk, hole, sant, new cut,
Unto the keeping of four knaves he'll put
His whole estate; at loadum, or at gleeke,
At tickle-me-quickly he's a merry greek;
At primifisto, post-and-payre, primero,
Maw, whip-her-ginny, he's a lib'ral hero;
At my-sow-pigged: but (reader, never doubt ye),
He's skilled in all games, except looke-about ye.
Bowles, shovel-groat, tennis, no game comes amiss,
His purse a nurse for anybody is . . .

¶*Ruffe, Slam, Trump, and Whisk are all forms of the game that became Whist and ultimately Bridge; Noddy and One-and-thirty are forms or terms of the game that Sir John Suckling, not long after, made into Cribbage; Sant is simply an English spelling of the French word* cent, *or 100, which we now call Piquet; Gleeke and Primero blossomed later as fads and died in due course; dice, tick-tacke* (backgammon), *doublets* (craps), *draughts* (checkers), *chess, bowles, shovelgroat* (shuffleboard) *and tennis are no strangers to us; and the others are obsolete or obscure.* ❡*As for Shakespeare, he knew his cards and his games well enough to scatter them liberally through his plays and sonnets. The following article, which appeared in Phi Beta Kappa's austere* American Scholar, *may serve to emphasize and even overemphasize the Shakespearean predilection for card allusions; it is, in fact, a hoax (an admirably ingenious one) with a host of far-fetched attributions, and its author's name is, of course, a pseudonym, but there are a sufficient number of correct interpretations to make it significant in its sphere.*

Cosmic Card Game

by THOMAS KYD

THE VULGAR ERROR that Shakespeare's *Antony and Cleopatra* is a tragedy about Antony and Cleopatra has been perpetuated by so-called learned men. An appallingly self-explosive note "elucidates" the text in the edition by the late Professor Kittredge:

> . . . she, Eros, has
> Pack'd cards with Caesar and false-play'd my glory
> Unto an enemy's triumph. (IV.xiv.18-20)

"Triumph," explains Kittredge with pathetic eagerness, meant not only a victory celebration but also "a trump card." It is not that the note is *wrong*. In its feeble way, it is, of course, *right*. What so distresses the quickened sensibilities of our time is that only after he had reached the fourth act of a work established by Mr. Eliot as Shakespeare's greatest was the commentator able to perceive, and then but dimly, one isolated detail of a pattern of imagery that articulates the entire drama and gives it form and meaning. He fails wholly to observe that the richly ambivalent word "triumph" was also the name of *the Elizabethan card game from which modern Whist and Contract Bridge have descended.**

There are in *Antony and Cleopatra* five laminated patterns of iterative imagery: the Chaos Pattern, the Bedclothes Pattern, the Insect Pattern, the Alcoholic-Beverage Pattern, and the Card Game Pattern. The last carries the theme and obtrudes upon the consciousness of the properly qualified reader the shifting partnerships, the play and false-play, the, so to speak, *brouillamini à jouer* in a Cosmic Game of Triumph. The first piece in the pattern is inserted in the first speech of the play:

> PHILO: His Captain's *heart,*
> Which in the scuffles of great fights hath burst
> The buckles on his breast, *reneges* all temper.
> (I.i.6-8)

The word "reneges" (occurring here and there only in Shakespeare) establishes Antony as a negligent, not dishonest, gamester, and juxtaposed with "great fights" sets up at once a paradoxical equation of the trivial with the momentous. Much of the effect of the Card Game imagery lies in the ironical excess or over-adequacy of the action of the drama as an objective correlative for the thematic pattern of language.

The word "heart" is the first of two-hundred-and-forty-seven instances (one instance I have eliminated as doubtful) in which the iconographic element in the pattern occurs. Each of the four rulers in the play is made to resemble an honor card in one of the four suits. Cleopatra is the queen of clubs (self-described as the trefoil or "full-blown rose . . . with Phoebus' amorous pinces black," I.v.28). Lepidus is the king of diamonds (utilizing as pun the Latin, *lapides,* gems, in color red, "Lepidus is high colour'd," II.vii.5). Octavius Caesar is the knave of spades ("he's but Fortune's knave," V.ii.3; in color black, "has a cloud in's face," III.ii.52). Antony is the king of hearts, as will so abundantly appear as to need no present illustration. If my reader will glance at the king of hearts and knave of spades in his modern deck, the design of which was standardized in Tudor times, he will note the marvelous consistency in the drama of allusions to "Antonius's beard" (II.ii.7) and "the scarce-bearded Caesar" (I.i.21). Lesser honor cards are Alexas (Cleopatra's "foul knave," I.ii.75), Eros (Antony's "dear knave," IV.xiv.14), and Thyreus ("This Jack of Caesar's," III.xiii.103). Through her unhappy state-marriage with Antony, Octavia of course figures as the queen of hearts. (That Shakespeare has injected into his poem, through this detail, a touch of human sentiment, the critic must concede even though he may not wholly approve.)

In what follows, two points must be kept in

* [George Lyman] Kittredge was right, the author wrong. Shakespeare can have meant only the trump card. The game would not fit the context.

mind: first, that in the imagistic play at cards, over which the cruder action of the drama lies as on a palimpsest, no higher card than a king is mentioned—the ACE *never,** and second, that although Antony, Cleopatra, Caesar and the rest are playing cards, they are also the cards *played.* The profound significance of the twin paradox, providing no less than the clue to the total meaning of the drama, will be treated in conclusion.

Although [the two men were] co-rulers of the Roman Empire, the words "competitor" and "partner" are used interchangeably wherever Antony and Caesar are concerned (I.iv.3; II.ii.22; II.vii.76; V.i.42 *inter alia*). In the first rubber, the competitor-partners have won a bid in hearts, owing largely to Caesar's ability to strengthen that suit by offering his sister Octavia to Antony. Caesar is dummy while Antony plays the hand:

ANTONY: Let me have your *hand.*
Further this act of grace; and from this hour
The *heart* of brothers govern in our loves
And sway our great designs.
CAESAR: There is my *hand.*
A *sister* I bequeath you, whom no brother
Did ever love so dearly. Let her live
To join our kingdoms and our *hearts.* (II.ii.148-54)

Graphically evoked is the picture of the two facing each other across the table, the cards in play before them. Antony leads the queen of hearts, and an onlooker later describes the tense moment to Cleopatra:

MESSENGER: I looked her in the *face,* and saw her *led*
Between her brother and Mark Antony.
(III.iii.12-13)

Backed by Antony's own king, the card is high and should establish the suit ("settle the *heart* of Antony," II.ii.246), but Caesar thinks it should have been reserved, "cherished," whereupon bickering begins between the competitor-partners. The card itself, termed by Caesar "poor castaway," thus plaintively laments:

Ay me most wretched
That have my *heart* parted betwixt two friends
That do afflict each other. (III.vi.76-78)

Now distrusting Antony's card sense, the prudent Caesar covers his stake by wagering against his own side, as has been his custom:

Caesar gets money
Where he loses hearts. (II.i.13-14)

Antony, resenting what seems to him alienated loyalty, charges his partner with laying reluctantly in the dummy hand such honor-cards as he may possess:

when perforce he could not
But pay me terms of *honour,* cold and sickly
He *vented* them. (III.iv.6-8)

The post-mortem in Act III, Scene vi, features Antony's querulous claim to a share in Caesar's winnings, and the dissolution of their partnership.

We must pause here to note the rare distinction in Shakespeare's artistry. Although we need not stain our page with the so-called historical approach to literature, or proceed to Shakespeare through the purlieus of the minor dramatists, brief mention may be made of Thomas Heywood. Those who have read *A Woman Killed with Kindness* with the attentiveness evoked by Mr. Eliot's devastating analysis will recall the metaphoric use of card game terms in the banal and sentimental course of Act III. The imagery in *Antony and Cleopatra,* while, of course, never so unspeakably jejune, is sometimes equally perspicuous, its superiority lying less in a guarded transparency than in a consistent sustenation—the true measure, after all, of the distance between Shakespeare and Heywood. Now observe how the master employs gaming imagery to forewarn us that even so seasoned a player as Antony will prove no match for Caesar. Antony says,

Be it art or hap
. . . the very dice obey him. (II.iii.33)

"Dice" being the plural of "die," and "die" signifying the climax of sexual experience as every schoolboy knows, at least in the better private institutions, "the very dice [climaxes] obey him" signifies that Caesar has his passions under almost repellently complete control. (Although it seems improbable that the number should be greater or less than seven, the present author has deliberated over whether the "dice" image may not offer an *eighth* type of ambiguity; prudently he shrinks back from making the suggestion until he may take counsel with his correspondents, one of whom is, unfortunately, en route to the Lower Punjab.)

In Act III the inevitable occurs, and Antony resumes his former partnership with Cleopatra, that avid gamester ("pour out the pack," II.v.54) who since the opening of the drama has been

* Of course not; the ace was not at that time the highest card but the lowest, just as it was at dice, whence the cast—(crabs, today called craps) lost automatically.

lamenting her forced abstention from play. Antony begins the game in an exhilarated mood:

My *playfellow*, your *hand*, this kingly seal
And *plighter of high hearts!* (III.xiii.125-26)

Observe that Antony insists upon frequent bids in hearts, although Cleopatra is permitted to play most of the hands. As the play proceeds, we become increasingly aware of Caesar at this table also, but now in the avowed role of formidable opponent. Antony grows irritated, complaining at the run of cards:

Of late, when I cried 'Ho!'
Like boys unto a muss, *kings* would start forth . . .
Take hence this *jack* . . . (III.xiii.90-93)

He sneers at Caesar's skill, suggesting that his servant Thyreus is as capable as his master, being "one that ties his points" (III.xiii.156). Dexterously developed is the imagistic foreshadowing of that climactic misplay when Cleopatra will lead her king (Antony) into Caesar's trump. Antony's words are a warning to his partner:

If I lose my *honour*,
I lose *myself*. (III.iv.22-23)

But the play is made, as signaled in the wry words of Canidius, "So our leader's *led*/ And we are women's *men*" (III.vii.70-71). We get Antony's anguished outcry, "O, whither hast thou *led* me, Egypt?" (III.xi.51), and his incredulous examination of the lost trick, "Where hast thou been, my *heart?*" (III.xiii.173). It was at this stage that Kittredge caught his one fleeting glimpse of Shakespeare's intention, and composed his little note on Antony's accusation that Cleopatra has "pack'd cards" with Caesar and "false-play'd" his glory "unto an enemy's triumph."

Without displaying that literal-mindedness so delectably satirized in *How Many Children Had Lady Macbeth?* by Mr. L. C. Knights, one of the distinguished *Scrutiny* wits, we may perhaps ask whether Cleopatra actually *did* pack cards with Caesar, and whether Dolabella's description of Antony ("he is pluck'd," III.xii.4) is to be taken at face value. That Cleopatra is a cheat goes without saying, and there is ample indication that there has been cheating in the present rubber. (Before it is over there are six kings in the deck: "Six kings already/Show me the way to yielding," III.x.33). Quite early we have heard of Antony "being barber'd ten times o'er" (II.ii.229), and it is quite possible that taking him to the barber has become habitual with her, but *it does not follow* that her cheating is designed to aid Caesar. Her lead in hearts seems to have been a genuine error, no doubt induced by confusion during her covert manipulation of the cards, and Antony himself finally adopts this view. He proceeds with the game, although with the poorest of hands, consisting, on the action level of the drama, only of servitors and old captains. These must be thought of as spot cards in the suit of hearts ("fiery spots," I.iv.12), and, as Enobarbus warns, capable of taking only "odd tricks." Antony, nevertheless, speaks with bravado:

Know, my *hearts*,
I hope well of tomorrow and will *lead* you.
(IV.iii.41-42)

A speech by Scarus, no doubt enigmatical to those who read on the plot level alone, becomes richly meaningful in the light of the Card Game Pattern:

I had a wound here that was like a T,
But now 'tis made an H. (IV.vii.7-8)

That is to say, the *hearts* ("H"), however low, are at the moment *trumps* ("T"). Antony wins his few "odd tricks" and Scarus eagerly takes them in:

Let us score their *backs*
And snatch 'em up. (IV.vii.12-13)

It will be remembered that the surface action of the drama in Act IV, Scenes v,vi,vii and viii, is entirely concerned with Antony's successful but hopelessly futile sortie against Caesar's encompassing army. The way in which the irony of this success-failure is underlined by the mood-music of trumpets is one of the most subtly amazing effects of the *Triumph* Imagery. The stage directions order trumpets to sound in all these scenes, and, in the last, Antony orders, "Trumpeter,/ With brazen din blast you the city's ears" (IV.viii.35-36). Now bearing in mind that, as even Kittredge perceived, "triumph" signifies "trump," it follows that "trump" signifies "triumph." Therefore "trumpets" (or "trump-ettes") signifies "triumph-ettes"—or *hollow victories.*

After Antony's "self hand" has taken his own life, has "triumph'd [trumped] on itself" (IV.xv.15), he may be considered as permanently retired from play. For a brief interval, Cleopatra contemplates playing alone, but for a person of her temperament there is no stimulus in Solitaire: "patience is sottish" (IV.xv.79). Her faith in a better run of cards is soon restored—"my hands I'll trust," (IV.iv.49)—and the fifth act finds her trying to match skill with Caesar. Eagerly she demands the deal—"Quick, quick, good hands!" (V.ii.39). The play in Act V, Scene ii, is quick and decisive. The stake, consisting of Cleopatra and her treasure, is won by Caesar through his finesse with Dolabella. "For the Queen, I'll take her," says the latter. A moment later we hear her dazedly ask, "Is't not your trick?" and the reply, "Your loss is, as yourself, great." Then comes Cleopatra's hopeless "He'll lead me then in triumph?" (V.ii.66,101,109), and the replay can be only Yes. She is now the trump card of Caesar, and the imagistic prophecy of Act II, Scene ii, line 189, where she is called "a most triumphant lady" is thus ironically fulfilled.

The manner in which our queen of clubs, by self-destruction, robs the winner of his triumph must be prefaced by a word of explanation. Throughout the drama, the lesser characters have themselves been busy at cards—their game not Triumph but one of a humbler sort. In Act I, Scene ii (rich in gaming imagery throughout), Charmian says, "Let me be married to three *kings* . . . and companion me with my mistress." Since her mistress is a queen, and only queens can "companion" with queens, it is obvious that Charmian is praying for a full-house-kings-high. Now nothing is more striking in *Antony and Cleopatra* than the spectacle of deterioration in its titular characters, and the way the imagery suggests progressive vulgarity, as when Antony invites Cleopatra to sit on his lap and play his trump cards ("ride on the pants triumphing," IV.iii.16). As Acts IV and V continue, the royal characters advert periodically to the more squalid game of their retainers, and we are thus prepared for the ruse by which Cleopatra saves herself from being led in trump by Caesar. The fatal asps are brought her by a *Clown,* and this *Clown,* far from being a tasteless intrusion upon the tragic close of the drama, is the crowning piece in the Pattern of Card Game Imagery. Into the game of Triumph is introduced, to Caesar's complete surprise, a type of card normally used only in the humble game of more lowly people—in a word, the joker.

It is from the humbler game that the valedictory imagery of *Antony and Cleopatra* is drawn. The lovers had been called in the opening scene of the drama "a mutual pair" and, in the concluding speech, we hear,

> No grave upon the earth shall clip in it
> A *pair* so famous. (V.ii.362-63)

The objection that a *pair* consists, not of a king and queen, but of two kings or two queens,* has been deftly met by the poet as early as Act I, Scene iv, lines 5-7, with Caesar's statement that Antony

> . . . is not more manlike
> Than Cleopatra, nor the queen of Ptolemy
> More womanly than he,

thus effecting that sexual homogeneity necessary to "a mutual pair." To the objection sometimes plaintively made that the reader's mind is unable to retain the relationship between two such widely separated pieces of data in an imagistic pattern, we can only reply, if reply we must, that there is considerable difference in the strength of human *minds,* and that if we must ignore Shakespeare's intention merely because of the incapacity of the "generality," we might as well exclaim at once, with Amy Lowell, "God, what are patterns for!"

And thus we leave them, a *famous pair,* but *clipped* even in their grave—enclosed, that is, in the mendacious atmosphere of a gambling dive or clip-joint. *It is a bitter play!*

Before putting into words my concluding revelation of the nature of *Antony and Cleopatra,* I must remark that the serious critic who would discharge with awareness his high office, and nurture such areas of sensibility as our era affords, must, sooner or later, as the greatest living critical, poetical and spiritual guide himself unerringly perceived, consider Shakespeare. It is a taxing ministry, because Shakespearean drama has been so "clapper-clawed with the palms of the vulgar"—the indiscriminate and undiscriminating hordes of mere readers and playgoers—that the mere task of de-degradation seems simply overwhelming. The only way in which we can combat the distressing pervasiveness of poetic non-perceptivity is by patient effort. The present admittedly incomplete survey of the imagery of *Antony and Cleopatra* must illustrate to those who have viewed the work as a mere chronicle of love and empire that what Shakespeare has actually done has been to show in conflict the rational Caesar and the passionate

* The author missed a trick here, the only serious flaw in his clever conceit. In the earliest English literature we encounter only "pair of cards" where today we would say "deck" or "pack of cards." The Oxford English Dictionary enters pair as "a set, not confined to two" with a citation as early as 1530 and in a specific sense as "a pack (of cards)," while deck did not show up until 1593 and must have been a neologism to Shakespeare, and pack came even later (1597). Therefore the objection that the author anticipates and jousts would not be valid if made.

Antony, with Cleopatra—a person of by no means unquestionable integrity—as a distinct factor in the latter's downfall. On the cosmic level, the new insights provided by adequate attention to the thematic imagery are even richer and more novel. The fact that the *ace* is never played and *never can be played** by worldly actors, the fact that the characters are both players at cards and *cards played* intimates to us that Man's Destiny Is Not Wholly In His *own hands.* Once we have grasped the thought, we are amazed that it has not been grasped before, either in connection with this great drama or with an even greater object of contemplation—human life in general. Now that the idea dawns upon us, we realize that it has struggled for expression elsewhere in Shakespeare, notably in the wood-working imagery in *Hamlet:*

> There's a divinity that shapes our ends,
> Rough-hew them how we will.

The message, and I use the word unashamedly, brought to us by Shakespeare is, then, in last analysis, the message brought us by Mr. Eliot—the lesson of humility. It is with humility that I proffer it to the world.

¶ *There could be arguments ad infinitum over the coincidence of the numbers derivable from a pack of playing cards with various key numbers in astronomy, mathematics, and other sciences. Rosicrucians and many Masons can plausibly relate certain playing-card numbers to the Great Pyramid in Egypt or to the Temple of Solomon at Jerusalem. Such incursions into the occult may be very ancient, but the earliest extant record is a French pamphlet published at Brussels in 1778, purporting to be the testimony of a soldier named Louis Bras-de-fer (arms of iron); it was translated and circulated in England within the year as a broadside titled:*

> THE PERPETUAL ALMANACK, OR GENTLEMAN-SOLDIER'S PRAYER-BOOK: *shewing how one Richard Middleton was taken before the Mayor of the city he was in for using cards in church during Divine Service: being a droll, merry and humorous account of an odd affair that happened to a private soldier in the 60th Regiment of Foot.*

THE SERJEANT commanded his party to the church, and when the parson had ended his prayer, he took his text, and all of them that had a Bible, pulled it out to find the text; but this soldier had neither Bible, Almanack, nor Common-Prayer Book, but he put his hand in his pocket and pulled out a pack of cards, and spread them before him as he sat; and while the parson was preaching, he first kept looking at one card and then at another. The serjeant of the company saw him, and said,

"Richard, put up your cards, for this is no place for them."

"Never mind that," said the soldier, "you have no business with me here."

Now the parson had ended his sermon, and all was over: the soldiers repaired to the church-yard and the commanding officer gave the word of command to fall in, which they did. The serjeant of the city came, and took the man prisoner. "Man, you are my prisoner," said he.

"Sir," said the soldier, "what have I done that I am your prisoner?"

"You have played a game at cards in the church."

"No," said the soldier, "I have not play'd a game, for I only looked at a pack."

"No matter for that, you are my prisoner."

"Where must we go?" said the soldier.

"You must go before the Mayor," said the serjeant.

So he took him before the Mayor; and when they came to the Mayor's house, he was at dinner.

When he had dined he came down to them, and said,

"Well, serjeant, what do you want with me?"

"I have brought a soldier before you for playing at cards in the church."

"What? That soldier?"

"Yes."

"Well, soldier, what have you to say for yourself?"

"Much, sir, I hope."

"Well and good; but if you have not, you shall be punished the worst that ever man was."

"Sir," said the soldier, "I have been five weeks upon the march, and have but little to subsist on; and am without either Bible, Almanack, or Common-Prayer Book, or anything but a pack of cards: I hope to satisfy Your Honour of the purity of my intentions."

Then the soldier pulled out of his pocket the pack of cards, which he spread before the Mayor; he then began with the Ace.

"When I see the Ace," said he, "it puts me in mind that there is one God only; when I see the Deuce, it puts me in mind of the Father and the

* Alas, it would have lost if played then; see note on page 11.

Son; when I see the Tray, it puts me in mind of the Father, Son, and Holy Ghost; when I see the Four, it puts me in mind of the four Evangelists, that penned the Gospel, viz. Matthew, Mark, Luke, and John; when I see the Five, it puts me in mind of the five wise virgins who trimmed their lamps; there were ten, but five were foolish, who were shut out. When I see the Six, it puts me in mind that in six days the Lord made Heaven and Earth; when I see the Seven, it puts me in mind that on the seventh day God rested from all the works which he had created and made, wherefore the Lord blessed the seventh day, and hallowed it. When I see the Eight, it puts me in mind of the eight righteous persons that were saved when God drowned the world, viz. Noah, his wife, three sons, and their wives. When I see the Nine, it puts me in mind of nine lepers that were cleansed by our Saviour; there were ten, but nine never returned God thanks; when I see the Ten, it puts me in mind of the Ten Commandments that God gave Moses on Mount Sinai on the two tables of stone."

He took the Knave, and laid it aside.

"When I see the Queen, it puts me in mind of the Queen of Sheba, who came from the furthermost parts of the world to hear the wisdom of King Solomon, for she was as wise a woman as he was a man; for she brought fifty boys and fifty girls all clothed in boy's apparel, to show before King Solomon, for him to tell which were boys, and which were girls; but he could not, until he called for water for them to wash themselves; the girls washed up to their elbows, and the boys only up to their wrists; so King Solomon told by that. And when I see the King, it puts me in mind of the great King of Heaven and Earth, which is God Almighty, and likewise his Majesty King George, to pray for him."

"Well," said the Mayor, "you have a very good description of all the cards, except one, which is lacking."

"Which is that?" said the soldier.

"The Knave," said the Mayor.

"Oh, I can give Your Honour a very good description of that, if Your Honour won't be angry."

"No, I will not," said the Mayor, "if you will not term me to be the Knave."

"Well," said the soldier, "the greatest that I know is the serjeant of the city, that brought me here."

"I don't know," said the Mayor, "that he is the greatest knave, but I am sure that he is the greatest fool."

¶[*This is apparently the end of the story; but in the broadside it was continued without a break to embrace a different but similar story that dealt with the calendar rather than the Bible:*

"When I count how many spots there are in a pack of cards, I find there are three hundred and sixty-five; there are so many days in a year. When I count how many cards there are in a pack, I find there are fifty-two; there are so many weeks in a year. When I count how many tricks in a pack, I find there are thirteen; there are so many [lunar] months in a year. You see, sir, that this pack of cards is a Bible, Almanack, Common-Prayer Book, and pack of cards to me."

Then the Mayor called for a loaf of bread, a piece of good cheese, and a pot of good beer, and gave the soldier a piece of money, bidding him to go about his business, saying he was the cleverest man he had ever seen.

¶[*The afterthought on the calendar probably came from a similar French pamphlet that antedated Bras-de-fer or Middleton by nearly a hundred years. This pamphlet went further: The four suits reminded the soldier of the four seasons, the twelve face cards reminded him of the twelve calendar months. Even in this seventeenth-century example there was the same mistake of counting 365 spots on the cards, a total patently impossible since it is not divisible by four and there are four equal suits. Counting jack as 11, queen 12, and king 13, you can get up to 364 and no farther.* ¶[*Another seventeenth-century (1683) manuscript tells how a parson rescued himself as cleverly as the soldiers Bras-de-fer and Middleton had done:*

The Parson that loved gaming better than his eyes made a good use of it when he put up his cards in his gown-sleeve in haste, when the clerk came and told him the last stave was a-singing. 'Tis true, that in the height of his reproving the Parish for their neglect of holy duties, upon the throwing out of his zealous arm, the cards dropt out of his sleeve, and flew about the church. What then? He bid one boy take up a card and asked him what it was—the boy answers the King of Clubs. Then he bid another boy take up another card.

"What was that?"

"The Knave of Spades."

"Well," quo' he, "now tell me, who made ye?" The boy could not well tell.

Quo' he to the next, "Who redeemed ye?" —that was a harder question.

"Look ye," quoth the Parson, "you think this was an accident, and laugh at it; but I did it on purpose to shew you that had you taught your children your catechism, as well as to know their cards, they would have been better provided to answer material questions when they come to church."

THE CURSE OF SCOTLAND

Just as crapshooters have their nicknames for throws of the dice ("box cars," "snake-eyes," "eighter from Decatur"), card players have nicknamed their cards. The most picturesque name is "the devil's bedposts" for the four of clubs; the most enigmatic, though the best known, is "the curse of Scotland" for the nine of diamonds. The late A. E. Manning-Foster, founder and editor of Bridge Magazine (London), explored the legends surrounding this fatal card:

"THE Curse of Scotland" is a popular name for the nine of diamonds, but nobody knows exactly why. There are at least six possible origins for the term, as follows:

(1) That in the once popular round game "Pope Joan," the nine of diamonds was called "the Pope," the Antichrist of Scottish reformers.

(2) That the nine of diamonds was the chief card in the game "Cornette," introduced into Scotland by the unhappy Queen Mary.

(3) That "Butcher" Cumberland wrote the orders for the Battle of Culloden (1746) on the back of the card. This is very doubtful.

(4) That the order for the massacre of Glencoe was signed on the back of this card.

(5) That the dispositions for the fatal field of Flodden (1513) were drawn up on it by James IV of Scotland. Both these last have only the slightest authority.

(6) That it is derived from the nine lozenges that formed the arms of the Earl of Stair, who was especially loathed for his connection with the massacre of Glencoe and the Union with England (1707).

The foregoing account overlooks the seventh and probably the best account: that Charles I (Stuart) was holding the nine of diamonds, about to play it in a card game, when he was arrested and started on his way to execution.

COUNTING THE CARDS

AMONG the many remarkable coincidences recorded in connection with the standard deck of playing cards, none is more remarkable than this: The number of letters in the names of the cards totals to exactly 52, the same as the number of cards in the deck, not only in English but in many other languages as well:

English		*French*		*Dutch*		*Swedish*		*German*	
ace	3	as	2	aas	3	ess	3	as	2
two	3	deux	4	twee	4	tvaa	4	zwei	4
three	5	trois	5	drie	4	trea	4	drei	4
four	4	quatre	6	vier	4	fyra	4	vier	4
five	4	cinq	4	vyf	3	femma	5	fünf	4
six	3	six	3	zes	3	sexa	4	sechs	4
seven	5	sept	4	zeven	5	ajua	4	sieben	6
eight	5	huit	4	acht	4	atta	4	acht	3
nine	4	neuf	4	negen	5	nia	3	neun	4
ten	3	dix	3	tien	4	tia	3	zehn	4
jack	4	valet	5	boer	4	knekt	5	Bube	4
queen	5	reine	5	vrouw	5	dam	3	Dame	4
king	4	roi	3	heer	4	konung	6	König	5
Total	52		52		52		52		52

Note that in French the queen must be *reine*, whereas she is most often referred to as *la dame;* and that in German the count is correct only if the digraph *ch* is counted as a single letter.

[Here is a bit of card curiosa that speaks for itself, though it has one flaw: With the popularity of "one-eyes" as wild cards in Poker, almost anyone may know (and the erudite editors of Games Digest should have known) the answer to No. 1. That would make the par score 1 instead of 0. With the rest of it we agree entirely.

Do You Know Playing Cards?

by GERTRUDE MCGIFFERT

THE editors of *Games Digest* are all card-players. They have spent a goodly portion of their lives doing nothing except look at playing cards. Therefore they were much interested in the list of questions contributed by Mrs. McGiffert. And what do you think happened?

Not one of us could answer a single one of the questions! That shows how observant card players are.

So here's the list; and if you take it honestly (no guessing) here's our recommended scoring:

Zero: Par!
1: Brilliant.
2: Colossal.
3: You cheat.

1. What king shows his profile?
2. What king has no mustache?
3. What king holds a battle-ax?
4. What king wears ermine?
5. What king holds no sword?
6. What king's beard is not parted?
7. What king has a daisy belt buckle?
8. What queen has a scepter?
9. What queen has bands of Grecian keys?
10. What queen has a long belt buckle?
11. What queen shows her hair next her face on one side?
12. What queen wears a breast pin?
13. What queen holds her flower between her first and second finger?
14. What jack wears a leaf in his cap?
15. What jack shows his full face?
16. What jack holds a leaf to his lips?
17. What jacks carry battle-axes?
18. What jack carries a staff?
19. What jack has no mustache?
20. What jack has two rows of curls?
21. What jack wears buttons on his coat?

Correct answers may be found in a deck of playing cards.

[Gallup-type surveys of card-playing began about 1940 and have since become annual phenomena. Each year's list of the "ten most popular games" has come to be almost as eagerly awaited as the lists of the ten best-dressed women and has all the validity of a Trendex or similar report on a TV show's popularity. We use the first such report; it had the most information of interest to card-players, and subsequent surveys have not shown any material change except of course that Gin Rummy has moved up into the top ten and Canasta suddenly appeared—and, lo, led all the rest.

Card-Playing in the U.S.A.

IN November 1940, the first nationwide study of card-playing in this country was conducted by the Association of American Playing Card Manufacturers.

In conducting the survey, door-to-door interviewers called upon homes in 24 U. S. cities representative of small, medium and large communities in every section of the country. Families interviewed were selected at random, except that the number of families in each of the four income brackets—wealthy, comfortable, getting along and poor—was carefully controlled to correspond with U. S. Census percentages.

In brief, the survey shows that cards are still the country's favorite social recreation and that Contract Bridge is still the most popular game—and on the increase.

More than four-fifths of U. S. families—83 per cent, to be exact—play cards, the survey indicates. And just in case this seems high, cards are found in 87 per cent of American homes. Most of the 4 per cent who own but do not play cards explained that they kept them on hand for "company" or other members of the family.

For comparison: 83 per cent of U. S. homes have radios, 36 per cent have telephones, 73 per cent have electricity.

Certainly, then, on the basis of the survey, more people play cards than take part in any other form of recreation except listening to the radio, going to the movies and reading. The playing of cards extends through all income levels, although decreasing from 99 per cent in the top bracket to 69 per cent in the poorest section of the population.

The most widely *known* card game, and undoubtedly the best known game of any kind, is Rummy, the survey indicates. Of all families interviewed, 49 per cent play Rummy, 45 per cent know Solitaire and 44 per cent play Contract Bridge.

Of the 77 different card games played in this

country (see below), eight are known to more than 22 per cent of the people interviewed, as shown below. Of the other 69 games, some are sectional, some are foreign, and the remainder are more or less familiar all over.

BEST-KNOWN CARD GAMES

(*Each symbol represents 3% of families interviewed who know how to play these games*)

Game	Families
Rummy	♠♠♠♠♠♠♠♠♠♠♠♠♠♠♠♠ 49%
Solitaire	♠♠♠♠♠♠♠♠♠♠♠♠♠♠♠ 45%
Contract	♠♠♠♠♠♠♠♠♠♠♠♠♠♠♠ 44%
Poker	♠♠♠♠♠♠♠♠♠♠♠♠ 37%
Auction	♠♠♠♠♠♠♠♠♠♠♠ 34%
Pinochle	♠♠♠♠♠♠♠♠♠♠♠ 33%
Hearts	♠♠♠♠♠♠♠♠♠♠ 30%
Five Hundred	♠♠♠♠♠♠♠ 22%

Of Bridge players asked, 60 per cent said they play as much or more today than they did five years ago.

While Bridge is increasing its hold, the survey indicates that other card games have declined slightly in popularity. Of the families interviewed, 43 per cent said they didn't play cards as much now as they did five years ago, 42 per cent said they played as much or more, and 15 per cent didn't know or didn't reply.

The surprising social significance of Bridge in America is perhaps best indicated by the frequency with which the game is played. Among both auction and contract players questioned, 41 per cent play once a week or *oftener* and another 16 per cent play once a fortnight.

Also of interest: 35 per cent of women Bridge players belong to a Bridge club. Here income makes a big difference. Among women Bridge players from the wealthiest group, 48 per cent are card-club members; 41 per cent in the next group belong; the figure slips to 33 per cent for the lower middle classification; and only 13 per cent of women players in the lowest bracket go to Bridge clubs. (These clubs, incidentally, are "Thursday afternoon" social affairs and not Bridge clubs as they are known in large cities.)

The popularity of cards among children was clearly indicated by the survey with 45 games mentioned by the families interviewed as "favorites." Surprising, however, was the number of adult games which children played—particularly was this true of Contract, Auction and Pinochle—and the number of "party" games at which many children can play.

Although two card games are slightly better known, Contract Bridge is by all odds the most popular and is played by far the most often. It is the favorite card game of 47 per cent of U. S. women and 30 per cent of the men interviewed.

The nine most popular card games and the percentage of persons preferring each:

WOMEN		MEN	
Contract	47%	Contract	30%
Auction	18%	Poker	22%
Pinochle	11%	Pinochle	21%
Rummy	7%	Auction	10%
500	6%	Rummy	6%
Poker	5%	500	4%
Whist	3%	Whist	3%
Solitaire	2%	Hearts	2%
Hearts	1%	Solitaire	2%

As for variations between income groups, the popularity of contract declines markedly from the wealthiest to the poorest brackets and the popularity of Pinochle increases by about the same proportions among both men and women. Poker among men, contrariwise, keeps its position in second place through all income groups. Apparently this grand old American game is also the most democratic.

Noteworthy is the prevalence of Auction Bridge, particularly in the lower income groups and in New England. Among women, it is apparently the most popular game for those who do not play contract.

77 CARD GAMES AMERICA PLAYS

(*Asterisk* indicates children also play this game*)

Rummy*
Solitaire*
Contract Bridge*
Poker*
Auction Bridge*
Pinochle*
Hearts*
Five Hundred*
Cribbage*
Whist*
Hi Five*
Carioca
Set Back*
Bézique
Euchre
Cassino*
Spoon
Americana
Michigan*
Concentration*
Battle*
Pig*
Three Pair
Sixty-six
War*
Black Jack or 21*
Red Dog
Russian Bank*
Go Fish (Fish)*
Fish Nor*
7-Up
Coon King
40 String
Strip*
Thirty-one*
Gin Rummy*
Slam
Michigan Bridge
Kitty
Bonanza
Oh Hell
Multiple Solitaire
Forty-five
Old Maid*
Hassenpfeffer
Pounce*
Slap Jack*
Datta
Pitch
Hump
Pedro*
Honeymoon Bridge*
Donkey*
5-Up
Tong
Deck Rummy
Liverpool Rummy*
Contract Rummy*
Chinese Rummy
Knock Rummy
Whistle
Banker and Broker*
Skat
Solo
Fan Tan*
Tripoli*
Seven and One Half
Biscola
Rekop*
Airplane*
Old Man's Bundle*
High Card*
Grown Up*
Baseball Rummy*
Books*
Snap*
Everlasting*

WHIST

[The most popular card authority of the nineteenth century was a London surgeon named Henry Jones, Jr., who signed his books with the pen name "Cavendish" because he was a member of the Cavendish Club when (in 1863) his first book was published. This book and most of Cavendish's other writings were on Whist, but he was a serious student of other games and their histories. The following essay, though published in the 1870s, remains as good a round-up of the earliest card games as has ever been written.

On the Origin and Development of . . . Card Games
by
CAVENDISH (HENRY JONES, JR.)

[The author has identified the Tarot cards as the first known to Europe and has drawn the conclusion (as we still do) that the game Tarok or Tarocchi played with them must have been the first game. His essay continues:]

ASSUMING that the original game of all was the *Tarocchi* of Venice, played with seventy-eight cards (fifty-six numerals and twenty-two tarots), the first alteration was probably made by the Florentines, who increased the emblematic pieces to forty-one, and invented the game of *Minchiate* with ninety-seven cards. After this all the changes in the pack were in the direction of reduction, it being probably found that packs consisting of so many cards were awkward to handle. Accordingly, a little later, the Bolognese diminished the pack to sixty-two (twenty-two tarots and forty numerals), the two, three, four and five of each suit being rejected. The game played with these cards was called *Tarocchino.* And the Venetians themselves, at a very early period, abolished all the true tarots and suppressed the three, four, five and six of each suit (the pack now consisting of forty cards), and termed the game played with these packs *Trappola.*

When cards traveled through Europe, the tarot cards found comparatively but little favor, though to this day tarot cards may be procured in Italy and in the south of France. Trappola cards (*Drapulir Karten*) are also still published at Vienna. But the vast majority of packs soon came to consist of fifty-two numeral cards, one of the four coat cards being removed from each suit. It seems not unlikely that on the loss of one of the pictures the ace was raised to its present rank, instead of the ten, in order to preserve the original number of cards of superior dignity. If so, this accounts for the lowest card ranking as the highest in so many games.

With these fifty-two cards, some being occasionally suppressed, various countries invented . . . and established their several games. No nations seemed content to adopt *en bloc* any game as it traveled to them. Though the varieties introduced were marvelously ingenious and numerous, the old fundamental elements were maintained, in most instances so closely that there is no great difficulty in tracing the pedigrees of the principal modern games, owing to their easily recognized family likenesses to older ones.

In order to do this it will be desirable to start with the early games and to trace their successive developments until the games now in vogue are reached.

In a *Canzone* of Lorenzo de Medici, Flush (*il Frusso*) and Bassett are referred to. The date of the *"Canti Carnascialeschi"* in which the *Canzone* appears is doubtful; but it is among the writer's early compositions. He died in 1492.

It may be assumed from the name *il Frusso* that a flush (cards of the same suit) was one of the objects, or the principal object, striven after by the players. No doubt this game was an early edition of Primero. Baretti's Italian Dictionary (Florence, 1832), under Frusso says, "What we now call Primiera and the English Primero." It should rather be the Spaniards, for Primero is only the Spanish form of the Italian Primiera. At Primiera a flush is the most important hand. Primero is undoubtedly a very old game, of either Italian or Spanish origin. It is mentioned by Berni (*Capitolo del Gioco della Primiera, 1526*) with *Bassetta, il Frusso, Tarocchi, Sminchiate,* and other games. [Richard] Seymour (*The Court Gamester,* 1734) says Ombre is an improvement of Primero "formerly in great Vogue among the *Spaniards.*" But Primero has no relation to Ombre. Primero is supposed by some to have been the oldest game played with numeral cards; but it is now pretty well ascertained that Trappola was earlier, and so also probably were Flush and Bassett, as the simpler games would naturally precede the more complex ones.

Primero was played in various ways and with packs of different degrees of completeness. Thus in Florence the sevens, eights, and nines were removed from the pack; in Rome they were kept.

The principal features of the game (as nearly as can be made out from old descriptions which are very obscure) were as follows: Four cards were dealt to each player, and the rest was made or set at the second card. This probably means that when two cards had been dealt a pool was formed, and then the other two cards were dealt. The first player might either stand or pass. If he passed he was at liberty to discard one or two of his cards, and so on with the others.

Any player having a good hand vyed on it, *i.e.,* raised the stakes, and finally the hands were shown. The principal hands were 1 flush, 2 prime, 3 point. The highest flush was the best, then the highest prime (all four cards held being of different suits); and if there was no flush or prime, the highest point won. The point was thus reckoned; seven (best card) counted for 21; six for 18; five for 15; four for 14; three for 13; two for 12; ace for 16; coat cards, 10 each. Also, if agreed, *quinola,* knave of hearts, might be made any card or suit. Another variation, probably of later introduction, was that four cards of a sort, as four sevens, were superior to a flush.

Primero was played also in France. It is included by Rabelais in the list of games that Gargantua played, under the name of *la Prime.* The celebrated history was finished about 1545;* but a portion of it was published earlier.

In France, the game of Prime, elaborated, appears to have been played under the name of *l'Ambigu ou le Meslé. La Maison des Jeux Académiques* (Paris, 1665) says *"Le Meslé s'appelle tant parce qu'il tient in effet quelque chose de tous les autres, et qu'en le voyant jouer on ne saurait discerner si c'est prime ou autre semblable."* In later editions of the Academy it is called *l'Ambigu* or the Banquet (literally a banquet of meat and fruit both together—*repas ou l'on sert en même temps la viande et le fruit*), and is stated to be an assemblage of different sorts of games. It was played with forty cards, all the figured cards being thrown out. Two cards were dealt to each player. The players then stood or passed; if the latter, they discarded one or both of their cards, and had others in exchange. The pool was next put down, and two more cards dealt to

* The History of Gargantua and Pantagruel, of course; the first volume was published in 1532, the fifth and last in 1562. The list of games appears in the first volume.

each player. Each then examined his hand and either stood or passed. Any one that stood might say *va* or go, and increase his stake or go better. If no one else increased the stake to equal the amount already gone, the person who backed his hand took the pool. But if two or more players chose to make *vade,* each of them might discard again or not, and then each that stood might pass or make the *renvi,* that is go better again. If no one stood the *renvi,* the player making it won. If any stood it, they were at liberty to *renvier* once more; and the stakes of those who stood the second *renvi* now being equal, the hands had to be shown. The winner took the pool, the *vade* and the *renvis,* and in addition certain payments from each of the other players, whether they stood the game or not. The *fredon,* four cards of the same denomination, was the best hand, next *flush-sequence,* (four cards of the same suit in sequence), next *tricon* (three cards of the same denomination), combined with *prime* (four cards of different suits), then *flush, tricon, sequence, prime,* and lastly *point.* Point was two or three cards of the same suit, the highest point being that which contained the most pips.

Primero was also played in England. Shakespeare represents the King (Henry VIII, act v, scene 1) as playing Primero with the Duke of Suffolk, and the game was fashionable in the time of Elizabeth. In J. Florio's *Second Frutes* (1591) the following description of Primero occurs:

"S.—Goe to, let us play at Primero then. . . . A.—Let us agree of our Game. What shall we plaie for? S.—One shilling stake and three rest. A.—Agreede, goe to, discarde. S.—I vye it; will you hould it? A.—Yea, sir, I hould it and revye it; but dispatch. S.—Faire and softly, I praie you. 'Tis a great matter. I cannot have a chiefe carde. A.—And I have none but coate cardes. S.—Will you put it to me? A.—You bid me to losse. S.—Will you swigg? A.—'Tis the least part of my thought. S.—Let my rest goe then, if you please. A.—I hould it. What is your rest? S.—Three crownes and one third, showe. What are you? A.—I am four and fiftie; and you? S.—Oh! filthie luck; I have lost it one ace."

Later than the sixteenth century, a bastard kind of Primero called Post and Pair was much played in the west of England. A pack of fifty-two cards was used. [Charles] Cotton wrote (*Compleat Gamester, 1674*): "This play depends much upon daring; so that some may win very considerably, who have the boldness to venture much upon the Vye, although their cards are very indifferent.

"You must first stake at Post, then at Pair; after this deal two cards apiece, then stake at the Seat, and then deal the third Card about. The eldest hand may pass and come in again if any of the Gamesters vye it."

Post would appear to have been the point, the best cards being two tens and an ace, counting one-and-twenty. A pair royal (three of a kind) beat everything else, and "wins all, both Post, Pair and Seat." What seat is, Cotton does not explain. It seems to have been a third stake won by the player who held the best card out of those last dealt, as was the case at the sister game of Brag.

Vying continued until all your antagonists were daunted and brought to submission. But "If all the Gamesters keep in till all have done, and by consent shew their Cards, the best Cards carry the game. Now according to agreement those that keep in till last may divide the stakes, or show the best Card for it."

The more modern game of Brag is evidently Post and Pair with variations. It was played at least as early as Hoyle's time, for Hoyle wrote "A short Treatise of the Game of Brag" in 1751. It was played with fifty-two cards. The players laid down three stakes apiece, one for the best whist card turned up in the deal (this is probably the "seat" of the older game); a second for the best brag hand (pair); and a third for obtaining thirty-one, or the number nearest to it (post). Three cards were dealt to each player, the last one all round being turned up, to decide the first stake. The next stake was won by the best brag hand, or by the boldest player in backing his hand. Two cards, viz., knave of clubs and nine of diamonds (according to Hoyle three braggers), were made favorite cards, and were entitled to rank as any card, like the *quinola* at Primero, natural pairs or natural pairs royal, however, taking precedence of artificial ones. Any player saying "I brag," and increasing his stake, won, if no one answered with a similar or larger deposit. If any one answered, the bragging continued as at Post and Pair, till one would brag no more or made the stakes equal and called a show. After Hoyle's date, flush-sequences, flushes, and sequences were added to the hands that might win in bragging.

For the third stake the players could draw cards from the stock to increase the point; but any one over-drawing lost his chance.

It only remains to observe that the game of Poker, originally played in America with fifty-two cards, may be described as developed Brag [with] the stakes for highest card and point omitted.

It is curious that the game of Poker, by many considered a new game, should be traceable to a game at least four hundred years old.

Thus, Flush becomes Primiera, Primero, or Prime. Prime is modified into Ambigu. The offshoots of the last are Post and Pair and Brag. And lastly, "throwing back" more nearly in some respects to the parent games, Poker, now a national game in America, is invented.

In Germany the game of Lansquenet, under the name of *Landsknechtspiel,* played with fifty-two cards, was a favorite, and by some authorities is called the national German card game. It is said by Bettinelli to have been a kind of Bassett or Faro (both very ancient) under another name. All these are mere games of chance, with an advantage to the dealer or holder of the bank. Of games of chance Lansquenet is about the simplest, depending only on whether a card of one denomination is turned up before a card of another denomination. It is, in fact, hardly a game at all, but merely a complicated way of playing pitch-and-toss with cards instead of coins; and this remark applies to every chance game from Bassett to Rouge et Noir. In Germany, Lansquenet seems to have been the most usual pitch-and-toss card game; but to elevate it to the dignity of a national card game, is to treat it with a respect it does not deserve.

Spain is credited with the invention of several games. Her claim to the invention of Primero has already been noticed; but preference has been given to the view that Primero is only the Spanish rendering of the Italian Primiera. *La Gana Pierde* was an early and popular game, and is no doubt the same game as *Coquimbert* (evidently a corruption of *qui gagne perd*), mentioned in the Gargantua list. In France a very similar, if not the same, game was called *Reversis,* just as there Primero, with a difference, was rechristened *Ambigu.* In the *Académie des Jeux** it is said that *Reversis* was originally Spanish, and that it was called *Reversis* because (in some respects) it was the reverse of all other games. If played in England it might have been under another name; Cotgrave [dictionary] says that a card game called Loosing-lodam (formerly played in England) was very similar to Reversis, and Urquhart translates the Coquimbert of Rabelais by "losing load him," probably a misprint for Losing-lodam. Modern Hoyles (including additional games not written by Hoyle) contain Reversis; but no one ever seems to play at it.

* A book of the rules of games, by the Abbé Bellecoeur, published in Paris in 1659.

Reversis was played with forty-eight cards, the tens being thrown out from a complete pack. Many old Spanish packs contain no tens.

The national game of Spain was and is Ombre. It is played by three persons with forty cards, the tens, nines, and eights being discarded. It is a very complicated game, and, on that account alone, one would suppose it must have had a simpler predecessor. But none of the writers on the subject have discovered any similar earlier and less complex game. It introduces an entirely new feature, viz.: that of playing with a partner or ally, instead of, as in the older games, every man's hand (in two senses) being against every one else's.

Ombre is a game of great merit, and was much played at one time in France and England. Modifications of it also were invented, viz.: *Ombre à deux, Tredille, Quadrille* (four players), *Quintille* (five players), *Sextille* (six players), and *Médiateur* or *Préférence,* which again has variations such as *Solitaire* and *Piquemedrille. Tresillio* and *Rocambor,* much played in Spanish South America, are simply Ombre except in the mode of marking.*

The invention of Piquet is generally attributed to France. It is called by Rabelais both *le Piquet* and *le Cent;* and the same game under the name of *Cientos* was known very early in Spain.

Piquet, under the name of Sant, a corruption of *Cent,* was played in England until nearly the middle of the seventeenth century, when the French name of Piquet was adopted, contemporaneously with the marriage of Charles I. to a French Princess.

It is, further, not unlikely that Piquet is a developed form of *Ronfa,* a game included in Berni's list. This is in all probability the same game as *la Ronfle* included in Rabelais' list. If these have no connection with Piquet, it is at least a remarkable coincidence that the point at Piquet (one of the most important features in the game) was anciently called *ronfle.*

Whether or not the French national game was a development of the German Sword-game, or of *Ronfa* and *Cientos,* it certainly, under the name of Piquet, became identified with France. Prior to the end of the seventeenth century the game of *Cientos, Cent,* Sant or Piquet was played with a pack of thirty-six cards, the twos,

* The game Solo is modern Ombre.

threes, fours and fives being left out; the sixes were then also withdrawn, and only thirty-two cards used, as at present.

Écarté may also be regarded as a game especially French. As now played it is of quite recent invention; but its earlier forms may be traced back to the time of Berni. He includes in his list *Trionfi,* which may be assumed to be the game called *Trionfo* in Spain (mentioned by Vives, a Spaniard, d.1541, in his "Dialogues" under the name of *Triumphus Hispanicus*). There can be little doubt but that these games are closely related to *la Triomphe* of Rabelais.

Triomphe was played in several ways, either *tête-à-tête,* or with partners, or as a round game. A piquet pack was used, the ace ranking between the knave and ten. Five cards were dealt to each player, by two and by three at a time, and the top card of the stock was turned up for trumps. The players were obliged to win the trick if able. The player or side that won three tricks marked one point; the winners of the *vole* [all five tricks], two points. The game was usually five up. If one side or player was not satisfied they might offer the point to the adversary. If he refused he was bound to win the vole or to have two scored against him.

The same game was played in England, and is described by Cotton under the name of French-Ruff. It appears from Cotton that the players might discard (though the passage is rather obscure), and offering the point is absent from his account of the game.

The family likeness of Triomphe or French-Ruff to Écarté scarcely needs pointing out. The main difference is the addition of a score for the king at Écarté.

The French settlers in America took Triomphe with them, and transformed it into Euchre, now [1878] a national game in the States.*

The game of Triomphe or French-Ruff must not be confused with the English game of Trump or Ruff-and-Honors, the predecessor of our national game of Whist.

Trump seems to have been entirely of English origin; at least no mention of it occurs in continental books on games, the nearest approach to it being *les Honneurs* mentioned by Rabelais. Trump was played in England as early as the beginning of the sixteenth century. The game of Ruff-and-Honors, by some called Slam, was probably the same game, or, if not, a similar game with the addition of a score for honors. It was played by four persons, with fifty-two cards, twelve cards being dealt to each and four left in the stock, the top card of which was turned up for trumps. The holder of the ace of trumps *ruffed, i.e.,* he put out four cards and took in the stock. The game was nine up, and, at the point of eight, honors could be called* as at long Whist.

The game, with a slight modification, was afterwards called Whisk or Whist. Cotton in the *Compleat Gamester,* 1674, says that "Whist is a game not much differing from this [*i.e.,* Ruff-and-Honors], only they put out the Deuces and take in no stock." The trump was the bottom card, and the game was nine up. Whist, then, was originally played with forty-eight cards, and the odd-trick, that important feature in the modern game, was, of course, wanting.

Not long after this the game was made ten up. Cotton, ed. 1709, says the points were "nine in all"; ed. 1721, "ten in all"; ed. 1725, "nine in all"; Seymour, ed. 1734, with which Cotton was incorporated, "ten in all"; and it may be assumed that, simultaneously with this change, the practice of playing with fifty-two cards obtained. While Whist was undergoing these changes, it was occasionally played with *swabbers* or *swobbers,* certain cards (not the honors) which entitled the holder to a stake independently of the general event of the game.

After the *swabbers* were dropped, our national card game having been known as Trump, Ruff-and-Honors, Slam, Whisk, and Whist-and-Swabbers, finally became Whist. Whist it was when Edmond Hoyle wrote (*A Short Treatise On the Game of Whist. By a* GENTLEMAN, 1742), and Whist it has remained.

¶[*There had been English literature on games before; Charles Cotton—adopted son of Izaak Walton and his collaborator in* THE COMPLEAT ANGLER (*1653*)*—put out his own* COMPLEAT GAMESTER *in 1674, and far more of a "Hoyle" it was than Hoyle himself would ever write. Richard Seymour prepared a similar compendium,* THE COURT GAMESTER, *about 1720, for "the little princesses," daughters of George I. But these and various pamphlets were confined*

* Other descendants of *Triomphe*: the English game Nap or Napoleon; the Irish Spoil Five and Forty-five.

* For many years, the rules of Whist permitted the "call." Honors were A, K, Q, J, and a partnership that held three honors scored 2 points. Game was 10, and when a side reached 8, either partner holding two honors would say, "Can ye one, partner?" If his partner held an honor, the game was won. The call was colloquially called the "canye" because of the form of the question.

to gambling games, betting, and cheating. True English literature on card games as an intellectual and respectable subject began with Whist. ¶*Without too great a stretch of the imagination we might attribute the entire mass of this literature to the introduction of hot drinks into England; the Irish historian Edward Lecky (in his* History of the Rise . . . of Rationalism, *1865) did not hesitate to go even further and attribute to this factor much of the intellectual renascence of eighteenth-century Europe. The coffeehouses and the chocolate houses brought together the intelligent middle classes and the exceptional nobility, starved for intellectual companionship. They sat, sipped, and talked. Not since ancient Greece had discussion been so free from dogmatic repression. No subject capable of logical exploration was immune to their scrutiny. Sooner or later the subject was bound to be a card game and Whist was the best candidate.* ¶*Mrs. Hargrave, who told us (page 2) about the origin of playing cards, now tells us how this revolution came about:*

The Reign of Hoyle

by CATHERINE PERRY HARGRAVE

In the winter of 1736 a set of gentlemen who frequented the Crown Coffee House in Bedford Row, of whom the first Lord Folkstone was one and Mr. Edmond Hoyle probably another, forsook Piquet for the ancient English game of Whist, which they studied at length and for the playing of which they laid down the following rules:

Play from the strongest suit.
Study your partner's hand as well as your own.
Never force your partner unnecessarily.
Play to the score.

And this same Mr. Hoyle, publishing *A Short Treatise on the Game of Whist* in 1742, raised the game forever from its lowly estate and made it one of the most enduring of "English games upon the cardes."

THE MYSTERY MAN OF WHIST

Of Mr. Hoyle himself we know almost nothing; he is perhaps the vaguest celebrity of his bewigged and beruffed age. It is said that he was educated for the law, but it was as a writer and instructor in games that he made his name. His first edition was printed in London by John Watts "for the author," but it was so pirated that all later editions were autographed by both author and publisher. For more than a hundred years it was supposed that the only copy of the original first edition was that in the Bodleian Library at Oxford, but recently [1934] another was offered for sale in New York. Of the piracies there are many and they may often be picked up for a song. They* were printed at Bath and reprinted at London in 1743, the title page announcing mysteriously that the book was written "By a Gentleman."

Like Charles Cotton and Richard Seymour, Mr. Hoyle entirely omits the actual directions for playing the game, the number of players, the deal, the lead and the object of the game. But his exposition of the four principles mentioned above is clear, concise and logical. Whist parlance has changed little in all these years. He writes of revokes, sequences and tenaces, and his rules for the play of the elder hand are a masterpiece. When he keeps score, however, he says "nine—love" or "four—love," love standing for nothing, just as it did in the tennis count of those days and as it does today.

COMPLAINTS OF THE MORALISTS

A London paper of about this time dourly complains: "There is a new kind of tutor lately introduced into some families of fashion in this Kingdom, principally to complete the education of the young ladies—namely, a gaming master, who attends his hour as regularly as the music,

* The antecedent is not clear here, but Mrs. Hargrave undoubtedly means that the earliest piracies were printed at Bath. The rather complex record of the editions is as follows: The true first edition was in manuscript, made by copyists and apparently intended for distribution only to Hoyle's private pupils; this was the only edition that Hoyle signed "By a Gentleman" and was published in December 1742. Hoyle's own second edition was the first printed edition, and on this one he put the line "By Edmond Hoyle, *Gent.*" It was published in London early in 1743, perhaps as early as January; but already the manuscript "By a Gentleman" had been set in type and was being printed and published by the pirates. Since Hoyle had a byline on his second edition, the pirates promptly added the same (often misspelling the name, "Edmund" instead of "Edmond"). Somewhere in the course of the second or third edition Hoyle began to sign every copy to foil the pirates, but the pirates simply forged his signature to their own copies and kept on selling. (The Library of Congress has a twelfth edition, catalogued as genuine and purportedly signed by Hoyle and his publisher, but actually a forgery). The pirates were wholly faithful: Every time Hoyle changed editions, they changed editions; every time he added material, they added the same material; every time he reset type, they reset type to conform; every time he signed his name to his copies, they signed his name to theirs. Even the Bodleian's copy cannot but be suspect.

dancing and French master, in order to instruct young misses in principles of the fashionable accomplishment of card playing. However absurd such a conduct in parents may appear, it is undeniably true that such a practise is now introduced by some, and will, it is feared, be adopted by many more."

But Dr. Johnson proclaims ponderously that "card playing generates kindness and consolidates society."

A SUBJECT FOR SATIRE

MEANWHILE Mr. Edmond Hoyle gave lessons not only to the young ladies and gentlemen of London but to their parents as well, selling his treatise to each pupil at first in manuscript form for a guinea a copy. When the printed edition appeared, it received the subtlest flattery of the time and, incidentally, the best possible advertising, through the popular satires it inspired. A play called *The Humours of Whist, as acted every day at White's and other coffee houses and assemblies* came out in the very year that he published the treatise on Whist. The action revolves about Professor Whiston, who is a caricature of Mr. Hoyle and who gives lessons to Sir Calculation Puzzle, an ardent scholar, who gets sadly muddled over Mr. Hoyle's calculations and always loses. There is a prologue, spoken by a waiter, which is a caricature of the introduction to the treatise and ridicules all that Mr. Hoyle says. The waiter tells, among other things, how he has spent forty years at the study of Whist, and he declaims,

"Who will believe that man could e'er exist
Who spent near half an age in studying Whist?
Grew gray with calculation, labor hard,
As if life's business centered on a card?
That such there is let me to those appeal
Who with such liberal hands reward his zeal.
Lo, Whist he makes a science, and our peers
Deign to turn schoolboys in their riper years."

The pupils, and especially Sir Calculation Puzzle, take delight in telling why plays do not turn out as they should according to theory. One of Sir Puzzle's explanations is that the dog ate his opponent's losing card "upon the pinch of the game," whereupon there was a new deal, "and faith, he won."

Mr. Hoyle later published *The Gamesters' Companion, The Accurate Gamester, The Polite Gamester* and *Hoyle's Games,* in which he gave directions for playing Quadrille, Piquet, backgammon and chess as well as Whist. After his death in 1769, there were later editions of them all, and *Hoyle's Games,* added to by each successive editor, is still triumphantly marching along.

Writers on card games of the early nineteenth century delight in grandiloquently quoting Lord Byron's "Troy owes to Homer what Whist owes to Hoyle," and the line is very true. Mr. Hoyle not only made the record of Whist an enduring one, but he made the game itself such a good one that it took its place beside Piquet and Quadrille, which had succeeded Hombre, in the play at the London clubs and the assemblies at Bath, and in Mr. Seymour's *Gamester* of 1754 it is among the games played at court.

Mr. Hoyle's treatise undoubtedly affected the play in the countryside as well, for the rare first edition which was recently offered for sale in New York was found at a county auction. Whist had long been the game of the country squires and clergymen, as well as of the citizenry of the cathedral towns—especially York, Durham, Lincoln and Oxford—and they must all have welcomed Mr. Hoyle's contribution to the game.

But it was not only in the big houses that Whist was played, but in the cottages and the little farm houses as well. Here, as in the homes of the squires, a rubber of Whist had been a common amusement long before the day that Mr. Cotton* wrote so disparagingly that "every child of eight years hath a competent knowledge of this game." Sir Roger de Coverly sent a string of hog's puddings and a pack of cards as a Christmas present to every poor family in his parish, and "two by honours and the odd trick" were as sure a sign of Christmas as frosts and Yule logs, mince pies and frumenty. There were little Whist societies throughout the countryside, and during the winter the lovers of the game "cut in" periodically at each other's houses.

But it was in London, and particularly in the coffee and chocolate houses, that the game had its most spectacular development. Here, long before Whist became the accepted game, gallant companies foregathered after the theater and sat playing at Piquet or Hombre or Faro until long after midnight. In their wake came swarms of adventurers, "rooks" and highwaymen, who mingled with the greatest statesmen and professional men in the kingdom and carefully spotted the heavy winners. When at length milord left with his winnings, his departure was not unobserved; often dark, cloaked figures stepped from the shadows and stopped his coach on lonely Hounslow Heath or Finchley Common, and once more the gold changed hands.

* In *The Compleat Gamester,* 1674; see page 23.

This condition was of course intolerable, and about the time Whist was coming into fashion several exclusive clubs were being opened—places where these purposeful kibitzers were not admitted. Of these the most important was White's, long a favorite haunt of England's greatest celebrities, and of this club *The Connoisseur* says in May, 1754: "The love of gaming has taken such entire possession of White's that it affects the common conversation of its members. All differences of opinion are settled by the sword or the wager, so that the only genteel method of adjustment is to risk a thousand pounds or take the chance of being run through the body. There is nothing, however trivial or ridiculous, which does not admit of a bet. Many pounds are lost on the color of a coach horse, an item in the news or a change in the weather. The birth of a child brings great advantages to persons not in the least related to the family, and the breaking off of a marriage affects many fortunes besides those of the people immediately concerned.

"But the most extraordinary practice is what in gaming dialect is called 'betting one man against another'—that is, wagering which of the two will live the longer. A player, perhaps, is pitted against a duke, or an alderman against a bishop. There is scarcely one remarkable person upon whose life there are not thousands of pounds depending, or one whose death will not leave several mortgages upon his estate."

An entry of November 4, 1754, in the club betting-book reads: "Lord Mountfort wagers Sir John Bland one hundred guineas that Mr. Nash outlives Mr. Cibber." Below the entry, in another handwriting, is the significant note: "Both Lord M. and Sir B. put an end to their own lives before the bet was decided."

It is hardly necessary to add that in such an atmosphere the game of Whist must have been played in deadly earnest—and it is not strange that Mr. Hoyle made such a point of his calculation of probabilities. In 1760, under his aegis, the code of laws of Whist of White's and Saunders' was drawn up; nine years later Mr. Hoyle died "full of years and honours."

¶*By the time Edmond Hoyle died in 1769, at the age of ninety (most reference books give the year of his birth as 1672, but this is a mistaken back-formation from one reference in the* Gentleman's Magazine, *which said Hoyle was ninety-seven when he died)—anyway, when Hoyle died he knew he had written the best-seller of his century. It had already seen sixteen editions and a seventeenth was on its way. Our friend (and, frequently, Bridge partner) Richard L. Frey tells (in the Introduction to* New Complete Hoyle*) what has happened since:*

Who Is Hoyle?

by RICHARD L. FREY

THE only truly immortal human being on record is an Englishman named Edmond Hoyle, who was born in 1679 and buried in 1769 but who has never really died.

Hoyle wrote "short treatises" on five different games. They were bound together in one volume in 1746. This was the first edition of *Hoyle's Games*. Within the year plagiarists were putting Hoyle's name on other books that gave rules and advice for playing games. By the end of the 19th century dozens of such books had appeared, different books by different writers, but all bearing the name of this same Edmond Hoyle. Into the twentieth century it has continued. Every few years, as sure as fate, one may see another book "by Hoyle" appear on the market. Let others toast Horatio Alger, Jr., or H. G. Wells, such supposedly prolific authors; Edmond Hoyle beats their output all hollow—and from the grave!

Furthermore, there are countless millions who own one of the innumerable Hoyle books and in whose minds Hoyle is a living man, "the man who wrote the book," who probably lives in New York or Los Angeles or Miami or wherever authors live, to whom a letter may be addressed if a ticklish problem arises, and who might even be gotten on the other end of a long-distance telephone call if the problem were sufficiently urgent.

No less does this concept of a living Hoyle persist among authors and publishers. In a recent book on Poker, the author castigated "Hoyle's laws"; his publisher, no doubt fearful that Mr. Hoyle would sue, softened the tone of the attack. (Hoyle himself died at least fifty years before Poker was invented.) The managing editor of a Reno newspaper, asked what rules were being followed in the Nevada gambling houses, replied, "Hoyle was out here and put the rules in his book." Not even the "experts" who write books and articles about rules are immune; constantly, in citing some law or other, they begin with "Hoyle says." Yet they might be quoting from any of hundreds of "Hoyle" books, of which at least ten different ones are still on sale. And Edmond Hoyle himself never wrote or saw a word of any of these books.

Among writers on games who know all about the Hoyle history, the prestige of the immortal old man is immense. Surely no one in history ever made a greater name for himself in the realm of games than Ely Culbertson. Nevertheless, Culbertson's book of games was called *Culbertson's Hoyle.* The worthiest successor to Edmond Hoyle, over a period that stretched from 1880 into the 1920s, was the old Scotsman R. F. Foster, but after a brief, futile effort to sell his *Encyclopedia of Games* he gave up and thereafter his book carried the simple and eloquent title *Hoyle.* If Edmond Hoyle has any peer in immortality, it's no gamester. It's Noah Webster.

¶*Of all that has been written about Whist, the most often quoted is one of the* ESSAYS OF ELIA. *Charles Lamb never told who "Sarah Battle" was. The general opinion has always been that she was modeled on his mother, but who can doubt that she was chiefly himself? This is the essay, which he wrote when he was on the staff of the* London Magazine *from 1820 to 1829.*

Mrs. Battle's Opinions on Whist

by CHARLES LAMB

A CLEAR FIRE, a clean hearth, and the rigour of the game." This was the celebrated wish of old Sarah Battle (now with God), who, next to her devotions, loved a good game of Whist. She was none of your lukewarm gamesters, your half-and-half players, who have no objection to take a hand, if you want one to make up a rubber; who affirm that they have no pleasure in winning; that they like to win one game and lose another; that they can while away an hour very agreeably at a card table, but are indifferent whether they play or no; and will desire an adversary who has slipped a wrong card to take it up and play another. These insufferable triflers are the curse of a table. One of these flies will spoil a whole pot. Of such it may be said that they do not play at cards, but only play at playing at them.

Sarah Battle was none of that breed. She detested them, as I do, from her heart and soul, and would not, save upon a striking emergency, willingly seat herself at the same table with them. She loved a thorough-paced partner, a determined enemy. She took, and gave, no concessions. She hated favors. She never made a revoke, nor ever passed it over in her adversary without exacting the utmost forfeiture. She fought a good fight: cut and thrust. She held not her good sword (her cards) "like a dancer." She sat bolt upright; and neither showed you her cards, nor desired to see yours. All people have their blind side—their superstitions; and I have heard her declare, under the rose, that hearts was her favorite suit.

I never in my life—and I knew Sarah Battle many of the best years of it—saw her take out her snuff-box when it was her turn to play; or snuff a candle in the middle of a game; or ring for a servant, till it was fairly over. She never introduced, or connived at, miscellaneous conversation during its process. As she emphatically observed, cards were cards; and if I ever saw unmingled distaste in her fine last-century countenance, it was at the airs of a young gentleman of a literary turn, who had been with difficulty persuaded to take a hand; and who, in his excess of candor, declared that he thought there was no harm in unbending the mind now and then, after serious studies, in recreations of that kind! She could not bear to have her noble occupation, to which she wound up her faculties, considered in that light. It was her business, her duty, the thing she came into the world to do—and she did it. She unbent her mind afterwards, over a book.

Pope was her favorite author: his "Rape of the Lock" her favorite work. She once did me the favor to play over with me (with the cards) his celebrated game of Ombre in that poem; and to explain to me how far it agreed with, and in what points it would be found to differ from, Quadrille. Her illustrations were apposite and poignant; and I had the pleasure of sending the substance of them to Mr. Bowles; but I suppose they came too late to be inserted among his ingenious notes upon that author.

Quadrille, she has often told me, was her first love; but Whist had engaged her maturer esteem. The former, she said, was showy and specious, and likely to allure young persons. The uncertainty and quick shifting of partners—a thing which the constancy of Whist abhors; the dazzling supremacy and regal investiture of Spadille—absurd, as she justly observed, in the pure aristocracy of Whist, where his crown and garter give him no proper power above his brother nobility of the aces; the giddy vanity, so taking to the inexperienced, of playing alone; above all, the overpowering attractions of a *Sans Prendre*

Vole—to the triumph of which there is certainly nothing parallel or approaching in the contingencies of Whist; all these, she would say, make Quadrille a game of captivation to the young and enthusiastic. But Whist was the *solider* game: that was her word. It was a long meal; not, like Quadrille, a feast of snatches. One or two rubbers might co-extend in duration with an evening. They gave time to form rooted friendships, to cultivate steady enmities. She despised the chance-started, capricious, and ever-fluctuating alliances of the other. The skirmishes of Quadrille, she would say, reminded her of the petty ephemeral embroilments of the little Italian states, depicted by Macchiavelli: perpetually changing postures and connections; bitter foes today, sugared darlings tomorrow; kissing and scratching in a breath;—but the wars of Whist were comparable to the long, steady, deep-rooted, rational antipathies of the great French and English nations.

A grave simplicity was what she chiefly admired in her favorite game. There was nothing silly in it, like the nob in Cribbage—nothing superfluous. No *flushes*—that most irrational of all pleas that a reasonable being can set up; —that any one should claim four by virtue of holding cards of the same mark and color, without reference to the playing of the game, or the individual worth or pretensions of the cards themselves! She held this to be a solecism: as pitiful an ambition at cards as alliteration is in authorship. She despised superficiality, and looked deeper than the color of things. Suits were soldiers, she would say, and must have an uniformity of array to distinguish them; but what should we say to a foolish squire, who should claim a merit from dressing up his tenantry in red jackets, that never were to be marshalled—never to take the field? She even wished that Whist were more simple than it is; and, in my mind, would have stripped it of some appendages, which in the state of human frailty may be venially, and even commendably, allowed of. She saw no reason for the deciding of the trump by the turn of the card. Why not one suit always trumps? Why two colors, when the mark of the suits would have sufficiently distinguished them without it?

"But the eye, my dear Madam, is agreeably refreshed by the variety. Man is not a creature of pure reason—he must have his senses delightfully appealed to. We see it in Roman Catholic countries, where the music and the paintings draw in many to worship, whom your Quaker spirit of unsensualizing would have kept out. You yourself have a pretty collection of paintings—but confess to me, whether, walking in your gallery at Sandham, among those clear Vandykes, or among the Paul Potters in the anteroom, you ever felt your bosom glow with an elegant delight, at all comparable to *that* you have it in your power to experience most evenings over a well-arranged assortment of the court cards?—the pretty antic habits, like heralds in a procession—the gay triumph-assuring scarlets—the contrasting deadly killing sables—the 'hoary majesty of spades'—Pan in all his glory!

"All these might be dispensed with; and with their naked names upon the drab pasteboard, the game might go on very well, pictureless. But the *beauty* of cards would be extinguished for ever. Stripped of all that is imaginative in them, they must degenerate into mere gambling. Imagine a dull deal board, or drumhead, to spread them on, instead of that nice verdant carpet (next to nature's), fittest arena for those costly combatants to play their gallant jousts and tourneys in!—Exchange those delicately turned ivory markers—(work of Chinese artist unconscious of their symbol—or as profanely slighting their true application as the arrantest Ephesian journeyman that turned out those little shrines for the goddess)—exchange them for little bits of leather (our ancestors' money) or chalk and a slate!"

The old lady, with a smile, confessed the soundness of my logic; and to her approbation of my arguments on her favorite topic that evening, I have always fancied myself indebted for the legacy of a curious Cribbage board, made of the finest Siena marble, which her maternal uncle (old Walter Plumer, whom I have elsewhere celebrated) brought with him from Florence: this, and a trifle of five hundred pounds, came to me at her death.

The former bequest (which I do not least value) I have kept with religious care; though she herself, to confess a truth, was never greatly taken with Cribbage. It was an essentially vulgar game, I have heard her say—disputing with her uncle, who was very partial to it. She could never heartily bring her mouth to pronounce *"Go,"* or *"That's a go."* She called it an ungrammatical game. The pegging teased her. I once knew her to forfeit a rubber [a five-dollar stake], because she would not take advantage of the turn-up knave, which would have given it her, but which she must have claimed by the disgraceful tenure of declaring *"two for his heels."* There is something extremely genteel in this sort of self-denial. Sarah Battle was a gentlewoman born.

Piquet she held the best game at the cards for two persons, though she would ridicule the pedantry of the terms—such as pique, repique, the capot—they savored (she thought) of affectation. But games for two, or even three, she never greatly cared for. She loved the quadrate, or square. She would argue thus: Cards are warfare: the ends are gain, with glory. But cards are war, in disguise of a sport: when single adversaries encounter, the ends proposed are too palpable. By themselves it is too close a fight; with spectators it is not much bettered. No looker-on can be interested, except for a bet, and then it is a mere affair of money; he cares not for your luck *sympathetically,* or for your play. Three are still worse; a mere naked war of every man against every man, as in Cribbage, without league or alliance; or a rotation of petty and contradictory interests, a succession of heartless leagues, and not much more hearty infractions of them, as in Quadrille. But in square games (*she meant Whist*) all that is possible to be attained in card-playing is accomplished. There are the incentives of profit with honor, common to every species—though the *latter* can be but very imperfectly enjoyed in those other games, where the spectator is only feebly a participator. But the parties in Whist are spectators and principals too. They are a theater to themselves, and a looker-on is not wanted. He is rather worse than nothing, and an impertinence. Whist abhors neutrality, or interests beyond its sphere. You glory in some surprising stroke of skill or fortune, not because a cold—or even an interested—bystander witnesses it, but because your *partner* sympathizes in the contingency. You win for two. You triumph for two. Two are exalted. Two again are mortified; which divides their disgrace, as the conjunction doubles (by taking off the invidiousness) your glories. Two losing to two are better reconciled than one to one in that close butchery. The hostile feeling is weakened by multiplying the channels. War becomes a civil game. By such reasonings as these the old lady was accustomed to defend her favorite pastime.

No inducement could ever prevail upon her to play at any game where chance entered into the composition *for nothing.* Chance, she would argue—and here, again, admire the subtlety of her conclusion—chance is nothing, but where something else depends upon it. It is obvious that cannot be *glory.* What rational cause of exultation could it give to a man to turn up sice ace* a hundred times together by himself? or before spectator, where no stake was depending? Make a lottery of a hundred thousand tickets with but one fortunate number—and what possible principle of our nature, except stupid wonderment, could it gratify to gain that number as many times successively, without a prize? Therefore she disliked the mixture of chance in backgammon, where it was not played for money. She called it foolish, and those people idiots, who were taken with a lucky hit under such circumstances. Games of pure skill were as little to her fancy. Played for a stake, they were a mere system of overreaching. Played for glory they were a mere setting of one man's wit—his memory, or combination-faculty rather—against another's; like a mock engagement at a review, bloodless and profitless. She could not conceive a *game* wanting the spritely infusion of chance, the handsome excuse of good fortune. Two people playing at chess in a corner of a room, while Whist was stirring in the center, would inspire her with insufferable horror and ennui. Those well-cut similitudes of castles and knights, the *imagery* of the board, she would argue (and, I think, in this case justly), were entirely misplaced and senseless. Those hard head-contests can in no instance ally with the fancy. They reject form and color. A pencil and dry slate (she used to say) were the proper arena for such combatants.

To those puny objectors against cards, as nurturing the bad passions, she would retort that man is a gaming animal. He must be always trying to get the better in something or other; that this passion can scarcely be more safely expended than upon a game at cards; that cards are a temporary illusion; in truth, a mere drama; for we do but *play* at being mightily concerned, where a few idle shillings are at stake; yet, during the illusion, we *are* as mightily concerned as those whose stake is crowns and kingdoms. They are a sort of dream-fighting; much ado; great battling, and little bloodshed; mighty means for disproportioned ends; quite as diverting, and a great deal more innoxious, than many of those more serious *games* of life, which men play without esteeming them to be such.

With great deference to the old lady's judgment in these matters, I think I have ex-

* Six-ace, or seven, the winning first cast at the old dice game hazard, ancestor of craps, just as it is at craps.

perienced some moments in my life when playing at cards *for nothing* has even been agreeable. When I am in sickness, or not in the best spirits, I sometimes call for the cards, and play a game at Piquet *for love* with my cousin Bridget—Bridget Elia.

I grant there is something sneaking in it; but with a toothache, or a sprained ankle—when you are subdued and humble—you are glad to put up with an inferior spring of action.

There is such a thing in nature, I am convinced, as *sick Whist.*

I grant it is not the highest style of man—I deprecate the Manes of Sarah Battle—she lives not, alas! to whom I should apologize.

At such times, those *terms* which my old friend objected to come in as something admissible. I love to get a tierce or a quatorze, though they mean nothing. I am subdued to an inferior interest. Those shadows of winning amuse me.

That last game I had with my sweet cousin (I capotted her)—(dare I tell thee how foolish I am?)—I wished it might have lasted for ever, though we gained nothing and lost nothing, though it was a mere shade of play: I would be content to go on in that idle folly for ever. The pipkin should be ever boiling that was to prepare the gentle lenitive to my foot, which Bridget was doomed to apply after the game was over; and, as I do not much relish appliances, there it should ever bubble. Bridget and I should be ever playing.

¶*Bulwer-Lytton in perhaps his best novel* (My Novel, *1853*) *described a famous Whist game among memorable—because so human—players. It is the typical after-dinner game of the typical English county family; it is exactly what went on in Whist for two centuries or more and, with just a bit more complexity, survives in Contract Bridge today. Please take our word that you will enjoy meeting the players in this Whist game, and that having met them you will like them all.*

from My Novel

by EDWARD BULWER-LYTTON

But see, Captain Barnabas, fortified by his fourth cup of tea, has at length summoned courage to whisper to Mrs. Hazeldean.

"Don't you think the Parson will be impatient for his rubber?"

Mrs. Hazeldean glanced at the Parson, and smiled; but she gave the signal to the Captain, and the bell was rung, lights were brought in, the curtains let down; in a few moments more the group had collected round the card table.

The best of us are but human—that is not a new truth, I confess, but yet people forget it every day of their lives—and I daresay there are many who are charitably thinking at this very moment that my Parson ought not to be playing at Whist. All I can say to those rigid disciplinarians is, "Every man has his favorite sin; Whist was Parson Dale's!—ladies and gentlemen, what is yours?" In truth, I must not set up my poor Parson nowadays as a pattern parson—it is enough to have one pattern in a village no bigger than Hazeldean, and we all know that Lenny Fairfield has bespoken that place, and got the patronage of the stocks for his emoluments! Parson Dale was ordained, not indeed so very long ago, but still at a time when churchmen took it a great deal more easily than they do now. The elderly parson of that day played his rubber as a matter of course, the middle-aged parson was sometimes seen riding to cover (I knew a schoolmaster, a doctor of divinity, and an excellent man, whose pupils were chiefly taken from the highest families in England, who hunted regularly three times a week during the season), and the young parson would often sing a capital song—not composed by David—and join in those rotatory dances, which certainly David never danced before the ark.

Does it need so long an exordium to excuse thee, poor Parson Dale, for turning up that ace of spades with so triumphant a smile at thy partner? I must own that nothing which could well add to the Parson's offense was wanting. In the first place, he did not play charitably, and merely to oblige other people. He delighted in the game—he rejoiced in the game—his whole heart was in the game—neither was he indifferent to the mammon of the thing, as a Christian pastor ought to have been. He looked very sad when he took his shillings out of his purse, and exceedingly pleased when he put the shillings, that had just before belonged to other people, into it. Finally, by one of those arrangements common with married people who play at the same table, Mr. and Mrs. Hazeldean were invariably partners, and no two people could play worse; while Captain Barnabas, who had played at Graham's with honor and profit, necessarily became partner to Parson Dale, who himself played a good, steady, parsonic game. So that, in strict truth, it was hardly fair—it was almost swindling—the combination of these two great dons against that innocent married couple! Mr. Dale, it is true, was aware of this disproportion of force, and had often proposed either to change partners or to give odds—propositions always scornfully scouted by the Squire and his lady, so that the Parson was obliged to pocket his conscience, together with the ten points which made his average winnings.

The strangest thing in the world is the different way in which Whist affects the temper. It is no test of temper, as some pretend—not at all! The best-tempered people in the world grow snappish at Whist; and I have seen the most testy and peevish in the ordinary affairs of life bear their losses with the stoicism of Epictetus. This was notably manifested in the contrast between the present adversaries of the Hall and the Rectory. The Squire, who was esteemed as choleric a gentleman as most in the county, was the best-humored fellow you could imagine when you set him down to Whist opposite the sunny face of his wife. You never heard one of those incorrigible blunderers scold each other; on the contrary, they only laughed when they threw away the game, with four by honors in their hands. The utmost that was ever said was a "Well, Harry, that was the oddest trump of yours. Ho-ho-ho!" or "Bless me, Hazeldean—why, they made three tricks in clubs, and you had the ace in your hand all the time! Ha-ha-ha!"

Upon which occasions Captain Barnabas, with great good humor, always echoed both the Squire's Ho-ho-ho! and Mrs. Hazeldean's Ha-ha-ha!

Not so the Parson. He had so keen and sportsmanlike an interest in the game that even his adversaries' mistakes ruffled him. And you would hear him, with elevated voice and agitated gestures, laying down the law, quoting Hoyle, appealing to all the powers of memory and common sense against the very delinquencies by which he was enriched—a waste of eloquence that always heightened the hilarity of Mr. and Mrs. Hazeldean.

MISS JEMIMA. It is only those horrid men who think of money as a source of happiness. I should be the last person to esteem a gentleman less because he was poor.

MRS. DALE. I wonder the Squire does not ask Signor Riccabocca here more often. Such an acquisition *we* find him.

THE SQUIRE'S VOICE FROM THE CARD TABLE. Whom ought I to ask more often, Mrs. Dale?

PARSON'S VOICE (*impatiently*). Come—come—come, Squire; play to my queen of diamonds—do!

SQUIRE. There, I trump it—pick up the trick, Mrs. H.

PARSON. Stop! stop! trump my diamond?

THE CAPTAIN (*solemnly*). Trick turned; play on, Squire.

SQUIRE. The king of diamonds.

MRS. HAZELDEAN. Lord! Hazeldean; why, that's the most barefaced revoke—ha—ha—ha! trump the queen of diamonds and play out the king! well I never—ha—ha—ha!

CAPTAIN BARNABAS (*in tenor*). Ha, ha, ha!

SQUIRE. Ho—ho—ho! bless my soul; ho, ho, ho!

CAPTAIN BARNABAS (*in bass*). Ho—ho—ho!

(*Parson's voice raised, but drowned by the laughter of his adversaries and the firm, clear tone of Captain Barnabas*) Three to our score! —game!

SQUIRE (*wiping his eyes*). No help for it, Harry—deal for me! Whom ought I to ask, Mrs. Dale? (*waxing angry*). First time I ever heard the hospitality of Hazeldean called in question!

MRS. DALE. My dear sir, I beg a thousand pardons, but listeners—you know the proverb.

SQUIRE (*growling like a bear*). I hear nothing but proverbs ever since we had that Mounseer among us. Please to speak plainly, ma'am.

MRS. DALE (*sliding into a little temper at being thus roughly accosted*). It was of Mounseer, as you call him, that I spoke, Mr. Hazeldean.

SQUIRE. What! Rickeybockey?

MRS. DALE (*attempting the pure Italian accentuation*). Signor Riccabocca.

PARSON (*slapping his cards on the table in despair*). Are we playing at Whist, or are we not?

(*The Squire, who is fourth player, drops the king to Captain Higginbotham's lead of the ace of hearts. Now the Captain has left queen, knave, and two other hearts—four trumps to the queen, and nothing to win a trick with in the two other suits. This hand is therefore precisely one of those in which, especially after the fall of that king of hearts in the adversaries' hand, it becomes a matter of reasonable doubt whether to lead trumps or not. The Captain hesitates, and, not liking to play out his good hearts with the certainty of their being trumped by the Squire, nor, on the other hand, liking to open the other suits, in which he has not a card that can assist his partner, resolves, as becomes a military man in such dilemma, to make a bold push and lead out trumps, on the chance of finding his partner strong, and so bringing in his long suit.*)

SQUIRE (*taking advantage of the much meditating pause made by the Captain*). Mrs. Dale, it is not my fault. I have asked Rickeybockey —time out of mind. But I suppose I am not fine enough for those foreign chaps. He'll not come—that's all I know.

PARSON (*aghast at seeing the Captain play out trumps, of which he, Mr. Dale, has only two, wherewith he expects to ruff the suit of spades, of which he has only one—the cards all falling in suits—while he has not a single other chance of a trick in his hand*). Really, Squire, we had better give up playing, if you put out my partner in this extraordinary way—jabber —jabber—jabber!

SQUIRE. Well, we must be good children, Harry. What!—trumps, Barney? Thank ye for that! (*And the Squire might well be grateful, for the unfortunate adversary has led up to ace, king, knave, with two other trumps. Squire takes the Parson's ten with his knave, and plays out ace, king; then, having cleared all the trumps except the Captain's queen and his own remaining two, leads off tierce major in that very suit of spades of which the Parson has only one— and the Captain, indeed, but two—forces out the Captain's queen, and wins the game in a canter.*)

PARSON (*with a look at the Captain which might have become the awful brows of Jove, when about to thunder*). That, I suppose, is the new-fashioned London play! In my time the rule was, "First save the game, then try to win it."

CAPTAIN. Could not save it, sir.

PARSON (*exploding*). Not save it!—two ruffs in my own hand—two tricks certain till you took them out! Monstrous! The rashest trump. (*Seizes the cards—spreads them on the table, lip quivering, hands trembling—tries to show how five tricks could have been gained—can't make out more than four—Captain smiles triumphantly—Parson in a passion, and not at all convinced, mixes all the cards together again, and, falling back in his chair, groans, with tears in his voice*—) The cruelest trump! the most wanton cruelty!

THE HAZELDEANS IN CHORUS. Ho-ho-ho! Ha-ha-ha!

(*The Captain, who does not laugh this time, and whose turn it is to deal, shuffles the cards for the conquering game of the rubber with as much caution and prolixity as Fabius might have employed in posting his men.*)

PARSON (*thrumming on the table with great impatience*). Old fiddledee!—talking of old families when the cards have been shuffled this half-hour?

CAPTAIN BARNABAS. Will you cut for your partner, ma'am?

SQUIRE (*who has been listening to Frank's inquiries with a musing air*).—Why do you want to know the distance to Rood Hall?

FRANK (*rather hesitatingly*). Because Randal Leslie is there for the holidays, sir.

PARSON. Your wife has cut for you, Mr. Hazeldean. I don't think it was quite fair; and my partner has turned up a deuce—deuce of hearts. Please to come and play, if you *mean* to play.

(*The Squire returns to the table, and in a few minutes the game is decided by a dexterous finesse of the Captain against the Hazeldeans. The clock strikes ten; the servants enter with a tray; the Squire counts up his own and his wife's losings; and the Captain and Parson divide sixteen shillings between them.*)

SQUIRE. There, Parson, I hope now you'll be in a better humor. You win enough out of us to set up a coach-and-four.

"Tut!" muttered the Parson; "at the end of the year, I'm not a penny the richer for it all."

And, indeed, monstrous as the assertion seemed, it was perfectly true, for the Parson portioned out his gains into three divisions. One-third he gave to Mrs. Dale, for her own special pocket money; what became of his second third he never owned even to his better half; but certain it was, that every time the Parson won seven and sixpence, half a crown, which nobody could account for, found its way to the poor-box; while the remaining third the Parson, it is true, openly and avowedly retained; but I have no manner of doubt that, at the year's end, it got to the poor quite as safely as if it had been put into the box.

Mr. Dale moved on; but as he passed Captain Barnabas, the benignant character of his countenance changed sadly.

"The cruelest trump, Captain Higginbotham!" said he sternly, and stalked by—majestic.

¶[*Few will maintain that Benjamin Disraeli the novelist was of the stature of the same Benjamin Disraeli the statesman; but the statesman's fame was enough to endow with intrinsic interest anything the novelist may have written about a card game—especially when it was played on the Road to Hell. This excerpt is from* THE INFERNAL MARRIAGE (1828). *Proserpine, her six happily infernal months ended, has reluctantly parted from Pluto and is on her way back to earth. With her she brings the spring flowers, of course, but can she appreciate this boon to mere mortals when she must leave her delightfully devilish husband and return to her cereal mother? As have so many of her sisters since, she seeks solace in a card game; and—how remarkable!—it gives a future Prime Minister a succession of opportunities to voice some political opinions not exclusively applicable to Whist.*

from The Infernal Marriage
by BENJAMIN DISRAELI

TRAVELERS who have left their homes generally grow mournful as the evening draws on; nor is there, perhaps, any time at which the pensive influence of twilight is more predominant than on the eve that follows a separation from those we love. Imagine, then, the feelings of the Queen of Hell as her barque entered the very region of that mystic light, and the shadowy shores of the realm of Twilight opened before her. Her thoughts reverted to Pluto; and she mused over all his fondness, all his adoration, and all his indulgence, and the infinite solicitude of his affectionate heart, until the tears trickled down her beautiful cheeks, and she marveled she ever could have quitted the arms of her lover.

"Your Majesty," observed Manto, who had been whispering to Tiresias, "feels, perhaps, a little wearied?"

"By no means, my kind Manto," replied Proserpine, starting from reverie. "But the truth is, my spirits are very unequal; and though I really cannot well fix upon the cause of their present depression, I am apparently not free from the contagion of the surrounding gloom."

"It is the evening air," said Tiresias. "Your Majesty had, perhaps, better re-enter the pavilion of the yacht. As for myself, I never venture about after sunset. One grows romantic. Night was evidently made for indoor nature. I propose a rubber."

To this popular suggestion Proserpine was pleased to accede, and herself and Tiresias, Manto and the captain of the yacht, were soon engaged at the proposed amusement.

Tiresias loved a rubber. It was true he was blind, but then, being a prophet, that did not signify. Tiresias, I say, loved a rubber, and was a first-rate player, though, perhaps, given a little too much to finesse. Indeed, he so much enjoyed taking in his fellow-creatures, that he sometimes could not resist deceiving his own partner. Whist is a game which requires no ordinary combination of qualities; at the same time, memory and invention, a daring fancy, and a cool head. To a mind like that of Tiresias a pack of cards was full of human nature. A rubber was a microcosm; and he ruffed his adversary's king, or brought in a long suit of his own with as much dexterity and as much enjoyment as, in the real business of existence, he dethroned a monarch, or introduced a dynasty.

"Will your Majesty be pleased to draw your card," requested the sage. "If I might venture to offer your Majesty a hint, I would dare to recommend your Majesty not to play before your turn. My friends are fond of ascribing my success in my various missions to the possession of peculiar qualities. No such thing: I owe everything to the simple habit of always waiting till it is my turn to speak. And, believe me, that he who plays before his turn at Whist, commits as great a blunder as he who speaks before his turn during a negotiation."

"The trick, and two by honors," said Proserpine.

"Pray, my dear Tiresias, you who are such a fine player, how came you to trump my best card?"

"Because I wanted the lead. And those who want to lead, please your Majesty, must never hesitate about sacrificing their friends."

"I believe you speak truly. I was right in playing that thirteenth card?"

"Quite so. Above all things, I love a thirteenth card. I send it forth, like a mock project in a revolution, to try the strength of parties."

"You should not have forced me, Lady Manto," said the captain of the yacht, in a grumbling tone, to his partner. "By weakening me, you prevent me bringing in my spades. We might have made the game."

"You should not have been forced," said Tiresias. "If she made a mistake, who was unacquainted with your plans, what a terrible blunder you committed to share her error without her ignorance!"

"What, then, was I to lose a trick?"

Next to knowing when to seize an opportunity," replied Tiresias, "the most important thing in life is to know when to forego an advantage."

"I have cut you an honor, sir," said Manto.

"Which reminds me," replied Tiresias, "that,

in the last hand, your Majesty unfortunately forgot to lead through your adversary's ace. I have often observed that nothing ever perplexes an adversary so much as an appeal to his honor."

"I will not forget to follow your advice," said the Captain of the yacht, playing accordingly.

"By which you have lost the game," quickly remarked Tiresias. "There are exceptions to all rules, but it seldom answers to follow the advice of an opponent."

"Confusion!" exclaimed the captain of the yacht.

"Four by honors, and the trick, I declare," said Proserpine. "I was so glad to see you turn up the queen, Tiresias."

"I also, madam. Without doubt there are few cards better than her royal consort, or, still more, the imperial ace. Nevertheless, I must confess, I am perfectly satisfied whenever I remember that I have the Queen on my side."

Proserpine bowed.

¶*Every protagonist of Whist as an intellectual game superior to chess must read with delight the following testimony of a uniquely eloquent advocate, Edgar Allan Poe; for the Whist adherents cannot grant the pretensions of a game* (chess) *in which there is no element of the unknown.*

from The Murders in the Rue Morgue

by EDGAR ALLAN POE

WHIST has long been noted for its influence upon what is termed the calculating power, and men of the highest order of intellect have been known to take an apparently unaccountable delight in it, while eschewing chess as frivolous. Beyond doubt there is nothing of a similar nature so greatly tasking the faculty of analysis. The best chess-player in Christendom *may* be little more than the best player of chess; but proficiency in Whist implies capacity for success in all those more important undertakings where mind struggles with mind. When I say proficiency, I mean that perfection in the game which includes a comprehension of *all* the sources whence legitimate advantage may be derived. These are not only manifold, but multiform, and lie frequently among recesses of thought altogether inaccessible to the ordinary understanding. To observe attentively is to remember distinctly; and, so far, the concentrative chess-player will do very well at Whist, while the rules of Hoyle (themselves based upon the mere mechanism of the game) are sufficiently and generally comprehensive. . . . But it is in matters beyond the limits of mere rule that the skill of the analyst is evinced. He makes in silence a host of observations and inferences. . . . He examines the countenance of his partner, comparing it carefully with that of each of his opponents. He considers the mode of assorting the cards in each hand, often counting trump by trump and honor by honor through the glances bestowed by their holders upon each. He notes every variation of face as the play progresses, gathering a fund of thought from the differences in the expression of certainty, of surprise, of triumph, of chagrin. From the manner of gathering up a trick he judges whether the person taking it can make another in the suit. He recognizes what is played through feint, by the air with which it is thrown upon the table. A casual or inadvertent word; the accidental dropping or turning of a card, with the accompanying anxiety or carelessness in regard to its concealment; the counting of the tricks, with the order of their arrangement; embarrassment, hesitation, eagerness, or trepidation—all afford, to his apparently intuitive perception, indications of the true state of affairs. The first two or three rounds having been played, he is in full possession of the contents of each hand, and thenceforward puts down his cards with as absolute a precision of purpose as if the rest of the party had turned outward the faces of their own.

¶*When James Hogg wrote about Whist he called himself "Portland," taking the name of his club, just as Cavendish and so many others did. Late into the last century it was not considered quite respectable for a gentleman to sign his name to a book.* ¶*The Portland Club of London might receive some mention here, for it must crop up from time to time throughout this book. Historically it is the premier card club of the world. For many years its members were drawn wholly from the nobility and landed gentry, and if a prince of the blood played Whist it would be at the Portland. Even today the bars at the Portland are not very far down, considering the spirit of the times, and only at the Portland Club is there a regular $2 a point Bridge game every afternoon.* ¶*The story that* *follows, by Hogg (or Portland—we don't begrudge him the pen name), is one of the early appearances of the "Mississippi Heart Hand" in the literature of Whist-family games. It is by no means the earliest; this hand had shown up more than a hundred years before. Nor will it be the last time. The setting is this: You hold* ♠—— ♡ A K Q J 10 9 ◇ A K Q J ♣ A K Q, *or some variant of it. With hearts trumps you cannot win more than six tricks, for your opponent holds the other seven hearts and all the high spades.*

A True Story of a Legacy

by PORTLAND (JAMES HOGG)

ABOUT ten o'clock one fine summer's night, a good many years ago, a gentleman who, from his sunburnt features, had evidently only lately arrived from abroad, and from a very hot climate, was walking alone in Cremorne Gardens, enjoying at once a fragrant Havana and listening to the music, to which the votaries of Terpsichore were merrily dancing on the circular platform. From the placid manner in which he listened and gazed on the bright scene before him, it was evident he was not an *habitué* of the gardens, or accustomed to join in the reveling. His walk was interrupted by a gentlemanly-looking man, who politely asked for a light to his cigar. This of course was given, and acknowledged by the lifting of his hat in the most pronounced fashionable form.

The stranger, who for convenience's sake it will be as well to call Robinson, was about to pass on his way, when his progress was stayed by an observation from the polite gentleman, to the effect that it was a charming evening and a very gay scene. To which not very original observation Mr. Robinson of course replied; and so a conversation began, and was continued during a walk round the grounds. Mr. Robinson was asked to try a very choice cigar, offered by—let us at once call him—Smith, which he accepted, and admitted to be excellent, better than he had smoked for a long time—better far than he had ever seen in the country he came from.

"Oh!" said Smith. "Are you a foreigner?"

"Yes, from Demerara," replied Robinson; "and I only reached England a day or two ago."

"How strange," rejoined Smith. "I have a friend who resides there; I wonder if you know him—his name is Jones. He was a doctor in the 161st, fell in love whilst serving with his regiment, married and settled in the island."

"I know him quite well," replied Robinson, "but by sight only. He is, I fear, a loose fish, and does not bear the best reputation. He is too fond of the good things of life. I saw him only a day before I left. He was at my lawyer's, on some business connected with his wife's estate, on which, as I heard, he was trying to raise money."

"I'm glad to hear the old boy is still in the land of the living," said Smith; "he always was fast, and will no doubt be so to the end of the chapter; but his heart was in the right place. He and I have not met for years."

The conversation, thus begun, was cemented by a drink at the bar, until at length Smith suggested that after all the place was "slow," and that except to those who wished to indulge in a flirtation with a fair one there was more real fun at Evans's. Robinson had heard of the place, would like of course to see it—beyond everything.

"What do you say then?" said Smith. "Let's go there at once."

Robinson assented, and a Hansom soon conducted them to Covent Garden. Smith kept up such a lively and interesting chat that Robinson mentally voted him a most agreeable fellow. The usual friendly dispute arose as to payment for the cab, in which Smith was the victor, and they were about to enter the hall of the celebrated Paddy Green, when Smith suddenly recollected it was far too soon to go in, as there would be no one there till after the theaters, and he suggested a cup of coffee and a cigar to pass away an hour. Nothing loth, Robinson assented, and they walked on till they reached a cigar shop, which, at the period of our history, existed opposite to the private-box entrance of one of the large theaters, a plain old-fashioned-looking shop, not well stocked with cigars, with a dark-colored curtain closely drawn across the inner window, so as completely to shut out the view of what was passing from the street, a similar curtain being drawn across the window in the shop door.

Smith, upon entering, asked the shopkeeper for one of his best cigars, and pointing to a room beyond, fitted up with tables and sofas—a sort of divan, in fact—inquired whether they could be supplied with coffee. The shopkeeper informed him that they could, and our friends were in the act of going into the room, when two gentlemen entered the shop, each talking in a loud voice, and both together, so loud and so earnestly as to call the attention of our friends to them.

"I tell you I'm right," said the first. "I'll lay a hundred to one—a thousand if you like."

"I know I'm right," said the other, "though I don't want to bet; I never do, as you know. Still, I'm not the less right."

"I'll tell you what I'll do," replied the first disputant, "I'll leave it to this gentleman—" pointing to Robinson—"and bet you four cups of coffee and cigars I'm right."

"Done," said the nonbetting gentleman, and all four walked into the inner room, where the question in dispute was submitted to Mr. Robinson. It was this: I hold king, knave, ten, and two small cards of a suit at Whist; which is the correct card to lead, as an original lead? Mr. Robinson decided it was the ten, and so awarded the bet in favor of the gentleman who had said he never betted, his friend appearing much chap-fallen at the decision, having been vehement in declaring it was the knave which should be led.

The coffee and cigars were brought in, and of course, the subject of Whist having been broached, the conversation as to the game was continued, until at length Smith observed, "I wonder if we could have a rubber here?" It was soon found that they could. Cards were produced, and Robinson and Smith were partners against the two strangers, who introduced themselves as Green and Brown by name. The stakes were at first for cups of coffee only, afterwards for half-crown points, and finally for half-sovereign points, with a sovereign on the rubber, Robinson and Smith continuing to be partners, and the play terminated by each losing between £5 and £10.

All four gentlemen then adjourned to Evans's, and quite late at night separated with an engagement for the following evening, at the same shop, when Robinson and Smith were to have their revenge. Smith insisted on walking with Robinson to his hotel, and on the road the latter imparted to his newly-found friend the interesting fact that he had come to England for the purpose of receiving a legacy amounting to £4,000, that he was to go to the Bank of England and receive the money in the course of a day or two; and that during the time he had been in town he was amusing himself with seeing the sights of London. Hence his visit to Cremorne.

Smith, before leaving, handed Mr. Robinson his card, adding how happy he should be to chaperone his newly found friend to some of the marvels of London, which, unless well directed, Mr. Robinson would be sure to miss. Robinson, quite delighted with his new friend, who had all the appearance and manners of a polished gentleman, invited him to dine at his hotel on the following day; and Smith, with some apparent hesitation, accepted; and so they parted for the night.

Smith was punctual to his dinner engagement, and after dessert and a bottle of port, they started in the direction of Covent Garden, to keep their appointment, and play the return rubber. Their opponents had not arrived, but made their appearance shortly afterwards, apologizing for being late, observing incidentally, that they had been dining with some friends in Eaton Square, and could hardly manage to get away—in fact, they had forgotten their engagement when making the appointment, but as they had won on the last occasion, they did not like to fail in their engagement. We may remark, by the way, that Green and Brown were each well dressed, in evening costume, and were tall, gentlemanly-looking men.

Coffee, cigars, and cards were produced, and play soon began, Messrs. Robinson and Smith again being partners. At first fortune favored them; they won back considerably more than they had lost. But the fickle goddess again deserted them, and Messrs. Robinson and Smith each lost £50 odd. In the case of our friend Robinson this was more than he had about him, and on the fact being stated by him, Mr. Smith forthwith drew out his pocketbook, and insisted, on behalf of his friend, in discharging the debt.

The play appeared to be even, and Mr. Robinson, who was a good sound player, though not brilliant or first class, was of opinion that Smith's play was slightly better than either Green or Brown. The result, it was evident, was entirely due to the marvelous ill-luck with which at every critical point of the several games their opponents scored honors, or had overwhelming hands.

Before separating, Smith stated that he had invited a few friends to a fish dinner on the following Monday, and would be glad if all of them would join. Mr. Robinson regretted his inability to do so, as he had an important engagement for that day with his lawyer, to go to the City. On which Smith insisted upon altering the day, and Tuesday was fixed upon, at the "Trafalgar."

After some general conversation Brown and Green left, and Robinson and Smith went to the lodgings of the latter in Weymouth Street,

Oxford Street. Here they had more smoke and chat, and to pass the time a game of Écarté for half a sovereign a game. Robinson played well and with good luck, and won £5 which Smith would insist on paying in cash, though Robinson owed him £25, the amount he had previously paid.

Smith had described himself as a law student, whose friends lived in the city, and as he was anything but a working man, in fact a very idle one, he offered on the following day (Sunday) to take Mr. Robinson to Richmond, and promised to call for him after church hours, and drive him down in his trap.

Mr. Robinson agreed to the suggestion, and on the following day, at about two o'clock, Smith drove to the hotel in a smart phaeton, accompanied by an equally smart groom, in unexceptionable livery of the quietest pattern; the whole turnout being of its kind perfect, the horse not less so than the appointments. The drive to Richmond was rapid, and on arriving at the Star and Garter, a glass of sherry and a biscuit discussed, dinner ordered, they went down the river, chartered a wherry, and pulled up to Teddington. Robinson was charmed with the scenery, and Smith made himself very agreeable, showing a perfect knowledge of all the river reaches, and of the dwellers by the waterside. The dinner, as in those days it used to be at the Star, was capital, the wine first-class, and the cigars afterwards; so, when Smith (who had insisted on paying) at ten at night had deposited Mr. Robinson in safety at his hotel, he declared with perfect truth that he had passed a delightful day. He should not be able to see Mr. Smith till the evening of the following day, when he hoped he would dine with him at his hotel. This invitation was accepted, and the friends parted. Mr. Robinson was very busy all the next day, for he was in Lincoln's Inn at his lawyer's by eleven o'clock. Here he met an uncle from the country, the surviving trustee of his father. Then there was a great signing of deeds, releases, and accounts, and a vast deal of legal formality to go through, until, about two o'clock, Mr. Robinson, his solicitor, and uncle took cab to the Bank of England, and the sum of £4,375 in crisp new Bank of England notes found themselves safely buttoned up in Mr. Robinson's breast coat pocket.

As they were leaving the office of the stockbroker, where the business was finally completed, by one of those singular "accidents," which at times happen to all of us, Mr. Smith passed. He started with surprise, but only acknowledged his acquaintance with Robinson by raising his hat, and walked on. His uncle asked who that was, and was informed that he was a friend of Dr. Jones, of Demerara.

The party then returned to Lincoln's Inn, and finished the signing of documents, and Robinson having seen his uncle off by a train at Euston, returned to his hotel at six o'clock, where he found Smith *just arrived.* After dressing, Robinson conducted Mr. Smith to a snug private room, where, at Smith's suggestion, he had ordered dinner to be served, the coffee room being voted a nuisance.

Here they had a capital little dinner and some famous old port; afterwards Mr. Robinson amused his friend with a quizzical account of his old uncle, the lawyer, and the whole business of the day. Robinson discharged his debt by a check on a London Bank, where he had that day opened an account. He then proposed a game of Écarté, and they played two games, each winning one, when Smith begged to be excused playing longer, pleading headache as an excuse, and he left early, promising to call for Mr. Robinson at four o'clock on the following afternoon, and drive him down to Greenwich. He should then, he observed, send back the trap, and they could return, whenever it suited them, by rail.

Mr. Smith was punctual to his appointment on the following day, and our friends were soon en route for Greenwich, where they arrived without accident. Smith ordered dinner at seven, for six persons, and then strolled out with Mr. Robinson into the Hospital, which they examined with great interest, and thence to the park, returning in good time for dinner. Green and Brown had arrived, and soon afterwards two other gentlemen made their appearance. It is unnecessary to give their names, as after they were introduced to Mr. Robinson they expressed their great regret at being unable to stay later than eight o'clock, having particular engagements in London, and they did in fact leave before the dessert was put on the table.

The dinner—served in a private room—was most recherché, and Robinson thoroughly enjoyed the fish, never before having partaken of such a repast. He did not fail either to do ample justice to the dry champagne or to the very "curious" old port; and when, after dinner, he was on the veranda overlooking the river, smoking his cigar, he declared he had never had so good a dinner in his life.

The evening being chilly, the windows were

soon closed, candles lighted, a card table set out, and the four sat down to Whist.

Smith, whilst walking in the Park, had hinted that he should try and increase the stakes, as he felt confident they should be able to get back the money they had lost; and accordingly at his suggestion it was agreed they should play pound points, with £5 on the rubber, giving and taking 5 to 2 in pounds.

The play began about nine, and by eleven o'clock our heroes found themselves losers of £100 each, this large amount being due to several bets which from time to time had been made on individual hands.

Smith appeared much excited at his losses. Robinson was calm and indifferent, but anxious no doubt to get back his money. Smith said he should have new cards, as those with which they had been playing only brought bad luck, and he rang the bell for the purpose, and ordered the waiter to bring two new packs of cards. He left the room, as he said, to wash, and on returning brought back the new cards, which he observed the fellow was crawling up the stairs with as he came past.

The game was resumed, and Smith and Robinson won the first rubber with the new cards. During the next game Robinson had to deal, and having shuffled the cards, placed them for Brown to cut. Smith *asked him to ring the bell, as he wanted some brandy and soda. Robinson left the table to do so,* and on his return proceeded to deal, and turned up the ace of spades.

Upon sorting his hand, he was astonished to find that he held, besides the ace, the king, queen, knave, ten and nine of trumps, ace and king of hearts, ace and king of clubs, with two small ones, and the queen of diamonds. He observed that he would bet 100 to 1 he won the game.

Green, who appeared to be intently studying his hand, said, "Don't be too sure of that; I think we shall make the odd trick."

Robinson replied it was impossible and added, "I'll bet you £1,000 to £50 upon it."

"Done," said Green, and amidst the greatest excitement the game proceeded.

Green led king of diamonds, to which his left-hand opponent followed suit, and so did Brown, and Mr. Robinson's queen fell. Green then led ace of diamonds; this Mr. Robinson trumped with the nine, and played the king of trumps. Green followed suit, but it was found that neither of the other players held a trump. Mr. Robinson then saw that Green had originally held seven trumps, while he had only six, one of which had been forced by the ace of diamonds, leaving him (after he had played the king of trumps) with four, while Green held five. On making this discovery, Mr. Robinson played king of hearts; this Green trumped and played knave of diamonds, which Mr. Robinson trumped, and then again changed his lead to king of clubs; but this was also trumped by Green, and the ten of diamonds led, and so Mr. Robinson was again forced. In the result, as the Whist-player will understand, Green, who held seven trumps and *six diamonds,* by forcing Mr. Robinson's hand, was left with the thirteenth trump, scored the odd trick, and won the bet.

Mr. Smith was profuse in his expressions of regret and condolence, observing that Robinson had no right to make such a bet, and that, for his part, he was disgusted at it, as he considered high play ought not to be tolerated, and that he would never have sanctioned it.

Mr. Robinson, when he recovered from the shock, said he would not play any more that night, and, drawing a checkbook from his pocket, he handed one to Mr. Green for £1,500, and to Mr. Brown (for by-bets) £200; Mr. Smith at the same time giving his check for £350, the amount he had lost.

Upon reaching the station the last train to London was found to have gone. After some delay, a brougham and pair was found, and the party reached town, Green kindly inviting them to dine with him at the Castle at Richmond, and saying he would give them a chance to get their money back. The invitation was accepted, and an early day appointed.

Smith did not accompany Robinson to his hotel as usual, pleading fatigue; but early next morning he called on Mr. Robinson and breakfasted with him.

Mr. Robinson was not in the best of spirits, and Smith appeared to be no less disgusted with the result of the past night's amusement. He hinted—rather than stated—his suspicions of Green. It was certainly *very* strange how constantly he won! It was *very* remarkable that two such hands should have been held! Though such things do—they say—happen with new cards, not properly made, and so on. Mr. Robinson listened; but was too indolent, or too indifferent, to reply; and so, breakfast being finished, they strolled out, and went to lionize London.

At night they visited the opera; and the following day Smith, whose attention to Mr. Robinson never flagged, took him to the Crystal

Palace, and dined there, returning early to town. Throughout the day Smith kept harping on their marvelous ill luck; and at length he said, "I shall only give myself one more chance, and if I don't get my money back tomorrow (the day appointed for dinner) I shall cut them, as I can't afford to lose so much money—and look here, old fellow," he added, "if you hear me offer to lay a bet over £50 you may lay your life to a guinea the game is in my hands, and lay it on heavy, so as to get your money back"; and with these words he left.

Mr. Robinson pondered on these words, and it must be admitted the thought entered his mind that the suggestion was *hardly* right, and that it partook somewhat of confederacy. His keen sense of honor however was a little sullied by his heavy losses, and he mentally desired to get his money back if he could.

The dinner at the Castle was all that could be desired, the wines perfect, the cigars first-class, and as usual the card table was set out in due course. Robinson and Smith won several rubbers in succession—some twenty points—with bets amounting to upwards of £100.

Robinson was in capital spirits. The play continued some time with varying success; then it come to Smith's turn to deal, and he turned up king of hearts. He rapidly glanced at his hand, and said (the game stood four all), "I'll bet 2 to 1 we win the game."

"Done," said Green. "I'll take it in monkeys if you like."

"No," said Smith.

On which Mr. Robinson laughingly said, "What *is* a monkey?"

This being explained to him, *and with a look at Smith, who nodded assent,* he said, "I lay it. £1,000 to £500."

The bet was accepted. Mr. Brown thereupon observed he would take £200 to £100 each side, and this bet was also laid, and the game proceeded.

At the third lead Brown played ace of clubs, to which Smith played a diamond, exclaiming, "I trump it!"

"Trump?" said Robinson. "Hearts are trumps!"

"No," replied Smith, in great excitement, "diamonds are trumps. I turned up king of diamonds."

He was of course undeceived by all three; on which he placed his cards on the table, but, taking them up again, played out the hand, and lost the odd trick and the game.

No sooner was the game over than, without a word, Smith rose, or rather staggered, from the table, and was making for a sofa, when he fell to the ground, apparently in a fit. His cravat was loosened, water thrown in his face, the window opened for air, but all without effect. A waiter was sent for a doctor, who promptly arrived, but only in time to see the patient just recover his consciousness, and in the act of taking some brandy. He explained that he had been subject to fits from boyhood, when too much excited, and that he was then all right again.

The medical gentleman, having pocketed his guinea, departed, and the play finished. Mr. Robinson on this night lost £1,500, which he paid to Green and Brown; and Smith lost £400, which he paid, and the party went back to London, Mr. Smith dropping Robinson at his hotel, and driving on with Green and Brown in Brown's brougham, Smith promising to call and see Mr. Robinson at his rooms on the following morning, to inquire after his health.

We doubt if Mr. Robinson went happily to his bed. He mentally cast up his losses, and was horrified at discovering that he was minus some £3,000, and he awoke to the unpleasant fact that if he went on at this rate he would soon arrive at the end of his legacy, so he wisely resolved to put up with his loss, and to play no more.

He slept uneasily, but after tossing about in his bed all night, he fell into a deep slumber from which, about eleven o'clock, he was awakened by a knock at his bedroom door. The waiter informed him that a gentleman named Brown wished to see him. Robinson requested he should be shown to the sitting room, and hastily getting from his bed, slipped on his dressing gown and slippers, and went to see him.

"Good morning, Mr. Robinson," said Brown. "You are no doubt astonished to see me early, but—sir—but—the fact is that Mr. Smith is a d——d scoundrel, and—in short, Mr. Robinson, you have been robbed, and I've come to make a clean breast of it."

Robinson was astounded; he thought it very probable that he had been robbed, but could not understand the reference to Smith, who had been so large a loser; and he said, "How dare you speak in that way of my friend."

"Your friend," retorted Brown; "your friend, indeed! He is a thief and a scoundrel. Not content with robbing you, he has now robbed me. Your friend! He it was who picked you up in Cremorne Gardens, where he followed you from your hotel. He it was who arranged your meeting with Green and myself. He it was who got up and paid for the dinners. He it is who has pocketed all the plunder, and he now robs me of my share; and I swore to him half an hour ago I'd come and tell you all. He changed and stacked the cards when you made the first heavy loss. The fit was sham; go to his lodging, and you'll find him with his friend Green laughing in their sleeves at you and at me. There, now, you know the whole truth."

As this history is but a dry narrative of facts, we will not stay to describe Mr. Robinson's feelings as the truth began to dawn upon his mind. He begged Brown to wait while he dressed, and, having swallowed a cup of tea, took a cab, and went to the office of his uncle's solicitor. That gentleman—an old and experienced man of the world—listened to the narrative in silence, put only a very few questions, and then said to Brown: "I believe, sir, every word you have said, and I shall advise Mr. Robinson to adopt very severe measures."

He then wrote a few lines on a sheet of paper, and presented it to Brown, saying, "Will you sign and agree to that?"

"Yes," said Brown, "I will," and he signed a consent to be detained in a lockup house at Mr. Robinson's pleasure, while inquiries were being made, so as to prevent the possibility of Smith or his agents getting at him, undertaking not to bring any action for false imprisonment. He was forthwith conducted to a celebrated sponging house in Chancery Lane, with instructions that he was not to see anyone, and that no letters were to be posted or delivered from him, and none to be received by him.

This done, Mr. Brown gave the solicitor a narrative of all the circumstances of the case. They may be shortly summarized thus: Mr. Smith learned by a letter from his friend at Demerara that Mr. Robinson was about to sail for England to receive a large legacy, and the hotel at which he was likely to stay was mentioned, he having accidentally heard it in the lawyer's office. Robinson was accurately described, and the writer hoped his friend Smith would "pull off a good thing," and not forget him. Smith watched the arrival of the mail steamer, and spotted Mr. Robinson as soon as he reached his hotel.

Due notice was given to Brown and Green, and for some days Robinson was watched, without affording an opportunity for an introduction. At length the visit to Cremorne gave the long-waited-for chance. Robinson was followed to the Gardens by the three confederates, and followed to town again after Mr. Smith had succeeded in getting him first to give a light to his cigar, and then, as we have seen, to go to the cigar shop in Drury Lane. Our readers will not require to be told that the subsequent treatment of Mr. Robinson was an organized scheme between the three, the object of course being plunder; and that up to a certain point all went well and smoothly; but when thieves fall out, et cetera, et cetera. So poor Mr. Robinson learned how he had been duped and robbed.

The sequel is soon told. The story was found to be strictly true, and was confirmed by a multitude of small but important circumstances. Smith and Green were arrested and taken before a magistrate, charged with conspiracy and cheating. Brown gave evidence against them, and they were fully committed for trial to the Old Bailey. At the trial, which took place at the next ensuing sessions, they were both convicted and sentenced, Smith to eighteen months' imprisonment and £1,500 fine, and Green to twelve months and £1,000 fine; and so this eventful history terminated.

NOTE: The writer assures his readers that every word of the above narrative is strictly true, and that the circumstances happened exactly as they have been detailed.

MORAL: Never play cards with strangers.

¶ *A whist game in a London card club provided the motive in this Sherlock Holmes story. The story has additional special interest, for in it Conan Doyle brought his hero back to life after supposedly having killed him some years before.*

The Adventure of the Empty House

by ARTHUR CONAN DOYLE

IT WAS in the spring of the year 1894 that all London was interested, and the fashionable world dismayed, by the murder of the Honourable Ronald Adair under most unusual and inexplicable circumstances. The public has already learned those particulars of the crime which came out in the police investigation, but a good deal was suppressed upon that occasion, since the case for the prosecution was so overwhelmingly strong that it was not necessary to bring forward all the facts. Only now, at the end of nearly ten years, am I allowed to supply those missing links which make up the whole of that remarkable chain. The crime was of interest in itself, but that interest was as nothing to me compared to the inconceivable sequel, which afforded me the greatest shock and surprise of any event in my adventurous life. Even now, after this long interval, I find myself thrilling as I think of it, and feeling once more that sudden flood of joy, amazement, and incredulity which utterly submerged my mind. Let me say to that public, which has shown some interest in those glimpses which I have occasionally given them of the thoughts and actions of a very remarkable man, that they are not to blame me if I have not shared my knowledge with them, for I should have considered it my first duty to do so, had I not been barred by a positive prohibition from his own lips, which was only withdrawn upon the third of last month.

It can be imagined that my close intimacy with Sherlock Holmes had interested me deeply in crime, and that after his disappearance I never failed to read with care the various problems which came before the public. And I even attempted, more than once, for my own private satisfaction, to employ his methods in their solution, though with indifferent success. There was none, however, which appealed to me like this tragedy of Ronald Adair. As I read the evidence at the inquest, which led up to a verdict of willful murder against some person or persons unknown, I realized more clearly than I had ever done the loss which the community had sustained by the death of Sherlock Holmes. There were points about this strange business which would, I was sure, have specially appealed to him, and the efforts of the police would have been supplemented, or more probably anticipated, by the trained observation and the alert mind of the first criminal agent in Europe. All day, as I drove upon my round, I turned over the case in my mind and found no explanation which appeared to me to be adequate. At the risk of telling a twice-told tale, I will recapitulate the facts as they were known to the public at the conclusion of the inquest.

The Honourable Ronald Adair was the second son of the Earl of Maynooth, at that time governor of one of the Australian colonies. Adair's mother had returned from Australia to undergo the operation for cataract, and she, her son Ronald, and her daughter Hilda were living together at 427 Park Lane. The youth moved in the best society—had, so far as was known, no enemies and no particular vices. He had been engaged to Miss Edith Woodley, of Carstairs, but the engagement had been broken off by mutual consent some months before, and there was no sign that it had left any very profound feeling behind it. For the rest of the man's life moved in a narrow and conventional circle, for his habits were quiet and his nature unemotional. Yet it was upon this easy-going young aristocrat that death came, in most strange and unexpected form, between the hours of ten and eleven-twenty on the night of March 30, 1894.

Ronald Adair was fond of cards—playing continually, but never for such stakes as would hurt him. He was a member of the Baldwin, the Cavendish, and the Bagatelle card clubs. It was shown that, after dinner on the day of his death, he had played a rubber of Whist at the latter club. He had also played there in the afternoon. The evidence of those who had played with him—Mr. Murray, Sir John Hardy, and Colonel Moran—showed that the game was Whist, and that there was a fairly equal fall of the cards. Adair might have lost five pounds, but not more. His fortune was a considerable one, and such a loss could not in any way affect him. He had played nearly every day at one club or other, but he was a cautious player, and usually rose a winner. It came out in evidence that, in partnership with Colonel Moran, he had actually won as much as four hundred and twenty pounds in a sitting, some weeks before, from Godfrey Milner and Lord Balmoral. So much for his recent history as it came out at the inquest.

On the evening of the crime, he returned from the club exactly at ten. His mother and sister were out spending the evening with a relation. The servant deposed that she heard him enter the front room on the second floor, generally used as his sitting room. She had lit a fire there, and as it smoked she had opened the window. No sound was heard from the room until eleven-twenty, the hour of the return of Lady Maynooth and her daughter. Desiring to say good night, she attempted to enter her son's room. The door was locked on the inside, and no answer could be got to their cries and knocking. Help was obtained, and the door forced. The unfortunate young man was found lying near the table. His head had been horribly mutilated by an expanding revolver bullet, but no weapon of any sort was to be found in the room. On the table lay two bank notes for ten pounds each and seventeen pounds ten in silver and gold, the money arranged in little piles of varying amount. There were some figures also upon a sheet of paper, with the names of some club friends opposite to them, from which it was conjectured that before his death he was endeavoring to make out his losses or winnings at cards.

A minute examination of the circumstances served only to make the case more complex. In the first place, no reason could be given why the young man should have fastened the door upon the inside. There was the possibility that the murderer had done this, and had afterwards escaped by the window. The drop was at least twenty feet, however, and a bed of crocuses in full bloom lay beneath. Neither the flowers nor the earth showed any sign of having been disturbed, nor were there any marks upon the narrow strip of grass which separated the house from the road. Apparently, therefore, it was the young man himself who had fastened the door. But how did he come by his death? No one could have climbed up to the window without leaving traces. Suppose a man had fired through the window, he would indeed be a remarkable shot who could with a revolver inflict so deadly a wound. Again, Park Lane is a frequented thoroughfare; there is a cab stand within a hundred yards of the house. No one had heard a shot. And yet there was the dead man, and there the revolver bullet, which had mushroomed out, as soft-nosed bullets will, and so inflicted a wound which must have caused instantaneous death. Such were the circumstances of the Park Lane Mystery, which were further complicated by entire absence of motive, since, as I have said, young Adair was not known to have any enemy, and no attempt had been made to remove the money or valuables in the room.

All day I turned these facts over in my mind, endeavoring to hit upon some theory which could reconcile them all, and to find that line of least resistance which my poor friend had declared to be the starting point of every investigation. I confess that I made little progress. In the evening I strolled across the Park, and found myself about six o'clock at the Oxford Street end of Park Lane. A group of loafers upon the pavements, all staring up at a particular window, directed me to the house which I had come to see. A tall, thin man with colored glasses, whom I strongly suspected of being a plain-clothes detective, was pointing out some theory of his own, while the others crowded round to listen to what he said. I got as near him as I could, but his observations seemed to me to be absurd, so I withdrew again in some disgust. As I did so I struck against an elderly, deformed man, who had been behind me, and I knocked down several books which he was carrying. I remember that as I picked them up, I observed the title of one of them, *The Origin of Tree Worship,* and it struck me that the fellow must be some poor bibliophile, who, either as a trade or as a hobby, was a collector of obscure volumes. I endeavored to apologize for the accident, but it was evident that these books which I had so unfortunately maltreated were very precious objects in the eyes of their owner. With a snarl of contempt he turned upon his heel, and I saw his curved back and white side whiskers disappear among the throng.

My observations of No. 427 Park Lane did little to clear up the problem in which I was interested. The house was separated from the street by a low wall and railing, the whole not more than five feet high. It was perfectly easy, therefore, for anyone to get into the garden, but the window was entirely inaccessible, since there was no waterpipe or anything which could help the most active man to climb it. More puzzled than ever, I retraced my steps to Kensington. I had not been in my study five minutes when the maid entered to say that a person desired to see me. To my astonishment it was none other than my strange old book collector, his sharp, wizened face peering out from a frame of white hair, and his precious volumes, a dozen of them at least, wedged under his right arm.

"You're surprised to see me, sir," said he, in a strange, croaking voice.

I acknowledged that I was.

"Well, I've a conscience, sir, and when I chanced to see you go into this house, as I came hobbling after you, I thought to myself, I'll just step in and see that kind gentleman, and tell him that if I was a bit gruff in my manner there was not any harm meant, and that I am much obliged to him for picking up my books."

"You make too much of a trifle," said I. "May I ask how you knew who I was?"

"Well, sir, if it isn't too great a liberty, I am a neighbor of yours, for you'll find my little bookshop at the corner of Church Street, and very happy to see you, I am sure. Maybe you collect yourself, sir. Here's *British Birds,* and *Catullus,* and *The Holy War*—a bargain, every one of them. With five volumes you could just fill that gap on that second shelf. It looks untidy, does it not, sir?"

I moved my head to look at the cabinet behind me. When I turned again, Sherlock Holmes was standing smiling at me across my study table. I rose to my feet, stared at him for some seconds in utter amazement, and then it appears that I must have fainted for the first and the last time in my life. Certainly a gray mist swirled before my eyes, and when it cleared I found my collar ends undone and the tingling aftertaste of brandy upon my lips. Holmes was bending over my chair, his flask in his hand.

"My dear Watson," said the well-remembered voice, "I owe you a thousand apologies. I had no idea that you would be so affected."

I gripped him by the arms.

"Holmes!" I cried. "Is it really you? Can it indeed be that you are alive? Is it possible that you succeeded in climbing out of that awful abyss?"

"Wait a moment," said he. "Are you sure that you are really fit to discuss things? I have given you a serious shock by my unnecessarily dramatic reappearance."

"I am all right, but indeed, Holmes, I can hardly believe my eyes. Good heavens! to think that you—you of all men—should be standing in my study." Again I gripped him by the sleeve, and felt the thin, sinewy arm beneath it. "Well, you're not a spirit, anyhow," said I. "My dear chap, I'm overjoyed to see you. Sit down, and tell me how you came alive out of that dreadful chasm."

He sat opposite to me, and lit a cigarette in his old, nonchalant manner. He was dressed in the seedy frockcoat of the book merchant, but the rest of that individual lay in a pile of white hair and old books upon the table. Holmes looked even thinner and keener than of old, but there was a dead-white tinge in his aquiline face which told me that his life recently had not been a healthy one.

"I am glad to stretch myself, Watson," said he. "It is no joke when a tall man has to take a foot off his stature for several hours on end. Now, my dear fellow, in the matter of these explanations, we have, if I may ask for your co-operation, a hard and dangerous night's work in front of us. Perhaps it would be better if I gave you an account of the whole situation when that work is finished."

"I am full of curiosity. I should much prefer to hear now."

"You'll come with me tonight?"

"When you like and where you like."

"This is, indeed, like the old days. We shall have time for a mouthful of dinner before we need go. Well, then, about that chasm. I had no serious difficulty in getting out of it, for the very simple reason that I never was in it."

"You never were in it?"

"No, Watson, I never was in it. My note to you was absolutely genuine. I had little doubt that I had come to the end of my career when I perceived the somewhat sinister figure of the late Professor Moriarty standing upon the narrow pathway which led to safety. I read an inexorable purpose in his gray eyes. I exchanged some remarks with him, therefore, and obtained his courteous permission to write the short note which you afterwards received. I left it with my cigarette-box and my stick, and I walked along the pathway, Moriarty still at my heels. When I reached the end I stood at bay. He drew no weapon, but he rushed at me and threw his long arms around me. He knew that his own game was up, and was only anxious to revenge himself upon me. We tottered together upon the brink of the fall. I have some knowledge, however, of baritsu, or the Japanese system of wrestling, which has more than once been very useful to me. I slipped through his grip, and he with a horrible scream kicked madly for a few seconds, and clawed the air with both his hands. But for all his efforts he could not get his balance, and over he went. With my face over the brink, I saw him fall for a long way. Then he struck a rock, bounded off, and splashed into the water."

I listened with amazement to this explanation, which Holmes delivered between the puffs of his cigarette.

"But the tracks!" I cried. "I saw, with my own eyes, that two went down the path and none returned."

"It came about in this way. The instant that the Professor had disappeared, it struck me what a really extraordinarily lucky chance Fate had placed in my way. I knew that Moriarty was not the only man who had sworn my death. There were at least three others whose desire for vengeance upon me would only be increased by the death of their leader. They were all most dangerous men. One or other would certainly get me. On the other hand, if all the world was convinced that I was dead they would take liberties, these men, they would soon lay themselves open, and sooner or later I could destroy them. Then it would be time for me to announce that I was still in the land of the living. So rapidly does the brain act that I believe I had thought this all out before Professor Moriarty had reached the bottom of the Reichenbach Fall.

"I stood up and examined the rocky wall behind me. In your picturesque account of the matter, which I read with great interest some months later, you assert that the wall was sheer. That was not literally true. A few small footholds presented themselves, and there was some indication of a ledge. The cliff is so high that to climb it all was an obvious impossibility, and it was equally impossible to make my way along the wet path without leaving some tracks. I might, it is true, have reversed my boots, as I have done on similar occasions, but the sight of three sets of tracks in one direction would certainly have suggested a deception. On the whole, then, it was best that I should risk the climb. It was not a pleasant business, Watson. The fall roared beneath me. I am not a fanciful person, but I give you my word that I seemed to hear Moriarty's voice screaming at me out of the abyss. A mistake would have been fatal. More than once, as tufts of grass came out in my hand or my foot slipped in the wet notches of the rock, I thought that I was gone. But I struggled upward, and at last I reached a ledge several feet deep and covered with soft green moss, where I could lie unseen, in the most perfect comfort. There I was stretched, when you, my dear Watson, and all your following were investigating in the most sympathetic and inefficient manner the circumstances of my death.

"At last, when you had all formed your inevitable and totally erroneous conclusions, you departed for the hotel, and I was left alone. I had imagined that I had reached the end of my adventures, but a very unexpected occurrence showed me that there were surprises still in store for me. A huge rock, falling from above, boomed past me, struck the path, and bounded over into the chasm. For an instant I thought that it was an accident, but a moment later, looking up, I saw a man's head against the darkening sky, and another stone struck the very ledge upon which I was stretched, within a foot of my head. Of course, the meaning of this was obvious. Moriarty had not been alone. A confederate—and even that one glance had told me how dangerous a man that confederate was—had kept guard while the Professor had attacked me. From a distance, unseen by me, he had been a witness of his friend's death and of my escape. He had waited, and then making his way round to the top of the cliff, he had endeavored to succeed where his comrade had failed.

"I did not take long to think about it, Watson. Again I saw that grim face look over the cliff, and I knew that it was the precursor of another stone. I scrambled down on to the path. I don't think I could have done it in cold blood. It was a hundred times more difficult than getting up. But I had no time to think of the danger, for another stone sang past me as I hung by my hands from the edge of the ledge. Halfway down I slipped, but, by the blessing of God, I landed, torn and bleeding, upon the path. I took to my heels, did ten miles over the mountains in the darkness, and a week later I found myself in Florence, with the certainty that no one in the world knew what had become of me.

"I had only one confidant—my brother Mycroft. I owe you many apologies, my dear Watson, but it was all-important that it should be thought I was dead, and it is quite certain that you would not have written so convincing an account of my unhappy end had you not yourself thought that it was true. Several times during the last three years I have taken up my pen to write to you, but always I feared lest your affectionate regard for me should tempt you to some indiscretion which would betray my secret. For that reason I turned away from you this evening when you upset my books, for I was in danger at the time, and any show of surprise and emotion upon your part might have drawn attention to my identity and led to the most deplorable and irreparable results. As to Mycroft, I had to confide in him in order to obtain the money which I needed. The course of events in London did not run so well as I had hoped, for the trial of the Moriarty gang left two of its most dangerous members, my own most vindictive enemies, at liberty. I traveled for two years in Tibet, therefore, and amused myself by visiting Lhasa, and spending some days with the head lama. You may have read of the remarkable explorations of a Norwegian named Sigerson, but I am sure that it never occurred to you that you were receiving news of your friend. I then passed through Persia, looked in at Mecca, and paid a short but interesting visit to the Khalifa at Khartoum, the results of which I have communicated to the Foreign Office. Returning to France, I spent some months in a research into the coal-tar derivatives, which I conducted in a laboratory at Montpellier, in the south of France. Having concluded this to my satisfaction and learning that only one of my enemies was now left in London, I was about to return when my movements were hastened by the news of this very remarkable Park Lane Mystery, which not only appealed to me by its own merits, but which seemed to offer some most peculiar personal opportunities. I came over at once to London, called in my own person at Baker Street, threw Mrs. Hudson into violent hysterics, and found that Mycroft had preserved my rooms and my papers exactly as they had always been. So it was, my dear Watson, that at two o'clock today I found myself in my old armchair in my own old room, and only wishing that I could have seen my old friend Watson in the other chair which he has so often adorned."

Such was the remarkable narrative to which I

listened on that April evening—a narrative which would have been utterly incredible to me had it not been confirmed by the actual sight of the tall, spare figure and the keen, eager face, which I had never thought to see again. In some manner he had learned of my own sad bereavement, and his sympathy was shown in his manner rather than in his words. "Work is the best antidote to sorrow, my dear Watson," said he; "and I have a piece of work for us both tonight which, if we can bring it to a successful conclusion, will in itself justify a man's life on this planet." In vain I begged him to tell me more. "You will hear and see enough before morning," he answered. "We have three years of the past to discuss. Let that suffice until half past nine, when we start upon the notable adventure of the empty house."

It was indeed like old times when, at that hour, I found myself seated beside him in a hansom, my revolver in my pocket, and the thrill of adventure in my heart. Holmes was cold and stern and silent. As the gleam of the street lamps flashed upon his austere features, I saw that his brows were drawn down in thought and his thin lips compressed. I knew not what wild beast we were about to hunt down in the dark jungle of criminal London, but I was well assured, from the bearing of this master huntsman, that the adventure was a most grave one—while the sardonic smile which occasionally broke through his ascetic gloom boded little good for the object of our quest.

I had imagined that we were bound for Baker Street, but Holmes stopped the cab at the corner of Cavendish Square. I observed that as he stepped out he gave a most searching glance to right and left, and at every subsequent street corner he took the utmost pains to assure that he was not followed. Our route was certainly a singular one. Holmes's knowledge of the byways of London was extraordinary, and on this occasion he passed rapidly and with an assured step through the network of mews and stables, the very existence of which I had never known. We emerged at last into a small road, lined with old, gloomy houses, which led us into Manchester Street, and so to Blandford Street. Here he turned swiftly down a narrow passage, passed through a wooden gate into a deserted yard, and then opened with a key the back door of a house. We entered together, and he closed it behind us.

The place was pitch dark, but it was evident to me that it was an empty house. Our feet creaked and crackled over the bare planking, and my outstretched hand touched a wall from which the paper was hanging in ribbons. Holmes's cold, thin fingers closed round my wrist and led me forward down a long hall, until I dimly saw the murky fanlight over the door. Here Holmes turned suddenly to the right, and we found ourselves in a large, square, empty room, heavily shadowed in the corners, but faintly lit in the center from the lights of the street beyond. There was no lamp near, and the window was thick with dust, so that we could only just discern each other's figures within. My companion put his hand upon my shoulder and his lips close to my ear.

"Do you know where we are?" he whispered.

"Surely that is Baker Street," I answered, staring through the dim window.

"Exactly. We are in Camden House, which stands opposite to our own old quarters."

"But why are we here?"

"Because it commands so excellent a view of that picturesque pile. Might I trouble you, my dear Watson, to draw a little nearer to the window, taking every precaution not to show yourself, and then to look up at our old rooms—the starting point of so many of your little fairy tales? We will see if my three years of absence have entirely taken away my power to surprise you."

I crept forward and looked across at the familiar window. As my eyes fell upon it, I gave a gasp and a cry of amazement. The blind was down, and a strong light was burning in the room. The shadow of a man who was seated in a chair within was thrown in hard, black outline upon the luminous screen of the window. There was no mistaking the poise of the head, the squareness of the shoulders, the sharpness of the features. The face was turned half-round, and the effect was that of one of those black silhouettes which our grandparents loved to frame. It was a perfect reproduction of Holmes. So amazed was I that I threw out my hand to make sure that the man himself was standing beside me. He was quivering with silent laughter.

"Well?" said he.

"Good heavens!" I cried. "It is marvelous."

"I trust that age doth not wither nor custom stale my infinite variety," said he, and I recognized in his voice the joy and pride which the artist takes in his own creation. "It really is rather like me, is it not?"

"I should be prepared to swear that it was you."

"The credit of the execution is due to Monsieur Oscar Meunier, of Grenoble, who spent some days in doing the molding. It is a bust in wax. The rest I arranged myself during my visit to Baker Street this afternoon."

"But why?"

"Because, my dear Watson, I had the strongest possible reason for wishing certain people to think that I was there when I was really elsewhere."

"And you thought the rooms were watched?"

"I *knew* that they were watched."

"By whom?"

"By my old enemies, Watson. By the charming society whose leader lies in the Reichenbach Fall. You must remember that they knew, and only they knew, that I was still alive. Sooner or later they believed that I should come back to my rooms. They watched them continuously, and this morning they saw me arrive."

"How do you know?"

"Because I recognized their sentinel when I glanced out of my window. He is a harmless enough fellow, Parker by name, a garroter by trade, and a remarkable performer upon the jew's-harp. I cared nothing for him. But I cared a great deal for the much more formidable person who was behind him, the bosom friend of Moriarty, the man who dropped the rocks over the cliff, the most cunning and dangerous criminal in London. That is the man who is after me tonight, Watson, and that is the man who is quite unaware that we are after *him*."

My friend's plans were gradually revealing themselves. From this convenient retreat, the watchers were being watched and the trackers tracked. That angular shadow up yonder was the bait, and we were the hunters. In silence we stood together in the darkness and watched the hurrying figures who passed and repassed in front of us. Holmes was silent and motionless; but I could tell that he was keenly alert, and that his eyes were fixed intently upon the stream of passers-by. It was a bleak and boisterous night, and the wind whistled shrilly down the long street. Many people were moving to and fro, most of them muffled in their coats and cravats. Once or twice it seemed to me that I had seen the same figure before, and I especially noticed two men who appeared to be sheltering themselves from the wind in the doorway of a house some distance up the street. I tried to draw my companion's attention to them; but he gave a little ejaculation of impatience, and continued to stare into the street. More than once he fidgeted with his feet and tapped rapidly with his fingers upon the wall. It was evident to me that he was becoming uneasy, and that his plans were not working out altogether as he had hoped. At last, as midnight approached and the street gradually cleared, he paced up and down the room in uncontrollable agitation. I was about to make some remark to him, when I raised my eyes to the lighted window, and again experienced almost as great a surprise as before. I clutched Holmes's arm, and pointed upward.

"The shadow has moved!" I cried.

It was indeed no longer the profile, but the back, which was turned toward us.

Three years had certainly not smoothed the asperities of his temper or his impatience with a less active intelligence than his own.

"Of course it has moved," said he. "Am I such a farcical bungler, Watson, that I should erect an obvious dummy, and expect that some of the sharpest men in Europe would be deceived by it? We have been in this room two hours, and Mrs. Hudson has made some change in that figure eight times, or once in every quarter of an hour. She works it from the front, so that her shadow may never be seen. Ah!" He drew in his breath with a shrill, excited intake. In the dim light I saw his head thrown forward, his whole attitude rigid with attention. Outside the street was absolutely deserted. Those two men might still be crouching in the doorway, but I could no longer see them. All was still and dark, save only that brilliant yellow screen in front of us with the black figure outlined upon its centre. Again in the utter silence I heard that thin, sibilant note which spoke of intense suppressed excitement. An instant later he pulled me back into the blackest corner of the room, and I felt his warning hand upon my lips. The fingers which clutched me were quivering. Never had I known my friend more moved, and yet the dark street still stretched lonely and motionless before us.

But suddenly I was aware of that which his keener senses had already distinguished. A low, stealthy sound came to my ears, not from the direction of Baker Street, but from the back of the very house in which we lay concealed. A door opened and shut. An instant later steps crept down the passage—steps which were meant to be silent, but which reverberated harshly through the empty house. Holmes crouched back against the wall, and I did the same, my hand closing upon the handle of my revolver. Peering through the gloom, I saw the vague outline of a man, a shade blacker than the blackness of the open door. He stood for an instant, and then he crept forward, crouching, menacing, into the room. He was within three yards of us, this sinister figure, and I had braced myself to meet his spring, before I realized that he had no idea of my presence. He passed close beside us, stole over to the window, and very softly and noiselessly raised it for half a foot. As he sank to the level of this opening, the light of the street, no longer dimmed by the dusty glass, fell full upon his face. The man seemed to be beside himself with excitement. His two eyes shone like stars, and his features were working convulsively. He was an elderly man, with a thin, projecting nose, a high, bald forehead, and a huge grizzled mustache. An opera hat was pushed to the back of his head, and an evening dress shirt-front gleamed out through his open overcoat. His face was gaunt and swarthy, scored with deep, savage lines. In his hand he carried what appeared to be a stick, but as he laid it down upon the floor it gave a metallic clang. Then from the pocket of his overcoat he drew a bulky object, and he busied himself in some task which ended with a loud, sharp click, as if a spring or bolt had fallen into its place. Still kneeling upon the floor he bent forward and threw all his weight and strength upon some lever, with the result that there came a long, whirling, grinding noise, ending once more in a powerful click. He straightened himself then, and I saw that what he held in his hand was a sort of gun, with a curiously misshapen butt. He opened it at the breech, put something in, and snapped the breech-lock. Then, crouching down, he rested the end of the barrel upon the ledge of the open window, and I saw his long mustache droop over the stock and his eye gleam as it peered along the sights. I heard a little sight of satisfaction as he cuddled the butt into his shoulder, and saw that amazing target, the black man on the yellow ground, standing clear at the end of his foresight. For an instant he was rigid and motionless. Then his finger tightened on the trigger. There was a strange, loud whiz and a long, silvery tinkle of broken glass. At that instant Holmes sprang like a tiger on to the marksman's back, and hurled him flat upon his face. He was up again in a moment, and with convulsive strength he seized Holmes by the throat, but I struck him on the head with the butt of my revolver, and he dropped again upon the floor. I fell upon him, and as I held him my comrade blew a shrill call upon a whistle. There was the clatter of running feet upon the pavement, and two policemen in uniform, with one plainclothes detective, rushed through the front entrance and into the room.

"That you, Lestrade?" said Holmes.

"Yes, Mr. Holmes. I took the job myself. It's good to see you back in London, sir."

"I think you want a little unofficial help. Three undetected murders in one year won't do, Lestrade. But you handled the Molesey Mystery with less than your usual—that's to say, you handled it fairly well."

We had all risen to our feet, our prisoner breathing hard, with a stalwart constable on each side of him. Already a few loiterers had begun to collect in the street. Holmes stepped up to the window, closed it, and dropped the blinds. Lestrade had produced two candles, and the policemen had uncovered their lanterns. I was able at last to have a good look at our prisoner.

It was a tremendously virile and yet sinister face which was turned towards us. With the brow of a philosopher above and the jaw of a sensualist below, the man must have started with great capacities for good or for evil. But one could not look upon his cruel blue eyes, with their drooping, cynical lids, or upon the fierce, aggressive nose and the threatening, deep-lined brow, without reading Nature's plainest danger signals. He took no heed of any of us, but his eyes were fixed upon Holmes's face with an expression in which hatred and amazement were equally blended. "You fiend!" he kept on muttering. "You clever, clever fiend!"

"Ah, Colonel!" said Holmes, arranging his rumpled collar. " 'Journeys end in lovers' meetings,' as the old play says. I don't think I have had the pleasure of seeing you since you favored me with those attentions as I lay on the ledge above the Reichenbach Fall."

The colonel still stared at my friend like a man in a trance.

"You cunning, cunning fiend!" was all that he could say.

"I have not introduced you yet," said Holmes. "This gentleman is Colonel Sebastian Moran, once of Her Majesty's Indian Army, and the best heavy-game shot that our Eastern Empire has ever produced. I believe I am correct, Colonel, in saying that your bag of tigers still remains unrivaled?"

The fierce old man said nothing, but still glared at my companion. With his savage eyes and bristling mustache he was wonderfully like a tiger himself.

"I wonder that my very simple stratagem could deceive so old a *shikari,*" said Holmes. "It must be very familiar to you. Have you not tethered a young kid under a tree, lain above it with your rifle, and waited for the bait to bring up your tiger? This empty house is my tree, and you are my tiger. You have possibly had other guns in reserve in case there should be several tigers, or in the unlikely supposition of your own aim failing you. These," he pointed around, "are my other guns. The parallel is exact."

Colonel Moran sprang forward with a snarl of rage, but the constables dragged him back. The fury upon his face was terrible to look at.

"I confess that you had one small surprise for me," said Holmes. "I did not anticipate that you would yourself make use of this empty house and this convenient front window. I had imagined you as operating from the street, where my friend Lestrade and his merry men were awaiting you. With that exception, all has gone as I expected."

Colonel Moran turned to the official detective.

"You may or may not have just cause for arresting me," said he, "but at least there can be no reason why I should submit to the gibes of this person. If I am in the hands of the law, let things be done in a legal way."

"Well, that's reasonable enough," said Lestrade. "Nothing further you have to say, Mr. Holmes, before we go?"

Holmes had picked up the powerful air-gun from the floor, and was examining its mechanism.

"An admirable and unique weapon," said he, "noiseless and of tremendous power: I knew Von Herder, the blind German mechanic, who constructed it to the order of the late Professor Moriarty. For years I have been aware of its existence, though I have never before had the opportunity of handling it. I commend it very specially to your attention, Lestrade, and also the bullets which fit it."

"You can trust us to look after that, Mr. Holmes," said Lestrade, as the whole party moved towards the door. "Anything further to say?"

"Only to ask what charge you intend to prefer?"

"What charge, sir? Why, of course, the attempted murder of Mr. Sherlock Holmes."

"Not so, Lestrade. I do not propose to appear in the matter at all. To you, and to you only, belongs the credit of the remarkable arrest which you have effected. Yes, Lestrade, I congratulate you! With your usual happy mixture of cunning and audacity, you have got him."

"Got him! Got whom, Mr. Holmes?"

"The man that the whole force has been seeking in vain—Colonel Sebastian Moran, who shot the Honourable Ronald Adair with an expanding bullet from an air-gun through the open window of the second-floor front of No. 427 Park Lane, upon the thirtieth of last month. That's the charge, Lestrade. And now, Watson, if you can endure the draught from a broken window, I think that half an hour in my study over a cigar may afford you some profitable amusement."

Our old chambers had been left unchanged through the supervision of Mycroft Holmes and the immediate care of Mrs. Hudson. As I entered I saw, it is true, an unwonted tidiness, but the old landmarks were all in their place. There were the chemical corner and the acid-stained, deal-topped table. There upon a shelf was the row of formidable scrapbooks and books of reference which many of our fellow citizens would have been so glad to burn. The diagrams, the violin case, and the pipe rack—even the Persian slipper which contained the tobacco—all met my eyes as I glanced round me. There were two occupants of the room—one, Mrs. Hudson, who beamed upon us both as we entered—the other, the strange dummy which had played so important a part in the evening's adventures. It was a wax-colored model of my friend, so admirably done that it was a perfect facsimile. It stood on a small pedestal table with an old dressing gown of Holmes's so draped round it that the illusion from the street was absolutely perfect.

"I hope you observed all precautions, Mrs. Hudson?" said Holmes.

"I went to it on my knees, sir, just as you told me."

"Excellent. You carried the thing out very well. Did you observe where the bullet went?"

"Yes, sir. I'm afraid it has spoilt your beautiful bust, for it passed right through the head and flattened itself on the wall. I picked it up from the carpet. Here it is!"

Holmes held it out to me. "A soft revolver bullet, as you perceive, Watson. There's genius in that, for who would expect to find such a thing fired from an air-gun? All right, Mrs. Hudson. I am much obliged for your assistance. And now, Watson, let me see you in your old seat once more, for there are several points which I should like to discuss with you."

He had thrown off the seedy frock coat, and now he was the Holmes of old in the mouse-colored dressing gown which he took from his effigy.

"The old *shikari's* nerves have not lost their steadiness, nor his eyes their keenness," said he, with a laugh, as he inspected the shattered forehead of his bust.

"Plumb in the middle of the back of the head and smack through the brain. He was the best shot in India, and I expect that there are few better in London. Have you heard the name?"

"No, I have not."

"Well, well, such is fame! But, then, if I remember right, you had not heard the name of Professor James Moriarty, who had one of the great brains of the century. Just give me down my index of biographies from the shelf."

He turned over the pages lazily, leaning back in his chair and blowing great clouds from his cigar.

"My collection of M's is a fine one," said he. "Moriarty himself is enough to make any letter illustrious, and here is Morgan the poisoner, and Merridew of abominable memory, and Mathews, who knocked out my left canine in the waiting room at Charing Cross, and, finally, here is our friend of tonight."

He handed over the book, and I read:

Moran, Sebastian, Colonel. Unemployed. Formerly 1st Bangalore Pioneers. Born London, 1840. Son of Sir Augustus Moran, C.B., once British Minister to Persia. Educated Eton and Oxford. Served in Jowaki Campaign, Afghan Campaign, Charasiab (despatches), Sherpur, and Cabul. Author of *Heavy Game of the Western Himalayas* (1881); *Three Months in the Jungle* (1884). Address: Conduit Street. Clubs: The Anglo-Indian, the Tankerville, the Bagatelle Card Club.

On the margin was written, in Holmes's precise hand: The second most dangerous man in London.

"This is astonishing," said I, as I handed back the volume. "The man's career is that of an honorable soldier."

"It is true," Holmes answered. "Up to a certain point he did well. He was always a man of iron nerve, and the story is still told in India how he crawled down a drain after a wounded man-eating tiger. There are some trees, Watson, which grow to a certain height, and then suddenly develop some unsightly eccentricity. You will see it often in humans. I have a theory that the individual represents in his development the whole procession of his ancestors, and that such a sudden turn to good or evil stands for some strong influence which came into the line of his pedigree. The person becomes, as it were, the epitome of the history of his own family."

"It is surely rather fanciful."

"Well, I don't insist upon it. Whatever the cause, Colonel Moran began to go wrong. Without any open scandal, he still made India too hot to hold him. He retired, came to London, and again acquired an evil name. It was at this time that he was sought out by Professor Moriarty, to whom for a time he was chief of the staff. Moriarty supplied him liberally with money, and used him only in one or two very high-class jobs, which no ordinary criminal could have undertaken. You may have some recollection of the death of Mrs. Stewart, of Lauder, in 1887. Not? Well, I am sure Moran was at the bottom of it, but nothing could be proved. So cleverly was the colonel concealed that, even when the Moriarty gang was broken up, we could not incriminate him. You remember at that date, when I called upon you in your rooms, how I put up the shutters for fear of air-guns? No doubt you thought me fanciful. I knew exactly what I was doing, for I knew of the existence of this remarkable gun, and I knew also that one of the best shots in the world would be behind it. When we were in Switzerland he followed us with Moriarty, and it was undoubtedly he who gave me that evil five minutes on the Reichenbach ledge.

"You may think that I read the papers with some attention during my sojourn in France, on the lookout for any chance of laying him by the heels. So long as he was free in London, my life would really not have been worth living. Night and day the shadow would have been over me, and sooner or later his chance must have come. What could I do? I could not shoot him at sight, or I should myself be in the dock. There was no use appealing to a magistrate. They cannot interfere on the strength of what would appear to them to be a wild suspicion. So I could do nothing. But I watched the criminal news, knowing that sooner or later I should get him. Then came the death of this Ronald Adair. My chance had come at last. Knowing what I did, was it not certain that Colonel Moran had done it? He had played cards with the lad, he had followed him home from the club, he had shot him through the open window. There was not a doubt of it. The bullets alone are enough to put his head in a noose. I came over at once. I was seen by the sentinel, who would, I knew, direct the colonel's attention to my presence. He could not fail to connect my sudden return with his crime, and to be terribly alarmed. I was sure that he would make an attempt to get me out of the way *at once,* and would bring round his murderous weapon for that purpose. I left him an excellent mark in the window, and, having warned the police that they might be needed—by the way, Watson, you spotted their presence in that doorway with unerring accuracy—I took up what seemed to me to be a judicious post for observation, never dreaming that he would choose the same spot for his attack. Now, my dear Watson, does anything remain for me to explain?"

"Yes," said I. "You have not made it clear

what was Colonel Moran's motive in murdering the Honourable Ronald Adair?"

"Ah! my dear Watson, there we come into those realms of conjecture, where the most logical mind may be at fault. Each may form his own hypothesis upon the present evidence, and yours is as likely to be correct as mine."

"You have formed one, then?"

"I think that it is not difficult to explain the facts. It came out in evidence that Colonel Moran and young Adair had, between them, won a considerable amount of money. Now, Moran undoubtedly played foul—of that I have long been aware. I believe that on the day of the murder Adair had discovered that Moran was cheating. Very likely he had spoken to him privately, and had threatened to expose him unless he voluntarily resigned his membership of the club, and promised not to play cards again. It is unlikely that a youngster like Adair would at once make a hideous scandal by exposing a well-known man so much older than himself. Probably he acted as I suggest.

The exclusion from his clubs would mean ruin to Moran, who lived by his ill-gotten card gains. He therefore murdered Adair, who at the time was endeavoring to work out how much money he should himself return, since he could not profit by his partner's foul play. He locked the door lest the ladies should surprise him and insist upon knowing what he was doing with these names and coins. Will it pass?"

"I have no doubt that you have hit upon the truth."

"It will be verified or disproved at the trial. Meanwhile, come what may, Colonel Moran will trouble us no more. The famous air-gun of Von Herder will embellish the Scotland Yard Museum, and once again Mr. Sherlock Holmes is free to devote his life to examining those interesting little problems which the complex life of London so plentifully presents."

THE MAN WHO REVOKED AT THE PORTLAND CLUB

From *Punch*, 1924; reproduced by permission of *Punch*.

❡[*The* Punch *cartoon does not exaggerate by much. The august Portland Club is as awesome an institution as England can boast; only at the Portland can a game of cards assume the gravity of a meeting of the Cabinet or the Admiralty. When a peer or a royal prince plays cards it is at the Portland.*

BRIDGE

❡Bridge was the greatest bombshell of all the card games. It showed up almost simultaneously in New York (1893) and London (1894). Within a matter of months it overturned the 400-year-old primacy of Whist. By the turn of the century it had done more for women's rights than a generation of suffragette agitation, for mixed Bridge replaced segregation by sexes as after-dinner routine. Bridge began as a fad but it did not die as fads do. It persisted and survived as a social phenomenon equivalent to dancing and jazz music. ❡There have been three games of Bridge. The one we play today we call Contract. The one that started it all was first called simply Bridge, but now we call it Bridge-Whist to emphasize its antiquity and distinguish it from its successors. In the earliest Bridge, the dealer named the trump (or he could "bridge" the prerogative to his partner, who was always the dummy). Then came Auction Bridge, with a new factor—bidding! It reached its peak just in time to catch the unrestrained demand for entertainment that followed hard on World War I. ❡Mah-jongg was in its heyday. In 1922 and 1923 Mah-jongg sets outsold radios. But Auction Bridge rode serenely and triumphantly over the Yellow Peril and by 1926 its ascendancy was absolute. Undoubtedly one of the factors favoring Auction Bridge was a series of short stories written by Sam Hellman for the Saturday Evening Post between 1923 and 1927. Mass magazines were not so common then as they are today, and the S.E.P.'s influence on public opinion was enormous. No better explanation can be advanced for the success of the Hellman Bridge stories. Sam Hellman himself was never more than an uninterested dabbler in Bridge. He played the game a few times because fashion so decreed. When the urgency subsided he quit. His stories used the classic hands (Duke of Cumberland, Mississippi Heart Hand), but only because someone happened to show them to him and he happened to write them down as fiction ideas. Yet he started or at least impelled a trend with his stories, of which the following was the first and most famous.

High Bridge

by SAM HELLMAN

I

THIS here game of Bridge is, you might say, the greatest of American indoor spats. They is lots of rows us married lads can work up over such domestical matters as slapping a monicker on the bambino or where-was-you-last-night-huh and the such, but them kinda lukeworn skirmishes ain't to be compared to the hell and hot water you can get into with the frau just by forgetting that the six of clubs ain't been played yet.

Before I was talked into falling for this Auction stuff, home life maybe wasn't just one swift song; but anyways, me and the misses could easy be mistaken for a coupla friends. Things ain't no more now like they used to was. A cuckoo dropping into our hut around breakfast time any morning after a session with the pestboards would get the idea that we was a pair of deaf and dummies marooned on a iceberg and not able to say nothing on the account of our fingers being frostbitten.

I've told you fellers before how I learned to play Bridge from a gambolier named High Spade Kennedy, and also from outta the book by McGullible, just to show up some friends of the frau, who was always bragging how much brains it took to get jerry to the game. After proving to them, by a trip to the cleaners, that such was not the case, I figured on retiring on my low rails; me, up to that time, not having no high opinions of any kinda pastime that the frills could get by with, without interfering with the piecework they was doing in the scandal shop. But this darn game is like whiskers. It just grows on you nilly-billy, and before I knows it, I've given Stud and Pinochle the grand razzazz and taken my chips to the auction house.

We plays two or three times a week, mostly with the Magruders, them perfect busts that started me off on the sport of kings and aces, and in a coupla months I could be third-degreed into admitting that they wasn't hardly nobody that I couldn't spot about two legs per rubber and knock for a trip to the check book. The wife, however, is got different ideas, which is, of course.

"How do you like my stuff?" I asks her one night, when we is still talking at the end of the game.

"Well," says she, "considering that you had all the cards and me for a partner, and the folks we was playing with don't know nothing about Bridge, you could maybe have done worser. You only trumped your own tricks about eight times and blocked yourself twice and finessed against me every ten minutes or so; but outside of that, I can't think of no more than a dozen things that you done wrong."

"From them praises you is singing to me," I remarks, "you must want something."

"I does," comes back Kate.

"Give it a name," I tells her.

"I want," says the misses, "that you should give a imitation of a gentleman of refineries and tastes when we goes up to the Sintons' next week."

"What for?" I desires to know. "Pete Sinton and me used to eat pie with the same knife, and even if he is got enough jack now to slip a ten-case note to every brunette in Africa, that boy ain't the kind to put on no dogs with."

"Maybe not," admits the misses, "but seeing that he ain't been around near you for a long time, they is a barely chance that his manners is got better than when he was barrooming with you. I hears that they has a wonderful place out in the country, with butlers scattered all over the house, and that they is a lotta swells coming to this party."

"How," I asks, "do we happen to bust in with the nifties?"

"That's easy," answers Kate. "Belle Sinton knows me and don't know you. You horns in by the mere accidents of marriage."

"I does, eh?" I yelps. "Suppose I ups and refuses to go."

"I ain't got no time to waste on no joke supposes like that," comes back the wife. "What I wants to say is this: If you don't act at the Sintons' like a gentleman should, you will maybe find out some more about them accidents of marriage I was telling you about. They is sure to be some Bridge playing there, and I don't wish that you should let the idea get around that the suspicion you got of the game was learned from a couple of yeggmen in the back room of a boiler factory."

"What," I inquires, "is wrong with the way I play?"

"It would take me, at the leastest, a week to even scratch the service," answers the frau; "but they is a few things I could mention right quick."

"Them being?" I asks.

"One of 'em being," says she, "the barrelhouse habit you has of slamming the cards down on the table like you was mad at 'em for having bit you. Another is the mean way you got of looking at me when I don't happen to lead the suit you thinks you wants but probably don't."

"Well," I remarks, "even a king may look at a cat."

"Yeh," returns the misses, "but not no deuce spot."

"What else is they," I asks, "that I does——"

"It ain't so much what you does in a Bridge game," cuts in the squaw, "as what you does to it. Auction, you may have heard by accident some place, is supposed to be a nice, quiet pastimes for people with cultures; but the way you plays it could easy be mistaken for a cross between a dog fight and a raid on a gambling den. You don't play Auction; you broadcasts it."

"Got any more trumps?" I asks, sarcastic.

"You is a gloating winner and a rotten loser," goes on Kate. "When you is ahead you is as full of conversation as a barker at a ballyhoo; when you is behind you ain't got no more to say than a deaf mutt; and, besides, you looks about as happy as a kid that's just been washed behind the ears, spanked and put to bed without nothing to eat except a dose of castor oil."

"What is you out for?" I asks. "The nonstop razz record?"

"I'll be making a record," says the wife, "if I can get you to act at the Sintons' like you was used to playing Bridge as if it was a decent parlor game instead of a excuse for dragging out samples of your temper line."

"I'll show you some right now," I yelps, real riled by the grand slams the frau's been scoring offa me with five honors in one hand. "If you was to know ten times as much as you knows about Bridge now, if any, you wouldn't hardly know nothing. You——"

"Maybe not," interrupted Kate, "but I could teach you that much, anyways."

"No, you couldn't," I shouts back, not noticing until too late that I has left the switch wide open and backed my train of thoughts into a blind alley. "You couldn't learn me nothing."

"You're right," says the millstone; "and now that you is holding both ends of the argument, they ain't nothing for me to do and I'm on my way to bed."

"You can call off that party date," I yells. "I ain't going."

"Write down any other jokes you knows," comes back the misses, "and we'll have 'em for breakfast."

II

I HAS my way as per usual, and Friday afternoon we leaves for the Sintons', our invite calling for us to stick around till Monday morning.

Pete's place out in the country is the real spiff in Class A shanties and could easy be palmed off by a good pest agent as the home of one of them infant prodigals out in Hollywood; besides the which, the grounds around the shack is big enough to hold the kinda crowds that turns out for them English sucker football games. Every tree and bush and blade of grass on the lot looks like it was planted personal with a ruler instead of a shovel.

I has to grin inwards at the idea of Baldy Pete Sinton, who used to think that a two-bit flop in a bed-house and a flock of hog and hen fruit was the last words in luxuries, living like a Roman umpire in a Spanish air castle, all littered up with butlers and scullery maidens and stable bridegrooms. Ten years before, me and him was panhandling around in the Oklahoma oil fields, and they wasn't enough real jack between us any time to buy a swimming suit for a tadpole; but he stuck longer 'an me and pretty soon a gusher up and hit him in the face. The rest is in the histories.

I ain't seen Pete since it begun raining barrels on him; but something tells me that all the flash and fussy feathers I pipes before me ain't his doings, but musta been brung on by the wife. I just can't imagine that lad using more'n one fork, if any, at a meal and the old imagine ain't so far wrong at that.

Pete's at the door when we breezes up, the same old Baldy, a little fatter than he used to was, and looking about as comfortable in his joy rags as a guy in a parade that's bust his last suspender button and got a garter dragging.

"Hello," he says, jovial. "How's the old low-down buzzard bird?"

"Do you mean it?" I asks.

"Sure, I does, you thieving scoundrel," he comes back.

"Good boy!" I answers, grabbing his mitts. "I thought maybe you was trying to be polite and make me feel at home, you lying horse robber."

"Gosh," says Pete, "it sounds great to be called that! How much dryer is you than usual?"

"Just as," I answers.

The wife in the meantime has been towed off by the misses of the roost and Sinton gives me the shoulder to follow him. We drifts upstairs and finally lands in a room at the back of the shack that looks like it got into the place by mistake. They ain't hardly nothing there excepting a coupla run-down chairs, a worn-out rug, smeared up with cigar ashes, and a rickety cabinet.

"My study," grins Sinton.

"What do you study here?" I asks. "Labels?"

"Yeh," comes back Pete, "and I is also taking lessons in Scotch," with the which he drags out a bottle and pours a set of stiff hookers.

"Over the river," says he.

"And through the woods," I replies. "Like old times, ain't it?"

"This room you is in," answers he, kinda mournful, "is all that is left of them. It's the only thing in the whole joint that belongs to me exclusive, and I had a grand battle with the burden to save that. The rest of this pile of stuck-up stucco is the wife's idea of what she calls a quiet nook out in the country."

"Well," says I, "that's what you draws for getting in the way of that damn gusher. If you'd 'a' done like me and beaten it outta Oklahoma in time, you could yet be enjoying the pleasures of poverties."

"Maybe you think they ain't got none," returns Baldy. "Wait till you see the bunch of dry holes that is up here for the week-end. They don't none of them know nothing excepting cards. I was gonna have you out with some regular folks, but the misses was keen on bringing your frau here this time on the accounts of hearing that she was good at this Bridge hop. Is she?"

"You want my opinion," I asks, "or hern?"

"How long you been hitched?" comes back Pete.

"Fifteen years," I answers. "Why?"

"Then you ain't got no opinions," says he. "What does she think about her game?"

"Well," I tells him, "Kate's got the idea that if she was to hook up with the guy that wrote the book——"

"She's gonna have that chance right here."

"What do you mean?" I inquires.

"Ever hear of a lad named Angus McGullible?" asks Baldy, right back.

"Sure!" I replies. "That's the bobo that learned me the game with his book—him and High Spade Kennedy."

"Oh," says Pete, "then you plays too?"

"In our set," I yawns, "one must. Is Angus one of your week-enders?"

"He'll be here tomorrow," answers Baldy. "That bimbo comes every Saturday and Sunday regular for his wages. If I should shut down this dump, that baby'd have to go to work. He lives a coupla miles or so down the road, and Belle uses him as a kinda side show to pull the come-ons in to her blowouts. They ain't hardly a session of Bridge outta the which that boy don't tote away at the leastest a hundred fish. He's been coming here, on and off, for six months now, and I ain't seen him dig yet."

"From the way you talks," I remarks, "I gathers Angus ain't your favorite color."

"If he was choking on a bone," says Pete, "I wouldn't even pat him on the back. I almost quit drinking Scotch because McGullible is. You being here, though, gives me an idea. Will you do me a favor?"

"I didn't bring my gat," I answers quick, "and I ain't so good at strangling like I used to was. Besides——"

"But you is still on friendly terms with a deck of cards, ain't you?" cuts in Baldy. "Seems to me like you was able in the old days to make the papers jump through hoops and say papa. Now——"

"Nothing doing," I interrupts, short. "I don't pull them things no more. The only aces that I plays with nowadays is them which is dealt to me honest."

"I know," says Sinton, "but in a pinch you could talk pretty to the pictures, couldn't you?"

"I suppose," I admits, modest. "But wouldn't you and me get in sweet if I was caught icing a deck? Lead me to this boy McGullible on the up and up, if all you want is to slip him a trimming. I ain't so worse at the game; and, besides, they is some snappy tricks I learned from High Spade Kennedy that maybe Angus don't know nothing about."

Pete shakes his head, dubious.

"Playing on the square," says he, "you wouldn't have no more chances of beating him than a jack rabbit, and I'd give my right arm to see that cuckoo knocked off the Christmas tree. One good walloping and maybe Belle and the other hens that lay around this place wouldn't think Angus was the curly bearcat like they does now. They ain't no question but that the boy's good. I've played around with the game enough to know that."

"Well," I remarks, "he's gotta to have the prominent cards like any one else to win."

"Not this bozo," comes back Baldy. "He don't have to have nothing. All you got to do is bid once or sneeze or something like that, and this baby knows what you got in your hand, and if it's anything good he'll make you discard it before you knows what all the shooting's for."

"Leave him to me," says I, "and I'll make you a present of his hide without working no skin game, neither."

"I got a case of Scotch," announces Pete, "that goes to the guy that can slap the red ink on Angus."

"Ship it now," I comes back, "so it'll be home when I get there."

III

AFTER I takes a pipe at the bunch of fluffs that Pete's wife has brung for the party, I'm kinda glad that the gusher hit him instead of me. They is six couples outside of us, and they ain't one of 'em that's worth one hurrah in Hades. I gets it from Baldy that they is all in the first hundred of the four, and they ain't none of the she-men in the layout that's done any work in three or four generations. It just gets me mean to be near 'em, and it takes hardly no times at all for me to get into their black looks.

Right after dinner that night one of the starched frails whose name is De Smythe, the original copy of which come over to this country with a Mayflower in one hand and a bottle of liquor in the other for the Indian real-estate business, throws a rope of pearls at the swine.

"You in trade?" she asks me.

"Sure," I comes back. "What you got—a second-hand washing machine or a baby buggy or something to swap?"

She cuts in with "Sir!" on ice.

"Oh," I goes on, "I didn't make you at first. You mean if I is in business. I'll tell the cock-eyed world I is."

"Oil?" she asks.

"Better'n that," I tells her. "I got the garbage-collection contract in the city; and believe me, it's some fat graft! We takes the stuff and——"

"How ghastly!" she gasps, and beats it.

A few minutes later Pete grabs me and pulls me off in a corner. He looks scared.

"What you been telling that De Smythe woman?" Baldy wants to know.

"Why?" I comes back.

"I musta give you too many shots in the arm before dinner," says Pete. "Whatever you pulled, she was about ready to leave the joint flat and I had one swell time squaring you."

"How'd you do it?" I inquires.

"I told her," says Sinton, "that you was worth eight million dollars, and had a funny sense of humor, for which you was noted when you was in Harvard. I explained your rough talk by saying you mixed a lot with your men in the gold mines."

"Gold mines!" I laughed. "She thinks I'm in the garbage-collection business."

"I fixed that too," says Pete. "Garbage, I tells her, is your contemptible way of talking about money, on account of you having so much of it. Watch your step, bo. The wife's nearly shot the roll and her nerves to get in with this gang of society saps."

"I see," says I, kinda sorry that I had done any kidding. "I'll keep my trap shut after this."

"When you has to," comes back Baldy, "chew the rag with 'em about cards or money. I've let the ideas get around that you is cuckoo on Bridge, and I even told 'em a funny antidote about how you and Charlie Schwab oncet played for ten dollars a point against the Rockefeller boys at a benefit for the I.W.W."

"Ten dollars a point, huh!" I remarks. "What kinda money do you shoot for around here?"

"Not no ten dollars," grins Pete. "Five cents is our limit."

"It'd better be," I comes back, "or that week-end of yourn ends right here with this Harvard boy."

Sinton musta spread the salve in pretty good shape, because when I gets to mingling with the gang later on, they is all trying to talk to me at oncet. While I ain't had much to do with the blue-buds, it don't take me long to get the idea that this bunch ain't the real cream at all, but a set of skimmilkers that is stalling around like they had a lotta jack, but on the lowdown is glad of the opportunities to mooch off birds like the Sintons. Maybe they is all from swell families, but they don't ring blue to me.

This Mrs. De Smythe makes a real fuss over me, bragging about how much she likes big, ragged men that has knocked Nature down for the count and picked its pockets without letting success change them from being simple, she pulling all of this ba-blah right in front of her husband, a little, sawed-off, watery-eyed misfoot that don't weigh no more than ninety-eight pounds, including the lip cheater and the manacle. Kate listens sorta blank to the rah-rah the jane is spilling; but before she has a chance of shooting a ball into the wrong pocket, the De Smythe wren drags me and the frau off to a Bridge table.

"I don't suppose," says she, "that they is much interest for you in a five-cent game, but——"

"That's all right," I cuts in, giving the wife the foot-office to look, listen and stop; "I just plays for the pleasures."

"I know you don't care for no more garbage," comes back Mrs. De Smythe. "That's just a joke me and your husband is got," she explains to Kate, who is giving us the pop eye.

I rings a quick change in on the subject and then we gets to playing. From the luck we has, Pete, who is looking on mosta the time, musta thought that I was cold-decking the game right along. For a hour I don't hold nothing that wouldn't be worth at least a three bid in something from Old Leather Vest hisself; and the few times I ain't got 'em, the wife's there with the pace cards. Besides, I puts over deep-sea finesses, bluffs and tricky shifts that musta made Baldy think that I was, anyways, doing some fingernail work on the back of the cards, even if the decks was honest.

Nothing don't come up in the talk to put me in bad with the yarn Sinton spilled about me, excepting once nearly when De Smythe asks me what my year was at Harvard.

"Please don't bring that up," I answers, giving the misses the toe-tip. "I had a sad experience when me and Ted Roosevelt was rooming together and I hates——"

He, being a polite bimbo, mumbles a excuse for being alive, which he should, and switches the conversation to gold mines, which I don't know nothing about and he don't neither, making it easy for me to give him a lotta valuable info about the subjects. They ain't nothing you can tell that cane-toter that ain't a eight-column head in a extra.

We plays along for maybe a other hour, and towards the end of the game most of the gang at the house is looking on, Pete having passed out the news, I guess, that some snappy Bridge was being demonstrated at Table No. 1. At the finish we is fifty-six smackers to the good and De Smythe shoves over his check.

"Here," says I, passing it and a wink to Baldy, "give this to the poor of the village."

While the rest of the bunch stands around downstairs getting free air and gas, me and Pete ducks up to his study to see if the Scotch needs any attention. It does.

"How did my work hit you?" I asks Sinton.

"Was all them aces dealt to you," he comes back, "or did you help yourself?"

"Wasn't you watching?" I inquires.

"Yeh," he admits; "but if you is as good now as you was oncet, the eye ain't got no more chance in a race with the hand than a crippled snail has with a scared rabbit."

"It was on the square," I tells Baldy. "Gimme them kinda cards and the same breaks tomorrow and I'll make McGullible look like his first lesson in Bridge was next week. All——"

"You don't know how strong that lad is," cuts in Pete, "and you don't know how wild I is to get Angus a good trimming in this house, or you wouldn't insist so much on being honest. Be a good kid and forget them scribbles of yourn for a coupla days. I must have that baby's goat and you gotta get it for me."

I tries to convince Baldy that I can beat McGullible on the square, me being all puffed up over my easy win over the De Smythes, and that he shouldn't ask me to do no slicker stuff; but it ain't no use. Sinton's made up his mind that he's gonna make Angus dig for oncet in his life and that I'm the bimbo to turn the trick. Finally I agrees, if the game is going agin me, to have a talk with the cards, which satisfies Pete. We discusses some details, and after another trip over the river and through the woods, I beats it to join the frau. She's in our room.

"Well," says I, putting my watch on the table, "it's a quarter to twelve. I'll give you fifteen minutes to do your stuff. What foxy passes has I pulled so far?"

"What right has I, a simple country girl," comes back the frau with satires, "to criticize the manners of a Harvard graduate? If I should say anything, for example, about your rough fork work, or them expressions you used in the game, you might leave me and run away to your gold mines with that frumpy Mrs. De Smythe; and what would I do then, poor thing?"

"That college-and-millionaire stuff," I explains, "was just a joke of Pete's to liven things up. But I has got a gold mine."

"Yeh?" inquires Kate.

"Yeh," I answers; "you. You got it over the rest of those cluckers like a big top over a side show."

I gets to sleep ten minutes to twelve.

IV

McGULLIBLE don't show the next day until after dinner. I only has to take one look at him to get hep to why Pete would pass up everything to dance at his funeral. He's one of them high-voiced lads, with a line of patter for the ladies that makes you think of men dressmakers that was once in the chorus. When Pete introduces me out on the porch, I feel like taking off my hat and kissing his hand.

"Do you play Bridge?" Angus asks me.

"One or two times," I tells him; "but I'm kinda sorry now that I learned it."

"How is that?" he wants to know.

"Well," says I, "when I first heard about the game I thought it was scientifical, like Pitch or Stud; but it ain't nothing but showdown. If you gets the papers you cop; if you ain't holding 'em you go way back and set down."

"You have a wrong idea," comes back McGullible with a sweet smile. "You must read my book on Bridge."

"Oh, you play, then?" I inquires, surprised.

"You musta heard of McGullible on Auction," cuts in Baldy.

"Seems like I did," says I; "but I sorta had a idea it was something about them hog-and-mule sales they has out in the sticks."

"What was the ideas of that line of hop?" asks Pete, when sweetie breezes away.

"Little advertising, bo," I tells him. "I'm gonna give that cream puff a grand trimming, and it'll sting more if the walloping comes from the kinda fathead he thinks I is. I tried the stunt oncet on a coupla the wife's side-kickers and it went with a wow."

"Then you'll play ball?" asks Sinton.

"Anything you'd do to that cuckoo'd be honest," I answers. "You act like I tells you. When me and Angus is playing and I gives you the tip-off, start something around the room like making a speech or yelling fire or busting a vase. My fingers maybe ain't so good like they was and I may need more time for my stuff. Got that?"

"I'd dynamite the house to hook that baby," says Baldy.

In about a hour the Bridge playing begins. Some other folks has dropped in from the neighborhood and they is enough for four tables. Sinton hisself don't sit in, him and the wife having put up a prize to be battled over, besides the regular stakes.

"If you're gonna get him," whispers Pete to me, "you gotta do it to-night. He just tole me he wouldn't be here tomorrow, and you maybe will have to do some fancy stuff in the other games to get in at the finish with him."

This progressive proposition, which Baldy framed before he knew about Angus beating it Sunday, kinda throws the works out, they being a chance of my not getting to hook up with McGullible; but it's got to be gone through with.

On the first round I draws the De Smythe hen for a partner, which don't worry me none, the frail being a pretty snappy trump slinger. Against us is the wife and a lad named Sullivan. We wins the heat without any troubles and moves on to scrap with the winners at the next table.

They ain't no use dragging out the prelims. Me and Mrs. De Smythe gets all the cards and spades in the deck and they ain't nothing for me to do excepting play 'em as I get 'em.

The last game works out like we has hoped, and we hooks up with Angus and a Mrs. Davey, being the only pairs that ain't been knocked for a goal some place or the other in the march around the room. McGullible hands me one of them pretty smiles.

"Would you care to make the stakes ten cents?" he asks.

"Ten cents or ten dollars," I comes back. "I got a fifty-fifty chance in any kinda showdown."

I looks around for Pete and I sees him standing at the other end of the room; but he's watching close and nods that he is ready to do his bit. My luck stays with me, and the first hand Angus deals me is the kind that plays itself. I grabs off four spades and four honors in one mitt and we is off to a grand start.

The next leg goes to McGullible. The boy does know how to play 'em. He don't get such a much to work with, but he can sure make sevens and eights act like kings and queens. His partner ain't no slouch neither, and keeps right in step with him.

It's my deal next and I hesitates a little. The way the cards has been running, I figures I got a pretty good chance of grabbing off the loot on the square; besides, I ain't so sure I can monkey with the deck and get away with it. Pete, who's been strolling back and forth between the table and the other side of the room, passes so he can catch my eye and he looks so darn begging that I gives him the high sign. Right away Baldy raises his hand and does his song and dance.

"Ladies and gentlemen," says he, "while I think of it, I want to tell you about tomorrow——"

I don't listen to no more. The way Sinton's standing, McGullible has to turn clean around to be polite, and the women folks also pays attention. Me, I got other work to do.

"That's all," I hears Pete say, and it's enough. I'm through. I passes over the deck to be cut, but making a cut a waste of time ain't no trick a-tall. Then I deals.

I ain't picked out nothing for myself excepting the ace, king, queen of hearts, the ace, king, queen of spades, the ace, king, queen, jack of clubs and, not to be too rough, only the king, jack and nine of diamonds. What the others is got I don't know and don't care a whole hell of a lot.

"One no trump," I announces.

"Two diamonds," comes along Angus.

My partner ain't got nothing to say and the Davey jane also pulls a clam.

I glances around and sees the wife and Baldy in back of me. I grins and bids "Three no trumps" just to show that Scotch cuckoo what I thinks of his force-up stunt. Angus passes and I'm ready to start the massacre when the Davey hen comes through with "Four diamonds."

"Four no trumps," I yelps.

"Five diamonds," says McGullible.

I looks my mitt over again, and am just ready to go to five no trumps when I changes my mind. I figure I can set that baby about four hundred, which'll win for us even if we lose the rubber game.

"Double," says I.

"Redouble," comes back Angus, right quick.

"Try and make it!" I snaps.

He tries and does, for a grand slam, doubled and redoubled. I loses all control of myselfs and heaves the cards across the room.

"Damn such a game!" I howls. "I'm through with it for life," and I beats it up to the room.

Cartoon *by* TONY SARG

The wife follows.

"What happened?" she asks. "You had such a wonderful hand."

"It oughta been," says I, grim. "I made it myself. Here's how it happened, though."

I grabs a piece of paper and draws a picture of it for her:

Mrs. De Smythe
♢ ———
♣ 10, 9, 6, 5, 3, 2
♠ 8, 7, 5, 4, 3
♡ 8, 4

Angus	*The Davey Hen*
♢ A, Q, 10, 7, 6	♢ 8, 5, 4, 3, 2
♣ ———	♣ 8, 7, 4
♠ ———	♠ J, 10, 9, 6, 2
♡ J, 10, 9, 7, 6, 5, 3, 2	♡ ———

Me
♢ K, J, 9
♣ A, K, Q, J
♠ A, K, Q
♡ A, K, Q

"I don't see yet," remarks Kate, after looking it over, "how anybody could make a grand slam against all them aces and kings. I guess I wasn't watching close."

"You wasn't," I comes back, "or you'da seen something that won't happen again in a million years. That De Smythe baby starts off by leading a club, which Angus trumps. Then he shoves out a heart, which I slaps my queen on and which McGullible's partner trumps. That frail leads a diamond and Angus takes my nine with a ten. It don't make no difference what I play, with him sitting over me with ace, queen, ten. McGullible sends out a heart and my king is trumped on the other side. Then she comes along with another trump and my jack's shot. Angus follows with a heart and Mrs. Davey uses her last trump to make a bum outta my ace of hearts. She leads back a spade, which McGullible grabs with a diamond. Then he leads the ace of trumps, snatching off my king, and his hearts are as good as wheat. Now do you see it?"

"You musta done something wrong," says Kate, shaking her head, "or it wouldn't have happened."

"I did," I admits, "but not in the playing. I stacked the deck for Angus."

Then the frau starts razzing me, but before she gets very far they is a knock. It's one of them dolled-up servants.

"A book," says he. "With the compliments of Mr. McGullible."

I takes a quick look. It's him on Auction.

¶[Every time the game changed, so did the heroes. Joseph Elwell had been the Apostle of Bridge-Whist, but Bridgewise he was already dead long before he was so sensationally murdered in 1920. When Auction Bridge arrived it brought a new prophet, Milton C. Work, the first of a long line of Philadelphia lawyers (the latest is Charles Goren) who have abandoned the bar for Bridge. Then came Contract and Culbertson. ¶[One man who stayed on top through all the transitional periods was Sidney Lenz. He had been a whiz at Whist, a bear at Bridge, an autocrat at Auction—for which game his book LENZ ON BRIDGE *is still a classic —and finally he became a celebrity at Contract, of which more later. The following is one of many Contract Bridge stories he wrote for Liberty, one of the major magazines of the twenties. [Twenty-six years ago when I played with him against Culbertson he was called "The Grand Old Man of Bridge." He is still around and not a day older.—O.J.]*

It Beats the Devil

by SIDNEY S. LENZ

FOR MORE than five years Burke Wilson had experienced every kind of bad luck that could be imagined. He had worked his way through college, studied law and passed the bar examination with very little to spare. The few cases he tried did not help his prestige. He had still to win his first suit, perhaps because his personality was not the sort that made a good impression at the start.

It had been a sore disappointment to lose his case today. Discouraged, despondent, and broke, he was retiring for the night when there was a tap on the door.

A dark, good-looking man entered.

"Mr. Wilson," he said, extending his hand, "you saw me in court today. Would you take it as an affront if I ventured to point out why you lost your case?"

Burke was too depressed for resentment.

"Go to it," he replied. "The breaks have been against me so long that I have no pride left."

"That's just it," answered the visitor. "Your spirit has been broken by your continued bad luck. I have specialized in luck, both good and bad. Unless I can put you one hundred per cent right, there is no obligation."

"Well, well!" Burke said. "So you are a psychoanalyst. I'm sorry, old man, but I couldn't raise a hundred dollars to save my soul."

The visitor smiled gently.

"It is not a question of money," he said, "and —why do you want to save your soul?"

"What's the big idea? Are you trying to work a Faust on me?" asked Burke.

"Possibly," answered the visitor. "Are you willing to take a chance?"

Burke was bewildered. However, dreaming or awake, he would see it through.

"Let's have your proposition," he said.

"It's like this," replied the strange guest. "I am prepared to guarantee you every happiness this world can give you for a period of—shall we say twenty years? After that time you belong to me."

"Seems fair enough," Burke answered facetiously. "I believe it is customary in these little matters to give a fellow a chance to escape when his time is up. How about it?"

"Most assuredly," replied his accommodating guest. "I'll give you any fifty-fifty chance for an out."

"Fine," Burke answered. "I'll sign on the dotted line."

"Right," said his guest. "I have an agreement here. I'll just add the escape clause. Have you a pen handy?"

"Back of the chair," said Burke, "you will find a couple of fountain pens in my coat. The one with the jade band has ink in it."

The visitor took a paper from his pocket, added a few lines, and passed the paper and pen to Burke. The legal phraseology was perfect. Burke signed. His visitor took the paper, bowed, and—was gone.

When Burke awakened the next morning he remembered every detail of his dream.

As he put on his coat, he noticed that one of his pens was missing. He must have left it in the office, although he was almost certain he had put it in his pocket.

"Say, Burke," said Bill King at luncheon that day. "You look a bit fagged. I'm driving to the races this afternoon. How about coming along?"

Burke and Bill had been together at college. They had a pleasant drive, and at the races Bill placed a few bets without much success. There was a big stake race that day with an odds-on favorite that looked to be unbeatable. As Bill got up to place a bet on the favorite, a man who looked somewhat familiar to Burke handed him an envelope and said:

"Wilson, will you do me a favor and place

Bridge *by* H. T. WEBSTER

1930; courtesy The New York *Herald Tribune*

this bet for me? I've been called away suddenly. See you later."

In the envelope was a hundred-dollar note and a card on which was written: "Devil's Imp—to win."

"Your friend is daffy," laughed Bill. "He has picked the rankest outsider."

Burke took the ticket at a hundred to one, and Devil's Imp won by six lengths.

With ten thousand dollars belonging to a man whose name he could not even remember, Burke was in a quandary. A personal in the newspaper did no good and he wondered uneasily whether his dream had anything to do with it.

King was very much impressed to find that Wilson had friends who could pick hundred-to-one shots as a matter of course, and was instrumental in getting him the most important client of his career. With new offices, new clothes, and a general appearance of affluence, his success was phenomenal. From a mediocre lawyer he changed into a silver-tongued orator.

The most wonderful girl in the world jumped at his offer of marriage. There were times when he pondered over his extraordinary change of luck and wondered if it had any bearing on the curious dream.

Wilson had changed very little in the past twenty years. He had a fine home, a loving wife, and a clever and pretty daughter who had won cups at golf, tennis, and Bridge.

Today in court he had won a decision in a difficult case. As he was about to leave the courtroom, a dark pleasant gentleman approached him.

"Remember me, Mr. Wilson? It is some years since we last met. My name is—Cifer."

It suddenly flashed on Wilson that this was the man of the race-track episode.

"Seems to me I am in your debt," Wilson answered.

"Would ten o'clock this evening be a good time to settle our business?"

"Sure thing," said Wilson. "See you at my home."

Seated in the library, awaiting his guest, Wilson's thoughts persisted in reverting not only to the day at the track but to the night before the day. Of course it was idiotic to associate the two events, but—

"Mr. Cifer," the butler announced.

"You are looking better today than you did twenty years ago," Mr. Cifer said. "I trust you have been prosperous and happy."

"Yes, I have," said Wilson simply. "And here is my check to cover my indebtedness to you."

"Your indebtedness? Isn't there something more?"

Wilson winced. He had tried to fool himself, but it was no use. Incredible as it seemed, the compact he had entered into had not been a dream but a reality. There was no escape.

"Mr. Cifer," he said, "will you . . ."

"Of course," replied Cifer. "All or nothing. Shall we toss a coin or cut the cards?"

Wilson remembered his joking remark about a final clause. Well, he would take it, although he knew it was hopeless against such an adversary. He took a deck of cards from a case and placed it before his guest.

"Let's cut," he said.

At that moment the door swung open and a vision of loveliness burst into the room.

"Father!" she cried. "I—" Then as Mr. Cifer rose, she continued, "I didn't know you were engaged."

"It's all right, Lucy. Mr. Cifer, this is my daughter."

Lucy glanced at the check and the deck of cards.

"Have you men been gambling?" she inquired severely.

"Oh, no," answered Cifer. "We were about to decide a—er—business matter by cutting the cards."

"What a poor way to decide anything," Lucy pouted. "I have been playing Bridge and we had a fuss about the play of a hand I was playing with Bruce. You know, father, he gets worse every day. Do you play Contract, Mr. Cifer, or am I boring you?"

"Not at all," replied Cifer. "I invented the game."

"Really," said Lucy. "You must be older than you appear to be."

"I am," answered Cifer.

Lucy brought to light a deck of cards she had been holding behind her back. "May I show you the deal?" she asked.

"Certainly," said Cifer.

Lucy held the deck with her fingers separating the four hands. She spread the cards on the table:

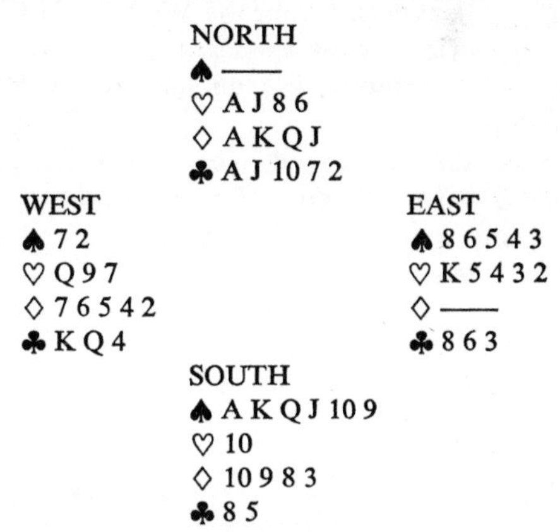

"I sat North and opened with a club. East bid a heart and Bruce bid two spades. With my wonderful hand and Bruce's jump bid, I was bound to bid for a slam; but there was no stopping my partner until he had bid for a grand slam in spades, which East doubled and Bruce redoubled. Because of the double West led the queen of her partner's suit, and there, with his declaration made to order for him, Bruce let them defeat him! Wasn't it awful?" she asked Cifer confidently.

He looked the hands over carefully before he answered:

"Miss Lucy, I am afraid your partner was not culpable this time. He had no way of getting rid of the losing club. It was simply an unfortunate distribution."

"If I had been playing the hand," Lucy said, "I would have made it without question."

"Not against good play," said Cifer.

"You wouldn't dare bet me?" Lucy asked pertly.

"I might," replied Cifer cautiously.

"All right," said Lucy. "I'll assume my father's side of your—'business matter.' "

"If you should lose," said Cifer, "you stand by his agreement?"

"Certainly," agreed Lucy.

"I've got you. Would you mind signing this card?" Cifer handed Lucy a fountain pen and a visiting card. Lucy signed and sat down to play the South hand.

"It is understood that after the first lead I play the East and West hands as I wish," said Cifer.

"Of course," said Lucy sweetly. "And I play the North and South hands the way Bruce should have played them."

Lucy took the queen of hearts with the ace and then led the jack. The king covered and Lucy trumped. Lucy played her five spades and discarded from the dummy one club and the four top diamonds. [From the West hand] Cifer followed twice on the spades, then discarded a club and a diamond, but on the last spade he hesitated.

"Now do be careful," cautioned Lucy in honeyed tones, "because if you give up a diamond, my four diamonds will be good and you will be sunk on the eleventh trick. If you discard a heart, the dummy will have two good hearts. And a club discard will be ruinous. So far, Mr. Cifer, you have done very well, but where do you go from here?"

"Hell!"

Whether Mr. Cifer was merely replying to Lucy's question or had lost his temper will never be known. He rushed out the door without another word.

Lucy picked up the card she had signed.

"What a queer name—L. U. Cifer," she read. "Such a nice man, but what a bad temper and so profane. Look, father. He forgot his fountain pen."

As Wilson placed the pen in his pocket, he noticed the jade band on the end.

¶*Of course such a commentator on the passing scene as Ring Lardner could not overlook such a daft phenomenon as Contract Bridge seemed to be as we entered the 1930s. He wrote several Bridge stories, but we consider the following best because it points a real moral about manners—even though we regret to say that Mr. Lardner's own bidding and play, much as he admired them himself, were no better than his hero Shelton's. Still he was better than the self-appointed experts with whom he played.*

Contract

by RING LARDNER

WHEN THE Sheltons were settled in their new home in the pretty little suburb of Linden, Mrs. Shelton was afraid nobody would call on them. Her husband was afraid somebody would. For ages Mrs. Shelton had bravely pretended to share her husband's aversion to a social life; he hated parties that numbered more than four people and she had, convincingly, so she thought, played the role of indifference while declining invitations she would have given her right eye to accept. Shelton had not been fooled much, but his dislike of "crowds" was so great that he seldom sought to relieve her martyrdom by insisting that they "go" somewhere.

This was during the first six years of their connubial existence, while it was necessary to live, rather economically, in town. Recently, however, Shelton's magazine had advanced him to a position as associate editor and he was able, with the assistance of a benignant bond and mortgage company, to move into a house in Linden. Mrs. Shelton was sure suburbanites would be less tedious and unattractive than people they had known in the city and that it would not be fatal to her spouse to get acquainted and play around a little; anyway she could make friends with other wives, if they were willing, and perhaps enjoy afternoons of Contract Bridge, a game she had learned to love in three lessons. At the same time Shelton resolved to turn over a new leaf for his wife's sake and give her to understand that he was open for engagements, secretly hoping, as I have hinted, that Linden's denizens would treat them as if they were quarantined.

Mrs. Shelton's fears were banished, and Shelton's resolution put to a test, on an evening of their second week in the new house. They were dropped in on by Mr. and Mrs. Robert French, who lived three blocks away. Mrs. French was pretty and Shelton felt inclined to like her until she remarked how fascinating it must be to edit a magazine and meet Michael Arlen. French had little to say, being occupied most of the while in a petting party with his mustache.

Mrs. Shelton showed Mrs. French her seven hooked rugs. Mrs. French said, "Perfectly darling!" seven times, inquired where each of the seven had been procured and did not listen to the answers. Shelton served highballs of eighty-dollar Scotch he had bought from a Linden bootlegger. French commented favorably on the Scotch. Shelton thought it was terrible himself and that French was a poor judge, or was being polite, or was deceived by some flavor lurking in the mustache. Mrs. Shelton ran out of hooked rugs and Mrs. French asked whether they played Contract. Mrs. Shelton hesitated from habit. Shelton swallowed hard and replied that they did, and liked it very much.

"That's wonderful!" said Mrs. French. "Because the Wilsons have moved to Chicago. They were crazy about Contract and we used to have a party every Wednesday night; two tables—the Wilsons, ourselves, and the Dittmars and Camerons. It would be just grand if you two would take the Wilsons' place. We have dinner at somebody's house and next Wednesday is our turn. Could you come?"

Mrs. Shelton again hesitated and Shelton (to quote O. O. McIntyre) once more took the bull by the horns.

"It sounds fine!" he said. "We haven't anything else on for that night, have we, dear?"

His wife uttered an astonished no and the Frenches left.

"What in the world has happened to you?" demanded Mrs. Shelton.

"Nothing at all. They seem like nice people and we've got to make friends here. Besides, it won't be bad playing cards."

"I don't know about Contract," said Mrs. Shelton doubtfully. "You've got good card sense, and the only time you played it you were all right. But I'm afraid I'll make hideous mistakes."

"Why should you? And even if you do, what of it?"

"These people are probably whizzes."

"I don't care if they're Lenz's mother-in-law."

"But you'll care if they criticize you."

"Of course I will. People, and especially strangers, have no more right to criticize your Bridge playing than your clothes or your complexion."

"You know that's silly. Bridge is a game."

"Tennis is a game, too. But how often do you hear one tennis player say to another, 'You played that like an old fool!'?"

"You're not partners in tennis."

"You are in doubles. However, criticism in Bridge is not confined to partners. I've made bonehead plays in Bridge (I'll admit it), and been laughed at and scolded for them by opponents who ought to have kissed me. It's a conviction of most Bridge players, and some golf players, that God sent them into the world to teach. At that, what they tell you isn't intended for your edification and future good. It's just a way of announcing 'I'm smart and you're a lunkhead.' And to my mind it's a revelation of bad manners and bad sportsmanship. If I ask somebody what I did wrong, that's different. But when they volunteer . . ."

It was an old argument and Mrs. Shelton did not care to continue it. She knew she couldn't win and she was sleepy. Moreover, she was so glad they were "going out" on her husband's own insistence that she felt quite kindly toward him. She did hope, though, that their new acquaintances would suppress their educational complex, if any.

On Wednesday night this hope was knocked for a double row of early June peas. Mrs. Shelton was elected to play with French, Mrs. Cameron and Mr. Dittmar. Mrs. Cameron was what is referred to as a statuesque blonde, but until you were used to her you could think of nothing but her nostrils, where she might easily have carried two after-dinner mints. Mr. Dittmar appeared to be continuing to enjoy his meal long after it was over. And French had to deal one-handed to be sure his mustache remained loyal. These details distracted Mrs. Shelton's mind to such an extent that she made a few errors and was called for them. But she didn't mind that and her greatest distraction was caused by words and phrases that came from the other table, where her husband was engaged with Mr. Cameron, Mrs. Dittmar and the hostess.

The French cocktails had been poured from an eye-dropper and Shelton maintained perfect control of his temper and tongue. His polite reception of each criticism was taken as a confession of ignorance and a willingness to learn, and his three table-mates were quick to assume the role of faculty, with him as the entire student body. He was stepped on even when he was dummy, his partner at the time, Mrs. Dittmar, attributing the loss of a trick to the manner in which he had laid out his cards, the light striking the nine of diamonds in such a way as to make her think it was an honor.

Mrs. Dittmar had married a man much younger than herself and was trying to disguise the fact by acting much younger than he. An eight-year-old child who is kind of backward hardly ever plays Contract Bridge; otherwise, if you didn't look at Mrs. Dittmar and judged only by her antics and manner of speech, you would have thought Dittmar had spent the final hours of his courtship waiting outside the sub-primary to take her home. Mrs. French, when she was not picking flaws in Shelton's play, sought to make him feel at home by asking intelligent questions about his work—"Do the people who draw the illustrations read the stories first?" "Does H. C. Witwer talk Negro dialect all the time?" And "How old is Peter B. Kinney?" Cameron, from whom Work, Lenz, Whitehead and Shepard had plagiarized the game, was frankly uninterested in anything not connected with it. The stake was half a cent a point and the pains he took to see that his side's score was correct or better proved all the rumors about the two Scotchmen.

Mrs. Shelton was well aware that her husband was the politest man in the world when sober; yet he truly amazed her that evening by his smiling acquiescence to all that was said. From the snatches she overheard, she knew he must be afire inside and it was really wonderful of him not to show it.

There was a time when Mrs. Dittmar passed and he passed and Cameron bid two spades. Mrs. French passed and Mrs. Dittmar bid three hearts, a denial of her partner's spades if Shelton ever heard one. Shelton passed and Cameron went three* hearts, which stood. Shelton held four spades to the nine, four diamonds to the king, two small hearts and the eight, six and five of clubs. He led the trey of diamonds. I am not broadcasting the battle play by play, but when it was over, "Oh, partner! Any other opening and we could have set them," said Mrs. French.

"My! My! My! My! Leading away from a king!" gurgled the child-wife.†

"That lead was all that saved us," said Cameron.

They waited for Shelton to apologize and explain, all prepared to scrunch him if he did either.

"I guess I made a mistake," he said.

"Haven't you played much Bridge?" asked Mrs. French.

"Evidently not enough," he replied.

"It's a game you can't learn in a minute," said Cameron.

"Never you mind!" said Mrs. Dittmar. "I've played Contract ever since it came out, and Daddy still scolds me terribly for some of the things I do."

Shelton presumed that Daddy was her husband. Her father must be dead or at least too feeble to scold.

There was a time when a hand was passed around.

"Oh! A goulash!" crowed Mrs. Dittmar.

"Do you play them, Mr. Shelton?" asked his hostess.

"Yes," said Shelton.

"Mrs. Shelton," called Mrs. Dittmar to the other table, "does your big man play goulashes?"

"Oh, yes," said Mrs. Shelton.

"You're sure you know what they are," said Cameron to Shelton.

"I've played them often," said the latter.

"A goulash," said the hostess, "is where the hand is passed and then we all put our hands together like this and cut them and the dealer deals five around twice and then three. It makes crazy hands, but it's thrilling."

"And the bidding is different," said Mrs. Dittmar, his partner at this stage. "Big man mustn't get too wild."

Shelton, who had dealt, looked at his hand and saw no temptation to get wild; at least, not any wilder than he was. He had the king, queen and jack of spades, four silly hearts, four very young clubs and two diamonds of no standing. He passed. Cameron bid three clubs and Mrs. Dittmar four diamonds. That was enough to make game (they already had thirty), and when Mrs. French went by, Shelton unhesitatingly did the same. So did Cameron. It developed that Mrs. Dittmar had the ace, king, jack, ten and another diamond. Cameron had none and Mrs. French reeked with them. The bidder was set two. Her honors counted one hundred and opponents' net profit was two hundred, Mrs. Dittmar being vulnerable, or "venerable," as Mrs. French laughingly, but not very tactfully, called it.

Cameron lighted into Mrs. French for not doubling Mrs. Dittmar, and Mrs. French observed that she guessed she knew what she was doing. Shelton hoped this would develop into a brawl, but it was forgotten when Mrs. Dittmar asked him querulously why he had not shown her his spades, a suit of which she held the ace, ten to five.

"We're lucky, partner," said Mrs. French to

* Obviously it was four hearts he bid.

† In those days a lead from a king was considered a serious error—even when it gained a trick. It was not a bad lead from this hand, though a club might have been better.

Cameron. "They could have made four spades like a breeze."

"I'd have lost only the ace of hearts and queen of diamonds," said Mrs. Dittmar, doubtless figuring that the maid would have disposed of her two losing clubs when she swept next morning.

"In this game, everything depends on the bidding," said Mrs. French to Shelton. "You *must* give your partner all the information you can."

"Don't coach him!" said Cameron with an exasperating laugh. "He's treating us pretty good."

"Maybe," said Mrs. French to Mrs. Dittmar, "he would have shown you his spades if you had bid three diamonds instead of four."

"But you see," said Mrs. Dittmar, "we needed four for game and I didn't know if he'd think of that."

And there was a time when Shelton bid a fair no trump and was raised to three by his partner, Cameron, who held king, queen, ten to five hearts and the ace of clubs for a re-entry. The outstanding hearts were bunched in Mrs. French's hand, Shelton himself having the lone ace. After he had taken a spade trick, led his ace of hearts and then a low club to make all of dummy's hearts good (which turned out to be impossible), he put over two deep sea finesses of the eight and nine of diamonds from the dummy hand, made four odd and heard Cameron murmur, "A fool for luck!"

"My! What a waste of good hearts!" said Mrs. Dittmar, ignoring the fact that they weren't good hearts, that if he had continued with them, Mrs. French would have taken the jack and led to her (Mrs. Dittmar's) four good spade tricks, and that with the ace of clubs gone, Shelton couldn't have got back in the dummy's hand with a pass from Judge Landis.

At the close of a perfect evening, the Sheltons were six dollars ahead and invited to the Dittmars' the following Wednesday. Mrs. Shelton expected an explosion on the way home, but was agreeably disappointed. Shelton seemed quite cheerful. He had a few jocose remarks to make about their new pals, but gave the impression that he had enjoyed himself. Knowing him as she did, she might have suspected that a plot was hatching in his mind. However, his behavior was disarming and she thought he had at last found a "crowd" he didn't object to, that they would now be neighborly and gregarious for the first time in their married life.

On the train from the city Friday afternoon, Shelton encountered Gale Bartlett, the writer, just returned from abroad. Bartlett was one of the star contributors to Shelton's magazine and it was he who had first suggested Linden when Shelton was considering a suburban home. He had a place there himself though most of his time was spent in Paris, and he was back now for only a brief stay.

"How do you like it?" he asked.

"Fine," said Shelton.

"Whom have you met?"

"Three married couples, the Camerons, the Frenches and the Dittmars."

"Good Lord!" said Bartlett. "I don't know the Dittmars but otherwise you're slumming. Cameron and French are new rich who probably made their money in a hotel washroom. I think they met their wives on an excursion to Far Rockaway. How did you happen to get acquainted?"

"The Frenches called on us, and Wednesday night we went to their house for dinner and Bridge."

"Bridge!"

"Contract Bridge at that."

"Well, maybe Dittmar's a contractor. But from what I've seen of the Frenches and Camerons, they couldn't even cut the cards without smearing them with shoe polish. You break loose from them before they forget themselves and hand you a towel."

"We're going to the Dittmars' next Wednesday night."

"Either call it off or keep it under your hat. I'll introduce you to people that are people! I happen to know them because my wife went to their sisters' boarding school. I'll see that you get the entree and then you can play Bridge with Bridge players."

Shelton brightened at the prospect. He knew his wife was too kind-hearted to wound the Camerons *et al.* by quitting them cold and it was part of his scheme, all of it in fact, to make them do the quitting. With the conviction that she would be more than compensated by the promised acquaintance of people they both could really like, he lost what few scruples he had against separating her from people who sooner or later would drive him to the electric chair. The thing must be done at the first opportunity, next Wednesday at the Dittmars'. It would be kind of fun, but unpleasant, too, the unpleasant part consisting in the mental anguish it would cause her and the subsequent days, not many he hoped, when she wouldn't be speaking to him at all.

Fate, in the form of one of Mrs. Shelton's two-day headaches, brought about the elimination of the unpleasant part. The ache began Wednesday afternoon and from past experience, she knew she would not be able to sit through a dinner or play cards that night. She telephoned her husband.

"Say we can't come," was his advice.

"But I hate to do that. They'll think we don't want to and they won't ask us again. I wish you'd go, and maybe they could ask someone in to take my place. I don't suppose you'd consider that, would you?"

Shelton thought it over a moment and said yes, he would.

Before retiring to her darkened room and her bed, Mrs. Shelton called up Mrs. Dittmar. Mrs. Dittmar expressed her sympathy in baby talk and said it was all right for Mr. Shelton to come alone; it was more than all right, Mrs. Shelton gathered, because Mrs. Dittmar's brother was visiting her and they would be just eight.

Shelton, who had learned long ago that his wife did not want him around when her head was threatening to burst open, stayed in town until six o'clock, preparing himself for the evening's task with liberal doses of the business manager's week-old rye. He was not going to be tortured by any drought such as he had endured at the Frenches'. He arrived at the party in grand shape and, to his surprise, was plied with cocktails potent enough to keep him on edge.

Mrs. Dittmar's brother (she called him her dreat, big B'udder) was an amateur jazz pianist. Or rather, peeanist. He was proving his amateur standing when Shelton got there and something in the way he treated "Rhapsody in Blue" made Shelton resolve to open fire at once. His eagerness was increased when, on the way to the dining room, Mrs. Dittmar observed that her B'udder had not played much Contract "either" and she must be sure and not put them (Shelton and B'udder) at the same table, for they might draw each other as partners and that would hardly be fair.

Dinner began and so did Shelton.

"A week ago," he said, "you folks criticized my Bridge playing."

The Camerons, Dittmars and Frenches looked queer.

"You didn't mind it, I hope," said Mrs. Dittmar. "We were just trying to teach you."

"I didn't mind it much," said Shelton. "But I was just wondering whether it was good manners for one person to point out another person's mistakes when the other person didn't ask to have them pointed out."

"Why," said Cameron, "when one person don't know as much about a thing as other people, it's their duty to correct him."

"You mean just in Bridge," said Shelton.

"I mean in everything," said Cameron.

"And the person criticized or corrected has no right to resent it?" said Shelton.

"Certainly not!"

"Does everybody here agree with that?"

"Yes," "Of course," "Sure," came from the others.

"Well, then," said Shelton, "I think it's my duty to tell you, Mr. Cameron, that soup should be dipped away from you and not toward you."

There was a puzzled silence, then a laugh, to which Cameron contributed feebly.

"If that's right I'm glad to know it, and I certainly don't resent your telling me," he said.

"It looks like Mr. Shelton was out for revenge," said Mrs. Cameron.

"And I must inform you, Mrs. Cameron," said Shelton, "that 'like' is not a conjunction. 'It looks as if Mr. Shelton were out for revenge' would be the correct phrasing."

A smothered laugh at the expense of Mrs. Cameron, whose embarrassment showed itself in a terrifying distension of the nostrils. Shelton decided not to pick on her again.

"Let's change the subject," said Mrs. Dittmar. "Mr. Shelton's a mean, bad man and he'll make us cwy."

"That verb," said Shelton, "is cry, not cwy. It is spelled c-r-y."

"Tell a story, Bob," said Mrs. French to her husband.

"Well, let's see," said French. I'll tell the one about the Scotchman and the Jew playing golf. Stop me if anybody's heard it."

"I have, for one," said Shelton.

"Maybe the others haven't," said French.

"They must have been unconscious for years," said Shelton, "but go ahead and tell it. I knew I couldn't stop you."

French went ahead and told it, and the others laughed as a rebuke to Shelton.

Cameron wanted things understood.

"You see," he said, "the reason we made a few little criticisms of your Bridge game was because we judged you were a new beginner."

"I think 'beginner' is enough, without the 'new'," said Shelton. "I don't know any old beginners excepting, perhaps, people old in years who are doing something for the first time. But probably you judged I was a beginner at Bridge because of the mistakes I made, and you considered my apparent inexperience justified you in criticizing me."

"Yes," said Cameron.

"Well," said Shelton, "I judge from observing Mrs. French eat her fish that she is a new beginner at eating and I take the liberty of stating that the fork ought never to be conveyed to the mouth with the left hand, even by a left-handed eater. To be sure, these forks are salad forks, not fish forks, as Mrs. Dittmar may believe. But even salad forks, substituting for fish forks, must not be carried mouthward by the left hand."

A storm was gathering and Mrs. Cameron sought to ward it off. She asked Mrs. Dittmar what had become of Peterson, a butler.

"He just up and left me last week," said Mrs. Dittmar. "He was getting too impudent, though, and you can bet I didn't object to him going."

" '*His* going,' " said Shelton. "A participle used as a substantive is modified in the possessive."

Everyone pretended not to hear him.

"This new one is grand!" said Mrs. Dittmar. "I didn't get up till nearly eleven o'clock this morning—"

"Eleven!" exclaimed Mrs. French.

"Yes. Imagine!" said Mrs. Dittmar. "The itta girl just overslept herself, that's all."

"Mrs. Dittmar," said Shelton, "I have no idea who the itta girl is, but I am interested in your statement that she overslept herself. Would it be possible for her, or any other itta girl, to oversleep somebody else? If it were a sleeping contest, I should think 'outsleep' would be preferable, but even so I can't understand how a girl of any size outsleeps herself."

The storm broke. Dittmar sprang to his feet.

"That's enough, Shelton!" he bellowed. "We've had enough of this nonsense! More than enough!"

"I think," said Shelton, "that the use of the word 'enough' three times in one short speech is more than enough. It grates on me to hear or read a word reiterated like that. I suggest as synonyms 'plenty,' 'a sufficiency,' 'an abundance,' 'a plethora.' "

"Shut your smart aleck mouth and get out!"

"Carl! Carl! Mustn't lose temper!" said Mrs. Dittmar. "Lose temper and can't digest food. Daddy mustn't lose temper and be sick all nighty night."

"Shelton just thinks he's funny," said Cameron.

"He's drunk and he'll leave my house at once!" said Dittmar.

"If that's the way you feel about it," said Shelton.

He stopped on the way out to bid Mrs. Dittmar's brother good-night.

"Good-night B'udder old boy," he said. "I'm glad to have met you, but sorry to learn you're deaf."

"Deaf! What makes you think I'm deaf?"

"I understood your sister to say you played the piano by ear."

Knowing his wife would have taken something to make her sleep, and therefore not afraid of disturbing her, Shelton went home, got out a bottle of Linden Scotch and put the finishing touches on his bender. In the morning Mrs. Shelton was a little better and came to the breakfast table where he was fighting an egg.

"Well, what kind of time did you have?"

"Glorious! Much more exciting than at the Frenches'. Mrs. Dittmar's brother is a piano-playing fool."

"Oh, wasn't there any Bridge then?"

"No. Just music and banter."

"Maybe the brother can't play Contract and I spoiled the party by not going."

"Oh, no. *You* didn't spoil the party!"

"And do we go to the Camerons' next Wednesday?"

"I don't believe so. Nothing was said."

They did go next Wednesday night to the palatial home of E. M. Pardee, a friend of Gale Bartlett's and one of the real aristocrats of Linden. After dinner, Mrs. Pardee asked the Sheltons whether they played Contract, and they said they did. The Pardees, not wishing to impoverish the young immigrants, refused to play "families." They insisted on cutting and Shelton cut Mrs. Pardee.

"Oh, Mr. Shevlin," she said at the end of the first hand, "why *didn't* you lead me a club? You *must* watch the discards!"

Author's Postscript: This story won't get me anything but the money I am paid for it. Even if it be read by those with whom I usually play —Mr. C., Mrs. W., Mr. T., Mrs. R. and the rest —they will think I mean two other fellows and tear into me like wolves next time I bid a slam and make one odd.

¶To the many readers who avidly follow the "Jackie" stories written regularly by Alphonse "Sonny" Moyse, editor of The Bridge World, we have this to say: Yes, Jackie is a real person. Her name is really Jackie. She is Sonny's wife. He portrays her faithfully. ¶To those who have not experienced the delight of reading the "Jackie" stories, we recommend the following as an unexpected treat.

Jackie's Legal Joist

by ALPHONSE MOYSE, JR.

MY OFFICE TELEPHONE jingled and rescued me from the throes of trying to discover the best percentage play in a highly complicated situation.

It was Jackie, and I had only to hear her Hello to know that she was upset. I might say, parenthetically, that she upsets easily.

"We're having a terrible fight out here," she said, "and you've got to settle it."

"Naturally," I agreed. "What kind of fight, and who's we?"

"Oh, I thought you knew. The girls—Eleanor and Kitty and Clare and myself. It's our Bridge day—my turn. You ought to know that!"

I apologized and asked gently what they were fighting about.

My wife was a bit snappy now. "The Bridge game, of course! It's a question of law."

I groaned and tried to save myself. "Look, honey, why don't you call Al Sobel, or Morehead, or somebody like that? They're very good on the laws. And besides, I can't very well decide an argument in which you're involved. It wouldn't be ethical."

"How did you know I was involved?" she demanded suspiciously.

"I knew," I said grimly.

"Well, that's just silly—of course you can decide. You've got a rule book there in your office, haven't you? All you have to do is turn to the right page."

"I suppose you think that's a cinch!" I said with some heat.

"Listen to me!" she snapped. "How can I tell you what happened if you keep interrupting all the time? This is just a simple case of an insufficient bid."

"Oh," I said, relieved. "Well, go ahead."

"Well, it was like this. Kitty and I were partners against Eleanor and Clare. Both sides were vulnerable, and we had sixty on score. I dealt and opened with one diamond, Eleanor passed, Kitty bid a notrump, and Clare overcalled with two spades. I had a long diamond suit and a good hand besides, so I jumped to four diamonds. I thought there might be a slam in the hand. I figured that—"

"Look," I said. "Never mind what you thought. That's not important. Just tell me what happened."

There was an ominous hiatus and then Jackie hissed, "So what I think isn't important!"

"Oh darling, darling, darling!" I moaned. "Please! I didn't mean that what you think isn't important—generally—I just meant . . ."

Her sniff was highly audible. "Well, you might be nicer about this. I don't call you for decisions very often."

"I'm sorry," I said soothingly. "Now, you were saying . . . ?"

She took a deep breath—I could hear it. "Well, as I said, I jumped to four diamonds, but Eleanor thought I had bid only two diamonds, and she bid two spades." She paused, and her expectancy was implicit.

I gulped. This was going to be bad! "Well, then what happened?" I asked cautiously.

"Why, of course Kitty and I said that she had to make the bid sufficient . . . but she won't!"

I wasn't surprised; I had known all along what was coming. "She won't, huh?" I said, feeling stupid. "Well, that's too bad."

An exasperated cluck came over the wire.

"What do you mean, too bad! She has to make it sufficient, doesn't she?"

"Theoretically," I said feebly. "What's her side of the matter?"

"Oh, she claims that I mumbled my bid and that it sounded like two diamonds. Kitty sneezed just as I bid, and Eleanor claims that it wasn't her fault—Eleanor's fault, I mean—that she couldn't hear me clearly."

I groaned louder this time. "Kitty sneezed!" I paused to steady my voice. "Well, of course, that makes a difference, but the rule committee left sneezes out of the book. How about Clare, and Kitty herself? What did they think you bid—two diamonds or four?"

"Clare admits that it sounded like four to her, and Kitty is absolutely sure that I said four!"

"So the sneeze didn't affect her hearing," I muttered. "Well, it looks as though Eleanor is hooked."

"Of course she is!" Jackie cried triumphantly. But then her voice dropped. "But she won't make her bid sufficient." Before I could say anything she said, "Wait a second. Eleanor wants to talk to you."

Eleanor cooed, "Hello, Sonny,"

I said, "Hello."

"Listen," she said earnestly, "that is just what happened. On the score, and all, I wasn't expecting Jackie to bid more than two diamonds, and then Kitty sneezed, so I was sure she did bid only two diamonds. Well, I was willing to take a chance and bid two spades, to defend the rubber, but gee whiz, my hand wasn't anywhere near good enough to bid four spades over four diamonds. I don't think that's fair."

I couldn't think of anything to say to that.

"It would be perfectly ridiculous for me to bid four spades on my rotten hand," she continued indignantly.

I had an inspiration. Sure, I was going to be yellow, but what the hell! "Look," I said, "you want to bid two spades, whereas Jackie and Kitty want you to bid four spades, I presume. Well, why don't you split the difference and bid three spades?"

There was a long pause while Eleanor considered my Solomonlike judgment. "We—ll, all right," she finally said, very reluctantly. "I might do that."

"Ask the others if that will satisfy them," I urged, beginning to glow self-righteously.

Jackie came back on the wire. "If we let her bid three spades, can I bid four diamonds again when it comes around to me?"

"Sure," I said. "By the way," I added curiously. "What are you playing for? Two cents a point?"

"Are you trying to be funny?" Jackie sneered. "We always play for a fortieth—you know that! Why?"

"Oh, nothing," I mumbled.

"Well, good-by," she said. "I guess you've settled it all right."

I assured her that it had been a pleasure, and we hung up.

When I got home the first thing I asked Jackie was how the famous hand had ended.

"Oh, we followed your decision. Eleanor changed her bid to three spades and when it was my turn I bid four diamonds again, just as you said I could."

"So that ended the rubber?" I said innocently.

"Well, sort of. Eleanor bid four spades, Kitty doubled, and they made an extra trick."

Bridge *by* H. T. WEBSTER

1932; courtesy The New York *Herald Tribune*

[Unfortunately, P. G. Wodehouse picked golf instead of Bridge to write about. We are convinced that if he had written about Bridge, he would have done it just as Stephen White did it in this story, one of a series that Mr. White wrote in his more frivolous days, when he was just a Bridge-playing reporter and not a foreign correspondent.

Character

by STEPHEN WHITE

(With a modest bow to P. G. W.)

"I NEVER would have believed it of him," said the Underbidder, looking up from his newspaper. "Though of course I scarcely knew him."

"I knew him better than you did," said the Doubler, "and I would have laughed if someone had suggested it."

"But here it is," said the Underbidder. "Two years for larceny and fraud. He admitted he was guilty."

"He always seemed like a perfect gentleman," sighed the Doubler. "I simply never would have believed it."

"And I," broke in the Old Kibitzer, "I suspected it all along."

Both men turned to him incredulously. "You knew it?" said the Underbidder. "You never mentioned it. You never said a word about it."

"Of course not," said the Old Kibitzer. "You probably would have laughed at me. Nevertheless, I repeat that I suspected it."

"How?" asked the Doubler. "What could have made you suspect him?"

"I saw him," said the Old Kibitzer awesomely. "I saw him pass a two-bid."

The two men looked at the Old Kibitzer in unbelief; then began to laugh. "Do you mean to sit there and tell us," said the Doubler, "that you would infer a criminal mind from a man's actions at a Bridge table?"

"Certainly," he was told. "A man who will pass a two-bid is capable of almost anything. He shows the temper of his mind with every move he makes at the table."

"You are talking nonsense," said the Underbidder. "Bridge is a game, you know."

"Certainly it is. At the same time it is a model of life itself. You two have just cut out of a rubber?" They nodded. "I see," said the Old Kibitzer, "that a few of our better flag-flyers are at the table. You will have quite a wait until you can cut in again, and I will be pleased to tell you a little story while you are sitting out. You will find it has a definite bearing on the subject."

I don't believe (began the Old Kibitzer) that either of you belonged to the Club when Harold Phillips joined it. It was several years ago, when we had quarters across the hall. He was in Law School at the time, and was forced to stay here in the city during one summer in connection with his studies, and with a good deal of his time unoccupied he took to dropping in at the Club now and then for a rubber or two.

He was well liked immediately. Of course, just out of college as he was, he had a tendency to radical ideas. He had moved with a free-thinking crowd at school, read the wrong books, and shared youth's love for the sensational: as a result he frequently bid three card majors and underled aces. However, as he became more acquainted with our little group he settled down considerably and by the end of the month he was being treated as one of the regulars. Everyone admitted that he was a personable young man, always with a quip on his lips, and a brilliant Bridge player.

Having joined the club in the summer, he was necessarily unacquainted with that large group of our members which leaves the city each year with the onset of hot weather and shows up again only when fall is upon us. Hence it was some months before he met Lucy Martin. This, of course, means nothing to either of you two gentlemen, since Lucy Martin was also before your time here. Let me say, however, that she was one of the brightest spots this club has ever possessed. She had, at that time, already won the Lady's Pairs twice, and finished well up in the lists regularly at the Wednesday afternoon duplicates. Her handling of dummy reversal hands was a delight to behold, and her cross-ruff technique was crisp and decisive. I have heard it said she was beautiful as well; it was probably true.

It happened that I was present when Harold and Lucy met. The club champion had been forced to break a date with Harold for our Monday night duplicate, and Harold had asked me to play with him. Needless to say I was pleased at the opportunity, and we were at Table 1, North and South, doing quite well, when Lucy, playing with old Mrs. Harris, came to our table. Naturally, when the two women sat down I began at once to count my cards—as required in the rules—and as a result I failed to notice that Harold had become strangely flustered and had turned a deep shade of unbecoming red. Mrs.

Harris told me of that later: she said also that his Adam's apple was quivering spasmodically and he was evincing a disposition to choke. In view of what happened immediately after, I can well believe it.

Harold was dealer on the first hand and passed. I opened the bidding light in third position, and was startled and shocked to hear Harold respond with three notrump. Need I say we were beaten two tricks, vulnerable? At the conclusion of play, I reached over to verify Harold's holding, and discovered he held a weak two honor-trick hand. Naturally, I began to remonstrate with him, but he seemed to be paying me no attention. His eyes were riveted on Lucy.

I scarcely should be forced to go into more details: you must realize by now that I had been victimized by love at first sight. Harold had become enamored of the girl without ever having seen her so much as play a card! Now that I look back on it, I believe she also was interested. The charming way in which she said "Not through the Iron Duke" as I played the second board should have made me suspect. However, Harold managed to pull himself together, and we succeeded in winning the duplicate with a 67.2 per cent score. Mrs. Harris and Lucy were third, East and West.

Harold would not even go over the boards with me. As soon as the last card had been played, he was after me to introduce him to Lucy. I had no reason to refuse, and I brought them together directly after the scores were out. He wasted no time asking her for an opportunity to play Bridge with her, and he was successful in his quest. Lucy was hardly to be rushed off her feet, of course, but she did promise him a Monday early in the succeeding month. He was like a man transported: it was a pleasure to look at him.

They played together when the day came, and soon they began to play together regularly. It was pleasant to watch them, for they made a lovely pair. Love had steadied Harold down; his psychics became less and less frequent and he was rebidding his cards as accurately as Culbertson himself, instead of wildly as had been his custom. Meanwhile, under his tutelage, Lucy was losing her weakness in squeezes and end-plays, and her opening leads had become things of beauty. They were consistent winners. And they were always together. I was with them when Harold first asked for her hand: she passed it to him and it was exactly what her bidding had indicated. It was all very idyllic.

As their Bridge improved their love burgeoned. Here at the Club we were all in favor of it, knowing as we did that they would be odds-on favorites in the sectional Husband and Wife Tournament. Ultimately, we all were convinced that the announcements would be out as soon as our big tournament was completed, late in February, for they were planning to compete in it together and could hardly be expected to let anything else interfere. It was, I repeat, charming.

I pass lightly over the months that intervened before the big event. It came at last, and they qualified handily for the final round. I played with the club champion, and we were eliminated in the qualifying rounds, although I have been assured that during both sessions I had not so much as touched a wrong card. On one hand, holding the ace, jack and two small spades, three hearts to the queen, the diamond—I beg your pardon? Well, another time, perhaps. At any rate, we were eliminated, and for that reason I was able to follow Harold and Lucy in the finals.

They entered the round in second place, because of the carryover, but in a strong position. The lead was held by two youngsters whom none of us knew: they were far out in front but no one expected them to hold up through the pressure of a final round. Behind the two leading pairs the field was strung out evenly, with several strong teams still in the contention. It looked like a stirring finish.

But as the round wore along I realized, following Harold and Lucy, that they were almost certain to win. Their game was rolling along smoothly and efficiently. On board seven Harold put in a brilliant bid, which I myself would scarcely have risen to, and they won a glorious score on the board. On board eleven Lucy delighted me with a double squeeze for another top. And at no time did they have a bad board: they were constantly average or better. Sixty-six per cent was what I calculated, and I am not often wrong.

It was late in the session when they met the leaders. One look at the two boys was sufficient to convince me that the pressure was telling on them: they were pallid and worn, and as they took their cards out of the board their hands were trembling. I wonder if anyone but a Bridge player can realize the strain that comes with a final round? The boys were showing every bit of it, and I felt sorry for them.

The first hand was uneventful. Lucy played the hand at three notrump, and although she attempted to set up an endplay she was able to take only nine tricks. However, the board was obviously flat, with no more than a point to be gained or lost by either side.

But the second board was a different story. Sitting behind Harold, I watched him wrestle with the bidding of the hand. He was faced with the problem which all tournament players dread: whether to bid three notrump on a hand and play it there, or to explore farther in a minor suit with an aim to investigating slam possibilities. Obviously, if the slam were not there and he chose to go beyond the three notrump level, he might find himself playing the hand at five diamonds, for a bad score. On the other hand, he suspected the slam, and was torn between the two courses of action. I struggled with him, and when he chose to go on, I suffered with him. Ultimately he bid six diamonds, and I held my breath as the dummy went down.

I might very well have sighed aloud with relief when I saw Lucy's hand. There were twelve tricks at diamonds, and only eleven at notrump; Lucy and Harold had put themselves into the perfect contract. All Harold had to do was lose a trick to the ace of trumps, draw the remaining trumps, and take the balance. Only a ruff could defeat him, and a ruff was most unlikely. It was perfection itself.

Harold won the opening lead, and returned a trump. On his left the boy showed out, but that made no difference, except to guarantee the contract. The other boy played a low trump, and Harold won the trick. He played another diamond, and much to his surprise the boy on his left, who had previously shown out, won the trick with the ace!

No one said anything for a moment, although we all were conscious of what had happened. Lucy broke the uncomfortable silence. "That was a revoke," she said. "You know your rights, partner?"

"I guess so," said Harold. "But it doesn't make any difference. We'll just forget it."

"Forget it!" exclaimed Lucy. "That was a revoke. We get that trick and another—if they take another."

"I have all the rest of the tricks," said Harold, "so we make six diamonds. As far as the revoke is concerned, I waive the penalty. Why should the kids lose the ace of trumps?"

"It's the rule," said Lucy. "A revoke is a revoke."

"Rule or no rule," said Harold. "I'm damned if I'll rub anything in. We have a good score on this board as it is, and when the day comes that the ace of trumps doesn't take a trick I'll quit the game."

At this point I informed Harold that his actions were contrary to the laws of duplicate. It was plainly stated, I told him, that in case of any infraction of the rules the tournament director must be called, and he must assign the proper penalty. There was no alternative, I pointed out.

"Listen here," said Harold. "These kids stand a chance of winning this event, and I won't see them lose it on a technicality. I won't call the director, and if anyone else does I'll claim that I didn't see any revoke. Or I'll revoke myself on the eleventh trick. Now let's get on with the tournament."

There was nothing we could do. The boys might have been able to rectify things, but they were new to tournament play in the first place, and in no condition to think clearly anyway. The move for the next round was called, and play went on.

But the sparkle was quite gone from Lucy and Harold's game. They were old campaigners, of course, and to the unpracticed observer all was as unruffled as ever, but the scores were hardly as consistent as they had been, and there were no more tops. They finished up with two averages, and instead of going over their private score, as they usually did, they parted immediately. Harold disappeared to the bar, I believe, and Lucy came over to talk to me. "Do you realize what Harold did?" she said. "He cheated. He deliberately broke the rules." Of course I had no option but to agree with her. She walked away, her eyes flashing.

I need scarcely tell you that when the scores were posted, Harold's refusal to claim the revoke had cost three and a half points, and they had lost the event by two. The two boys had gone all to pieces and finished sixth, but another pair had come up and eked out the win. Warwick and Hutchins, to be precise. Harold and Lucy were second.

They never spoke to each other again. Lucy was heartbroken, but she was adamant. "I'm glad I found out in time," she told me one day. "He was a common cheat, and I never realized it."

I approached Harold about it one day, but he was brusque. "I don't wish to discuss it," he said, and though I brought it up time and again he walked away from me each time. Strangely enough, here in the Club the sympathy was mostly for Harold, although I remonstrated every chance I had, and even went so far as to read to several of the more stubborn sympathizers the rule in question.

Harold resigned from the club soon after, and we heard little more of him. We did discover, however, that soon after he left, his true colors showed themselves again, and he took up a freak slam-bidding convention. He went from bad to worse, even dabbling with an artificial one-club system, and the last I heard he had given up Bridge entirely after moving to another city.

Lucy was married shortly after, to an excellent Bridge player from Philadelphia—a friend, I might add of Blackwood himself. She writes occasionally, never failing to mention her relief over having escaped so closely a marriage to so unscrupulous a man. She is happy, though scarcely rolling in wealth: indeed, she is forced to run weekly duplicates in her home to eke out the family income. But in her last letter she tells me that her husband has promised to give up drinking, and that they stand a good chance of winning the National Mixed Pairs this spring.

"And so, gentlemen," concluded the Old Kibitzer, "I think you will agree that Bridge can bring out a man's character."

"Let me ask you something," said the Underbidder. "What was that man's name again?"

"Harold Phillips," said the Kibitzer. "You know him?"

"I don't know," said the Underbidder. "Somehow the name sounds familiar."

"I can help you," said the Doubler. "You saw it in a newspaper. He was just made a Justice of the State Supreme Court—the youngest in history."

"Very likely," said the Old Kibitzer. "He was, as I said, a lawyer. But do not change the subject. Will you admit, now, that Bridge brings out a person's character?"

"I will," said the Doubler. "But don't press me for details!"

¶*Here is more Bridge fiction in which you will meet some charming people, to the exact extent that people from* The New Yorker *can be charming. It takes a while for these charming people to get around to their Bridge game, but we know you will not be bored waiting.*

My Lady Love, My Dove
by ROALD DAHL

It has been my habit, for many years, to take a nap after lunch. I settle myself in a chair in the living room with a cushion behind my head and my feet up on a small square leather stool, and I read until I drop off.

On this Friday afternoon, I was in my chair and feeling as comfortable as ever with a book in my hands—an old favorite, Doubleday and Westwood's *The Genera of Diurnal Lepidoptera* —when my wife, who has never been a silent lady, began to talk to me from the sofa opposite. "These two people," she said, "what time are they coming?"

I made no answer, so she repeated the question, louder this time.

I told her politely that I didn't know.

"I don't think I like them very much," she said. "Especially him."

"No, dear, all right."

"Arthur. I said I don't think I like them very much."

I lowered my book and looked across at her lying with her feet up on the sofa, flipping over the pages of some fashion magazine. "We've only met them once," I said.

"A dreadful man, really. Never stopped telling jokes, or stories, or something."

"I'm sure you'll manage them very well, dear."

"And she's pretty frightful, too. When do you think they'll arrive?"

Somewhere around six o'clock, I guessed.

"But don't *you* think they're awful?" she asked, pointing at me with her finger.

"Well . . ."

"They're too awful, they really are."

"We can hardly put them off now, Pamela."

"They're absolutely the end," she said.

"Then why did you ask them?" The question slipped out before I could stop myself, and I regretted it at once, for it is a rule with me never to provoke my wife if I can help it. There was a pause, and I watched her face, waiting for the answer—the big white face that to me was something so strange and fascinating there were occasions when I could hardly bring myself to look away from it. In the evenings sometimes—working on her embroidery, or painting those small intricate flower pictures—the face would tighten and glimmer with a subtle inward strength that was beautiful beyond words, and I would sit and stare at it minute after minute while pretending to read. Even now, at this moment, with that compressed, acid look, the frowning forehead, the petulant curl of the nose, I had to admit that there was a majestic quality about this woman, something splendid, almost stately; and so tall she was, far taller than I—although today, in her fifty-first year, I think one would have to call her big rather than tall.

"You know very well why I asked them," she answered sharply. "For Bridge, that's all. They play an absolutely first-class game, and for a decent stake." She glanced up and saw me watching her. "Well," she said, "that's about the way you feel, too, isn't it?"

"Well, of course, I . . ."

"Don't be a fool, Arthur."

"The only time I met them I must say they did seem quite nice."

"So is the butcher."

"Now Pamela, dear—please. We don't want any of that."

"Listen," she said, slapping down the magazine on her lap, "you saw the sort of people they were as well as I did. A pair of stupid climbers who think they can go anywhere just because they play good Bridge."

"I'm sure you're right, dear, but what I don't honestly understand is why—"

"I keep telling you—so that for once we can get a decent game. I'm sick and tired of playing with rabbits. But I really can't see why I should have these awful people in the house."

"Of course not, my dear, but isn't it a little late now—"

"Arthur?"

"Yes?"

"Why, for God's sake, do you always argue with me. You *know* you disliked them as much as I did."

"I really don't think you need worry, Pamela. After all, they seemed quite a nice, well-mannered young couple."

"Arthur, don't be pompous." She was looking at me hard with those wide gray eyes of hers, and to avoid them—they sometimes made me quite uncomfortable—I got up and walked over to the French windows that led into the garden.

The big sloping lawn out in front of the house was newly mown, striped with pale and dark ribbons of green. On the far side, the two laburnums were in full flower at last, the long golden chains making a blaze of color against the darker trees beyond. The roses were out too, and the scarlet begonias, and in the long herbaceous border, all my lovely hybrid lupine, columbine, delphinium, sweet William, and the huge, pale, scented iris. One of the gardeners was coming up the drive from his lunch. I could see the roof of his cottage through the trees, and beyond it, to one side, the place where the drive went out through the iron gates on to the Canterbury road.

My wife's house. Her garden. How beautiful it all was! How peaceful! Now, if only Pamela would try to be a little less solicitous of my welfare, less prone to coax me into doing things for my own good rather than for my own pleasure, then everything would be heaven. Mind you, I don't want to give the impression that I do not love her—I worship the very air she breathes—or that I can't manage her, or that I am not the captain of my ship. All I am trying to say is that she can be a trifle irritating at times, the way she carries on. For example, those little mannerisms of hers—I do wish she would drop them all, especially the way she has of pointing a finger at me to emphasize a phrase. You must remember that I am a man who is built rather small, and a gesture like this, when used to excess by a person like my wife, is apt to intimidate. I sometimes find it difficult to convince myself that she is not an overbearing woman.

"Arthur!" she called. "Come here."

"What?"

"I've just had a most marvelous idea. Come here."

I turned and went over to where she was lying on the sofa.

"Look," she said, "do you want to have some fun?"

"What sort of fun?"

"With the Snapes."

"Who are the Snapes?"

"Come on," she said. "Wake up. Henry and Sally Snape. Our week-end guests."

"Well?"

"Now listen. You say they're such nice, polite, well-mannered people. Right? And I say they're a couple of nasty little social climbers. Well . . ." She hesitated, smiling slyly, and for some reason I got the impression she was about to say a shocking thing. "Well—let's find out which of us is correct. That should be easy enough. All we've got to do is listen to what they have to say about us when they're alone together—"

"Now wait a minute, Pamela—"

"Don't be an ass, Arthur. Let's have some fun

—some real fun for once—tonight." She had half raised herself up off the sofa, her face bright with a kind of sudden recklessness, the mouth slightly open, and she was looking at me with two round gray eyes, a spark dancing slowly in each. "Why shouldn't we?"

"What do you want to do?"

"Why, it's obvious. Can't you see?"

"No, I can't."

"All we've got to do is put a microphone in their room."

I admit I was expecting something pretty bad, but when she said this I was so shocked I didn't know what to answer.

"That's exactly what we'll do," she said.

"Here!" I cried. "No. Wait a minute. You can't do that."

"Why not?"

"That's about the nastiest trick I ever heard of. It's like—why, it's like listening at keyholes, or reading letters, only far, far worse. You don't mean this seriously, do you?"

"Of course I do. Just for the first five minutes after they get into their room. That's when people talk."

I knew how much she disliked being contradicted, but there were times when I felt it necessary to assert myself, even at considerable risk.

"Pamela," I said, snapping the words out sharply. "I forbid you to do it!"

She took her feet down from the sofa and sat up straight. "What in God's name are you trying to pretend to be, Arthur? I simply don't understand you."

"That shouldn't be too difficult."

"Tommyrot! I've known you do lots of worse things than this before now."

"Never!"

"Oh yes I have. What makes you suddenly think you're a so much nicer person than I am?"

"I've never done things like that."

"All right, my boy," she said, pointing her finger at me like a pistol. "What about that time at the Milfords' last Christmas? Remember? You nearly laughed your head off and I had to put my hand over your mouth to stop them hearing us. What about that for one?"

"That was different," I said. "It wasn't our house. And they weren't our guests."

"It doesn't make any difference at all." She was sitting very upright, staring at me with those round gray eyes, and the chin was beginning to come up high in a peculiarly contemptuous manner. "Don't be such a pompous hypocrite," she said. "What on earth's come over you?"

"I really think it's a pretty nasty thing, you know, Pamela. I honestly do."

"But listen, Arthur. I'm a *nasty* person. And so are you—in a secret sort of way. That's why we get along together."

"I never heard such nonsense."

"Mind you, if you've suddenly decided to change your character completely, that's another story."

"You've got to stop talking this way, Pamela."

"You see," she said, "if you really *have* decided to reform, then what on earth am *I* going to do?"

"You don't know what you're saying."

"Arthur, how could a nice person like you want to associate with a stinker?"

I sat myself down slowly in the chair opposite her, and she was watching me all the time. You understand, she was a big woman, with a big white face, and when she looked at me hard, as she was doing now, I became—how shall I say it—surrounded, almost enveloped by her, as though she were a great tub of cream and I had fallen in.

"You don't honestly want to do this microphone thing, do you?"

"But of course I do. It's time we had a bit of fun around here. Come on, Arthur. Don't be so stuffy."

"It's not right, Pamela."

"It's just as right"—up came the finger again—"just as right as when you found those letters of Mary Proberts' in her purse and you read them through from beginning to end."

"We should never have done that."

"*We!*"

"You read them afterward, Pamela."

"It didn't harm anyone at all. You said so yourself at the time. And this one's no worse."

"How would *you* like it if someone did it to *you?*"

"How could I *mind* if I didn't know it was being done. Come on, Arthur. Don't be so flabby."

"I'll have to think about it."

"Maybe the great radio engineer doesn't know how to connect the mike to the speaker?"

"That's the easiest part."

"Well, go on then. Go on and do it."

"I'll think about it and let you know later."

"There's no time for that. They might arrive any moment."

"Then I won't do it. I'm not going to be caught red-handed."

"If they come before you're through, I'll simply keep them down here. No danger. What's the time, anyway?"

It was nearly three o'clock.

"They're driving down from London," she said, "and they certainly won't leave till after lunch. That gives you plenty of time."

"Which room are you putting them in?"

"The big yellow room at the end of the corridor. That's not too far away, is it?"

"I suppose it could be done."

"And by the bye," she said, "where are you going to have the speaker?"

"I haven't said I'm going to do it yet."

"My God!" she cried. "I'd like to see someone try and stop you now. You ought to see your face. It's all pink and excited at the very prospect. Put the speaker in our bedroom, why not? But go on—and hurry."

I hesitated. It was something I made a point of doing whenever she tried to order me about, instead of asking nicely. "I don't like it, Pamela."

She didn't say any more after that; she just sat there, absolutely still, watching me, a resigned, waiting expression on her face, as though she were in a long queue. This, I knew from experience, was a danger signal. She was like one of those bomb things with the pin pulled out, and it was only a matter of time before—bang! and she would explode. In the silence that followed, I could almost hear her ticking.

So I got up quietly and went out to the workshop and collected a mike and a hundred and fifty feet of wire. Now that I was away from her, I am ashamed to admit that I began to feel a bit of excitement myself, a tiny warm prickling sensation under the skin, near the tips of my fingers. It was nothing much, mind you—really nothing at all. Good heavens, I experience the same thing every morning of my life when I open the paper to check the closing prices on two or three of my wife's larger stockholdings. So I wasn't going to get carried away by a silly joke like this. At the same time, I couldn't help being amused.

I took the stairs two at a time and entered the yellow room at the end of the passage. It had the clean, unlived-in appearance of all guest rooms, with its twin beds, yellow satin bedspreads, pale-yellow walls, and golden-colored curtains. I began to look around for a good place to hide the mike. This was the most important part of all, for whatever happened, it must not be discovered. I thought first of the basket of logs by the fireplace. Put it under the logs. No—not safe enough. Behind the radiator? On top of the wardrobe? Under the desk? None of these seemed very professional to me. All might be subject to chance inspection because of a dropped collar stud or something like that. Finally, with considerable cunning, I decided to put it inside the springing of the sofa. The sofa was against the wall, near the edge of the carpet, and my lead wire could go straight under the carpet over to the door.

I tipped up the sofa and slit the material underneath. Then I tied the microphone securely up among the springs, making sure that it faced the room. After that, I led the wire under the carpet to the door. I was calm and cautious in everything I did. Where the wire had to emerge from under the carpet and pass out of the door, I made a little groove in the wood, so that it was almost invisible.

All this, of course, took time, and when I suddenly heard the crunch of wheels on the gravel of the drive outside, and then the slamming of car doors and the voices of our guests, I was still only halfway down the corridor, tacking the wire along the skirting. I stopped and straightened up, hammer in hand, and I must confess that I felt afraid. You have no idea how unnerving that noise was to me. I experienced the same sudden stomachy feeling of fright as when a bomb once dropped the other side of the village during the war, one afternoon, while I was working quietly in the library with my butterflies.

Don't worry, I told myself. Pamela will take care of these people. She won't let them come up here.

Rather frantically, I set about finishing the job, and soon I had the wire tacked all along the corridor and through into our bedroom. Here, concealment was not so important, although I still did not permit myself to get careless, because of the servants. So I laid the wire under the carpet and brought it up unobtrusively into the back of the radio. Making the final connections was an elementary technical matter and took me no time at all.

Well—I had done it. I stepped back and glanced at the little radio. Somehow, now, it looked different—no longer a silly box for making noises, but an evil little creature that crouched on the tabletop with a part of its own body reaching out secretly into a forbidden place far away. I switched it on. It hummed faintly but made no other sound. I took my bedside clock, which had a loud tick, and carried it along to the yellow room and placed it on the floor by the sofa. When I returned, sure enough the radio creature was ticking away as loudly as if the clock were in the room—even louder.

I fetched back the clock. Then I tidied myself up in the bathroom, returned my tools to the workshop, and prepared to meet the guest. But first, to compose myself, and so that I would not have to appear in front of them with the blood, as it were, still wet on my hands, I spent five minutes in the library with my collection. I concentrated on a tray of the lovely *Vanessa cardui*—the "painted lady"—and made a few notes for a paper I was preparing, entitled "The Relation Between Color Pattern and Framework of Wings," which I intended to read at the next meeting of our society in Canterbury. In this way I soon regained my normal grave, attentive manner.

When I entered the living room, our two guests, whose names I could never remember, were seated on the sofa. My wife was mixing drinks.

"Oh, *there* you are, Arthur," she said. "Where *have* you been?"

I thought this was an unnecessary remark. "I'm so sorry," I said to the guests as we shook hands. "I was busy and forgot the time."

"We all know what *you*'ve been doing," the girl said, smiling wisely. "But we'll forgive him, won't we, dearest?"

"I think we should," the husband answered.

I had a frightful, fantastic vision of my wife telling them, amidst roars of laughter, precisely what I had been doing upstairs. She *couldn't*—she *couldn't* have done that! I looked round at her and she, too, was smiling as she measured out the gin.

"I'm sorry we disturbed you," the girl said.

I decided that if this was going to be a joke, then I'd better join in quickly, so I forced myself to smile with her.

"You must let us see it," the girl continued.

"See what?"

"Your collection. Your wife says that they are absolutely beautiful."

I lowered myself slowly into a chair and relaxed. It was ridiculous to be so nervous and jumpy.

"Are you interested in butterflies?" I asked her.

"I'd love to see yours, Mr. Beauchamp."

The Martinis were distributed and we settled down to a couple of hours of talk and drink before dinner. It was from then on that I began to form the impression that our guests were a charming couple. My wife, coming from a titled family, is apt to be conscious of her class and breeding, and is often hasty in her judgment of strangers who are friendly toward her—particularly tall men. She is frequently right, but in this case I felt that she might be making a mistake. As a rule, I myself do not like tall men either; they are apt to be supercilious and omniscient. But Henry Snape—my wife had whispered his name—struck me as being an amiable, simple young man with good manners, whose main preoccupation, very properly, was Mrs. Snape. He was handsome in a long-faced, horsy sort of way, with dark-brown eyes that seemed to be gentle and sympathetic. I envied him his fine mop of black hair, and caught myself wondering what lotion he used to keep it looking so healthy. He did tell us one or two jokes, but they were on a high level and no one could have objected.

"At school," he said, "they used to call me Scervix. Do you know why?"

"I haven't the least idea," my wife answered.

"Because cervix is Latin for nape."

This was rather deep and it took me a while to work out.

"What school was that, Mr. Snape?" my wife asked.

"Eton," he said, and my wife gave a quick little nod of approval. Now she will talk to him, I thought, so I turned my attention to the other one, Sally Snape. She was an attractive girl with a bosom. Had I met her fifteen years earlier I might well have got myself into some sort of trouble. As it was, I had a pleasant enough time telling her all about my beautiful butterflies. I was observing her closely as I talked, and after a while I began to get the impression that she was not, in fact, quite so merry and smiling a girl as I had been led to believe at first. She seemed to be coiled in herself, as though with a secret she was jealously guarding. The deep-blue eyes moved too quickly about the room, never settling or resting on one thing for more than a moment; and over all her face, though so faint that they might not even have been there, those small downward lines of sorrow.

"I'm so looking forward to our game of Bridge," I said, finally changing the subject.

"Us too," she answered. "You know we play almost every night, we love it so."

"You are extremely expert, both of you. How did you get to be so good?"

"It's practice," she said. "That's all. Practice, practice, practice."

"Have you played in any championships?"

"Not yet, but Henry wants very much for us to do that. It's hard work, you know, to reach that standard. Terribly hard work." Was there not here, I wondered, a hint of resignation in her voice? Yes, that was probably it; he was pushing her too hard, making her take it too seriously, and the poor girl was tired of it all.

At eight o'clock, without changing, we moved in to dinner. The meal went well, with Henry Snape telling us some very droll stories. He also praised my Richebourg '34 in a most knowledgeable fashion, which pleased me greatly. By the time coffee came, I realized that I had grown to like these two youngsters immensely, and as a result I began to feel uncomfortable about this microphone business. It would have been all right if they had been horrid people, but to play this trick on two such charming young persons as these filled me with a strong sense of guilt. Don't misunderstand me. I was not getting cold feet. It didn't seem necessary to stop the operation. But I refused to relish the prospect openly, as my wife seemed now to be doing, with covert smiles and winks and secret little noddings of the head.

Around nine-thirty, feeling comfortable and well fed, we returned to the large living room to start our Bridge. We were playing for a fair stake—ten shillings a hundred—so we decided not to split families, and I partnered my wife the whole time. We all four of us took the game seriously, which is the only way to take it, and we played silently, intently, hardly speaking at all except to bid. It was not the money we played for. Heaven knows, my wife had enough of that, and so, apparently, did the Snapes. But among experts it is almost traditional that they play for a reasonable stake.

That night, the cards were evenly divided, but for once my wife played badly, so we got the worst of it. I could see that she wasn't concentrating fully, and as we came along toward midnight she began not even to care. She kept glancing up at me with those large gray eyes of hers, the eyebrows raised, her nostrils curiously open, a little gloating smile around the corners of her mouth.

Our opponents played a fine game. Their bidding was masterly, and all through the evening they made only one mistake. That was when the girl badly overestimated her partner's hand and bid six spades. I doubled and they went three down, vulnerable, which cost them eight hundred points. It was just a momentary lapse, but I remember that Sally Snape was very put out by it, even though her husband forgave her at once, kissing her hand across the table and telling her not to worry.

Around twelve-thirty my wife announced that she wanted to go to bed.

"Just one more rubber?" Henry Snape said.

"No, Mr. Snape. I'm tired tonight. Arthur's tired, too. I can see it. Let's all go to bed."

She herded us out of the room and we went upstairs, the four of us together. On the way up, there was the usual talk about breakfast and what they wanted and how they were to call the maid. "I think you'll like your room," my wife said. "It has a view right across the valley, and the sun comes to you in the morning around ten o'clock."

We were in the passage now, standing outside our own bedroom door, and I could see the wire I had put down that afternoon and how it ran along the top of the skirting down to their room. Although it was nearly the same color as the paint, it looked very conspicuous to me. "Sleep well," my wife said. "Sleep well, Mrs. Snape. Good night, Mr. Snape." I followed her into our room and shut the door.

"Quick!" she cried. "Turn it on!" My wife was always like that, frightened that she was going to miss something. She had a reputation, when she went hunting—I never go myself—of always being right up with the hounds whatever the cost to herself or her horse, for fear that she might miss a kill. I could see she had no intention of missing this one.

The little radio warmed up just in time to catch the noise of their door opening and closing again. "There!" my wife said. "They've gone in." She was standing in the center of the room in her blue dress, her hands clasped before her, her head craned forward, intently listening, and the whole of the big white face seemed somehow to have gathered itself together, tight like a wineskin.

Almost at once, the voice of Henry Snape came out of the radio, strong and clear. "You're just a goddam little fool," he was saying, and this voice was so different from the one I remembered, so harsh and unpleasant, it made me jump. "The whole bloody evening wasted! Eight hundred points—that's four pounds!"

"I got mixed up," the girl answered. "I won't do it again, I promise."

"What's *this?*" my wife said. "What's going on?" Her mouth was wide open now, the eyebrows stretched up high, and she came quickly over to the radio and leaned forward, ear to the speaker. I must say I felt rather excited myself.

"I promise, I promise I won't do it again," the girl was saying.

"We're not taking any chances," the man answered grimly. "We're going to have another practice right now."

"Oh, no, please! I couldn't stand it!"

"Look," the man said, "all the way out here to take money off this rich bitch and you have to go and mess it up."

My wife's turn to jump.

"The second time this week," he went on.

"I promise I won't do it again."

"Sit down. I'll sing them out and you answer."

"No, Henry, *please!* Not all five hundred of them. It'll take three hours."

"All right, then. We'll leave out the finger positions. I think you're sure of those. We'll just do the basic bids showing honor tricks."

"Oh, Henry, must we? I'm so tired."

"It's absolutely essential you get them perfect," he said. "We have a game every day next week, you know that. And we've got to eat."

"What is this?" my wife whispered. "What on earth is it?"

"Shhh!" I said. "Listen!"

"All right," the man's voice was saying. "Now we'll start from the beginning. Ready?"

"Oh, Henry, please." She sounded very near to tears.

"Come on, Sally. Pull yourself together."

Then, in a quite different voice, the one we had been used to hearing in the living room, Henry Snape said, *"One* club." I noticed that there was a curious lilting emphasis on the word "one," the first part of the word drawn out long.

"Ace queen of clubs," the girl replied wearily. "King jack of spades. No hearts, and ace jack of diamonds."

"And how many cards to each suit? Watch my finger positions carefully."

"You said we could miss those."

"Well—if you're quite sure you know them?"

"Yes, I know them."

A pause, then "A *club."*

"King jack of clubs," the girl recited. "Ace of spades. Queen jack of hearts, and ace queen of diamonds."

Another pause, then "I'll say *one* club."

"Ace king of clubs . . ."

"My heavens alive!" I cried. "It's a bidding code! They show every card in the hand!"

"Arthur, it couldn't be!"

"It's like those men who go into the audience and borrow something from you and there's a girl blindfolded on the stage, and from the way he phrases the question she can tell him exactly what it is—even a railway ticket, and what station it's from."

"It's impossible!"

"Not at all. But it's tremendous hard work to learn. Listen to them."

"I'll go *one heart,"* the man's voice was saying.

"King queen ten of hearts. Ace jack of spades. No diamonds. Queen jack of clubs . . ."

"And you see," I said, "he tells her the *number* of cards he has in each suit by the position of his fingers."

"How?"

"I don't know. You heard him saying about it."

"My God, Arthur! Are you sure that's what they're doing?"

"I'm afraid so." I watched her as she walked quickly over to the side of the bed to fetch a cigarette. She lit it with her back to me and then swung round, blowing the smoke up at the ceiling in a thin stream. I knew we were going to have to do something about this, but I wasn't quite sure what, because we couldn't possibly accuse them without revealing the source of our information. I waited for my wife's decision.

"Why, Arthur," she said slowly, blowing out clouds of smoke. "Why, this is a *marvelous* idea. D'you think *we* could learn to do it?"

"What!"

"Of course. Why not?"

"Here! No! Wait a minute, Pamela . . ." But she came swiftly across the room, right up close to me where I was standing, and she dropped her head and looked down at me—the old look of a smile that wasn't a smile, at the corners of the mouth, and the curl of the nose, and the big full gray eyes staring at me with their bright black centers, and then they were gray, and all the rest was white flecked with hundreds of tiny red veins—and when she looked at me like this, hard and close, I swear to you it made me feel as though I were drowning.

"Yes," she said. "Why not?"

"But Pamela . . . Good heavens . . . No . . . After all . . ."

"Arthur, I do wish you wouldn't *argue* with me all the time. That's exactly what we'll do. Now, go fetch a deck of cards; we'll start right away."

THE ODD HISTORY OF CONTRACT BRIDGE

[Harold S. Vanderbilt is perhaps best known as a yachtsman. Yachting is a sport in which his record is roughly equivalent to Babe Ruth's in baseball and Bobby Jones's in golf; but to card-players he is primarily the father of Contract Bridge. Not only did he invent the game, but as early as the 1920s he worked out several basic aspects of Contract Bridge bidding, and it is often amusing to see them turn up one by one in these 1950s as "new" ideas of other players. [Numerous publications have carried accounts of the origin of Contract Bridge but we are happy to present here Mike Vanderbilt's own story, the first time it has been published.

The Origin of Contract Bridge
by HAROLD S. VANDERBILT

MY experience as a player of games of the Whist family—first Bridge, then Auction Bridge, and finally Contract Bridge—dates from the turn of the century when my mother persuaded Joe Elwell to give us some Bridge lessons in Newport, Rhode Island. I played Bridge until Auction appeared in 1907. Elwell became a few years later my favorite Auction Bridge partner, and remained so until his still unsolved murder in June, 1920.

In the early Twenties I played Plafond occasionally. I liked Plafond's main virtue: namely, that you could not score a game unless you bid it. I disliked slam bonuses at Auction, even though they were necessarily modest. They irked me because they were awarded for unbid slams. But their very existence put ideas into my head And so—influenced perhaps by this like and dislike—I began to think about devising a new game of the Whist family. I had seen Whist go, Bridge come and go, Auction come. Was it time for Auction to go? I thought so and christened my game Contract Bridge after its principal divergence from Auction Bridge: having to contract for a game in order to make one. In view of this drastic change I foresaw, as I dreamed up my new game, that slam premiums would have to be vastly increased in order to make it worth while to risk the loss of an otherwise certain game. The increases in trick and game values and in rubber premiums and penalties followed more or less automatically in the wake of the higher slam premiums, and, for simplicity's sake, I adopted the decimal system—round figures—in scoring.

I did not foresee a rather obvious result of all these increases in points scored; nor did I realize what was happening until years later when, as we were revising the International Contract Bridge Code in London, the Portland Club representative said, "You know the thing that has made your game so very popular is those big figures. Mrs. Smith just loves to say proudly to Mrs. Jones: 'My dear, you know I set Mrs. Snooks 1,400 points.' "

The first chance I had to test my new game was on a ten-day cruise on board the steamship *Finland* en route from California to Havana via the Panama Canal in November 1925. I was traveling in company with three friends* who agreed to try the game. So I produced my scoring table, which we changed slightly during the voyage, but by the time we reached Havana it was very similar to the one in use today. It differed principally in that no-trumps counted 35 points per trick, and doubled penalties increased in an ascending scale as the number of tricks increased. Today there is only one increase—from the first to each subsequent doubled undertrick—a change adopted more, I think, in the interests of simplicity than of equity.

My scoring table provided at the outset for lower penalties for a side that had not won a game, to enable it to "fly the flag" at not too great a cost and to add variety, singularly lacking in Auction, to the new game. But we were at a loss for a word to describe a side that is subject to higher penalties. A young lady we met on the boat—none of us can recall her name—who had played some strange game in California that called for higher penalties under certain conditions, gave us the word used in that game, and "vulnerable"—what a perfect description—it has been ever since.

After we got back to our respective homes in New York and Boston we made no particular effort to popularize our newborn game. It never occurred to me that it was destined to sweep the world, or that its eventual promoters were to make millions. I explained the scoring to a number of my friends. I may even have supplied them with typewritten scoring tables. Without

* Frederic S. Allen, Francis M. Bacon III, and Dudley L. Pickman, Jr.

exception, they all instantly gave up Auction. Like the flu, the new game spread by itself, despite the attempts of the old Auction addicts—too old to change—to devise a vaccine to stop it.

In 1927 the Whist Club published its first Laws of Contract Bridge, after making me a member of the Card Committee to assist in devising them; and the first important Contract Bridge Tournament was held in Cleveland, Ohio, in the fall of 1928, for the cup then newly presented by me and still competed for annually.

Such, in brief, is the story of the origin and childhood of Contract Bridge.

¶ *The biggest news story known to Contract Bridge, or any other card game for that matter, was the Culbertson-Lenz match, played in the winter of 1931-32. It made Contract Bridge the big game of the century and Ely Culbertson the big name of Contract Bridge. Undeniably it all came about through Culbertson's remarkable publicity genius.* ¶ *At the start of 1931 Ely Culbertson was already a leading Bridge authority. In 1929 he had founded* The Bridge World, *only American monthly magazine on the game; in 1930 he had published an outstandingly successful book; and he had two years of consistent tournament victories. But the names of the former Auction Bridge authorities were still better known. Culbertson decided to beat them at their own game. Here, in two chapters from his autobiography (*THE STRANGE LIVES OF ONE MAN, *1940), he tells his own story of how he did it.*

from The Strange Lives of One Man

by ELY CULBERTSON

THE SYSTEMIC WAR

IN September, having established the Culbertson organizations in France and in England, we returned to America. On the day of our arrival I went to see my new offices in the General Electric Building, on Lexington Avenue at Fifty-first Street. The three little cubbyholes at 45 West Forty-fifth Street had grown into a row of offices, with over a hundred employees on a payroll of $15,000 a month and, indirectly, a staff of certified Culbertson teachers earning several million dollars a year for themselves. I had planned the various Bridge departments well, for even during the few months of my absence they had grown tremendously. As I passed from one department to another, each run by its own manager, I wondered at this fairyland, America, that could make such things possible.

We were engaged in every possible form of commercial and intellectual activity connected with Bridge and cards, and everywhere the war cry, "Culbertson System, Culbertson System, Culbertson System" rang out.

But I was not content. I jumped in to organize new departments and to build new roads into the mass mind. I surveyed the newspaper syndicate field and signed a contract with Jack Wheeler, President of the Bell Syndicate. We became quite friendly, and with his help I organized a unique class of pupils. This was the only class I taught, and I accepted no fees; in fact, I even lost a little money to them in our "penny-ante" Bridge games—to their great satisfaction. My class consisted of Jack Wheeler; Bruce Barton, of the Batten, Barton, Durstine and Osborne Advertising Agency; Frank Crowninshield, editor of *Vanity Fair;* Kent Cooper, general manager of the Associated Press; Deac Aylesworth, president of the National Broadcasting Company and R.K.O.; Grantland Rice; Sumner Blossom, editor of *American Magazine;* Rex Cole; and Pete Jones. These "pupils" of mine controlled the most important publicity outlets. I naturally expected no special favors in publicity from my friends, and none was ever given. But I wanted them to understand the game of Contract Bridge, and to appreciate the great news value of Contract to the best classes of American men and women.

We held regular weekly sessions at different homes, and soon they became Contract enthusiasts. Proudly proclaiming that they had been taught by "the master himself," they tested their knowledge of the Culbertson System on their friends—which may easily explain why, for a few weeks, the sale of my books took an alarming drop. Although they were among the country's greatest masters of the mass mind, they sometimes mistook minimum responses for forcing bids, and vice versa. After all these years, undaunted, I am still trying to teach them the game. But I doubt that they'll ever really learn it.

Meanwhile, clouds were gathering that would soon break out in a storm and threaten to sweep away everything that Jo and I had built. In the early spring, even before our trip to Russia, things had begun to happen among my rival Bridge authorities. The golden tree in which Work, Whitehead, and Lenz had built such comfortable nests began to be shaken violently. The sales of their books, enormous at first, had stopped almost overnight. I had now become a menace not to one authority, but to all of them. None of them was strong enough any more to fight me individually. The time had come for me to stand alone and hack my own trail through the jungle of the mass mind. Having occupied the best positions everywhere, I calmly awaited the inevitable combine and onslaught.

The best-known authorities, though politely hostile to me, were gentlemanly enough; but some of their camp followers began sniping—with innuendoes, petty slander, whispering campaigns. A particularly lugubrious story was being circulated all over the country. It seems that I had played Poker with a crowd of society women in Pasadena. One poor lady lost a small fortune and couldn't pay. I took all her jewels. But next day, her husband visited me and, at the point of a gun, reclaimed the jewels!

Personally, I enjoy whispering campaigns; they are wonderful publicity, and their effect is always the opposite of that intended. Besides, they are invariably funny.

I laughed at the various juicy stories in which I was represented as a mysterious foreigner, a "Roosian with a past" who could show a trick or two to Casanova and other less glamorified gigolos. This of course was very romantic and made the ladies flock to the system.

I laughed less when it was persistently insinuated that I had fraudulently posed as an American and that even my name was not real. As an answer I joined the Society of the Sons of the American Revolution.

In March, information came to me from the enemy camp that all twelve of the leading authorities were meeting to plan an alliance against "that Culbertson."

I knew this was the beginning of a strange war—a Systemic War, which might come to be known as the "war for royalties," in which the "have-nots" allied themselves against the "forcing two-bid." Too late did they realize that the enemy was powerfully entrenched behind his Standard Table of Honor-Tricks, his flanks protected by forcing takeouts and shutout bids. Their only chance was for each to sacrifice his system and agree on one system. And now the twelve leading authorities—Lenz, Work, Whitehead, Shepard, and smaller fry—led by their business manager, F. D. Courtenay—got together for a final onslaught.

Early in June I received a visit from Mr. Courtenay, a fluid speaker of agreeable appearance. In private life he is a fine fellow, and I was really sorry to see him mixed up in such a highly specialized and complex business as Bridge.

"What you need is a good business manager, Mr. Culbertson," he had previously told me several times.

And finally I had said, "What you mean, Mr. Courtenay, is that you want me to be the business and you the manager."

Little did I expect at the time that Mr. Courtenay, in spite of himself, was destined to become the greatest publicity agent I ever had.

The object of Mr. Courtenay's latest visit was to inform me that he had conceived a brilliant plan; he had organized a corporation—"Bridge Headquarters." All the bridge authorities would be members of it, forming an advisory council. They had agreed to scrap their systems and adopt one "Official System." They would write only one book, dividing the royalties in proportion among the major and minor luminaries.

"We have all the twelve leading authorities, Mr. Culbertson," Mr. Courtenay exulted. "Won't you be the thirteenth?"

"I'm sorry, Mr. Courtenay, but I'm very superstitious. And besides, what is the aim of your organization?"

"We want standardization of Contract."

"But it's already standardized. You know it!"

"The greatest of the authorities don't agree with you. The people want a system that is official."

There was no use sparring. "Now look here, Mr. Courtenay," I said, "let's leave the 'people' out of this. As I see it, it's a combine of twelve Bridge authorities whose books do not sell against one who happens to be successful. You naturally don't expect me to join and divide the fruits of years of hard work with twelve other fellows who tried their best to keep me out of Bridge!"

"I think you'd be well advised to join, Mr. Culbertson. It's twelve against one, and in this country the majority rules."

"You're saying, in effect, join up or else . . ."

"Oh, no, Mr. Culbertson! I'm not threatening. In fact, we didn't expect you to come in. Perhaps it's better this way, after all. Maybe you're right—maybe thirteen is an unlucky number."

And Mr. Courtenay left.

I waited. The Systemic War broke out a week later with a nation-wide release from "Bridge Headquarters" announcing "the biggest news story that Bridge has ever produced." The story gave the impression that all the authorities had gotten together to promulgate a new standard system and that thereafter, according to the New York *Journal,* "Africans and New York clubmen will speak the same language . . ." The advisory council announced that the new system would be produced "within a week or so" and hired two Culbertson ghosts—Robert Brannon and Victor Smith, former employees of mine—to write the book. It was to be along the lines of Sidney Lenz's "One, Two, Three" which I dubbed *"Ein-Zwei-Drei."* I wondered how a system could be produced within a "week" when Jo and I had worked years.

I struck back with gas bombs of laughter and derision. My answer was printed in the *Herald Tribune*:

BRIDGE EXPERT SUPPORTS CHALLENGE WITH $10,000
Culbertson Offers to Meet Group That Has New Bidding System

Ely Culbertson, Bridge expert, pitted against twelve other masters of the game who have merged to found a uniform system of bidding, announced yesterday that he had placed $10,000 in a bank to cover a challenge made by him to the other group to play 220 rubbers of bridge.

Mr. Culbertson's $10,000 would be pitted against only $1,000 of the group, the losings and winnings to go as a donation to the New York Infirmary, according to the terms.

Quoting Mr. Culbertson: "Furthermore, if Mr. Courtenay, who fancies himself no slouch as an authority on Bridge, will agree to play me one hundred rubbers, I will agree that should he win I will not only give up my system but take a job with his company selling Bridge supplies."

The twelve experts were silent on the challenge. That I had expected, for they could not find a combination of two players on the advisory board who would have a good chance to defeat us in a long match. Mr. Courtenay, apparently confusing the challenge with the ancient code of dueling, answered with a somewhat bewildering release. *The New York Times* printed it:

For several hundred years it has been the custom among sportsmen of all nations to issue a challenge but to offer the opponents the choice of weapons and to let them specify the time and place. When, and if, Mr. Culbertson cares to conform to the elements of good sportsmanship, the advisory council of "Bridge Headquarters" will be most happy to oblige him.

It was a most peculiar statement. My counterattack was printed, among other papers, in the New York *World-Telegram:*

"That's okay!" said Mr. Culbertson. "The challenge, as to time, is good until the cows come home. The place? In their Bridge Headquarters, Inc., if they want it. As to weapons, I'd prefer a score pad and a deck of fifty-two cards—not a pinochle deck. If these conditions are not fair, I'll accept any reasonable suggestion."

As for sportsmanship, Mr. Culbertson blandly left it for the public to decide.

Players all over the country excitedly followed this barrage of releases. Bridge had become front-page news.

I closely studied the public reaction to the announcement of the Official System. Many people were obviously impressed. In public, I kept up my breezy, cheerful attitude; at home, Jo and I passed many anxious nights. We knew the time had come for the biggest fight of our lives. To all appearances we were on top of the world; only Jo and I realized how shaky our position really was. We were still ephemeral little Bridge gods, playthings of public fancy to be pulled down tomorrow and forgotten day after tomorrow. We had made our bid—and it was a forcing bid—but arrayed against us were all the most formidable and most intelligent Bridge authorities, who had been in the field for years. Even Jo's first teacher, Sidney Lenz, was in the enemy camp.

"Their scheme is very cunning," I said to Jo. "They're trying to make me appear in the public mind as a lone wolf, a selfish crackpot."

"Yes," Jo said, "and the 'Official System' is a very clever name. You know how people are. They have no time to go into detailed analyses and determine which is better. They'll listen to their old authorities, especially if they are united."

"But surely, Jo, the real students of the game won't let them pull the wool over their eyes. They'll analyze the methods carefully and they'll know what's what."

"That's true. But there are only a few thousand of them. What can they do against Work, Lenz, and others, with their newspaper syndicates, tremendous radio outlets, lectures, and teachers? They'll swamp us."

"Don't worry, darling. We're no weaklings, either. We have ideas, and they count more than everything else." I tried to console her, but there was no conviction in my voice.

"Ideas are not enough. The best we can hope for is years of struggle with a pack of hungry experts at our heels."

"Not necessarily. I have a little plan."

"What, again?" Jo was usually both pleased

and frightened whenever I pulled out of the hat one of my "little plans."

"You just mentioned a pack of hungry experts at our heels. Well, my plan is simple. We'll make them the fox, and turn ourselves into a pack of hounds."

"And how do you propose to do it?"

"We'll challenge Lenz himself to a pair match! He's their greatest player."

"But, Ely, you know that Lenz is far too clever to accept the challenge with any of the members of the advisory council as partner." Jo was visibly disappointed.

"That's just the point. I'm going to challenge him and let him choose as partner any expert he wishes, in or outside the council. It can be Sims, [Michael T.] Gottlieb, or anyone else. If we can pull down Lenz, we'll pull down the whole bazaar!"

Jo thought a long time. Then she said, "You know what will happen to us if we lose."

"We'll be ruined."

"Completely. The mass of Bridge players will follow the winner."

"That's true, Jo, but I think the risk of our losing is relatively slight. I'll prove it to you."

And I brought out a few sheets of paper covered with calculations. "These," I explained, "are the figures from some hands bid and played by Lenz. Although he's known by millions as the greatest player in the country, that's largely because of his playing, not his bidding. I also have analyzed the advantages of our system over his. All in all, I'm sure we ought to beat Lenz, regardless of how good his partner may be, by at least seven per cent. An average rubber is about a thousand points, so that ought to give us an advantage of about seventy points a rubber."

"But, Ely, suppose we get bad cards?"

"I wouldn't play less than a hundred and fifty rubbers, which would make the chances overwhelmingly against any luck variation of more than four per cent. Even if they get four per cent the best of the cards, that will still leave us with a three per cent, or thirty points a rubber, advantage." *

Jo understood me perfectly. But she also understood that if anything went wrong in my calculations of that tiny "four per cent" or the tinier "three per cent," it would mean a disaster to us. Events proved later that while the agreed stake was only a few thousand dollars, to go to charity, the actual stake was one of the greatest in the history of cards or sports—at least one million dollars. For that was the minimum price of public favor to Lenz or Culbertson.

* As it turned out at the end of our match, we held twenty-six fewer aces and thirty-four more kings than Lenz's side.—E. C.

THE BATTLE OF THE CENTURY

IT WAS now October, and still no word from Lenz. The Official System, as I had feared, was becoming a serious rival. It was not a good system; it contained a hodgepodge of my ideas smothered under a strange sauce prepared by twelve other cooks. But the cooks' names were imposing. I simply had to smoke Lenz out of his reluctance to play a match. He was not afraid to play anyone, anywhere; but he was a wealthy man and just as much interested in magic and Ping-Pong (he was a champion) as in Bridge.

I renewed my challenge. I used all my ingenuity to force him. I kidded him; I brought to bear terrific pressure from his own friends; I made full use of the discredit that his silence brought on the Official System; and I maneuvered through his publisher, Dick Simon. Finally, Lenz had to accept. The match was to take place on December 7, 1931, at the Hotel Chatham. One hundred and fifty rubbers were to be played, which meant about one thousand hands. Jo and I had to play together in at least seventy-five rubbers; for the balance of the match she could have a substitute. We were to play the Culbertson System, and Lenz, with his partner, Oswald Jacoby, his *"Ein-Zwei-Drei"* variant of the Official System. By special permission of the West Point authorities, Lieutenant A.M. Gruenther was to be general referee. Colonel G.G.J. Walshe, Bridge editor of the London *Times,* Deac Aylesworth, and Frank Crowninshield were to be honorary referees. A formal contract was drawn up to provide for all contingencies, and it was signed with more fanfare and publicity trappings than world's champion prize fighters have ever seen.

I now turned my entire attention to the preliminary publicity for the match. I carefully worked out the three basic themes to be played on the mass mind. They were:

1. This is the perennial struggle of a young, loving married couple against the forces of adversity—in this case exemplified by twelve "jealous" authorities who combined against them. (Object: to arouse sympathy.)

2. This is a grudge match between Lenz and Culbertson—a fight between the giants of Bridge. (Object: to arouse dramatic interest.)

3. This is a battle of systems, to decide which is the better system for players to use. (Object: to arouse self-interest.)

I began to play these themes to the nation with hundreds of variations and thousands of repetitions. I played them first of all through my teachers; they were bombarded with special circular letters giving them inside information, stories, advice, suggestions. As a result, the themes spread all over the country in ever-increasing word-of-mouth waves of publicity—first from teachers, then from their pupils, and then from the pupils' friends. I played my theme songs through the radio on national hookups and through local stations with my radio teachers. I played them through inserts in my books; through the *Bridge World* Magazine, special articles in other magazines, circular letters to department stores, inserts in Bridge supplies; through club chairmen, formation of committees of well-known men, and newspaper releases. I organized team-of-four championships among newspapermen and gave them a trophy. I "backed" Bridge editors for local newspapers all over the country. And everywhere the same themes, the same three *leitmotifs;* the young couple . . . grudge fight . . . battle of systems. It rang true because it was true.

As a result, the match was a general topic of conversation at every Bridge and dinner table long before it actually began. An atmosphere of tense expectancy had been created. Three weeks before the date set, I knew the match would be one of the biggest publicity tidal waves in the history of sports.

I went to see Jack Wheeler and arranged to write a special daily story of the match to be put on the wires and cables for newspapers all over the world. At the same time, I had Jo signed up for her story with another syndicate. I also visited Kent Cooper of the Associated Press. In all my publicity preparations, this was the first time I had personally seen anyone officially connected with the dissemination of news. I had never asked a favor of any editor. To do so is both stupid and insulting. As a rule, editors have to print a news story whether or not they like the person involved; and if there is no news story, they would make themselves ridiculous by printing it. I saw Cooper merely to inform him that from my reports I believed the demand for nation-wide coverage would probably exceed his wildest anticipations, and to suggest that he take the necessary steps to be prepared for the landslide. He, of course, already realized that the match would be a good story; and he had sufficient confidence in me to take stock in a prediction which, to anyone else, would have seemed the raving of a Bridge crackpot.

As a result, the AP began to lay heavy cables right into our apartment at the Chatham Hotel, assigned two of their first-rank men to the match, and prepared for a play-by-play coverage. Later, Western Union and Postal Telegraph established branches in our spare room. They had six employees on practically twenty-four-hour duty, so that the story of the match and of every play could be filed through lines of twenty-four cables directly from the apartment to all parts of the world.

When Jo saw what was being done to her home she was horrified. "To think that I would live to see the day when Western Union and Postal Telegraph opened up branches in my own home!"

And I thought of the day I had asked her to marry me, when I had said, "Darling, I'll give you the greatest home a woman ever had!"

The arrangements for the match were very elaborate. From the elevators, one passed through a long corridor, at the end of which was a large drawing room. In the corridor there was a long table where coffee, various concoctions from chafing dishes, and drinks were served. Only invited guests could witness the match, and no one, except newspapermen, was allowed to remain more than fifteen minutes, after which he had to leave the drawing room so that someone else could take his place. Almost from the start of the match there was a continuous line moving into the drawing room and out of it. The room itself was divided into two parts, separated by a very large screen. I saw to it that the cracks in the screen were big enough to let the guests take a good peek at the players, for the visitors were not permitted into the sanctum sanctorum, which was reserved for the players, the scorers, and the referees. There was a row of chairs behind the screen; the visitors filed in, sat down, peeped through the cracks for fifteen minutes if they wished, and filed out. All this in the most complete silence. During the match, thousands came and reluctantly left—leaders in society and the professions, presidents of banks and corporations, generals and bishops, motion-picture stars and champion prize fighters. They all sat or stood behind the screen, their eyes glued to the cracks, trying to catch a glimpse of the players' faces, and the flash of a card being played.

It was the greatest peep-show in history.

The match was played in two sessions daily —afternoon and evening, with selected days set aside for rest. At first, fortune smiled on Lenz and Jacoby. At the end of the twenty-seventh rubber, our opponents' lead reached the imposing figure of 7,030 points.

Jo was seriously worried. The night before she had told me, "Ely, I'm afraid you'll break down under this terrific strain. How can you play the hardest match of your life and at the same time annotate the hands after each play, write your daily article, keep up a stream of interviews with newspaper reporters, talk on the radio, plan publicity stunts, and run the whole show?"

"Don't worry, Jo dearest. I'm at my best like this." But inwardly I made an iron resolution to stop Lenz.

This lead of our opponents was their high-water mark. Cool, relentless defensive play on our part and precise bidding information not only stayed their advance but actually reduced their lead—despite their better cards. When the opportunity came for attack bidding, we wore down their gains until a few days later we led by 2,000 points—and never again lost the lead.

During the Christmas holidays Jo left the game and somehow managed to give a happy Christmas to the children. I played alternately with [Theodore] Lightner and [Waldemar] von Zedtwitz.

After January 1, 1932, our lead jumped to 17,000 points. It was then that Jacoby withdrew. Some newspapers intimated that he had quit under fire, and he issued the following statement:

In the excitement of last night, quite natural to many Bridge matches, I have been unfortunately misquoted, both in regard to my partner, Mr. Lenz, and my opponent, Mr. Culbertson.

I consider Mr. Culbertson one of the few truly great practical and analytical players in the world, and no list of the first five players of the world can reasonably be made up without including his name.

While we all make mistakes, I have learned during this match to respect, even more than before, his subtle and most imaginative game.

As for Mr. Lenz, it would be, to say the least, presumptuous on my part not to hold him in highest regard, both as a gentleman and as the Grand Old Man of Bridge, to whom we all owe so much.

Our differences are of ideas and methods of treating Bridge; not of personal friendship. However, I have now become convinced that these ideas are so radically distinct that it would be unfair to him for me to re-enter the match.

I will always remember with gratitude the high honor that Mr. Lenz has done me by selecting me as his partner, and only regret that I could not have done better.

(signed) OSWALD JACOBY

Commander Winfield Liggett took Jacoby's place, and brought luck to Lenz; for from then on, our lead was reduced.

Edward J. O'Neil, Associated Press sports writer, gave a witty sidelight on the match:

NEW YORK, Dec. 17—(AP)—In the fine, big drawing room of the Ely Culbertsons' they're at it again and the "shush-shushing" rings louder up and down the corridors of the stately Chatham Hotel than the few innocuous sounds that must be stilled for the spectacle.

In this corner, under the blazing lights, sits "Papa" Lenz.

"Papa" holds his hand close to his sharp nose and peers down at the cards through nose glasses that are slipping down. An old Poker player from the looks of him, and beside him on one side, like a saber gleaming, is Ely Culbertson, the slim, eager fellow with the thinning hair who has made "big business" of Contract Bridge as surely as Tex Rickard put prize fighting into the multimillionaire class. Now that Mrs. Culbertson has quit temporarily to make Christmas for her babies, a thin, studious fellow whose nose twitches, "Ted" Lightner by name, plays the accompaniment for the dazzling Culbertson.

The elect among the witnesses—four of them at a time—can peer through cracks in a pair of leather screens and watch the goings-on. And if you think this Contract Bridge thing hasn't gripped the imagination of the sports world, look who's sneaking a peek for himself—Monsieur Jacques Curley of Madison Square Garden, master of the largest herd of wrestlers in captivity.

"Look," whispers Mr. Curley excitedly. "Why I could put this thing in the Garden and get about 25,000 more entries and charge admission and it would be a sensation. Why . . ."

Mr. Curley paused and brushed his ear as though something were bothering him. It was the conversation of the masters at work, filtering through the screen.

"As I was saying," he went on, still brushing his ear, "I could offer cash prizes and invite the Culbertsons and the Lenzes and everyone else. We could put them all inside a big glass enclosure, thousands of them, with big score boards overhead to tell the plays, and charge admission."

Mr. Culbertson's voice comes through the screen again.

"What's the bid," he asks, "three diamonds?"

Mr. Lenz had been watching him scratching on a pad, paying practically no attention to what was going on.

"No . . . No . . . No!" he shouts, "It's two spades! If you'd pay some attention you'd know. Will you please quit writing and pay some attention!"

"What are we playing anyway," asks Mr. Culbertson, benignly, "Contract?"

"Mumblepuppy," snorts Mr. Lenz.

"Whist mumblepuppy," digs Mr. Culbertson.
Mr. Curley beams happily.

Curley came to me and, almost bitterly, reproached me for my lack of real showmanship. "Why didn't you come to see me?"

I laughed. I told Curley that in the show I was running, mere thousands of dollars was chicken feed. I was playing for stakes that transcended mere money, to a gate of at least ten million kibitzers who, in the privacy of their own homes, heard on the radio and watched in the newspapers every move we made.

My ideas of publicity were exactly opposite to those of Curley's. The keynote of my publicity was to reproduce as closely as possible the actual conditions of a home with a Bridge game in it, so that millions of other Bridge players in their own homes could participate in our little dramas, errors, and comedies, which would be so much like their own.

As weeks went by and the match progressed toward its conclusion, the story took more and more space on the front pages of the newspapers throughout the world. A Bridge hand had become news—interesting news—as fresh as today's murder.

Jo was the heroine of the match, and Edwin C. Hill waxed truly elegiac in the New York *Sun*:

> Her intellectual radiance and personal charm are too bright and warm to be dimmed even by that perpetual exhibition of skyrockets and Roman candles to whom she is married. Sitting night after night in the Hotel Chatham, with a trio of emotional and edgy-nerved gentlemen, her calm composure under the strain that has cracked masculine restraint must be pleasant in the sight of the gods.
>
> There in her East seat, eyes veiled by drooping lids—motionless, except for a flicker of white fingers as the cards drop or as a jeweled cigarette holder cuts an arc—she seems detached—immeasurably removed from bickering, and back-biting—gentle, tolerant, forbearing, slightly superior. No visitor to Ely Culbertson's Greatest Show on Earth and Educational Exhibition can fail of that impression.

Robert Neville [of the *Herald Tribune*] well summarized the match:

> The Culbertson score continued to mount until it assumed tremendous proportions. . . . The final six rubbers were played at top speed. The Culbertsons took the 149th rubber. They were then more than 7,000 points ahead.
>
> "Well, I can't lose now, because I'm not going to bid," Mr. Culbertson announced. "I just won't bid."

The match made not only Bridge but journalistic history. Usually a news story lives but one day, and it is a good story if it trails into the next day; it is a big story if it lives a week. Our story lived for six weeks, surviving the break for the Christmas holidays. More words were printed on this match than on the Lindbergh flight or on any murder case except the Hall-Mills trial. Some two million words—the equivalent of twenty-five large books—appeared in the newspapers alone. I no longer counted our publicity by words, but by yards. Before the match began, I had naïvely ordered from a clipping bureau an extra set of clippings for my personal use. Three months later the superintendent of the hotel complained that there was no more storage room left. I went down and took a look. Bushels were piled on bushels of editorials, cartoons, comments, news stories in every conceivable language. Soon after that I received a bill from the clipping bureau. I had forgotten all about it. It was for two thousand, one hundred and fifty dollars! They had had to keep a special staff for the sole purpose of gathering those clippings.

¶Robert Neville was one of the reporters assigned to cover the Culbertson-Lenz match. Because he did it so well he was pressed into service as a reluctant Bridge columnist for the New York Herald Tribune *and it was years before he could escape. He is now a foreign (Istanbul) bureau chief for* Time *and* Life. *¶Mr. Neville's eyewitness report of the match, which follows, was written as the Introduction to a book that the chief referee, Lieutenant (!) Alfred M. Gruenther, was to write. The book was never published. Perhaps General-to-be Gruenther became too busy preparing for his future jobs as Supreme Commander of NATO and president of the American Red Cross. Perhaps the publisher changed his mind. One thing is sure: Gruenther never started anything he didn't finish. ¶And now the floor is Bob Neville's:*

Peeking Through the Screen

by ROBERT NEVILLE

CONTRACT BRIDGE cast off its swaddling clothes on the evening of December 7, 1931, when in a drawing-room on the tenth floor of the Hotel Chatham, New York, Mr. and Mrs. Ely Culbertson, Mr. Sidney S. Lenz and Mr.

Oswald Jacoby sat down to a card table and began a game of 150 rubbers.

The quondam parlor game of Bridge was converted on that night to the status of a national spectacle, comparable to the gridiron, World Series baseball games or a national political convention. The swollen army of Bridge players and Bridge lovers in these United States, which, it was rumored, even outnumbered the country's current unemployed, turned their faces toward the Chatham that evening as if it were their Mecca and waited for the latest tidings of a Culbertson finesse, a Lenz end play, a Jacoby squeeze.

It was an auspicious occasion, albeit hectic and frantic, on that opening night. Fully five hours before the first hand was dealt the Culbertson drawing-room was a seething mass of cameras, radio microphones, Kleig lights, sound newsreel apparatus, photographers, reporters and that ever-present and irreducible number of kibitzers. The players were photographed in groups and individually. Mr. Culbertson and Mr. Lenz were asked first to smile at each other and then to scowl, first to wish each other the best of luck and then publicly to hope that the other would hold nothing but Yarboroughs during the match.

After three hours of such preliminaries, players, referees and distinguished guests sat down to a sumptuous eight-course dinner, which was interrupted by the necessity of making speeches over the radio. Mr. Culbertson recited a little doggerel about "All the Lenz Aces and all the Lenz Kings," and Mr. Lenz, the vegetarian, took another swallow of spinach. The Culbertson babies, "Fifi" Joyce and "Jump-bid" Bruce, were then put to bed after emerging unexpectedly from the sanctum of their nursery in blue satin nighties, a screen was put up around the handsome playing table, the room was cleared of all extraneous persons, and Lieutenant Alfred M. Gruenther, the referee from West Point, announced that Hand No. 1 Rubber No. 1, of the historic tilt between the Lenz "Official" One-Two-Three System and the Culbertson (Approach-Forcing) System of bidding was about to be dealt.

But the Lieutenant was more or less optimistic. There were still preliminaries, the least important of which was a little pre-match game that augured bad for Mr. and Mrs. Culbertson. Mr. Frank Crowninshield, Mr. Bruce Barton and Mr. Lenz sat down at the table for a hand of cutthroat. The bidding over, it was Mr. Lenz's play. He put down what at first seemed like the ten of spades, but it changed right in front of the players to the ace. Mr. Barton jumped up from the table, threw down a $10 bill and said, "I'm through!" The magic of Mr. Sidney Lenz, who used to hobnob with the late Harry Houdini, had worked. The odds jumped up in favor of the Lenz-Jacoby combination.

It was a strange card game, unlike any that had yet been held. While the playing end of the Culbertson drawing-room was more or less sacrosanct for players, referees and the ever-silent secretary, Mrs. Aileen McCabe (who, it was rumored, worked so fast that she took down not only the bidding and the plays, but also every word spoken), there were endless queues of Bridge players, Bridge teachers and other curious persons each evening who wanted to get into the other end of the room for a peek through the screen at the famed foursome.

Down the hall were the press rooms and telegraph rooms, resembling nothing so much in this reporter's memory as a World Series set-up. The Culbertson-Lenz match, indeed, was a sporting event of major importance from the angle of the newspapers. The Associated Press and the United Press had two men there to cover the event, one to write that dear old "crowd" story and another to write the Bridge. Two New York morning newspapers had two reporters covering the affair from the beginning. The *Evening Standard,* the *Morning Chronicle* and the *London Times* had special stories sent from the Chatham wire rooms. The *Chicago Evening News* even sent a man. The best feature writers of the *Chicago Tribune* and the *Baltimore Sun* came up one evening for a glance and subsequent feature stories appeared. Heywood Broun, the Scripps-Howard columnist, wrote a little piece about the match before he ever saw it, and then came up one evening and was promptly made Mr. Lenz's referee. Another piece subsequently appeared. Two of the reporters covering the affair had never played a game of Bridge before. Before the match had finished its course at the Waldorf-Astoria they had developed their own systems, the most exotic feature of which was to bid on three-card suits headed by the ace and jack.

But there was much for the reporter unskilled in the devious methods of bidding and the more intricate plays to do during the match. It was soon discovered that this was no technical event for the person who wanted to avoid technicalities. For many the "crowd" story became the real story. There were juicy little tales about "Ossie" ordering venison steaks a minute before the playing was to begin; about Mr. Culbertson insisting upon eating a rare broiled steak while figuring out a difficult hand; about Mr. Lenz virtually falling asleep while Mr. Culbertson was deciding on the wrong way to finesse; about Mr. Jacoby devouring a basket of strawberries while a hand was being dealt; about Mr. Culbertson's objections to the squashing of Russian boots on the other side of the screen; about the inconsequential, though heated, argument between the 250-pound Sir Derrick Wernher and the slight 140-pound Ely Culbertson, and, above all, about the sign over one of the doors in the Culbertson corridor which reminded the visitors that inside children were sleeping—"and dreaming."

There was a little note each night about the chronic and admitted lateness of Mr. Culbertson. He arrived at the match before the starting hour only one evening, and he said his watch was bad then. Mr. Lenz chronically objected to the persistent photographers. Mr. Culbertson insisted on beginning an evening's play with the question, "Have you changed your system?" Whenever one of his partners played a hand, Mr. Culbertson would assume the dummy's right to leave the room, and when the cards had all been played Mr. Lenz would cry out to the attendant, Lieutenant Gruenther or whoever happened to be present, "Page Ely!" On the closing night he said he had been saying those two words in his sleep.

There were distinguished visitors galore. Those who sat in the seats of the mighty in the Bridge world came night after night. Mr. Charles M. Schwab, Judges John J. Freschi and Joseph E. Corrigan, Mr. Henry W. Taft, the Grand Duchess Marie of Russia, Mr. Frank Morgan, Mr. Chico Marx, Mr. and Mrs. Marshall Field, 3rd, Mrs. Vincent Astor, Mr. Franklin P. Adams—these were only a few of those who dropped in from time to time to see this "slice of life" from the American scene.

Professor Albert Shaw, of whistling and New York University fame, deemed it an expedient time to unburden himself of many of his ideas of Bridge and Bridge players. Mr. F. Dudley Courtenay, of Bridge Headquarters, Inc., kept the air lively with a couple of statements, as many withdrawals and then withdrawals of the withdrawals. The *World-Telegram* saw fit to print five hands of a Poker match. The newspapers were crammed with news about a marathon dice game in Iowa to decide which was better—"the cotton roll" or the "straightaway." There was a 100-game checker match projected in another part of the Hinterland.

The newspapers gloried in some of the plays. They headlined the news that Mr. Lenz had once forgotten trumps. They featured the fact that Mrs. Culbertson led out of turn and allowed Mr. Jacoby to cash in on a small slam. A notrump bid that the Culbertsons failed to set was heralded throughout the land. And the morning after these admitted "boners" the players received challenge after challenge—from San Diego to Bangor, from Miami to Seattle. The worst dub in the world could defeat such play, it was intimated. There were so many challenges that Mr. Culbertson was finally moved to declare publicly that the next person who challenged him would have to eat his *Contract Bridge Blue Book,* cover, glue and all.

The match moved to the Waldorf-Astoria on December 23rd, the day before Christmas Eve, without a hitch. More than seventy-five rubbers had been played by that time. Mr. Culbertson sent his opponents in the match *Blue Books* for Christmas. There had been much discussion about this mysterious publication, and Mr. Culbertson freely charged that neither Mr. Lenz nor Mr. Jacoby had read it. The author autographed the presents with the flourish, "To the grand old man of Bridge," for Mr. Lenz; "To the rising young star of Bridge," for Mr. Jacoby.

Mr. Culbertson wished Mr. Lenz and Mr. Jacoby better luck in their new surroundings, but his wish was in vain. The change in scenery did Mr. Lenz little good. The Culbertson score continued to mount until it assumed tremendous proportions. There was a matinee session on the Saturday after Christmas. Mr. Culbertson came bouncing in with a teddy bear he had received from his daughter, and the bear became the latest and the only completely silent kibitzer. During the course of the afternoon Mr. Culbertson, like a good Englishman, ordered his tea. "Ossie" followed suit. Mr. Lenz ordered water. Mr. Culbertson's live "Teddy Bear," Theodore A. Lightner, said and ordered nothing.

As the match progressed the visitors became more numerous. Friends of friends of the players came to the Waldorf in hordes. A Boston business man said he had come all the way from the Bay State simply to look at Mr. Lenz and Mr. Culbertson. A middle-aged couple from Kentucky pleaded for admittance on the ground that they came from the sticks and wanted to tell their neighbors all about the sights of New York. Mr. Lewis Copeland admitted them solely because they had told the truth. Clara Bow

Drawing *by* JEFFERSON MACHAMER

called up the press room one night to ask about the results. Jack Curley, the wrestling impresario, came up to look over the possibilities of a gate in Bridge. He was impressed by the potentialities in Bridge, but virtually wept to see the number of dollars that were going to waste because no admission was being charged. Countless persons expressed surprise to find that there was no balcony from which the game could be watched.

Then there was the night when Mr. Jacoby folded up his tent and stole away. His psychics had proved too much for Mr. Lenz. The smiling Commander Winfield Liggett, Jr., took his place. Mr. Culbertson adopted two new partners for one-night stands—Mr. Michael T. Gottlieb and Mr. Howard Schenken. Mr. Gottlieb and Mr. Schenken sat in on particularly tragic evenings for them. The former held mediocre hands when he played; the latter busts. Mr. Gottlieb was witness to the fact that he and Mr. Culbertson sustained a loss of more than 2,000 points; Mr. Schenken more than 5,000. "We did not play tonight—we were kibitzers," Mr. Culbertson said that evening.

On the day preceding the last session Mr. Culbertson busied himself with writing a poem, "Sid Hamlet on Contract," in the manner of the immortal Shakespeare. It was a parody of the famous soliloquy, "To be or not to be," and began: "To bid or not to bid, that is the question."

The final six rubbers were played at top speed. Mr. Lenz and Commander Liggett seemed unwilling to prolong the match unduly. They were tired and wanted to get it over with. The Culbertsons (Mrs. Culbertson had returned for the last night) took the 149th rubber. They were then more than 7,000 points ahead.

"Well, I can't lose now, because I'm not going to bid," Mr. Culbertson announced. "I just won't bid."

Mr. Culbertson passed the first hand. It held three aces, but was not a game hand.

"It'll give the kibitzers something to talk about if you pass an opening two-bid," Lieutenant Gruenther said.

But the indomitable Mr. Culbertson held such good hands that he was forced to bid. He and Mrs. Culbertson walked right through the last rubber and Mr. Lenz and Commander Liggett did not object. The match was officially over, but not actually. There were congratulations galore and there were news reels to satisfy and radio speeches to give. The referees met and officially awarded Mr. Lenz's $1,000 check to the "eternal unemployed," the New York Infirmary for Women and Children.

The next evening Mr. Culbertson gave a dinner to the press. Heywood Broun made a brief speech about Utopia. He was a radical, he said, and he believed in a Utopia; but why, he asked, couldn't we have Contract Bridge in Utopia and why not the Approach-Forcing System? After the dinner, for a change, Bridge was played. Mr. Culbertson played incognito. His partner revoked on him on one hand. At another time one of his opponents made an unconventional lead which cost him game. He was impressed. Mr. Lenz went back to his golf, his Ping-Pong, his magic, his Camelot and his chess with José R. Capablanca. Mr. and Mrs. Culbertson left for Havana.

THE GA-GA AGE OF CONTRACT

When Contract Bridge was young and all the rage, from about 1929 to 1932, publicity-seekers and newspaper editors alike found it irresistible. You couldn't pick up your daily paper without reading bits like this:

TRUMPED WIFE'S ACE: HE'S SINGLE NOW

SEATTLE—Because he trumped his wife's ace in a Bridge game, William Ellis was a single man today.

"In spite of the presence of two of our friends who were playing against us," Ellis told the Court yesterday, "my wife completely lost her temper when I spoiled her play. She threw an alarm clock at me and knocked out one of my teeth. Then she packed my clothes and ordered me out of the house."

Judge Robert M. Jones granted him a divorce.

CUT GLASS HAS ITS USES

CHICAGO—Mrs. Lila Gray Colyer, who held 13 Diamonds at Bridge and won the contract at six no-trump, after a spade bid by an opponent, is suing for divorce. When she was set 12 tricks her husband, so the complaint avers, hit her with a cut-glass bowl, the nearest missile.

¶ *A man in North Carolina, on a losing streak, swore he would shoot the next man who dealt him a bad hand; on his own next deal he dealt himself a Yarborough and dutifully killed himself. A king of Afghanistan was deposed for his Bridge-playing habits: pictured playing cards are repugnant to the Islamic religion. But unquestionably the high spot was "The Bennett Murder Case" (so called; legally it was homicide, not murder, for Mrs. Bennett was acquitted). It happened in the autumn of 1929 and the following are contemporary reports, the first two from the New York Journal, the last from the Bell Syndicate.*

The Hands Behind the Fatal Family Bridge Game

TRAGEDIES, comedies, and the broadest farce have stalked in the wake of many a Bridge game ever since the vogue became far-flung. It is doubtful if any of these cases have equaled the Bennett disaster in intensity and intricacy.

The details of Bennett's death must necessarily depend largely on that version of the shooting given by the Hoffmans; for Mrs. Bennett, held on a charge of first-degree murder, has been too hysterical to give completely her side of the affray.

The couple lived in a fashionable Park Manor apartment at Kansas City. They were decidedly "well off." Bennett, who had been married to Myrtle Bennett for eleven years, had, by ambitious application of his talents, become a highly paid perfume agent. His yearly salary and commissions came to $35,000, and sometimes reached $40,000.

The Sunday Bennett was slain dawned peacefully for both principals in the oncoming tragedy. Bennett and Hoffman, who lives in the same block, played eighteen holes of golf at the exclusive Indian Hills Country Club. They then went back to the Bennetts' apartment, their appetites whetted, to enjoy an "ice-box lunch." For the afternoon, a foursome was proposed, with Mrs. Hoffman and Mrs. Bennett participating.

"As the game went on," Mrs. Hoffman said, "the Bennetts' criticisms of each other grew more and more caustic. Finally a spade hand was bought by them in the following manner: Bennett bid a spade. My husband overcalled with two diamonds. Mrs. Bennett promptly boosted the original spade bid to four. I passed. Mrs. Bennett, as dummy, laid down a rather good hand. But her husband went set.

"This seemed to infuriate his wife and she began goading him with remarks about 'bum Bridge players.' He came right back at her. I don't remember the exact words. This kept up for several minutes. We tried to stop the argument by demanding cards, but by this time the row had become so pronounced that Bennett, reaching across the table, grabbed Myrtle's arm and slapped her several times.

"We tried to intervene, but it was futile. While Mrs. Bennett repeated over and over, in a strained singsong tone, 'Nobody but a bum would hit a woman,' her husband jumped up and shouted, 'I'm going to spend the night at a hotel. And tomorrow I'm leaving town.' His wife said to us, 'I think you folks had better go.' Of course, we started to do so."

While the Hoffmans were putting on their things Mrs. Bennett dashed into the bedroom of her mother, Mrs. Alice B. Adkins, and snatched the family automatic from a dresser drawer. "John's going to St. Joseph," she explained to the older woman, "and he wants to be armed."

Bennett had gone to his "den," near the bathroom, to pack for the intended trip. Hoffman, adjusting his muffler, turned back and saw his friend alone for the moment. While Mrs. Hoffman waited in the doorway, her husband advanced toward Bennett, hoping to say a word or two that would dispel his angry depression.

The two men were in conversation as Mrs. Bennett darted in, pistol in hand. Bennett saw her, ran to the bathroom, slammed the door just as two bullets pierced the wooden paneling. Hoffman, rigid with astonishment, remained in the den. His wife, hearing the shots, ran down the hall and began pounding on the door of the next apartment.

It is thought Bennett died from two bullets fired as he neared the door leading to the street. He staggered to a chair—the Hoffmans agree—moaning, "She got me." Then he slumped, unconscious, to the floor.

Mrs. Bennett was standing at the other side of the living room, the gun dangling loosely from her fingers. As Bennett fell, her daze broke. She ran toward him. Police found her bent over him, giving vent to wild sobs.

Post Mortem

by SIDNEY S. LENZ

THIS innocuous-looking deal at the Bridge table resulted in the killing of John G. Bennett by his wife. The distribution of the cards and the quicktrick strength is quite conventional, although the play lends itself to various very interesting situations.

Bennett dealt and bid one spade. Hoffman overcalled with two diamonds. Bennett's partner, his wife, jumped his declaration to four

The Fatal Hand

NORTH
Mr. Bennett
♠ K J 9 8 5
♡ K 7 6 2
◇ 8 5
♣ K 10

WEST
Mrs. Hoffman
♠ 4
♡ Q 9 4
◇ K J 7 6 3
♣ Q 7 5 3

EAST
Mr. Hoffman
♠ Q 7 2
♡ A J 3
◇ A Q 10 9 2
♣ J 6

SOUTH
Mrs. Bennett
♠ A 10 6 3
♡ 10 8 5
◇ 4
♣ A 9 8 4 2

spades, and all hands passed. In the play of the cards the contract was set one trick.

Dissecting the bidding and play academically, I would say that the original spade bid was unsound.

Bennett's proper procedure would have been to pass, making a secondary bid if the other players made any declaration. After the spade bid Hoffman was justified in bidding two diamonds. As a matter of fact, Hoffman had a sound opening bid of a diamond. Now we come to a dramatic situation: the jump to four spades by Mrs. Bennett.

On actual values, Mrs. Bennett held close to three raises for an original spade bid, as evidenced by the result. With every card badly located in the opposing hands and an improper initial bid, it required perfect defense to defeat the bid by only one trick. Actually the contract might have been made if the declarant had been a lucky guesser. After the bid of four spades, the one point open to discussion is whether it would have been good strategy for Hoffman to have doubled.

Many players would have done so, but it would have been very bad play. The guarded spade honor would have been located in Hoffman's hand and in all likelihood the contract would have been made.

In the play of the cards Hoffman had the choice of two opening leads. Either the ace of diamonds or the jack of clubs would have been correct play. Hoffman chose the former, and when the singleton diamond appeared in dummy, the jack of clubs was the logical switch. Bennett won with the king and led the jack of spades. Hoffman did *not* "cover an honor with an honor."

Hoffman, nevertheless, was playing properly. It is erroneous to cover unless such play stands a chance to set up a good card for self or partner. Hoffman could not set up a spade trick for himself, and he knew his partner held but one spade—if any. With the high cards in dummy and Hoffman's hand, the original bidder must have had at least five spades to the king. Of course, the declarant could not afford to finesse with nine cards of the suit. The chance of the queen falling in two leads appeared favorable, with only four cards missing. If the finesse was to be taken, the percentage favored taking it against Mrs. Hoffman. First, because Hoffman had bid and shown length in the diamond suit. If Mrs. Hoffman could obtain the lead and come through the king of hearts it would have been ruinous. Therefore, the ace of spades went up, and on the return Mrs. Hoffman did not follow suit, so even if the finesse had been in the mind of the player it was now known to be impossible.

The king of spades won; the last diamond was trumped in dummy, and the ace of clubs taken in. Then the nine of clubs was led, covered by the queen and trumped by Bennett. Hoffman overtrumped and led the ace and a low heart, defeating the contract for one trick, since the declarant was unable to get in dummy to discard on the two good clubs and lost another heart trick.

There unquestionably was a good chance to win the contract if Bennett had played just a bit better. The two trump leads were simply guesses, but at the fifth trick it was bad play to trump the diamond. The clubs should have been established first; then the fourth trump in dummy would have been a re-entry card for the good clubs and the adversaries would have been held to one trick each in spades, hearts, and diamonds. That is, if Hoffman had played as he did and cashed in the ace of hearts.

If Hoffman had refused to lay down the ace of hearts until Bennett played the king, two tricks in hearts must be lost by the declarant.

How Bennett Could Have Saved His Life

by ELY CULBERTSON

FIRST, in the bidding, his hand did not justify an opening bid. Scientific tests and the concrete experience of millions of Bridge players have proved that a hand must contain 2½ honor-tricks for a sound opening bid. The hand Mr. Bennett dealt himself had barely 2 honor-tricks, and, while it is infrequent that the penalty for unsound bidding is as severe as this, all Bridge players have learned by sad experience that behind this rule there is both logic and safety. Mrs. Bennett was perhaps a trifle optimistic in raising her husband's bid of one spade to four. The decision is close. The conservative or pessimistic player would bid three spades and leave the final determination of attempting game to the question of whether or not the opening hand had any values whatever over a minimum bid. The hand contains 5½ playing tricks. In other words it has two full raises and one optional raise. Mrs. Bennett chose to give the optional raise at once.

We have heard of lives depending on the play of a card. It is not often that we find that figure of speech literally true. Here is a case in point. Mr. Bennett had overbid his hand. Of that there can be no doubt, but even with this, so kind were the gods of distribution that he might have saved his life had he played his cards a little better. Mr. Hoffman opened the diamond ace, then shifted to the club suit when he saw the dummy void of diamonds, and led the club jack. This Mr. Bennett won with his king and started to pull the adverse trumps. Here again he flirted with death, as people so frequently do when they fail to have a plan either in the game of Bridge or the game of life. He still could make his contract and save his life. The proper play before drawing the trumps would have been to establish the club suit, after ruffing the last diamond in the closed hand, upon which to discard losers in his own hand. Suppose Mr. Bennett, when he took the club trick with his king, had led his last diamond and trumped it with one of dummy's small trumps. He could then lead a trump and go up with the king . . . Now he would lead the club ten, and, when East followed suit, his troubles would be over. He would play the ace of clubs and lead the nine or eight. If West put up the queen, Mr. Bennett should trump and let East overtrump if he pleased. If East, after winning this trick, led a heart, the contract and a life would be saved. If he led a diamond the same would be true. A lead of the trump might still have permitted the fatal denouement but at least Mr. Bennett would have had the satisfaction of knowing that he had played the cards dealt him by fate to the very best of his ability.

¶*The following is more than a classic and historic example of spot-news Bridge reporting. It would be a classic whatever its subject. Bridge matches are seldom inherently dramatic, except to the players involved, and this report concerns only a quarter-final match in one of numerous national tournaments played every year. Indeed, the same scene has occurred at dozens of tournaments, often in matches with much more at stake. So the dramatic effect came rather from the reporter's artistry than from the news he had to report.* ¶*The writer, Walter Lister, was then on The New York Post, where this story appeared; some years later he became managing editor of the Philadelphia* Bulletin. ¶*To reassure the curious: The winning team in this story did go on through the semifinals and finals to win the tournament.*

Sims Team Saved by von Zedtwitz

RITZ CROWD GOES WILD AS BARON NOSES OUT MRS. CULBERTSON WITH 190 POINTS. LAST HAND TELLS STORY

by WALTER LISTER

NEW YORK, N. Y., Oct. 29, 1932.—The most dramatic match in the history of Contract Bridge ended at two o'clock this morning when the all-star team of Messrs. P. Hal Sims, Willard S. Karn, Waldemar von Zedtwitz and Harold S. Vanderbilt defeated a team captained by Mrs. Ely Culbertson by a whisker margin of 190 points for the right to enter the semifinals today.

The last hand told the story.

Mrs. Culbertson and her partner, William J. Huske, had finished play against Mr. Sims and Mr. Karn shortly after one o'clock. Mr. von Zedtwitz and Mr. Vanderbilt, the two slowest players in the world, were still plodding along against the other two members of Mrs. Culbertson's team, Messrs. Samuel Fry, Jr., and Louis H. Watson.

The ballroom of the Ritz-Carlton was clustered with groups of players, kibitzers and friends. Mrs. Culbertson, coming from her table, was greeted by her husband.

"How are you doing?" he demanded.

SET SIMS TEAM 1400

MRS. CULBERTSON, the only woman left in the tournament, smiled wearily.

"We set Hal Sims 1400 points, but I still think that we lost," she said.

The Vanderbilt table still had ten boards to play. Mrs. Culbertson sank into a soft chair in a corner of the ballroom, prepared to admit defeat. Three boards were played.

The word came from the referee, Lieutenant Alfred M. Gruenther:

"It's very close."

Hal Sims, a shaggy giant, strode restlessly about the ballroom. Mrs. Sims, a great player in her own right, sat huddled at one side of the ballroom, wide-eyed, eager for wisps of information. Mrs. Culbertson bemoaned that she had been set on a bid of six spades—a very tough hand—which she might have made by a somewhat crazy guess. Mr. Culbertson agreed with her that it was too bad, tried to play the hand and confessed that he also might have figured it wrong.

"ONE BOARD TO GO"

SUDDENLY from the Vanderbilt-von Zedtwitz table came the bulletin:

"One board to go—Mrs. Culbertson leading by 310 points."

There was a scramble for the previous result on the board. Mrs. Culbertson and Mr. Huske had played it at four spades and had been set two tricks, not vulnerable.

Mrs. Culbertson sat up. Mr. Culbertson was galvanized into striding about the room. Mr. Sims and Mr. Karn prepared to concede defeat.

Another bulletin from the Vanderbilt-von Zedtwitz table:

"Von Zedtwitz has the contract at five diamonds."

Five diamonds to make, on hands which had been set two at four spades!

Hal Sims, marching restlessly up and down, paused in front of his wife.

"It's all over," he said. "It can't be made. They have to lose a heart, a spade, and—wait a minute—"

He strode around several groups, brows knitted, and came back, eyes gleaming.

"HAS A PLAY FOR IT"

"HE HAS a play for it," said Mr. Sims. "He has a play for five diamonds. I just thought of it."

Far to the other side of the room Mr. Waldemar von Zedtwitz, former Baron of the Holy Roman Empire, who renounced his title to gain American citizenship, played with interminable deliberation.

Mr. Culbertson and Mr. Sims got a deck of cards. They laid out the hand on a table, according to Mr. Sims' directions. Mr. Sims remembered Dummy as having one too many trumps. All the players and kibitzers and reporters gathered around this table while Mr. Sims and Mr. Culbertson fought vicariously the battle being waged at the other table.

If the Sims team lost, it would be the first time in Vanderbilt Cup history that it had failed to reach the finals. It would also put a period to the ambition of Mr. Vanderbilt, donor of the trophy, to have his name engraved upon the trophy.

CROWD GOES WILD

FROM THE FAR SIDE of the room there came a sudden end to lethargic play. There was the slap-slap-slap of cards upon the table as Mr. von Zedtwitz, aristocratic, frail, combative, made up his mind and slammed the cards home.

There was a shout from Lieutenant Gruenther, sole privileged kibitzer:

"The Baron makes five diamonds."

The ballroom crowd went wild.

"Waldy came through again," shouted some one, remembering that in 1930 Mr. von Zedtwitz, then a member of the Culbertson team, had snatched victory out of apparent disaster by making five hearts when he had been doubled at three.

The players leaped up from their table. The cards were left strewn in such a mess that Lieutenant Gruenther had to recall the contestants to straighten them out for proper recording and analysis.

Mrs. Culbertson pushed through the throng surrounding Mr. von Zedtwitz, who for years had been her partner on the Culbertson team.

"As long as it was you, Waldy—congratulations," she said.

Newspaper men fought to copy down the cards of the final, decisive hand. They had no sooner finished than some sixteen experts gathered around the table to play the hand double dummy.

"The hand can't be beaten at five diamonds," came the chorus. "It's a laydown."

The hand was:

South—Dealer
Neither side vulnerable

NORTH
Mr. Fry
♠ Q 9 3
♡ A K Q 2
◇ 10 9 6
♣ Q 9 2

WEST
Mr. von Zedtwitz
♠ 6 5 2
♡ J 7 6 3
◇ A Q 6 5 2
♣ J

EAST
Mr. Vanderbilt
♠ K J 8 7
♡ 9
◇ K 8 3
♣ A K 6 5 4

SOUTH
Mr. Watson
♠ A 10 4
♡ 10 8 5 4
◇ 7 4
♣ 10 8 7 3

The bidding:

South	West	North	East
Pass	Pass	1 ♡	Double
2 ♡	3 ◇	Pass	

Up to this point the bidding was the same at both tables. When Mr. Huske sat East, however, he had made a shaded three spade bid, which Mrs. Culbertson had carried to four. Mr. Vanderbilt, studying the situation at length, decided to raise the diamonds to four rather than to show the spades. He was actuated by two things. First, he reasoned that South's raise in hearts guaranteed strength in spades, since a double of a major suit now usually shows support for the other major. Second, he disliked having to ruff hearts with his four-card spade suit. Mr. von Zedtwitz—"shooting," perhaps—carried the diamond bid to five.

Mr. Fry led the king of hearts, and after dummy's singleton heart was spread, shifted to the nine of spades. Dummy played the jack. Mr. Watson won with the ace and returned a heart.

The heart return is unexceptionable. It happened to give Mr. von Zedtwitz a chance to make his contract. A diamond return—or a diamond lead to the second trick by Mr. Fry—would have beaten the contract. It is, perhaps, enough to say that the sixteen experts, viewing the hand, declared that the contract was a laydown.

Mr. von Zedtwitz, ruffing the heart return in dummy, led the ace of clubs and then a small club, which he ruffed. He then led a heart to dummy, ruffed it and returned another club, which was ruffed. He then laid down three rounds of trumps, gambling on a 3-2 break, led a spade to dummy's king, and discarded his losing heart and spade on dummy's two good clubs. It was by no means a defeat for Mr. Watson and Mr. Fry, but it was a magnificent triumph for Mr. von Zedtwitz.

THE PEOPLE WHO PLAY BRIDGE

¶*George S. Kaufman is celebrated as the best Bridge player in the world of the theater and the wittiest man in the world of Bridge. In this book his life and works will inevitably appear here and there*—passim, *as the scholars say.*

On Certain Fine Points of the Game

by GEORGE S. KAUFMAN

IN THE course of a misspent life I have naturally devoted considerable time to Bridge. In my day I played all of the various forms of the game that have led gradually to modern Contract—Auction Bridge, Bridge Whist, straight Whist, postoffice, and, years before that, the old game of shinny, which was played with sticks out in the street and which really bears very little resemblance to Contract Bridge as we know it today. Perhaps I shouldn't even have mentioned it.

During these years, of course, I have read many articles on the fine points of the game, written by the world's Bridge masters. But in this article, if I may be so bold, I would like to touch on a few superfine points—points which even the experts have heretofore overlooked. I don't know how the experts came to overlook these points—unless maybe they've been so busy writing articles that they haven't had a chance to play Bridge. At all events, here they are:

The Kibitzer's Double. This is used very rarely—in fact, it can be used only once in his life by any given kibitzer, because generally he gets killed right after using it. The advantages of the Kibitzer's Double must be at once apparent to the expert. The kibitzer, who occupies a chair between North and East, let us say, is frequently in a position to double with absolute assurance that the contract will be defeated. It must always be read as a penalty double, there being only one case on record where a kibitzer doubled for a takeout—and got out. One point should be noted here in connection with the scoring. Only half of the additional points are credited to the winning side, the other half going to help bury the kibitzer.

The Forced Lead. This is an extremely fine play, for experts only. Frequently, at some point in the play of the hand, a player will know that the lead of a certain suit by his partner is necessary to defeat the contract. The procedure is as follows: After some deliberation the player suddenly remembers that he must put in an important telephone call, and excuses himself. He then calls up a trusted friend and tells him to call the club immediately and get Mr. John Jones, his partner, on the telephone and instruct him to lead the desired suit. This is a positive signal and cannot possibly be misread unless the wires get crossed.

Head-Shaking Device. Frequently, a player who does not like his partner's lead will indicate his distaste for it by shaking his head. This is, of course, a definite indication, but often uses so much of a player's energy that he cannot concentrate on the further play of the hand. The Little Gem Head Shaker, which clamps onto the back of the chair, automatically shakes the player's head for him and frees his mind for future plays. Can be bought at any sports store. Experts, please ask for larger size.

Choice of Seats. This is a matter that is generally given entirely too little attention. How can one tell which is the lucky seat? I once knew an expert who, following the usual custom, simply selected the seat that had won the previous rubber. The seat itself was all right, but the expert neglected to look at the ceiling. If he had done so he would have noticed a piece of loose plaster, which subsequently dropped on him just as he was playing four spades doubled. As he fell unconscious on the floor, his cards dropped face up on the table, which meant that he could not take any finesses. Not only was he killed by the plaster, but he thereby lost the hand by one trick.

What to Do While Jacoby Is Away from the Table. It is estimated by experts that Oswald Jacoby is away from the table 73.6 per cent of the playing time of any given rubber. Even the experts have been accustomed to wasting this time—as a rule they simply sit at the table and say, "Where is that b——?" The time, however, can be used in playing other games, reading the papers, going to the theater, making trips out of town, etc. In one case, during one of Mr. Jacoby's most extended absences, one of the women at the table had a baby. Under the rules, of course, the cards had to be dealt over again.

A Reply to Mr. George S. Kaufman

by OSWALD JACOBY

[*Bridge World*] EDITOR'S NOTE: Mr. Jacoby, who has played a great deal of Bridge with Mr. Kaufman, wrote this article in an effort to show that he can write almost as well as Mr. Kaufman can play Bridge.

IN THE last issue of *The Bridge World* was published an article, "On Certain Fine Points of the Game," by a man named Kaufman, who, I understand, is a new contributor to that magazine.

I must take considerable exception to this article, particularly as my name appears in it. I have no acquaintance with Mr. Kaufman unless one would count having played Bridge with him, and even though I have played Bridge with him it has never been more than seven times in one week.

Mr. Kaufman recommends the head-shaker device, but this contraption is obviously inferior to the long-distance kicker, with which instrument a player may kick his partner any time that he desires without letting the opponents see that he is doing so. The kicker not only serves the same purpose as the head-shaker but inflicts much-deserved punishment on partner at the same time.

Mr. Kaufman shows a woeful lack of knowledge of the rules of the game. Under the choice of seats he refers to the case when a piece of plaster fell on declarer's head, not only killing the unfortunate declarer but also causing him to be set one trick doubled. It seems impossible that Mr. Kaufman is unfamiliar with the rule about Gabriel's Trump, which clearly states that upon the death of any player during the course of a rubber from any cause other than being shot by partner the entire rubber shall be null and void.

Finally, Mr. Kaufman concludes his article with a paragraph on what to do when Jacoby is away from the table. If only he had written on what to do when Jacoby is *at* the table!

¶*P. Hal Sims was a worthy great of Contract Bridge but it is the works of his wife, Dorothy, that will endure — if only because, in a moment of rebellion against all rules and conventions, she made the first psychic bid on record. Mrs. Sims has numerous odd habits. She wears a mink coat in the middle of July. She travels around the world at least once a year. She dictates her writings to a machine and then transcribes them herself. And she writes what she thinks about almost any subject. We quote here from* Psychic Bidding, *published in 1932.*

from Psychic Bidding
by DOROTHY RICE SIMS

PSYCHICS AND "SUDO-SYCICS"

Psychics are to Bridge what futurism is to art —a camouflage for lack of knowledge.

Some years ago, at the Independent Exhibition in Paris, a group of artists tied a paint brush to a mule's tail, backed him up to a canvas, and "A Winter Sunset" was conceived. Nature took its course, and this painting was pronounced the masterpiece of the year. Similarly, the psychic in unskilled hands is as aimless as the brush at the end of the tail. A stab in the dark—the wheel of chance spins round and the player anxiously watches the little ball to discover whether he is a genius or a fool.

It is essential that there be a positive reason for every strategic bid. Aces and kings have their definite valuations, but when they have deserted us, situations may be sometimes molded to create pseudo-values to head off the imminent attack.

In this book I hope to give some idea of the motives and aims which should actuate the strategical bids which, under the name of "psychics," are being extensively misused by many players, who have observed the effects of these bids without investigating their logical basis. Psychics are the fourth dimension of Bridge—making aces out of spaces.

The origin of the psychic was probably the old camouflage double or shift bid. At Auction Bridge this was about the only trap employed with the exception of calling for a lead over a notrump with a singleton ace and then running off your own suit after the declarer rebid notrump.

The first psychic I ever bid was at the Knickerbocker Whist Club about ten years ago. I was playing Auction Duplicate. I, as dealer, picked up five spades with the ace, king, and five hearts with the ace, king. Not knowing which to bid, as in Auction Duplicate the combined honors are a very important factor, I bid a club. My partner bid a heart, which gave us top on the board. She had five hearts to the queen, jack, and four spades to the queen. Had I bid a spade, she would have passed. After this, I saw possibilities of carrying on strategic research along these lines.

I have had amazing results at times with psychic doubles—overcalling with voids and singletons—but as these are only gambling bids and often as disastrous as profitable, I shall not discuss them much nor advocate them in this book.

The origin of the name "psychic" is humorous. I was writing an article for the old Auction Bridge Magazine. My spelling is notoriously bad. I was trying to spell "psychological" but stuck. "Sycic" was as far as I could go. Good psychological bids have since been called "psychics" and bad ones "sycics."

* * *

The psychic is a mental cocaine that gives the addict the delusions of brilliancy. Cocaine instills fear; so do psychics. Every hand to the addict presents problems. You have a weak hand—fear. The opponents must have game. You bid to stop them from bidding. You have a good hand—fear—you must conceal its count and veil its honors. You are afraid of one suit—fear again—so you blindly bid your weakness: forcing bids from your partner, frantic denials by you, and you are swallowed under in a sea of doubles.

So it goes. Big hands—you bid to conceal weakness. Weak hands—you bid in a camouflage of strength. Important hands—unimportant hands—all reach gigantic proportions in the hysterical reaching out for the star of brilliancy.

If one psychic comes to grief, out comes another and another. If one should win, your vanity is fattened. You are a superman, so out comes another and another, and you sit trembling and perspiring like a drug addict.

Psychics are for a lost cause, but to the feverish mind of the sufferer every hand is a lost cause from the moment he touches it.

[This New Yorker brief by E. J. Kahn, Jr., based on a typographic snafu in the [former] New York Sun, is one of the most brilliant tours de force ever written about Contract Bridge. Every one of the Bridge players mentioned in it considers himself immortalized by the mention and, as Thomas Jefferson would have said, by right ought to be right. [It appeared in the issue of May 31, 1941.

Dummy, Dummy! Who's Dummy?

by E. J. KAHN, JR.

WITH the exception of my grandfather, all of the Bridge players I know often glance at the summaries of Bridge hands carried in the newspapers. My grandfather does not care to have his simple, rugged game altered by the gratuitous advice of experts, but other Bridge-fanciers take occasional delight in having unfolded for them the mysteries of the Vienna coup or the triple squeeze. A few weeks ago, while reading the *Sun,* I noticed a report on the progress of the Masters' Individual Bridge Championship, an annual affair as important to Bridge fans as the individual shoot at Sea Island, Georgia, is to skeet-shooters. "The final round," said the *Sun,* "produced a few spectacular results, one of the most outstanding being a hand on which most North and South players reached a small slam and made an extra trick." The *Sun* forthwith printed a box score of the hand and the accompanying bidding, as follows:

South, dealer. Neither side vulnerable.

	NORTH	
	♠ A K Q J	
	♡ K 4 3	
	◇ A Q 9	
	♣ Q 4 2	
WEST		EAST
♠ 10 3 2		♠ 8 7 6 4
♡ 9 8 6 5		♡ J 10
◇ K 8 7		◇ 6 4 3 2
♣ 8 6 5		♣ 10 7 3
	SOUTH	
	♠ 9 5	
	♡ A Q 7 2	
	◇ J 10 5	
	♣ A K J 9	

BIDDING ON THE HAND.

The bidding:

Lebhar	Glick	Fry Jr.	Fry
South	North	Jacoby	North
1 C	1 S	South	Pass
1 N T	6 N T	1 C	Hymes
7 N T	Gerst	Double	East
Fuchs	East	Appleyard	2 S
West	Pass	West	
Pass	Pass	1 S	
Pass		All Pass	
All Pass			

Any Bridge player, even my grandfather, would admit that the results indicated by this chart are spectacular. At first glance, they are also somewhat puzzling. I carried the item around with me for a while, studying it at odd moments, and I finally decided that I could understand it and moreover reconstruct from it the scene at that Bridge table. It wasn't an easy job; none of the participants in the game was credited by the *Sun* with saying more than a word or two at a time, and I had to figure out the intervening thoughts and reactions solely from my meagre knowledge of the temperament of Bridge players. My reconstruction begins just after the cards were dealt. At that point, I figure, the reporter assigned to the tournament, a young man with little or no sense of direction, asked the four men at the table to tell him exactly where they were sitting, to insure the accuracy of his account. This is what they said, and why they said it:

LEBHAR: South. (*Lebhar is a sound, sensible fellow. He is sitting South and would naturally say so.*)

GLICK: North. (*He doesn't hear the* Sun's *question, as he is telling a kibitzer named Fuchs the title of a play he has recently seen. Actually, Glick is sitting West.*)

FRY, JR.: Jacoby. (*This answer is just silly. It will become clear, as we go on, that Fry, Jr., is a spirited but alarmingly absent-minded fellow. He's sitting North.*)

FRY: North. (*Playing against his son in major competition always makes him nervous. He knows he's sitting East but decides that the other players are having fun with the* Sun *reporter and that he'll string along; he doesn't want to seem old-fashioned.*)

After these geographical preliminaries, the men hitch up their chairs and get down to the serious business of bidding:

LEBHAR: One club. (*With three and a half quick tricks, he'd be a fool not to say it.*)

GLICK: One spade. (*He figures that if he*

tosses in a psychic bid, he might confuse his opponents.)

FRY, JR.: South. (*Obviously, he's badly rattled.*)

FRY: Pass. (*He can't decide exactly what is going on, so he'll bide his time.*)

LEBHAR: One no trump. (*Although the bidding appears to be screwy, he hopes things will get straightened out. He holds a powerful hand and wants to play it.*)

GLICK: Six no trump. (*Having bluffed originally, he might as well go the whole hog, he thinks. This is the final round of the tournament and the other players are getting on his nerves; he'd like to get the hell out of the joint and into a Turkish bath.*)

FRY, JR.: One club. (*Hopelessly muddled by now, he remembers dimly that Lebhar said "One club" a while back. Fry, Jr., is peculiarly fascinated by everything Lebhar says and often repeats his partner's words, just because he likes the way they sound.*)

FRY: Hymes! (*An ejaculation. Any father might say it under the circumstances.*)

LEBHAR: Seven no trump. (*He's furious.*)

GLICK: Gerst. (*He is evidently asking Gerst, an elderly retainer at the bridge club, to come over and empty an ashtray into which Lebhar has been angrily depositing the shredded remnants of a scoring pad.*)

FRY, JR.: Double. (*Aside from the fact that he is doubling his own partner's bid, this is a perfectly proper remark.*)

FRY: East. (*He has suddenly remembered what he should have said way back at the beginning and is trying to straighten himself out.*)

LEBHAR: Fuchs. (*Mr. Fuchs, the kibitzer, has remained commendably quiet so far. Now Lebhar is requesting him to pay exceptionally careful attention. Most people, when playing a seven-no-trump contract, doubled, insist on having an outside witness looking on, so that if they are successful they will have impartial corroboration for the story they plan to tell their wives.*)

GLICK: East. (*This is an aside, addressed to Fry. Glick is simply acknowledging Fry's last word and is saying, in effect, "Oh—East. You mean you should have said that before."*)

FRY, JR.: Appleyard. (*The word "East" started him off on a train of thought, too. Its destination happens to be an appleyard he was fond of as a boy. As he says this, he looks in a happy, reminiscent way at his father.*)

FRY: Two spades. (*There is no rational explanation for this; perhaps it's a typographical error.*)

LEBHAR: West. (*Close, but not an exact transcription. What Lebhar is actually saying is "Gerst." The ashtrays need emptying again. Besides, Lebhar wants a drink, quick.*)

GLICK: Pass. (*He feels that the sooner this is over, the better.*)

FRY, JR.: West. (*A statement undoubtedly based on Lebhar's "Gerst," which Fry, Jr., misunderstood. Since he has been parroting Lebhar all along, it is illogical to expect him to stop now. If he had heard Lebhar say "Gerst," he would have said "Gerst," too.*)

FRY: (*He is speechless by now, and no wonder.*)

LEBHAR: Pass. (*He would be happy if they cut out the kidding and laid down some cards.*)

GLICK: Pass. (*If only the rest of the boys would follow his example!*)

FRY, JR.: One spade. (*He thinks he is imitating Lebhar again, but is so confused, what with his father glaring at him and the rest of the boys drumming angrily on the table, that by mistake he imitates Glick instead.*)

FRY: (*Still speechless.*)

LEBHAR: Pass. (*He's grimly determined to keep a grip on himself, no matter what.*)

GLICK: (*He has passed twice already, so this time he just nods.*)

FRY, JR.: All pass! (*Being absent-minded, he has failed to notice that the other players have done little but pass for some time. Fry, Jr., probably thinks he is doing them a favor by issuing this sweeping order to stop the bidding. They'd have stopped by themselves long ago if it hadn't been for him.*)

FRY: (*He doesn't say anything; isn't even thinking of bridge.*)

LEBHAR: All pass! (*It took quite a while, but he has finally collapsed under the strain and has begun to imitate Junior. It is a tribute to Lebhar's durability that he held out as long as he did.*)

The *Sun's* comment on this extraordinary episode was a masterpiece of subtle criticism. "Score for Fuchs and Gerst on this hand," it said, "was minus 1,520." I do not blame the *Sun* for losing patience with the contestants and attributing the whole mess to a couple of fellows who we know were merely dumping ashes and leaning on shoulders. Perhaps the only man who really relished this singular incident was my grandfather. I showed him the story and his eyes lit up. "Those so-called experts play like a lot of damn fools," he said. "I could have bid the hand better myself."

[Bridge is astonishingly free from cheating — more so than any other card game known — and it is even relatively free from the minor unethical conduct that falls in the twilight zone between scrupulous and ethical player. But even in the best circles there are some clever souls who can observe the letter while violating the spirit. They are called coffeehousers, and in the following article, which appeared originally in Cosmopolitan, Sam Fry defines them and exposes some of their stratagems.

Coffeehousing

by SAMUEL FRY, JR.

THERE'S a story about a well-known Bridge player who was losing in a high-stake game and seemed depressed about it. A hand was dealt, and our friend sank lower into the depths. Each time the bidding came around to him he literally groaned out his *pass.* The opponents got to game, and when he doubled the bid no one took it too seriously—apparently he was too disgusted to concentrate. When the dummy hand was shown he began shaking his head, practically throwing away his cards and conceding the contract. The declarer can hardly be blamed for not playing "sad sack" for the five missing trumps and just about *every* missing high card. The hand went down four tricks doubled, two of them due to overbidding, undoubtedly induced by the moans, and two to errors in the play.

This is just one instance which proved that Contract Bridge cannot be a purely abstract science. The physical and emotional composition of people makes it virtually impossible for a hand to be played without the players' obtaining more information than can be gained from the bids and the fall of the cards.

There is a type of player who takes advantage of this fact, like the lad in the first paragraph. He hopes the line of demarcation between natural emotional reactions and histrionics is so vague that no one will notice when he puts one over. This fellow has become known as a "coffeehouser."

During the last century, card games were played in the back rooms of English pubs and coffeehouses. The personnel of these games was mixed; a lord and a highwayman might be partners at Whist. You couldn't bring your own marked deck to these games, but that was about the only rule.

So the verb "to coffeehouse" and the nouns "coffeehouse" and "coffeehouser" have been chosen by the inner circle of Contract Bridge players today to describe a certain large group of petty larcenists of the card table. The coffeehouser does not violate any national or state laws, nor does he even deviate, strictly speaking, from the laws of Contract Bridge. A "coffeehouse" is any extracurricular act, remark, mannerism, or voice intonation that has as its deliberate objective either assisting one's partner or deceiving one's opponents. The only defense against coffeehouse ethics is not to play where they are employed—unless you are a master of the art yourself.

Probably the most widely used bit of "coffee" is the well-known "slow pass." This fellow has just under the values to make a bid, but, after all, one's partner should be notified that he is not as friendless on the deal as a simple quick pass would indicate. So the coffeehouser shows just the proper amount of hesitation and indecision before passing. His partner catches the current and immediately becomes more aggressive than he has any right to be.

Somewhat more subtle is the *intimidation* slow pass. This is directed at the enemy and is not meant to influence partner. Your partner has raised your one spade bid to two after the opponents have tossed in an overcall of two hearts. You have a minimum bid and two spades looks plenty high enough, but you also have no real defense against an opposing three-heart contract, which may be bid at your left if you pass too rapidly. So you huddle over partner's two-spade bid, trying to look like a man who is thinking of going on to game. When you finally pass, your opponent with the heart suit and not much defense against even four spades may be sufficiently impressed to abstain from making a winning three-heart bid.

We've all seen the *fumble.* It occurs during the play. A club is led, and our perverted friend has a singleton. He carefully fumbles around as if trying to decide which of several clubs to play, before finally deciding on following suit with the only one he has. Another common type of fumble is the one without the honor. A jack of a suit is led by declarer. The coffeehouser wants to protect *his partner's* queen, so he acts as if he has the lady himself and is contemplating covering the jack but finally decides against it. Of course, if he's playing against a student of the school of coffeehousing, his partner will immediately be played for the queen.

Then there's the fellow who makes casual remarks. Dummy will put his hand down at a six contract, the hand including among other securities the ace, jack, and a few small trumps. The coffeehouser has the king and a small trump which, being under the ace, will almost surely be trapped. He looks admiringly at dummy and then disgustedly says to declarer, "I suppose, added to everything else, you have a hundred honors." This is supposed to convey to declarer that the speaker obviously doesn't have an honor in trumps, and declarer is now expected to abandon finessing for the king and to try to drop it singleton in the other hand. It has worked.

Also there's the seemingly guileless and frequently pretty female player who is declarer at a game contract. When dummy goes down, she abuses her partner for not having bid a slam. Actually it is touch and go whether or not she can make even four odd on the hand. The defense, feeling their cause is hopeless, defend rather carelessly, and the doubtful four is made simple. Maybe I overrate this gal—possibly she really thinks she can make six, being an optimist by nature and a dumb Bridge player by birth.

The male opposite to this lady is the mournful fellow who sees his dummy at a doubled contract and then acts as if the losses on the hand will be enough to pay for a DC-6. Actually he has a choice of finesses to make his contract, and the defense, lulled to a sense of false security, make the careless play or plays that eliminate his guess.

The use of voice intonations to fill in the gaps not covered by a bidding system is a compulsory freshman course at the School for Advanced and Applied Coffeehousing. Everyone knows that one spade by you, one no trump by your partner, TWO SPADES! by you shows four tricks and is almost a forcing bid; whereas one spade, one no trump, two spades says, "Partner, if you bid any more I'll break your neck." There's a player I know who has such amazing control of his voice that he can grade it to within a quarter of a trick.

The use of such expressions as "content" or "satisfied" (instead of pass) during the bidding is frowned upon by the true coffeehouser, as being really too crude. Similarly "I double" for a takeout double, and "crack" for a business double, to avoid partnership misunderstandings, has become old-fashioned. If you pull one of them it's not your ethics but your manners that will be questioned.

The following bit of coffeehousing was engineered in the depression days of the early thirties by one of the well-known experts of that time. Think what you will of it morally, if you appreciate a true work of art, you'll remain to cheer. This fellow picked up the following mess of tripe: spades—none; hearts—8 6 3 2; diamonds—5 4 3 2; and clubs—K 8 5 4 3 2. Furthermore, he was vulnerable and his partner, an overbidding type of player, opened the bidding with one spade, and that sky's-the-limit look on his face. Our operative was more than equal to the occasion, however. After second hand passed, his response, surely made inadvertently, was one club. You remember the rules for an insufficient bid at that time (they're slightly changed now): you made your bid sufficient in any way you wished, and your partner was barred from bidding again. Our boy blissfully made his bid sufficient with two clubs. His partner had an apoplectic stroke, but he made two clubs for a small plus score on a hand which would have cost the team something like 1,400 at four spades doubled, had the bidding continued.

When we come to the Alcatraz Coup we are traveling in a new sphere of Bridge masterminding and a new high in coffeehousing. Here is the hand on which the inventor won a life membership in the Coffeehouse League of America:

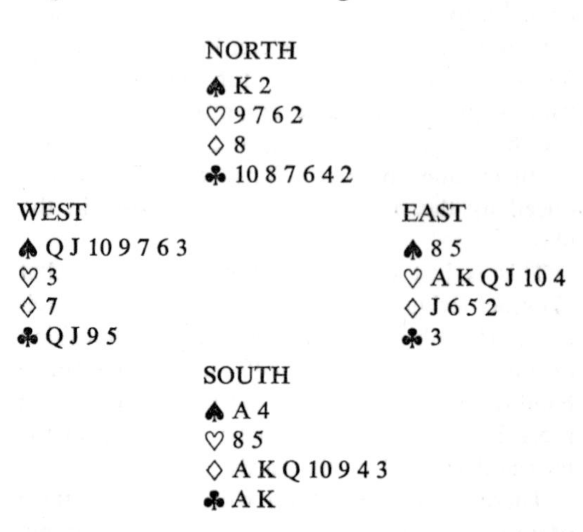

Our hero, vulnerable, held the rock-crushing South hand, and we must assume he came by it honestly. The West player, not being vulnerable, opened with three spades, North passed, East bid four hearts, and South's five-diamond bid closed the auction. West opened his singleton heart and South now took stock. He had two heart losers and probably no other losing tricks, as the jack of diamonds *should* drop on the ace, king or queen, with only five missing. But why not be surer? thought our clever friend. Why not try to find out if West has the diamond jack and, if he hasn't, East can be finessed for it, which play will be necessary if East has four cards in the suit. On the bidding it was obvious to South that the heart lead was a singleton. When East won the opening heart and continued with another high heart, our hero, instead of following suit on the second round, trumped with the nine of diamonds. West, having no more hearts but no higher trump, discarded a spade. South now, being in plenty of time under the rules because he had not played to the next trick, corrected his revoke with the appropriate self-critical remarks about his carelessness. He played his losing heart on trick two, won East's club lead at trick three, and then, having marked East with the jack of diamonds, entered dummy with the spade king and led a diamond through East and finessed the ten spot; thereby making a hand on which you and I (I hope) would have played the percentages, not finessed the diamond, and gone down.

Note, incidentally, that our enterprising lad's little coup also would have brought him rich rewards under other circumstances. Had his nine of diamonds at trick two been overruffed with the jack, he would have corrected his revoke on schedule and graciously (because the rules so state) permitted West to replace the jack in his hand. But now, if East continued with a third heart, as he obviously would, South would know to trump with one of his three top honors, and then play to drop West's jack on the other two, as his only hope.*

Here is a honey. The perpetrator was playing in a tournament, and his opponents were climbing gaily up to a contract of seven clubs, clubs having been bid originally by the opponent on his *left.* All during the bidding he was practically falling asleep; when the final contract of seven clubs was reached, he suddenly sort of half came to and led a low trump. The lead, of course, was out of turn and the declarer, having the right to call a lead, chose another suit in which he had some stronger fear of a possible loser. When dummy went down, the declarer saw that his only problem was picking up the trump queen, for which he could finesse through either opponent. He reasoned that since our pal had, innocently thinking it was his lead, chosen a low trump it couldn't have been from the queen—after all the man wasn't *completely* asleep. So dealer played the ace of trump on which all followed with a low one, and then led through young Machiavelli's partner and finessed the jack. Our man roused himself sufficiently from his coma to pounce on said jack with the queen and defeat the grand slam, which could have been made.

* A very nice story—we hate to detract from it in any way. But the fact is, this hand was never actually played. It was invented by one of the editors—to wit, Oswald Jacoby—to demonstrate to the Bridge Laws Committee a flaw in the revoke law. This particular law has not been changed, so perhaps the committee was not impressed.

There are thousands of Bridge players who regularly indulge in all of the little tricks outlined above. They are respected citizens of their communities, kind to cripples and little children, and one hundred per cent honest in all their non-Bridge dealings. Some of them are reformed Poker players and think such tactics are a legitimate part of the game. In Poker, of course, anything goes. But Bridge is a different game—the bidding and play in themselves are sufficiently complex, and no player should be obliged to cope with a coffeehouser's distractions. What, however, is he going to do?

¶ *There is some more on coffeehousing, among other rich meat, in our next selection, a chapter from Fred Schwed, Jr.'s* THE PLEASURE WAS ALL MINE, *a volume of spoofing essays that are all as delightful as this one. We should note that any resemblance to actual persons or places is not at all coincidental. They all exist, just as Fred says; in fact, both of the editors have on occasion been among the guests in his Bridge coterie—which is either very gracious or remarkably deceitful, for we did not know until we read it in Fred's book that our presence was not enthusiastically encouraged.* ¶ *We are sure you will chuckle, grin and guffaw your way through this as we did. Not the least of its charm is the illustrations by Walt Kelly. Our only regret is that this particular chapter does not contain one of Fred's bonnest mots: "I belong to a club," he said, "the way Uncle Tom belonged to Simon Legree."*

from The Pleasure Was All Mine

by FRED SCHWED, JR.

IT IS with a feeling of positive physical relief that I now turn to a sport where the insteps never ache, the breath never comes in agonized gasps, and if one sweats profusely it is not from bodily exertion but only from terror, or because the apartment is overheated.

In the game of Contract Bridge, thirteen cards are dealt to each of four players, one at a time, in clockwise rotation. After that a variety of things may happen. For example, there was that time when a lady, sitting East, procured a revolver and shot her husband, sitting West. An understanding jury found her not guilty. This case, however, must not be taken as typical. In our Bridge game, since there are no women players for reasons I shall try to set forth later, and since all of us are gentlemen and sportsmen, we settle our differences less drastically. Screaming, shrieking, and bursting into uncontrollable sobs, yes. Shooting, no. That is our Code. Besides, if the man who was shot happened to be behind (and most of our members seem usually to be behind), you can picture for yourself the troublesome litigation that would be necessary to collect what he had lost. There would be further complications if the incident took place before the play of the hand was completed.

Our bridge club, I must hasten to explain, is not a Bridge Club. We have no clubhouse, membership committee, or duplicate nights; no stranger, his voice throbbing with suppressed passion, ever phones us to ask what is the rule when South reneges on the tenth trick in a deal where East originally held fourteen cards. Neither do we have a regular employee to answer the phone and say, "I am sorry, Mrs. Murgatroyd, but Mr. Murgatroyd has not been in this afternoon." We are just a group of about a dozen who meet irregularly during the cold months at each other's homes. The home at which each game is played is not decided by rotation but by a device hoary with tradition. It is the home of the member whose wife happens to be away on a visit, or feeling good-natured for some reason, or reclining in a hospital.

Our club is so steeped in antiquity that no one can recall just how the original membership came about. Take the case of the excitable Monty, who seems to have been a member since the dawn of Harold W.* Vanderbilt. When the question comes up, as it not infrequently does —"Who the hell ever invited this Frenchman into this game in the first place?" no one seems to know. Each member points accusingly at another. If we had only thought to appoint a historian earlier, my task would now be simplified.

Members are permitted to bring guests, but the practice is not enthusiastically encouraged, for we are discriminatory Bridge players. A guest is liable not to be up to the speed of our game and this is embarrassing all round. Occasionally a guest is way ahead of our speed and this has its disadvantages also. And we once had a guest who would always say, when covering an honor with an honor, "Not through the Iron Duke!" So you can see we have become a pretty finicky organization, like a beach at Newport. There is one situation, however, in which our rigid selectivity is relaxed. This is when only three or seven players show up—not enough for either one or two tables. On such occasions we become more democratic. We would then welcome into our game the Iron Duke himself, or any other financially solvent male who knew enough about the game to keep score.

That there are flaws in our organization is apparent and will become more apparent. At a real Bridge Club there are always (except on a rare Christmas Eve) enough players to make a table instantly. But real Bridge Clubs have flaws too—at least as I remember them, which was during the depression. I understand that things have picked up with them since, as with what have they not?

At that time I got the impression that Bridge Clubs were made up chiefly of people who had less than three friends. Else why should we all be paying dues and a card fee for the privilege of cutting various objectionable partners? To make the picture less appetizing, these clubs were full of young men who had no money but expected to procure some by counting up to thirteen carefully and executing squeeze and throw-in plays. Each of these young men thought he had discovered an easy, pleasant way of making a living, but each was mistaken. There are unexpected obstacles. The chief one is that the other three players are also trying to make a living and have no money either. I once made bold to ask the late Mr. P. Hal Sims about this industry. Even he took a dim view of it, although at that time he could win from anyone in the world. "It is increasingly difficult to find wealthy opponents," he explained. "People of vast wealth are not like you and me. When they play Bridge they prefer to play for a tenth of a cent a point. That is why they have vast wealth."

Previous to the depression, when I lived on the southern shore of Long Island, most of the Bridge I played was Commuting Bridge. This is a rough, tough sport, only less wearing on the contestants than water polo, which it slightly resembles. The train most of the games were on was the Long Island's crack express, "The Pedestrian," leaving Penn Station at 5:36. To be sure to get a game players would begin arriving at

* for Stirling.

5:10, politely jostling. This meant that if their office happened to be in shambles at 4:45, it was left in shambles till next morning. There are many subtleties to Commuting Bridge which have never been set down in the Bridge books. For instance, during Daylight Saving Time a seat on the aisle is just as good as a seat by the window. In winter a seat by the window is figured to be worth two hundred points by the time the train gets to Jamaica because then the window acts as a makeshift, but still effective, mirror.

In this type of Bridge the players are all acquainted, but the kibitzers are random strangers. Yet a rare intimacy springs up between kibitzer and player before the train has emerged from under the East River. It is commonplace for the kibitzer in the seat directly behind you to edge so far forward that in the excitement of a slam hand he nuzzles your ear, like a pet. Conductors on the Long Island, in addition to their regular duties (supplying cards, collecting tips), sometimes had to restrain passionate kibitzers from seizing and shaking players whose bids or plays had deeply disappointed them. These kibitzers—sitting Southwest and Northeast—had no money stake in the game; they were just perfectionists. Incidentally, a kibitzer with halitosis is a very poor thing. It is strange that the Listerine people have never played up this angle. "Not even West would tell him the real reason that East had trumped his good queen."

I have mentioned earlier that some things are more fun if you don't know too much about them. The history of Contract is an excellent example. Not only Commuting Contract but also stationary Contract (the variation where the table and players stand still in one place) was a more robust diversion at that time. Mr. Vanderbilt invented the game and everybody immediately began playing deliriously. Several years went by before the average player knew what the hell he was doing. Hearts were high, tempers were short, diamonds were trumps, and there was often a club mixed up among the spades. Conventions were numerous, conflicting, and confusing. When a newcomer cut into a game he recited something that sounded rather like a high church credo:

"I believe in the distributional no-trump, two and a half tricks first and second hand, takeout double on the first two rounds of bidding only. I consider psychics an abomination. Amen."

His partner-to-be then intoned *his* articles of faith. A workable *modus vivendi* was thus consummated. Then the cards were dealt, the new partnership scientifically bid up to three no-trump and went down four tricks, doubled and redoubled.

Few were the players who, after a bid or two, seeing six cold staring them in the face, would go ahead and bid six. No, they must engage in seven rounds of subtleties first. There are the devotees of the Tom Sawyer school of bidding, and the breed is not yet extinct. You will recall that when Tom and Huckleberry Finn wanted to rescue Jim from the cabin, Huck wanted to lift the bedpost off Jim's chain and walk him out the door, but Tom said no, that wasn't the way they did things in *The Count of Monte Cristo*. Tom's method included such things as filing the chain for a week with a manicure file and concealing the filings by swallowing them, and leaving by the window via bedsheets tied to the lightning rod.

Bridge was not played on the morning trains going in to the city, but only discussed. Each partner would plump himself down next to some unfortunate and describe various catastrophes of the previous evening in detail. Each would prove that it hadn't been *his* fault, and they couldn't have been more earnest about it if they had been each trying to beat a murder rap before the grand jury.

Pop was particularly bitter about serving as an unwillingly appointed one-man jury in these cases. He claimed that he boarded the train in the morning to read his paper, compose his thoughts, and be transported to the island of Manhattan—not to be a Father Confessor for bum Bridge players. Such was Pop's genius that

he soon worked out his own technique for dealing with these emergencies. This is how he explained his system to us boys:

"I take a comfortable seat by myself, open my paper, and assume an expression which clearly says, 'I am holding this seat for my long-lost uncle, who will presently join me and divulge some family secrets of a confidential nature.' This is a good part of my system, except that it never works. Well, before Woodmere, someone lowers himself into the other seat and says:

" 'Listen to this, Fred. Last night Adolph was my partner and he opens with one spade, vulnerable. I hold a singleton spade, six hearts to the ace jack, and nothing else.'

"This goes on without any pause for breath for maybe as much as ten minutes. But I only listen up to the phrase, 'He opens with one spade, vulnerable,' which clearly indicates the tenor of his confidences. I immediately let my thoughts roam into greener pastures, perhaps consider what may be expected of the market at the opening, perhaps con some favorite lines of poetry to myself. But the moment he stops talking, I am instantly ready for him. I just say, with deep sympathy and understanding:

" 'The trouble was, he was only considering his own hand. He failed to consider what yours might be, although you had shown him, by your bidding.' At this point the mug cries, 'That's just it, Fred, that's just it!' I have made a friend for life, and what is more I have only had my attention diverted from more important matters for a couple of brief moments."

People felt passionately about their Contract when the game was young. Often the defense of the propriety of a man's bid took precedence over the propriety of his lady. Those were the days of rival systems, and holy wars were waged about them. Will he who is old enough ever forget the challenge match of five hundred* rubbers between the teams of Lenz and Culbertson? It was without doubt the most overpublicized event of small importance in the history of news. The game was played, for weeks, in New York hotels, and from Reykjavik to Ceylon's sunny isle people waited breathlessly to learn if Mrs. Culbertson finessed that jack successfully. (She usually did.)

Those glad, mad days are gone forever. I guess it was that match that took the first fine careless rapture out of Contract. The Culbertson system, or systems much like it, were universally established. Worse yet, most of the nation's players got to understand the system fairly well. As a result, since then the game has suffered from a lack of misunderstanding. It was the misunderstanding that used to produce all those piquant results, redoubled.

The need for a greater degree of misunderstanding can be illustrated from the situation at our club, a situation which has been bothersome for years now. After a decade of play we naturally know each other's games pretty well

* 150.

and it is naturally not necessary to ask each other every time we cut whether partner plays Blackwood or not.* This familiarity with each other's styles takes something off the edge of the excitement, but as I have pointed out, that can no longer be helped. Our problem goes deeper in this direction and concerns one of our members, Monty, whose exceptional genius for conveying information to his partner through his bidding has caused a stir in our game since the nineteen thirties. To illustrate the delicate nature of our problem I will describe a typical table:

Sitting North is Monty,† a small dapper man of Gallic extraction, highly excitable at the Bridge table and also everywhere else.

Sitting South is Jack, who plays Bridge much better than he plays golf. If I were forced to find any flaw in his game it would be his conviction that if he is only allowed to play a hand at three no-trump, he will make it, no matter what the twenty-six cards at his disposal happen to be. He is more frequently right about this than I can understand.

I am sitting West in my customary gentlemanly fashion. (I am writing this book in order to buy more chips so that I can continue to sit West.)

Across from me at East is Allie, our eldest member by half a dozen years. He is the undisputed Dean of our game, a position he is entitled to for his skill at cards, his character as a friend, his probity as a sportsman, and his ownership of a book of rules. He is (and I'm not kidding) one of the most brilliant of players. He can execute every subtle maneuver of the game, with the exception of winning.

Seated about us, impatiently spilling ashes, are three kibitzers, who are restlessly awaiting the arrival of Albert to make up a second table in the dining room. Frantic telephone calls have revealed that Albert has chosen this most inappropriate of moments to take his three children to the zoo. It has been moved and seconded that he feed the children to the bears so that he will be on time next week. Monty is dealing, and the previous hand is being discussed in a scientific way by seven people all at once. The door opens and a beautiful woman enters, the wife of our host of the afternoon. She is a vision of delight, hospitality, and the *couturier's* art. Someone has slopped part of a highball on her rosewood end table. No one even says hello to her except me, and I have to make it brief because Allie is now quietly encouraging me.

"Look, Fred," he says earnestly. "At this point the rubber is exactly even. If we each give them [*he makes a rapid mental calculation*] say, eight dollars, maybe they will accept it, call this rubber off, and let us cut again. You can see that the situation is otherwise hopeless. With my lack of luck, and your lack of ability, pitted against Jack's fine play and Monty's cheating—"

"I do *not* sheet," exclaims Monty, a claim he has been making for years with no improvement in his convincinglessness or his pronunciation.

"Who dealt?" I ask impatiently, for I find these side issues childish.

"I did," says Monty, and then, "I bid . . . [*pause of one full second*] whan hairt."

Pandemonium.

Allie flings his cards on the table (but face down) and swears by the honor of his many ancestors that he will never in his life play cards again with Monty. I try to say something placating, but it is like placating a slightly wounded tiger. Jack dissolves into laughter and the three kibitzers spring to their feet, simultaneously trying to soothe Allie and to explain to Monty, for the thousandth time, that that is no way for a sportsman to make his opening bid. Monty restates for the thousandth time his original premise, "I do *not* sheet," and turns purple to give his statement more emphasis.

To the player who plays "friendly Bridge," or "social Bridge," all this fury will be incomprehensible. (Monty, who never plays friendly or social Bridge, still claims that it is incomprehensible to him.) But to Allie, and to many other purists, the difference between the toneless announcement "One heart" and "I bid [*pause*] *one* heart" is as comprehensible a difference as there is between the exultant "Hey, partner, I open with two no-trump!" and H. T. Webster's sullen "Who dealt this mess? Pass." I shall shortly quote, without permission, Dean Allie himself on this particular point. In general, ideal Bridge morality requires that all of the early part of the auction shall be made in the same tone of voice and at the same speed. Bridge is the only game in which, to be scrupulously honest, one must do more than just obey the rules. Monty, because of his tempestuous Gallic temperament, is either incapable or unwilling to do this. Myself, I do not pass judgment; it is a matter between Monty and his own peculiar gods.

Experienced players will be quick to point

* But we ask anyway.—fsjr.

† Any suggestion or even implication that Monty cheats is hereby specifically denied by me. I do not in any way say this. It is the other fellows who say it. I would not say it because I know Monty well and I also knew the libel laws well.—fsjr.

out that there is one effective recourse, and one only, against infractions of this kind. That is to cease to play cards with the offender. However, this recourse is of no use at all to us in the case of Monty. In the first place, he is more fun to have in the game than anyone else, and in the second place, in spite of all the unfair advantages he takes, he keeps us all in Chevrolets.

Allie, in spite of the matured wisdom garnered over decades of play (he started with Whist at the age of four), still cannot appreciate this philosophy. A while ago his bitterness overflowed into artistic creation. He composed a didactic memorandum, or White Paper, setting forth how this type of Tonal Bidding might be standardized so that henceforward there would be no more misunderstandings at all. If I could write anything as good I would sell it, but Allie just scrawled it off on small pieces of paper and circulated it among the membership. The memorandum takes up such delicate matters as "What to Do with the Near-Bid Hand," "The Lightning Pass," "The Shaded Raise," "Vocal Distinctions between Doubles," and "How to Handle the Two-Suiter."

Allie's treatise in its entirety would doubtless prove too technical for the ordinary layman—especially the honest and aboveboard layman like the reader, who has never dreamed that such shameful gambits existed. The following sample explains, in considerable detail, Allie's position on the opening bid previously described.

HOW TO HANDLE THE TWO-SUITER

Anyone can bid a two-suit hand properly with a little instruction, provided he does not mind how high the bidding goes in the process. The problem is how to indicate that you have two biddable suits without getting beyond your depth before reaching the final contract.

Again, credit must go to Monty for pioneer work in coping with this problem. He has devised a method which consists of showing this two-suiter by starting his call with the words "I bid," and then waiting an appreciable length of time before stating his suit. Thus: "I bid . . . one heart."

No one will deny that this method is basically sound, since if he had no other suit to announce but hearts he would make his bid promptly. This method is simple to handle and it is effective. The only trouble with it is that it is not foolproof.

To illustrate, Jack's hesitation after an "I bid" frequently means no more than that he is temporarily absorbed in that young lady across the street on Beekman Place who leaves the Venetian blinds up while doing her physical-culture exercises. Again, Fred's hesitation after the "I bid" may indicate a two-suiter, but it is just as likely to mean that Fred is not sure whether he is playing Contract Bridge at all or whether he is playing Auction Pinochle. (There is usually good evidence that he thinks it is Auction Pinochle.)

I suggest that we remove the doubt by adopting the convention of counting aloud between the statement "I bid," and the naming of the suit when the bidder wants his partner to appreciate the two-suit nature of his hand. Thus: "I bid—one-two-three-four-five—a heart" would be unmistakable.

Jack's wife, Aggie, is a frequent hostess for the club. She is an excellent creature, nobly planned, and one of her many virtues is that she does not particularly mind her domicile's smelling faintly of abandoned cigar butts from Sunday evening through Tuesday morning. She is also clever at hypnotizing the children out of the living room immediately upon the arrival of a fourth. After being duly sworn she testifies as follows:

That one time Barney, a loving husband and homemaker, rushed in a little late and rather perturbedly asked permission to phone. He dialed his home and then said:

"Hello, Lucy? How's it look now? Un-huh . . . Uh, uh-huh. Well, that's good. I think it ought to be all right. Bye," and turning away from the phone, said, "Let's cut."

"Is anything wrong with Lucy?" asked Aggie solicitously.

"No, not Lucy. It's the kitchen. Stove sort of exploded and it was on fire when I left. But the firemen seem to have it under control now. Looks like you and me, Fred. Gee, I've been having bad luck like this for two months now."

There were, Aggie adds, muttered complaints that Barney was holding up the game with this long conversation.

Aggie further deposes that on the afternoon of December 28, 1947, ten players arrived at her house and that no one of them mentioned the weather, though their hats were variously stacked with from one to five inches of snow. During the next four and a half hours no one looked out the window although the greatest blizzard in history was occurring on the other side of the pane. At the end of the game she insists that Allie, Barney, and I stepped out into the darkness and into a chest-high drift and that there was an appreciable interval before we found out why we were not making forward progress. Allie was complaining bitterly for a change:

"I suppose you will never learn, Fred, that business doubles should be made when you have taking tricks, not just when you are annoyed, or bored, or vengeful. And that is especially true on slam bids when you—say, what the hell *is* this stuff, snow?"

Such earnest fascination with card playing is often condemned by more intellectual and spiritual types. "It is only a little short of revolting," they say, "the way you 'serious' Bridge players spend hours together, never exchanging any real ideas outside the game. You are so taken up with your childish pastime that you even omit the small niceties of companionship."

This charge hurts my feelings, and it is not true. We do speak of other things. With only a little strain on my memory I can remember twice when we did this.

Monty and I were partners for one of those long, nightmarish rubbers for which our partnership is so justly famous. At the rubber's expensive end Monty threw his remaining worthless cards in and declaimed hopelessly:

"That steenking Schwed, he nevaire holds a card!"

I regarded him with quiet disdain. "I did not know that you were acquainted with my uncle," I said coldly.

"Huh?" said Monty.

Allie was quick to help him. "Why, certainly," explained Allie. "You've heard of Sailing Baruch, haven't you? Well, Freddie has an uncle named Stinking Schwed. Very wealthy man, old Stinking Schwed, but as you have just observed, he never holds a card."

I would be doing my reputation as a resourceful Bridge player a grave injustice if I were to leave the reader with the impression he may have gotten of my skill from some of the comments that have been made on it. Those were the idle taunts of my companions motivated by a desire to be funny, or by jealousy. So I shall describe an extremely technical situation and how I handled it, and Allie's precise judgment of my play.

I had bid up to the staggering contract of seven spades. It was Allie's lead against this sure grand slam, and as he moodily tried to make one of thirteen hopeless choices, his partner, Monty, led out of turn. The tenseness of the situation had been too much for poor Monty. Like an eagle pouncing on his prey, I grasped the situation. "Lead out of turn! Lead out of turn!" I cried, and then remorselessly to Allie, "Now you lead your highest club." Allie, in stoical despair, led his highest club.

Well, in an effort to make a long story short, it turned out that Monty didn't have a club, so he trumped and set me one trick, and of course the club lead was the only one that could set me. All by myself I had discovered a play even more abominable, and far more costly, than the classic one of trumping partner's ace. I felt I should try to utter a few words of apology to my partner, Barney.

"Gee," I muttered, "I guess I am not good at calling leads out of turn."

"At long last, thank heavens," said Allie fervently, "we have discovered Freddie's Weakness."

Next Sunday afternoon, foul weather permitting, our club will meet again. As it happens, the host this time will be Monty. Eight or nine of us will drink his Scotch, Jack will burn a hole in his rug, Allie will comment acidly on his morals, and four or five of us will walk away with his money. Gee, it will be fun. I am praying for rain and, oddly enough, so is Monty.

¶*Stephen Potter's classic* GAMESMANSHIP, *when it was published in 1947, burst like a pyrotechnical rocket of enlightenment on everyone but the clubgoing card-player (and miscellaneous country-clubgoing golf and tennis players) who had teethed on identical principles. The subtitle of the book describes it completely: "The art of winning games without actually cheating." The book introduced a new word, or at least a word so old that it became new again, the* ploy, *a device or stratagem to put one's opponent at a disadvantage without giving him grounds for appeal to any committee of elderly and respectable men. Mr. Potter pays only cavalier attention to card games, but even though this excerpt be shallower than a well and narrower than a church door it will serve him that hath ears to hear.*

from Gamesmanship

by STEPHEN POTTER

BRIDGE AND POKER

MISS Violet Watkins—name of ill-omen in gamesmanship circles on the Welsh border—has said that "Gamesmanship can play little part in Bridge and Poker, which are themselves games of bluff."

The association of the word "bluff" with gamesmanship does small service to the art. True, there is a difficulty with Poker. There are those who believe that the sole duty of the Poker gamesman is to build up his reputation for impenetrability and toughness by suggesting that he last played Poker by the light of a moon made more brilliant by the snows of the Yukon, and that his opponents were two white-slave traffickers, a ticket-of-leave man and a deserter from the Foreign Legion. To me this is ridiculously far-fetched, but I do believe that a trace of American accent—West Coast—casts a small shadow of apprehension over the minds of English players.

Bridge, up to 1935, was virgin ground for the gamesman, but every month—owing largely I believe to the splendid work of Meynell—new areas of the game are being brought within his field. I will name one or two of the principal foci of research, in the new but growing world of bridgemanship.

1. INTIMIDATION.

We are working now on methods by which the gamesman can best suggest that he usually moves in Bridge circles far more advanced than the one in which he is playing at the moment. This is sometimes difficult for the mediocre player, but a primary gamescover of his more obvious mistakes is the frank statement, with apologies, that the rough and ready methods of this ordinary kind of Bridge, played as it is for amusingly low stakes, are constantly putting him off. "Idiotic. I was thinking I was playing duplicate." Refer to the "damnably complicated techniques" with which matchplay is hedged around. During the post-mortem period after each hand, give advice to your opponents immediately, before anyone else has spoken about the general run of the play. Tell the opponent on your left that "you saw her signalling with her third discard?" At first she will not realize that you are speaking to her, then she will not know what you are talking about, and will almost certainly agree. Invent "infringements" committed by your opponents in bidding, tell them that "it's quite all right—doesn't matter—but in a match it would be up to me to ask you to be silent for three rounds. Then if your partner redoubles, my original bid resumes its validity." Refer frequently to authorities. Mention the Portland Club and say, "I expect you've only got the 1939 edition of the rules. Would you care to see the new thing I've got here? 'For members only'?" Never say, "It doesn't matter in the least what you throw away because I am leading this card at random anyhow." Refer to some formula in the *Silver Book of End-Play Squeezes.*

It is usual, as part of intimidation play, to *invent a convention* (if playing with a fellow-gamesman as partner). Explain the convention to your opponents, of course, e.g.:

GAMESMAN: Forcing two and Blackwood's, partner? Right? And Gardiner's as well? O.K.

LAYMAN: What's Gardiner's?

GAMESMAN: Gardiner's—oh, simply this. Sometimes comes in useful. If *you* call seven diamonds *or* seven clubs and then one of us doubles without having previously called no trumps, then the doubler is telling his partner, really, that in his hand are the seven to queen, *inclusive,* of the next highest suit.

LAYMAN: I think I see . . .

GAMESMAN: The situation doesn't arise very often, as a matter of fact.

The fact that the situation does not arise more often than once in fifty years prevents any possible misunderstanding with your partner.

This phase of Intimidation Play is often called "Conventionist" or "Conventionistical."

2. TWO SIMPLE BRIDGE EXERCISES FOR BEGINNERS.

(a) *The deal.* Better than ten books on the theory of Bridge are the ten minutes a day spent in practicing how to deal. A startlingly practiced-looking deal has a hypnotic effect on opponents, and many's the time E. Hooper has won the rubber by his "spiral whirl" type of dealing. A good deal of medical argument has revolved round this subject. "Hooper's deal" is actually said to have a pulverizing effect on the Balakieff layer of the cortex. Myself, I take this *cum grano salis.*

(b) *Meynell's misdeal.* This is, in essence, the counter-game to intimidation play. Against a pair of opponents who know each other's game very well indeed, who have played together for years, and who pride themselves on the mechanical and unhesitating accuracy of their bidding, it is sometimes a good thing to make a misdeal deliberately (so that your partner has fourteen and yourself twelve, say; or the disparity may be even greater—see Fig. 12). Then pick up the cards and begin a wild and irrational bidding sequence. This will end, of course, in a double from E or W. As you begin to play the hand, discover the discrepancy in cards. The hand is then, of course, a washout. Your opponents will (a) be made to look foolish, (b) be annoyed at missing an easy double, (c) be unable to form a working judgment of your bidding form.

NORTH
♡ K 10 x x x x
♠ x x x
◇ J 10 x
♣ Q J x x x

SOUTH
♡ Q J
♠ A x x
◇ x x x
♣ 10

Fig. 12. Bridge hand. Distribution after typical Meynell misdeal.

3. SPLIT BRIDGE.

The old splitting game in golf foursomes has already been described.* Of late years—it is, in fact, the most recent development in Bridge—we have seen the adaptation of splitting, and the reshaping of it, for the junior game.

The art of splitting, in Bridge, is, quite simply, the art of sowing discord between your two opponents (East and West).

* "The art of fomenting distrust between your two opponents."

There is only one rule: BEGIN EARLY.

The first time the gamesman (South) makes his contract, the situation must be developed as follows:

GAMESMAN (South): Yes, just got the three. But I was rather lucky (*lowering voice to a clear whisper as he speaks to East*) . . . as a matter of fact your heart lead suited me rather well. I think . . . perhaps . . . if you'd led . . . well, almost anything else . . .

Ten to one West will seize this first opportunity of criticizing his partner and agree with Gamesman's polite implications of error. The seed of disagreement is sown. (Particularly if East had in fact led a heart correctly, or had not led one at all.) At the same time the gamesman's motto MODESTY AND SPORTSMANSHIP is finely upheld. It is never his skill, but an "unlucky slip by his opponent," which wins the trick.

BRIDGE ANECDOTES

Stories about card games recur in every generation, and nearly every one has been told about nearly every prominent player or authority. The three most famous are Bridge stories. We let Frank Crowninshield (from his book THE BRIDGE FIEND*) tell the first two, simply because he could tell a story better than anyone else. The third comes from George Beynon, dean of American tournament directors and Bridge publicists, who greatly enjoyed the ninetieth-birthday party the American Contract Bridge League gave him a few years ago—but came in to work bright and early the next morning.*

The Slight Misunderstanding

I HAVE often been asked about the case of the young man at Saratoga, and, as a very perplexing moral question is involved in it, I shall quote it and allow my readers to solve the ethical problem for themselves.

It was during the August races. The youth was asked to make up a rubber with some very rich men who were known to be heavy plungers on the turf. He assented, but, before beginning, he asked them what the table stakes were.

"Well," said Mr. G., in whose rooms at the United States Hotel the game was being played, "we have been playing five, but we can raise or lower the stakes if you wish."

Mr. F., the hero of the story, said that the points were perfectly satisfactory to him, and the game went on smoothly enough for four or five rubbers, when the session closed, and the three plungers plunged into a "low-neck" cab and drove off to the races.

As they were leaving, Mr. G. thanked Mr. F. for making up the game and informed him that he would send him, on the following day, a check for what he, F., had won.

The next afternoon F. was thunderstruck to receive G.'s check for three thousand two hundred dollars. He knew that, at five-cent points, he had won about thirty dollars. He accordingly wrote G. a polite little note saying that he fancied a mistake had been made, as he had only been playing five-cent points, and enclosing the check for correction.

Mr. G. replied that the check was perfectly correct; the stakes, he explained, had been five-dollar points and not five-cent points. He added that if F. had lost at the session, he, G., would have expected payment from him on a five-dollar basis and politely insisted upon F.'s keeping the check.

Query: What was F. to do?

—FRANK CROWNINSHIELD

The Green Suit

HERE is a diverting Bridge story, told, I believe, by a Mr. F. C. in New York. I think that the tale has appeared in print but it is too curious and horrible an adventure not to be included in this budget of bridge anecdotes. I shall relate the story in Mr. C.'s own words:

"The other evening I was dining comfortably at a New York club with an inveterate Bridge fiend, and we were amusing ourselves by comparing notes as to the most terrible tragedies which had ever befallen us at the Bridge table. I began by narrating to him the horrors of an English house party which I had unwillingly 'honored,' and where, for three evenings, I had played Double Dummy, for farthing points, with a deaf hostess to the accompaniment of a full Hungarian band. I also mentioned a saddening and memorable game which I had played, very late at night—at a Newport house—where the four twos were removed from the pack and four jokers inserted in their places, those jokers all having a higher value than the aces.

" 'My dear boy,' said my friend, the fiend, 'your stories are as mild as a night in June. Prepare yourself for a tragedy more terrifying than any tale told by Edgar Allan Poe.

" 'It was,' " he continued, " 'at the Hotel Splendide-Royal in Aix-les-Bains. I was playing twenty-cent points—one franc—which is just double my usual limit. I had lost six consecutive rubbers. I had cut, each rubber, against a peculiarly malevolent-looking Spaniard, who had a reputation at cards which was none too savory. There had been trouble about him only the day before at the Villa des Fleurs, where he had been mixed up in a somewhat unpleasant Baccarat scandal. He was a crafty and sullen Bridge player and I had conceived a most cordial dislike to him. To make matters worse, he had twice doubled my make of hearts and had twice scored up the game as a consequence. I contained my feeling of antipathy as best I could and bided my time.

" 'Finally—it was hideously late and the card-room waiter was snoring in the service-closet—my time for revenge arrived. It was my deal, and I saw at a glance that I had dealt myself an enormous hand. I could hardly believe my eyes. I held nine spades with the four top honors, the bare ace of clubs, the bare ace of hearts and the king and queen of diamonds. Here was a certainty of eleven tricks at no trumps, and, very possibly, twelve or thirteen. I looked at the Spaniard, whose turn it was to lead, and smiled exultantly.

" 'No trumps, I said, the note of triumph quite perceptible in my voice. Quick as a flash the Spaniard had doubled—and quick as another I had redoubled.

" 'When, however, he had jacked it up to 96 a trick, I hesitated, but of course went at him again with 192. Ah, ha! I said to myself. Mr. Bird of ill-omen, you are my prey, my chosen victim for the sacrifice.

" 'The price per trick had soon sailed up to 1,512, and I ventured to look at my partner. He was chalky white about the gills and his eyes seemed to stare idiotically into space. His agonized expression prompted me to say "Enough."

" 'Suddenly I had a terrible feeling of alarm. Had I, perhaps, mistaken the queen of diamonds for the queen of hearts? If so, my king of diamonds was bare and the mysterious Spaniard might run off twelve fat diamond tricks before I could say "Jack Robinson." With a sinking heart I looked at my hand again—all was well! The queen was surely a diamond. I looked at the olive-skinned gentleman from Spain and begged him to lead a card. I felt a great joy welling up within me. Revenge—sooeet r-r-revenge.

" 'At this moment the Spaniard led a card. I looked at it nervously. As soon as my eyes beheld it my heart seemed to stop beating. He had opened the ace of a strange green suit; a suit which I had never seen before; a suit all covered with mysterious figures and symbols. I felt strangely giddy, but discarded one of my beautiful spades. I looked at my partner who was the picture of despair. He said, mechanically and as though life had lost all beauty for him, "Having no hyppogryphs?" to which icy inquiry I answered in a strange, hissing whisper, "No gryppolyphs."

" 'The Spaniard followed with another green card, a king, this time, and again I played one of my priceless spades. The leader smiled a mahogany smile and proceeded to run off his entire suit of thirteen green cards. He then scored up a grand slam, the game, and a rubber of 10,450 points, or $2,090. I felt my brain reeling, and then and there fainted away with my head on the card table. Soon, however, I thought I felt my Spaniard tugging at my coat-sleeve. My anger at this was beyond all bounds. I opened my eyes, prepared to strike the crafty foreigner in his wicked face, and saw—my servant standing by my bed with my breakfast tray in his hands and my bathrobe on his arm.' "

—FRANK CROWNINSHIELD

The Base Canard

GEORGE BEYNON very likely feels like stout Cortez, or, if you prefer, Balboa. It was Mr. Beynon who discovered, amid a pile of clippings, the story in the Minneapolis *Journal* anent the group who wrote to Mr. Culbertson for some technical information and received a bill for "professional services."

The discovery is, indeed, one to be proud of. All of us, when we were young, used to like to go a-hunting for this story. We would find it in Pullman smoking cars, in barber-shop Poker games and even on the lips of our mothers. Every now and then we would find a perfect specimen in some country weekly. The newspapers seldom honored the story, however, nor could it ever be found in sheets whose circulation ran as high as 1,000. So far as we can remember, the Minneapolis *Journal* is the first big-city, reputable daily whose copy readers have been sufficiently naïve to let the tale go through.

In one of the first few issues of the Work-Whitehead Bridge Bulletin, or perhaps in its immediate successor, the original Auction Bridge Magazine, the research student can read in bold headlines, "Please Deny This Lie If You Hear It." "Outrageous Canard," the headline goes on to say, "Circulated About Mr. Work." The story beneath the headline tells of how Mr. Work is said to have charged one hundred dollars for his technical answers. It appeals to readers to let Mr. Work know the name of anyone telling this scurrilous story.

In the course of his life Mr. Work must have answered hundreds of thousands of letters; Mr. Culbertson today answers thousands weekly. Neither has once charged for information. In fact, no Bridge expert ever charged for answering these letters. Alas, he wouldn't get paid even if he did.

The hundred-dollar story didn't die when Contract came in and the name of Culbertson rose over the name of Work as the outstanding authority. In fact, inasmuch as Culbertson's name became even better known than Work's had been, the story was heard more often than ever.

And, we should like to point out, the story was still a hundred-dollar story. No Supreme Court decision had come along to enjoin price-fixing. Gossipers who wanted to tell the story were *scared* to have Mr. Culbertson charging anything less than a round century.

Then the Supreme Court acted, and bang! went the price. Reference to Mr. Beynon's department will reveal the sad fact that today, what with the depression and the sad demise of the NRA, the Minneapolis *Journal* had Mr. Culbertson sending a bill for a paltry ten-spot.

—*from* THE BRIDGE WORLD

¶ *We might go on to say that in the usual extension of this story, the recipient of the bill runs to his lawyer and asks, "Do I have to pay this?" The lawyer answers, "Yes, he is an expert and is entitled to payment." The next day the victim receives his lawyer's bill for $50.* ¶ *The other Bridge chestnuts go somewhat as follows:*

THE small-town expert visits New York and finds himself in a game with Work-Whitehead-Lenz, Culbertson-Sims-Jacoby, or what have you. When he returns home they ask him, "What did they say about your game?" He answers, "They never criticized me once. The only thing any of them said was once when I turned up a card while dealing and (Culbertson, Work) said, 'Why, the so-and-so can't even deal.' "

TWO young ladies enter a Bridge school and one of them says, "My friend wants to take a Bridge lesson." —"And how about you?" the instructor asks. —"Oh, no, I learned yesterday."

TWO little old ladies enter a big Bridge tournament and find themselves opposed to two famous experts. On the first hand one of the little old ladies bids one club and everyone passes. She plays the hand and goes down one. "Where do you ladies come from?" one of the experts asks, making polite conversation. "Mississippi," they answer. "And you came all the way from Mississippi just to go down one at one club!" "It's just as well we did," says the little old lady. "If we'd stayed in Mississippi we'd have been down two."

¶*Most Bridge anecdotes can be divided by personalities—those who actually have wit and those who have such a reputation for wit that every funny saying is sooner or later attributed to them, as for example malapropisms are to Samuel Goldwyn. There are Lochridge stories (Charles S. Lochridge), Kaplan stories (Fred D. Kaplan), Sims stories, Culbertson stories, Vanderbilt stories, George S. Kaufman stories, and the occasional stories about world figures.*

Lochridge Stories

FOR at least three rounds Lochridge's partner should have passed, but he kept on trying to take the contract. Finally Lochridge prevailed. At the end of the play his partner apologized. "I wouldn't have kept on bidding," he explained, "but the lady at my right inadvertently showed me her hand and I knew where every card was." "Do you think I'm blind?" Lochridge asked.

IN A Masters' Individual Tournament, Lochridge's partner had just finished playing a hand. The contract was four spades and he had gone down one. "Could I have done better?" he asked. "Yes," said Lochridge, "double-dummy you could have gone down two."

Kaplan Stories

IT SHOULD perhaps be mentioned that Fred Kaplan was long the *enfant terrible* of expert Bridge. Woman partners he reduced to tears, male partners he incited to murder. Once Kaplan, playing in a mixed-pair tournament (in which his partner was necessarily a woman), had strictly instructed his partner not to raise him without four trumps. Along came a hand on which he bid spades, she raised, and Kaplan became declarer at a spade contract. After the opening lead she laid down three trumps—the ace, king, and queen. Kaplan pulled out his watch and said, "I'll give you just twenty seconds to produce another spade."

KAPLAN has been widely credited with bidding "the fourth and last spade," but so have other players. This one is authenticated: Kaplan was bidding hearts, his partner spades. They bid up to a point at which he had bid six hearts, his partner six spades. Kaplan now bid seven no trump. "That saves a round of bidding," he explained.

Sims Stories

AT ALL tournaments, Hal Sims would take a half-dollar from his pocket, toss it, slap it down on the table, and bet each woman who came to his table two to one that she could not call it, heads or tails. Obviously the odds are even, two to one odds offer a distinct advantage, and Bridge players being keen on percentages all the women took him up on the bet. Sims always won. "I always put it down tails," he explained. "A woman is constitutionally incapable of saying 'tails' if she can say 'heads' instead."

SIMS was very proud of his ability to locate the opponents' high cards by psychology, when reasoning failed. He claimed never to have misguessed the location of a queen when he had a two-way finesse. So two players decided to frame him, and rang in a cold deck.

The key card was the queen of hearts. At the crucial moment Sims slapped the jack of hearts on the table and glared at both opponents. The one on his left followed quickly with a low heart. The one on his right lighted a cigarette. Sims slammed down his hand and said, "There's something wrong with this deck. Both you pigeons have the queen of hearts." And sure enough, both of them did.

Litvinoff

MAXIM LITVINOFF, Soviet foreign secretary in the years before World War II and exiled in disgrace when he could not forestall the war, was called back to power suddenly when Germany invaded Russia in June 1941. He told the story in a game in Washington, where he was sent as ambassador.

"I had just bid a grand slam," he recalled, "and the dummy was about to go down—when the telephone rang. The message recalled me to Moscow, at once. I dashed upstairs, packed a bag—"

"But how did the grand slam come out?" he was asked. (After all, it was a Bridge game.)

"I never stopped to find out," he said.

"Maxim Maximovitch," said one of the players sadly, "you will never make a Bridge player."

The foregoing story is well authenticated, yet we cannot but doubt it when we consider the next story, told about Winston Churchill—in 1922.

Churchill

WINSTON CHURCHILL, who recently played Bridge in New York homes, is the hero of the most dramatically interrupted rubber.

On the eve of declaration of war by England to Germany, Mr. Churchill, then head of the British Admiralty, worn out by suspense and anxiety sought relief in a rubber of Bridge with Lord Beaverbrook and two friends. In the midst of spirited bidding came a knock on the door and a special messenger holding an enormous sealed box. Churchill broke the seal and fished out a thin sheet of paper. It read "Germany declared war on France." Thus from the strategy of pasteboard battlefields where armies are annihilated by abstract symbols to their remote ancestor and prototype—war.

Paderewski

THERE is no question about Mr. Paderewski's ability to make the most of the cards he holds. One of his closest friends declared, "I have been playing Bridge with Mr. Paderewski for fourteen years, and he has never improved a bit. But there was never any room for improvement."

There are two reasons for this excellence. The first is that Mr. Paderewski has an extraordinarily mathematical mind. He will take one glance at a complicated Bridge score and instantly arrive at the correct total. He adds three and even four columns of figures at the same time with ease. When he was playing once with the treasurer of a New York bank and performed this feat, the banker, amazed, asked how he did it.

"It is easy," said Mr. Paderewski. "I simply visualize all the columns at once."

"Well," said the banker, "I have been dealing with figures all my life and I should never attempt it."

The millionaire partnership of Harold S. Vanderbilt and Waldemar von Zedtwitz has always been much written about—because Vanderbilt invented modern Contract Bridge; because they have been one of the greatest and most conspicuously successful pairs in the history of the game; but chiefly because they are both colorful personalities as well as great players in their own right. And both play with the utmost concentration, deliberation, and determination to win.

Vanderbilt and von Zedtwitz Stories

VANDERBILT and von Zedtwitz were playing in the semifinal round of the Vanderbilt Cup tournament, which that year was at the old Ritz-Carlton Hotel in New York. Vanderbilt had just bid three spades and it was up to von Zedtwitz. As he was pondering his bid, a passing waiter stumbled and spilled an entire pitcher of ice water over his shoulders.

Absently, von Zedtwitz shook the ice cubes off his shoulders. "Don't do that again," he said to the waiter; "I don't like it. —Four diamonds."

VANDERBILT was in a tough game in a New York club. It was a relatively high-stake game, but it had been fairly even, and after two hours' play Vanderbilt was minus two dollars on the back score.

He was due to take a midnight train to Chicago—but he was out two dollars. He looked at his watch. Ordinarily he would be leaving now; there wasn't really time to start a new rubber—but he was out two dollars.

He said, "One more rubber."

The train was due to leave at midnight. It was almost midnight. The rubber was over; Vanderbilt was out twenty-three dollars.

He said, "One more rubber."

His office called; the attendant came and reminded him of the train. The second rubber was finished. Vanderbilt had won it. But it wasn't quite enough; Vanderbilt was out six dollars.

He said, "One more rubber."

His office called again; the starter at Grand Central Station was frantic; the train should have left three minutes ago. The game proceeded. Vanderbilt won the rubber. It was worth eighteen dollars. Now he was winning, by twelve dollars. He excused himself and dashed off. His car was waiting; the train pulled out less than thirty minutes late. (Yes, they have been known to hold trains for a man who is a director of thirty-seven railroad corporations.)

Does anyone seriously want to argue that two dollars, or six dollars, could hold a man who more than once has paid a million dollars for a yacht?

George S. Kaufman Stories

GEORGE KAUFMAN walked into Crockford's Club and sat down to kibitz. Just as he settled himself in his chair, a pair bid four hearts, were doubled, and went down 800. The rubber proceeded wildly. Nobody seemed able to make any contract. Fully half an hour later it was still going on. At this point the same pair bid four hearts, were doubled, and went down 800. Kaufman rose from his chair. "This is where I came in," he observed; and he walked out.

ONE OF THE well-known New York club players is Percy Uris (pronounced your-us), member of a famous construction firm. It so happened, however, that as late as the 1950's he and George Kaufman had never chanced to be in the same game, so they had never met. One afternoon Kaufman cut into a game at the Cavendish Club in New York. Uris, the only player in the game he did not already know, rose and introduced himself. "My name is Uris," he said. "Your name is minus," acknowledged Kaufman, warmly returning the handshake.

. . . and William Shakespeare

How shall we try it? We'll draw cuts. —*Comedy of Errors*
Well, sit we down. —*Hamlet*
Who calls? —*Julius Caesar*
I'll call for clubs. —*The Merchant of Venice*
Who bids thee call? I do not bid thee call. —*The Merchant of Venice*
Clubs—clubs. —*Two Gentlemen of Verona*
Hit the woman who cried out clubs. —*Henry VII*
A spade—a spade. —*Hamlet*
Why a spade? —*Timon of Athens*
Thou bid'st me to my loss. —*Cymbeline*
I would be glad to hear some instructon from my fellow partner. —*Measure for Measure*
Mark our contract. —*The Winter's Tale*
But an Ace. —*Midsummer Night's Dream*
What means that trump? —*Timon of Athens*
We will yet have more tricks. —*Merry Wives of Windsor*
You have put him down, lady, you have put him down. —*Much Ado About Nothing*
There's but one down. —*Macbeth*
There were two honors. —*Henry IV*
Come on, then, let's to bed. Ah, sirrah, by my fay, it waxes late. —*Romeo and Juliet*

How Good Is Ike's Bridge Game?

SINCE 1942, when Dwight D. Eisenhower was sent to take charge in Europe, his Bridge playing has been recurrently noted in the newspapers and he has usually been described as a Bridge "expert." The question is, what is an expert and just how good is Ike's Bridge?

Ike is exclusively a Rubber Bridge player, so he cannot be officially rated as are the 50,000* tournament-playing members of the American Contract Bridge League. However, some of the best American players (notably Oswald Jacoby and the late Ely Culbertson) have [made] convincing reports of his prowess.

President Eisenhower, it seems clear, is not overrated as a Bridge player. Said Culbertson, "He plays in the same class as Al Gruenther." (General Alfred Gruenther is Ike's favorite Bridge partner and for nearly thirty years [until his retirement in 1956] was considered the best Bridge player in the United States Army.) The consensus is that in the best Bridge-club games, the President would be on a par with anyone except the "pros," and that if he played in official tournaments he could be at least a Senior Master (the second highest rank).

Said Jacoby, "I know a lot of persons who play good Bridge. They have learned how the game should be played. But their play is wooden. The President obviously plays intelligent Bridge. He thinks about what he does and what he does is done with good reason. He's the nicest person at the Bridge table that I've ever played with. He doesn't get excited about winning or losing but he plays hard. He plays better Bridge than golf; he tries to break 90 at golf; at Bridge you would say he does break 80."

In a Bridge game, Eisenhower is serious and studious. He does not play "Poker Bridge," the style of play in which one tries primarily to fool the opponents by unconventional play. Rather, he tries to do the right thing. While both styles of play can be effective, the majority of topflight players favor the straightforward game that Eisenhower plays. Eisenhower plays a simple bidding system. The Blackwood slam con-

* This figure was low even for 1955, when this article was published. The A.C.B.L. had 75,000 members in 1957.

vention is the only artificial bidding device he uses.

Eisenhower bids and plays fast and decisively. He does not hog the bidding and try to play all the hands (traditionally a weakness of men in commanding positions). He often chooses a trump as an opening lead, which if anything is a strong point in his game, for the average player leads trumps too seldom.

No one could possibly enjoy a Bridge game more than Eisenhower does. In November 1942, the invasion of North Africa was all in readiness but some 800 Allied ships were fogbound off the African coast. "What'll we do now?" the other ranking officers asked. "Let's have a game of Bridge," Eisenhower replied. So they did. Eisenhower, Gruenther, General Mark Clark and Commander Harry Butcher, Ike's Naval Aide, played Bridge until the fog lifted and the invasion could begin.

In January 1946, when Clark was American Commander in occupied Austria and Gruenther was his Chief of Staff, Eisenhower summoned them to join him at a mountain resort in the Alps. When they arrived, Eisenhower was waiting for them with one of his staff officers, Brigadier General Raymond Moses. The first thing he said was, "Let's play some Bridge."

During the war, when he was working long hours seven days a week, Ike had few possibilities for Bridge but whenever possible he would assemble the best players among his staff officers and have a game. It was almost his only effective form of relaxation. Since Bridge itself is a difficult and nerve-straining game, especially when played seriously, this may seem like a paradox; yet the explanation is simple. In his official capacity, Eisenhower was constantly faced with tough decisions. Any decision, if wrong, could cost thousands of lives. The most relaxing thing he could do was to play a game in which the problems were tough, the solutions difficult, but the consequences of error were just a few hundred harmless points written down on a scorepad.

—from SPORTS ILLUSTRATED

PROBLEM HANDS AND CURIOSITIES

¶*Many card games have developed a large literature of problems and of card-playing situations so unusual that they make the* aficionado *exclaim with delight. By far the largest group is in Whist and Bridge, but there is a respectable number in other games. Most of these problems are "double dummy," which means that every player is assumed to know the location of every card and will always make the most advantageous play, even though such a play might be logically impossible in actual play.* ¶*We begin with the largest group, the Whist and Bridge problems.*

The Mississippi Heart Hand

ACTUALLY the most famous curiosity of the Whist family is "the Duke of Cumberland's hand," which is used in Sam Hellman's Bridge story on page 51. According to the legends (which vary), one or the other of two Dukes of Cumberland, the son of George II or the son of George III, lost £20,000 betting that he could win the odd trick—that is, seven tricks in all—when he held ♠ AKQ ♡ AKQJ ◇AK ♣ KJ97, and clubs were trumps. Actually he could not win a single trick, as Mr. Hellman's story explains. This Whist hand was first published in a book by Edmond Hoyle in 1750, but it was no doubt already old stuff with the hustlers who preyed on Whist players. There is almost no limit to the ingenuity of a hustler seeking to cheat in a card game.

The next-most-famous curiosity, also a standard cheater's device, is equally ancient. Variations of it appeared in Hoyle's books from 1746 on, and the full deal was published in Thomas Mathews' *Advice to the Young Whist Player* in 1803. This was the most popular cheaters' hand in Whist, when large bets were made on who would win the odd trick; in the literature of Whist nearly every story about cheating makes this hand its theme. But the hand really came into its glory when the original game of Bridge arrived.

In this original game of Bridge, the dealer always played the dummy and had the right to name the trump suit, but either side—whichever won more than six tricks—could score toward game. The value per trick could be doubled and redoubled indefinitely, and if both sides were stubborn enough there could be perhaps thirty doubles and redoubles. If the game started at one cent a point, by this time a single trick could be worth a million dollars. The "Mississippi" in the name of the Mississippi Heart Hand comes from a story that the hand was used by Mississippi River steamboat gamblers—and perhaps it was—though Poker was their game; but there is no authenticated record of any such instance. This is the famous hand in which the whole idea is to win the odd trick:

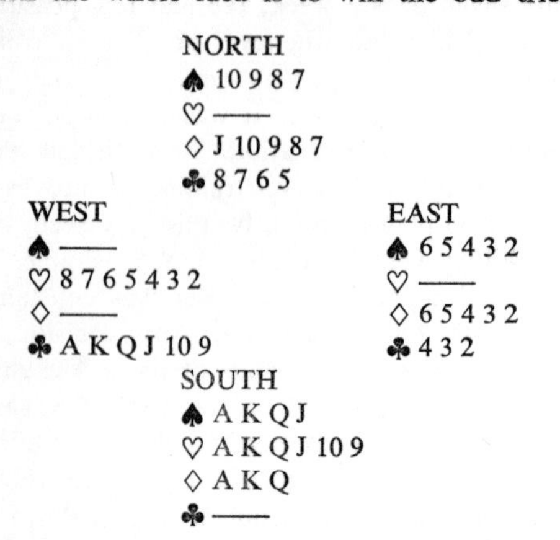

South deals and makes hearts trumps. West doubles, South redoubles, and so on; it is only a question of which becomes tired or impatient first. West leads a club and South can make only his six high trumps, so West gets the odd trick. This hand may be varied in many ways, but the theme is always the same.

The first of the celebrated Whist problems was published in the 1860s by James Clay, who had then been for more than a generation England's most revered Whist authority. Since it seemed very difficult to the best players of that time but would be child's play to even a fair Bridge player today, it has historical significance as a clue to the deplorably meager science of Whist. Mr. Clay attributed the hand to an unnamed Vienna player. It has been suggested that this was merely a device for introducing a problem he himself had invented, but from his writings it would not appear that he had sufficient skill—unless like Cavendish, the great British authority of the next generation, he "stumbled on it." The following article by F. M. Urban tells the whole story.

The Great Vienna Coup

by F. M. URBAN

THE Great Vienna Coup" originally was the name of a Double Dummy problem in Whist, proposed by James Clay. Here are the hands:

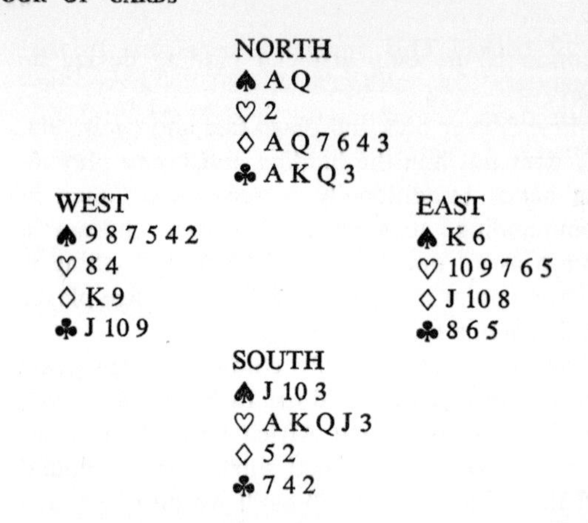

Clubs are trump. North leads and makes all 13 tricks.

The problem is not particularly difficult for a modern player. One begins with clubs and at the fourth trick the lead of the trey squeezes East. Unguarding spades or diamonds obviously loses at once, and it seems best to discard a heart. At the fifth trick North plays the ace of spades and then, putting South in, takes five rounds of hearts. North discards the queen of spades and 6, 4 and 3 of diamonds. On the lead of the last heart at the tenth trick East must discard either the king of spades or a diamond, and loses all the tricks in either case.

The play is typical of many similar problems in which one begins with a squeeze and continues with the play of a card which apparently unguards a suit. There are hundreds of problems which are solved in this way and the term "Vienna Coup" has become generic. It does not designate a particular problem any more, but a whole group of problems, which are all solved by the same method. It is difficult for us to imagine that there was a time when this play was something new, but it must have offered an entirely different aspect to Mr. Clay's contemporaries who did not know how to engineer a squeeze. A person unacquainted with this technique may puzzle many a weary hour over this problem without finding the solution. If you doubt it, present Mr. Clay's problem to a player who has just mastered the rudiments of the game and watch his efforts.

Mr. Clay introduces his problem with the following words: "I may permit myself to present to my readers one of the most beautiful problems I have ever seen. It occurred a few months back in actual play in Vienna, and at Double Dummy. Its story runs thus: The most celebrated player in Vienna had to play the hands North and South. As soon as the cards were exposed, he exclaimed: 'Why, I shall make all 13 tricks.' This appeared impossible to the bystanders, for, although his hands were, between them, of commanding strength, still his adversaries' hands, between them, held every suit guarded, except the trump. Large bets were made against the accomplishment of the feat, which was, however, performed; and it became evident that, if hands North and South are rightly played, hands East and West are utterly helpless, and, in spite of three guarded suits, must lose all 13 tricks. I give the four hands . . . and withhold the key to the mystery, in the hope that my readers will be at the trouble of finding it for themselves."

Mr. Clay's problem proved a hard nut to crack for the Whist players of his time. Henry Jones, better known by his *nom de plume* "Cavendish," worked three days on it without finding the solution, only in the end to stumble into it by accident. Mr. William Pole says in his *Philosophy of Whist*: "Problems in Double Dummy are sometimes given as puzzles for solution, and one famed one especially, called the 'Vienna Coup,' is so difficult that any one who can solve it, even after long study, is considered deserving of great credit." Messrs. Clay, Jones and Pole evidently believed in the excessive difficulty of this problem and their view probably was correct for the Whist players of their time.

It hardly is true for the Bridge players of our day. I showed Mr. Clay's problem to several of my friends whom I considered good players, and none disappointed me by failing to find the solution within a reasonable time. Mr. Pole's judgment must be turned upside down in order to apply to our times: Nobody can be considered a good player who does not solve The Great Vienna Coup within the few minutes which one has at one's disposal for thinking at the card table during actual play. What Mr. Clay calls "the key to the mystery" is in the possession of every good player today, which proves that the ordinary run of our players have a better understanding of the game than the star performers of former generations.

In one respect, however, my friends did not equal the record of the inventor of this coup: None of them found the solution at first sight and on the first attempt. Remember that the hands were offered to them as a problem and that a Bridge player of our times has infinitely more practice in squeezing than any Whist-playing contemporary of Mr. Clay ever could have. One cannot help admiring the feat of that unknown Viennese player who recognized the problem in actual play and solved it at a glance. This probably is the most memorable test of the analytic powers of a Whist or Bridge player.

The name of the player who invented The Great Vienna Coup probably will remain unknown. Mr. Clay merely calls him "the most celebrated player in Vienna," a statement with which we certainly will agree, and says that the hands were played a few months back, referring presumably to the date of writing. We do not know when Mr. Clay prepared his manuscript and unfortunately there is no certainty as to the date of the first appearance of his book. The above quotation is taken from the 1881 edition of *The Laws of Short Whist and a Treatise of the Game*. This is a "new and revised" edition and I never had a copy of the first edition in my hands. Catherine Perry Hargrave mentions several editions, but apparently has not seen the first edition either, from which one may conclude that the first edition is very rare.

There must be some conjecture as to the date of the first edition of this book, but it probably is 1864 or thereabout. The *Laws of Short Whist,* which are bound together with Mr. Clay's treatise, were agreed upon by the London clubs in April, 1864, and one may take it that the printing was rushed as much as possible, since it evidently was of great importance for the players to have the new rules in print. The first edition probably was completely sold out to players and small books which are constantly in use do not survive any great length of time. This is the reason why no copy of the first edition is to be had—neither new nor second hand—even if you offer a prize for it.

If our argument is correct, the game which Mr. Clay watched took place late in 1863 or in the beginning of 1864. Remains the question as to the name of the player who invented The Great Vienna Coup. This is a pretty little case in identity to unravel for an amateur detective. At first blush one might believe that this is not too hard. There were not so many clubs at Vienna in the early sixties which an Englishman could visit in order to watch a game. "The most celebrated player" must have been a person of some repute—at least among the card-players—and one might believe that it should be easy to identify this man to whom all Bridge players owe a debt of gratitude. Unfortunately this is not the case, and all my efforts in this direction have so far failed. Printed or written records are not extant and all persons with direct knowledge of Viennese Whist players at these distant times* are dead. However, I have not given up

* This was written in 1930.

hope yet, and it may happen that suddenly some person will turn up who can tell us the name of the father of all squeeze plays.

One of my many attempts to identify the inventor of The Great Vienna Coup led to results too funny not to be mentioned here. I had the idea that some person at Vienna might have some information about Viennese Whist players around 1864, and it seemed a good move to bring the case before the public by means of one of the large dailies. The *Neue Freie Presse* very courteously agreed to print Mr. Clay's problem with my comment.

The result was negative, but my little note brought forth some of the most extraordinary correspondence. At least it seemed extraordinary to me then. There are many excellent and delightful players in Vienna, but there are in this town an astonishing number of people who labor under the idea of being the best players in the world. These hidden champions resent the praise bestowed on anybody else and take it as a personal insult to hear somebody else being called "the most celebrated player in Vienna," even if that person must have died half a century ago. One of my correspondents, ignoring the issue, challenged me to name this most celebrated player of Vienna, because he wanted to watch his game and form an opinion on it. Incidentally, he would form an opinion as to the value of my judgment, but he gave me to understand that he did not think much of it anyhow. I did not answer. What good would it have been to tell that the inventor of The Great Vienna Coup will remain the most celebrated player of Vienna, no matter what happens?

The Deschapelles Coup

GUILLAUME DESCHAPELLES was a Frenchman born in 1780, died in 1847, whom James Clay called "incomparably the finest Whist player the world has ever known." While we can hardly trust Mr. Clay's opinion, it is probable that M. Deschapelles was truly a fine player. His reputation was as great in chess as in Whist. It is unfortunate that he left us no book to judge him by. He did project a major opus on Whist, the first volume of which was published in 1842; but this volume concerned itself exclusively with proposed changes in the Whist laws and he never got around to writing the second volume, which was to have been on skillful play. If the Deschapelles Coup was a sample of his play, the second volume would have been worth reading.

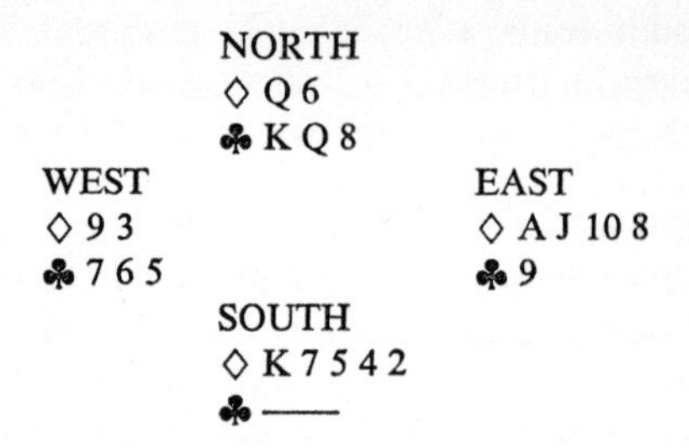

All the trumps were out. M. Deschapelles held the South cards. He led his king of diamonds and of course East won it with the ace, which gave North the remaining tricks. Of course, East could have thwarted the design by refusing to take his ace, but this does not detract from the excellence of the lead, and there are many cases in which there is no play that will counter the Deschapelles Coup.

The Whitfield Six

WILLIAM H. WHITFIELD was a professor of mathematics at Cambridge University. By his time (he was born in 1856) double-dummy problems had advanced far beyond the Vienna Coup, but still they had not approached—and have not since equaled—a six-card problem he composed in 1884. Though it would seem that any six-card problem is exhaustible by trial and error within a few hours, prizes offered for a solution in 1885 were not once claimed and the best Whist players insisted that there must have been some typographical error in printing the problem. There was not.

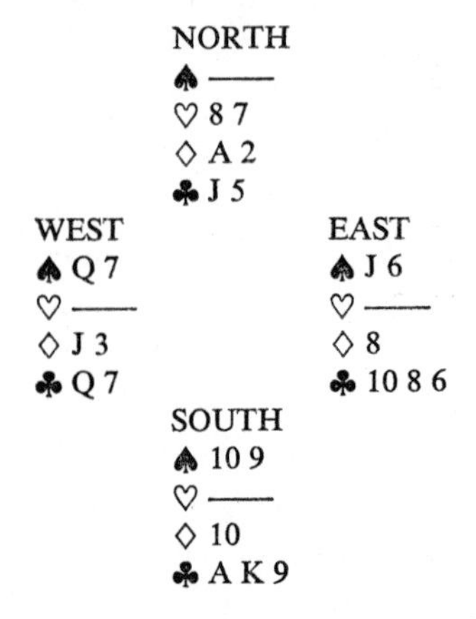

Hearts are trumps, South leads, and North-South must win all six tricks.

Those who wish to try the solution may pause here. For all others, this is the solution:

The key play is the first play: South leads the ace of clubs and North plays the jack. Next South leads a spade and trumps it with the seven of hearts. The eight of hearts is led from the North hand. East discards a diamond, South a diamond. West discards a spade, since his partner has the high spade still.

North now plays the ace of diamonds and East is squeezed. If he lets his spade go, South discards a club; if East discards a club, South discards his spade and his two clubs are high.

The essential part of the play is that after the first play West must hold his blank queen of clubs, for otherwise South could win an extra trick by finessing through East's ten.

Novelty Problems

THE following was one of a series of "penalty problems" in which the proposition was: A violation of the Bridge laws permits a player to choose one of alternative penalties. Which should he choose? In this case an opening lead out of turn created the problem, for in those times declarer was permitted to "call a lead" in addition to the options granted to him today. The bidding was Culbertsonian, era 1936-39, when "asking bids" were Culbertson's favored slam method.

South, dealer
North-South vulnerable

NORTH
♠ K J 7 3
♡ J 10 4 2
◇ A J 5
♣ K 8

WEST
♠ —
♡ A 7 3
◇ Q 9 7 4
♣ Q J 10 7 3 2

EAST
♠ 8 5 2
♡ 6
◇ K 10 6 2
♣ A 9 6 5 4

SOUTH
♠ A Q 10 9 6 4
♡ K Q 9 8 5
◇ 8 3
♣ —

The bidding:

South	West	North	East
1 ♠	2 ♣	3 ♠	4 ♣
4 ◇ ?[1]	Pass[2]	5 ◇[3]	Pass
5 ♠	6 ♣[4]	6 ♠	Pass
Pass	Pass		

[1] An asking bid. South hopes to find his partner with the ace of hearts and with the diamond suit controlled.

[2] A double would have been bad, because any double of an asking bid makes it easier for the other side to exchange information.

[3] This shows the ace of diamonds, but denies any other ace.

[4] On analysis, this is a bad bid, for it drives the opponents to a slam; however, if West could guess the position of the important outstanding honors, and finesse against the king of clubs and the jack of diamonds, he could make six clubs.

While South was studying his hand, and wondering just what North would show up with, East led the ace of clubs—out of turn.

This gave South the right to call a lead of any suit from West, or to call the ace of clubs a penalty card and force East to play it at his first opportunity.

South was perplexed, because he thought of all these things:

If he called a heart lead, the defenders might take the heart ace and get a ruff in hearts.

If he called a diamond lead it might knock out North's ace, with the heart suit not yet established.

If he called a club lead, East's ace would no longer be a penalty card. If North held the club king it would be finessed on the opening lead, and would never have any value.

If he called a spade lead, West might be void of spades, whereupon he could lead anything he chose. This would open the way to a disastrous heart or diamond lead.

If South chose to call the club ace a penalty card, West could lead anything he wished to lead, again making possible the heart or diamond lead.

Remember, South thought of all these possibilities without seeing the hand of any other player. He gets full credit for realizing all the danger he was facing, even though he never did arrive at the best solution to the problem.

We can see all the hands, and have the advantage of knowing that if South chose any of the penalties listed above, he would go down one or more at his slam contract.

What should South have done?

THE ANSWER

WE CAN give the answer immediately, because it is very simple.

South should have laid his hand down on the table, face up. This would make South the dummy, and North the declarer. The lead of the ace of clubs would stand, for with North the declarer, East would be the rightful leader.

This would protect North's king of clubs, if he had it. If not, it would still give North a start on the defenders, for the opening club lead would be ruffed in the South hand, and North could go about developing whatever tricks he had without having a valuable stopper knocked out on the first round—and without risking a heart ruff.

Study of the hands shows that it was necessary to establish the king of clubs to make the hand; it was also necessary to prevent an immediate heart ruff. Proper use of East's lead out of turn was the only thing which could have given North and South their vulnerable small slam.

South, after thinking of all the dangers, failed to apply the correct remedy, and called for a spade lead. West, having no spades, laid down the Ace and a small heart. But it is just as well that he did, because South had no right, on the cards, to make the slam, whether East led out of turn or not. A courteous exchange of errors did not affect the proper result of the hand. No one can feel bad when, despite unusual legal tangles, everything comes out as it should.

¶*S. J. Simon, the brilliant and eccentric British player who died so untimely a death in 1953, was both clever and profound in his writing, but never at the same time. His book* WHY YOU LOSE AT BRIDGE, *the only one published in the United States, was a minor classic along the former lines; his last book, published posthumously,* DESIGN FOR BIDDING, *was equally noteworthy in the department of profundity. The following problems are typical "Skip" Simon in his lighter vein.*

"All-In" Bridge

by S. J. SIMON

THERE is in the book of rules a section devoted to the proprieties of the game. Forget it.

In the school to which this article is dedicated it is perfectly legitimate to kick your partner under the table. The difficulty is to manage it. The way is usually barred by long-legged opponents tapping each other's soles in Morse.

Candidates for admission to the school are required to take an entrance examination to satisfy the Board that their Bridge has attained the required standard of foulness. Unsuccessful candidates are referred for six months and advised a course of practical study at a crammer. A list of recommended "crammer" clubs may be had on application to the Board.

As an indication of the standard required last year's examination paper is appended. The pass mark is 50 per cent—75 per cent and over gets first honors and carries with it the award of playing penny Bridge in obscure suburban clubs under a pseudonym.

To clarify the type of answer expected, here is an easy example taken from the Entrance Examination of 1930. Old rules.

N.-S. vulnerable. North dealer.

You are East and hold:

♠ x x x ♡ x x x ◇ x x x ♣ x x x x

North appears to be doing a quiet gloat. Glancing over his hand you note that he holds:

♠ A K Q ♡ A K Q ◇ A K Q J ♣ A K Q

What should you do?

Answer: Bid two clubs—a forcing bid—out of turn. South will now demand a new deal.

So now you understand.

THE COLLEGE OF "ALL-IN" CONTRACT

Entrance Examination

(Candidates are requested to write on one side of the paper only.)

1. West is an honest palooka. There is in his make-up no cunning, guile, or deceit—only a certain amount of greed. What he is doing in this game is not quite clear, but anyway here he is and it is up to you to make the most of him for quite clearly he won't be here long.

You are South, dealer, vulnerable. You bid one spade. West bids one no-trump. North bids seven spades. West doubles. North redoubles. The queen of hearts is led. Your combined hands are:

NORTH
♠ Q J x x x x
♡ A x
◇ A K Q x x
♣ —

SOUTH
♠ A 10 x x x
♡ K x x
◇ x x
♣ A Q x

On seeing dummy West smiles luxuriously and leans back in his chair. It is quite clear he holds K x of trumps.

How should you proceed?

2. Playing the Two-Club Convention, North deals and bids two clubs. East passes. You (South) hold:

♠—♡—◇—♣ A K Q J 10 9 8 7 6 5 4 3 2

North is a confirmed singleton-of-your-suit notrumpist. A void throws him into a rescue-at-any-price panic. It is utterly useless therefore to bid seven clubs. He is certain to take it out into seven notrumps.

What should you do?

NORTH
♠ K Q 6 5
♡ K Q 7
◇ Q 8 4
♣ K J 9

SOUTH
♠ A 4 3 2
♡ J 6 3
◇ 5 2
♣ A Q 8 4

You are South, playing a contract of four spades, West having bid and rebid diamonds. East is a player who hates to waste anything.

The king of diamonds is opened, on which East plays the ten—clearly the beginning of an echo. West follows with the ace of diamonds. The danger is obvious. East will trump the third diamond and force out your ace of trumps, thus setting the contract one trick if West holds three spades.

What is your best chance to stop him?

NORTH
♠ 7 5 2
♡ K 8
◇ A K Q
♣ A Q 6 4 3

SOUTH
♠ 9
♡ A Q 10 9 6 2
◇ 10 4 3
♣ K 8 5

You are South. The contract is six hearts. West opens ace of spades, followed by king of spades which you trump. On the second round of trumps West shows out. However the contract can still be made on a coup if East holds three clubs.

It is extremely unlikely however that East does hold three clubs. If he does West holds eleven cards in spades and diamonds and would surely have taken part in the bidding, which he failed to do. You must play on the assumption that East holds two clubs only. There is still hope, for East does not know you hold the king of clubs.

The correct procedure is as follows: Call the waiter and order a pack of cigarettes. Trance till the cigarettes arrive. Play a small club from your hand, allow West to follow, and now go into another and longer trance. Emerge from it to play the queen of clubs, and simultaneously thrust the newly opened pack of cigarettes under West's nose. Heave sigh of relief when queen wins, triumphantly play ace of clubs and a third club. East is now almost certain to place you with a doubleton in clubs and refuse to ruff.

Question. Why is it necessary to waste a cigarette on West?

ANSWERS

TO "ALL-IN" BRIDGE

1. The best chance is to curse your partner as convincingly as possible, ending up with "Partner, how could you put me in seven, missing both the ace and king of trumps?" Now with a resigned air lead small spade from your hand. West is a greedy player and will probably fall for it.

2. Make an underbid of one club. Correct it to seven clubs. Partner is now silenced.

Candidates who found the answer of "Pass" are awarded half marks. This bid at least insures getting a part score.

3. At the second trick stretch a languid hand toward dummy and touch the queen of diamonds—by mistake. Say "Curse it! Played." Play it. East, who never wastes anything, will now be too cheap to trump the third round of diamonds.

4. To stop him from stretching his hand across the table on the play of the club queen, thus revealing that he does not hold the king and so encouraging East to trump the third round.

THE TAROT AND FORTUNE-TELLING

[The mystery and romance of playing cards are nowhere more evident than in the Tarot, that ancient pack whose exotic names and colorful designs bring out the gypsy in all of us. William Lindsay Gresham based his ingenious thriller, NIGHTMARE ALLEY, on the tarots and their mysticism, and in the following excerpt we let him introduce the Tarot to you. The setting is a good old American carnival troupe on its special train, chugging through the night from the last one-night stand to the next.

from Nightmare Alley

by WILLIAM LINDSAY GRESHAM

FOR THE long haul the Ackerman-Zorbaugh Shows took to the railroad. Trucks on flatcars, the carnies themselves loaded into old coaches, the train boomed on through darkness—tearing past solitary jerk towns, past sidings of dark freight empties, over trestles, over bridges, where the rivers lay coiling their luminous way through the star-shadowed countryside.

In the baggage car, among piles of canvas and gear, a light burned high up on the wall. A large packing case with auger holes bored in its sides to admit air, stood in the middle of a cleared space. From inside it came intermittent scrapings. At one end of the car the geek* lay on a pile of canvas, his ragged, overalled knees drawn up to his chin.

Around the snake box men made the air gray with smoke.

"I'm staying." Major Mosquito's voice had the insistence of a cricket's.

Sailor Martin screwed up the left side of his face against the smoke of his cigarette and dealt.

"I'm in," Stan said. He had a jack in the hole. The highest card showing was a ten in the Sailor's hand.

"I'm with you," Joe Plasky said, the Lazarus smile never changing.

Behind Joe sat the hulk of Bruno, his shoulders rounding under his coat. He watched intently, his mouth dropping open as he concentrated on Joe's hand.

"I'm in, too," Martin said. He dealt. Stan got another jack and pushed in three blues.

* A sub-Skid Row alcoholic who pretends to eat rats and chickens alive.

"Going to cost you to string along," he said casually.

Major Mosquito, his baby head close to the boxtop, stole another glance at his hole card. "Nuts!"

"Guess it's between you gents," Joe said placidly. Bruno, from behind him, said, "Ja. Let them fight it out. We take it easy this time."

Martin dealt. Two little ones fell between them. Stan threw more blues in. Martin met him and raised him two more.

"I'll see you."

The Sailor threw over his hole card. A ten. He reached for the pot.

Stan smiled and counted his chips. At a sound from the Major all of them jumped. "Hey!" It was a long-drawn fiddle scrape.

"What's eating you, Big Noise?" Martin asked, grinning.

"Lemme see them tens!" the Major reached toward the center of the snake box with his infant's hand and drew the cards toward him. He examined the backs.

Bruno got up and moved over behind the midget. He picked up one of the cards and held it at an angle toward the light.

"What's eating you guys?" Martin said.

"Daub!" Major Mosquito wailed, taking his cigarette from the edge of the box and puffing it rapidly. "The cards are marked with daub.* They're smeared to act like readers. You can see it if you know where to look."

Martin took one and examined it. "Damn! You're right."

"They're your cards," the Major went on in his accusing falsetto.

Martin bristled. "What d'ya mean, my cards? Somebody left 'em around the cookhouse. If I hadn't thought to bring 'em we wouldn't have had no game."

Stan took the deck and riffled them under his thumb. Then he riffled again, throwing cards face down on the table. When he reversed them they were all high ones, picture cards and tens. "That's daub, all right," he said. "Let's get a new deck."

"You're the card worker," Martin said aggressively. "What do you know about this? Daub is stuff you smear on the other fellow's cards during the game."

"I know enough not to use it," Stan said easily. "I don't deal. I never deal. And if I wanted to work any angles I'd stack them on the pick-up until I got the pair I wanted on top of the deck, undercut and injog the top card of the top half, shuffle off eight, outjog and shuffle off. Then I'd undercut to the outjog—"

"Let's get a new deck," Joe Plasky said. "We won't any of us get rich arguing about how the cards got marked. Who's got a deck?"

They sat silent, the expansion joints of the rails clicking by beneath them. Then Stan said, "Zeena has a deck of fortunetelling cards we can play with. I'll get them."

Martin took the marked deck, stepped to the partly open door and sent the cards flying into the wind. "Maybe a new deck will change my luck," he said. "I been going bust every hand except the last one."

The car shook and pounded on through the dark. Behind the open door they could see the dark hills and a sliver of moon setting behind them with a scattering of stars.

Stan returned and with him came Zeena. Her black dress was relieved by a corsage of imitation gardenias, her hair caught up on top of her head with a random collection of blond hairpins.

"Howdy, gents. Thought I'd take a hand myself if I wouldn't be intruding. Sure gets deadly back in that coach. I reckon I've read every movie magazine in the outfit by this time." She opened her purse and placed a deck of cards on the box. "Now you boys let me see your hands. All clean? 'Cause I don't want you smooching up these cards and getting 'em dirty. They're hard enough to get hold of."

Stan took the deck carefully and fanned them. The faces were an odd conglomeration of pictures. One showed a dead man, his head skewered with ten swords. Another had a picture of three women in ancient robes, each holding a cup. A hand reaching out of a cloud, on another, held a club from which green leaves sprouted.

"What do you call these things, Zeena?" he asked.

"That's the Tarot," she said impressively. "Oldest kind of cards in the world. They go all the way back to Egypt, some say. And they're sure a wonder for giving private readings. Every time I have something to decide or don't know which way to turn I run them over for myself. I always get some kind of an answer that makes sense. But you can play Poker with 'em. They got four suits; wands are diamonds, cups are hearts, swords are clubs, and coins are spades. This bunch of pictures here—that's the Great Arcana. They're just for fortunetelling. But there's one of 'em—if I can find it—we can use for a joker.

* Daub is a pastelike paint that comes in tiny, round tin boxes, in blue and red to match standard playing-card colors. Readers are any marked cards.

TRADITIONAL TAROTS:

Left, "the fool"—precursor of the joker; right, "the hanged man" which the players in this game (see below) *mistakenly use as joker; center, "the juggler."*

Here it is." She threw it out and placed the others back in her purse.

Stan picked up the joker. At first he couldn't figure out which end was the top. It showed a young man suspended head down by one foot from a T-shaped cross, but the cross was of living wood, putting out green shoots. The youth's hands were tied behind his back. A halo of golden light shone about his head and on reversing the card Stan saw that his expression was one of peace—like that of a man raised from the dead. Like Joe Plasky's smile. The name of the card was printed in old-fashioned script at the bottom. *The Hanged Man.*

"Holy Christ, if these damn things don't change my luck, nothing will," the Sailor said.

Zeena took a pile of chips from Joe Plasky, anted, then shuffled and dealt the hole cards face down. She lifted hers a trifle and frowned. The game picked up. Stan had an eight of cups in the hole and dropped out. Never stay in unless you have a jack or better in the hole and drop out when better than a jack shows on the board. Unless you've got the difference.

Zeena's frown deepened. The battle was between her, Sailor Martin, and the Major. Then the Sailor dropped out. The Major's hand showed three knights. He called. Zeena held a flush in coins.

"Ain't you the bluffer," the Major piped savagely. "Frowning like you had nothing and you sitting on top of a flush."

Zeena shook her head. "I wasn't meaning to bluff, even. It was the hole card I was frowning at—the ace of coins, what they call pentacles. I always read that 'Injury by a trusted friend.' "

Stan uncrossed his legs and said, "Maybe the snakes have something to do with it. They're scraping around under the lid here like they were uncomfortable."

Major Mosquito spat on the floor, then poked his finger in one of the auger holes. He withdrew it, chirruping. From the hole flicked a forked thread of pink. The Major drew his lips back from his tiny teeth and quickly touched the lighted ember of his cigarette to the tongue. It flashed back into the box and there was the frenzied scraping of coils twisting and whipping inside.

"Jesus!" Martin said. "You shouldn't of done that, you little stinker. Them damn things'll get mad."

The Major threw back his head. "Ho, ho, ho, ho! Next time I'll do it to you—I'll make a hit on the Battleship *Maine*."

Stan stood up. "I've had enough, gents. Don't let me break up the game, though."

Balancing against the rock of the train, he pushed through the piled canvas to the platform of the next coach. His left hand slid under the edge of his vest and unpinned a tiny metal box the size and shape of a five-cent piece. He let his hand drop and the container fell between the cars. It had left a dark smudge on his finger. Why do I have to mess around with all this stuff? I didn't want their dimes. I wanted to see if I could take them. Jesus, the only thing you can depend on is your brains!

In the coach, under the dimmed lights, the crowd of carnival performers and concessioners sprawled, huddled, heads on each others' shoulders; some had stretched themselves on newspapers in the aisles. In the corner of a seat Molly slept, her lips slightly parted, her head against the glass of the black window. How helpless they all looked in the ugliness of sleep. A third of life spent unconscious and corpselike. And some, the great majority, stumbled through their waking hours scarcely more awake, helpless in the face of destiny. They stumbled down a dark alley toward their deaths. They sent exploring feelers into the light and met fire and writhed back again into the darkness of their blind groping.

At the touch of a hand on his shoulder Stan jerked around. It was Zeena. She stood with her feet apart, braced easily against the train's rhythm. "Stan, honey, we don't want to let what's happened get us down. God knows, I felt bad about Pete. And I guess you did too. Everybody did. But this don't stop us from living. And I been wondering . . . you still like me, don't you, Stan?"

"Sure—sure I do, Zeena. Only I thought—"

"That's right, honey. The funeral and all. But I can't keep up mourning for Pete forever. My mother, now—she'd of been grieving around for a year but what I say is, it's soon enough we'll all be pushing 'em up. We got to get some fun. Tell you what. When we land at the next burg, let's us ditch the others and have a party."

Stan slid his arm around her and kissed her. In the swaying, plunging gait of the train their teeth clicked and they broke apart, laughing a little. Her hand smoothed his cheek. "I've missed you like all hell, honey." She buried her face in the hollow of his throat.

Over her shoulder Stan looked into the car of sleepers. Their faces had changed, had lost their hideousness. The girl Molly had waked up and was eating a chocolate bar. There was a smudge of chocolate over her chin. Zeena suspected nothing.

Stan raised his left hand and examined it. On the ball of the ring finger was a dark streak. Daub. He touched his tongue to it and then gripped Zeena's shoulder, wiping the stain on the black dress.

They broke apart and pushed down the aisle to a pile of suitcases where they managed to sit. In her ear Stan said, "Zeena, how does a two-person code work? I mean a good one—the kind you and Pete used to work." Audiences in evening clothes. Top billing. The Big Time.

Zeena leaned close, her voice suddenly husky. "Wait till we get to the burg. I can't think about nothing except you right now, honey. I'll tell you some time. Anything you want to know. But now I want to think about what's coming between the sheets." She caught one of his fingers and gave it a squeeze.

In the baggage coach Major Mosquito turned over his hole card. "Three deuces of swords showing and one wild one in the hole makes four of a kind. Ha, ha, ha, ha. *The Hanged Man!*"

FORTUNETELLING

For centuries, devotees of the occult have studied the Tarot. Every phase of fact and fantasy has resulted. Literally millions have believed that the Tarot actually holds and can reveal the key to future events. A few years ago Macy's put some Tarot cards on sale and asked Geoffrey Mott-Smith to write a booklet to go with them. He read almost twenty books and boiled them down to the following. The description of cartomancy that follows does not represent the opinion of the editors (or of Mr. Mott-Smith). The folly of trusting to a pack of cards to predict the future can easily be seen if you realize that every shuffle produces a new fortune. However, it is pleasant fantasy, provided you don't take it seriously.

The Tarot

by GEOFFREY MOTT-SMITH

For six hundred years and more, the pack of playing cards known as the Tarot has engrossed and entertained the Western world.

With these famous cards, mystics at medieval carnivals foretold the future; mathematicians delved into the laws of probabilities and the doctrine of chances; kings and their courtiers, as well as the common folk, played games for pastime or for stakes.

Hundreds of books have been written about the Tarot. Occultists have related it to ancient Egypt, to the Hebrew Cabala, to the most ancient rites of divination.

Hundreds of games have been played with the Tarot; these time-honored playing cards have given birth to, or have influenced, nearly every card game we play today.

Most ancient of these games is the one called Tarocchi in Italy, Tarock in Germany, Tarot in France. Throughout Central Europe, after these many centuries, it is still the most popular game.

For fortunetelling, the Tarot is still supreme and thousands still delve into its mysteries daily.

The Tarot will be described in detail on the following pages; but for the reader who is not familiar with it, it may be briefly described thus:

The full Tarot comprises 78 cards.

Of these, 56 cards constitute what we would call "regular playing cards." There are four suits of 14 cards each—ten numbered cards, and four picture cards. In the Tarot pack, these are the *Minor Arcana.*

The other 22 cards are the *tarots,* or *Major Arcana* (French *atouts*). They are pictorial cards, symbolic of all that is worldly, spiritual, and occult.

Through the centuries, the Major Arcana has changed little. In every country today, as for the past 600 years and more, the first tarot bears a picture of a juggler, the twelfth is the hanged man, the twenty-first is the world, the lowest is the fool, precursor of the joker in the modern pack.

The Minor Arcana, the 56-card portion of the Tarot, has changed much both in design and in structure, with the time, the country, and the game. From it the French took the 52-card "standard" pack that the English and Americans use; they also made a 32-card pack used in many countries. The Germans made a 36-card pack. The Italians and Spanish made a 40-card pack.

ORIGIN OF THE TAROT

THERE are many legends about the origin of playing cards; all are undependable, most of them can be proved false, and some are downright ridiculous. We do not actually know when or where playing cards were first made and used. We do not know when they were first introduced into Europe, or where, or by whom.

As with dice, dominoes, and chess, the conclusion seems inescapable that playing cards developed through a long process beginning with remotest antiquity. They were made in China as early as the tenth century A.D. and possibly before. Playing cards were introduced into Europe at least as early as the fourteenth century, probably in the thirteenth century.

The oldest known European playing cards are the *Tarot,* and undoubtedly came to the rest of Europe from, or by way of, Italy. The Tarot is made up of two separable packs, which may have been separate originally. The suit cards are analogous to the paper and bone cards of India and China, and may well have derived from them. The tarots, or Major Trumps, may have developed independently at a later time in Europe. Indeed, a conjecture has been advanced that, whether or not true, at least explains. It is made by William Marston Seabury in a privately printed monograph (1951). He points out how appropriate are the Major Trumps as illustrations of the main divisions of the *Divine Comedy* of Dante Alighieri (1265-1321). If they were indeed "invented" for this purpose, we can understand how they apparently suddenly became known throughout Europe without leaving historical traces of a prior period of "development."

The Major Trumps have been modified from time to time by occultists intent upon carrying out their own symbolism. In the course of time the Tarot has become so packed with meaning that a large book, literally, is required to explain it. We may wonder what there was in the simple pictures of the early Tarot to evoke the words of Eliphas Levi (1860): "As an erudite Kabalistic book, all combinations of which reveal the harmonies preëxisting between signs, letters and numbers, the practical value of the Tarot is truly and above all marvelous. A prisoner devoid of books, had he only a Tarot of which he knew how to make use, could in a few years acquire a universal science, and converse with an unequalled doctrine and inexhaustible eloquence." The answer of the occultist would no doubt be that the esoteric significance was inherent in the Tarot from the beginning, and that elaboration of design is merely a way to make it more manifest.

A final note: Mystery envelops the origin of the very word *tarot.* Dictionaries define the word as a pack of cards used to play a game known in Italian as Tarocchi, "of obscure origin." This merely deepens the mystery. Could the game precede the cards? Modern design has provided a pat folk etymology for some future lexicographer. On the rim of the wheel in Card 10 are placed the letters ROTA, the Latin word for *wheel.* The letters can be read as TAROT. Unfortunately for etymology, the letters are not shown on any cards of the fourteenth century.

FORTUNETELLING WITH THE TAROT

THE Tarot has been used for cartomancy (divination by cards) since earliest days; the Gypsies have been particularly adept at this art. The allegorical aspect of the Major Arcana established a natural link with other forms of divination, notably astrology and numerology. Some acquaintance with these arts is a powerful reinforcement to cartomancy.

QUERENT AND CARTOMANTE

A *querent* is one who seeks the advice of a person having divinatory powers; a *cartomante* is a diviner who uses cards. All experience teaches that cartomancy on one's own behalf is uncertain at best, often frustrating and unreliable. The reason seems to be the difficulty of laying aside one's preconceptions and of putting one's conscious mind *en rapport* with one's own subconscious. By the same token, the cartomante usually finds it easier to deal with a total stranger than with a friend.

THE NATURE OF DIVINATION

It cannot be too much emphasized that the prerequisite for all divination is some *power of intuition.* This power has been variously defined: the ability to "size up" people, or to perceive a person's secret feelings, or to communicate directly with his subconscious mind. Actually, most people possess it to a higher degree than they realize.

Neither cards nor any other paraphernalia can take the place of intuition, but they are the vehicles by which it is focused. In occult theory, they are also the medium whereby a querent's subconscious mind exposes itself to the view of the cartomante.

What can divination undertake to do? To many people, the sole interest is in the prediction of future events. But the art is primarily concerned with disclosing the querent's character, interests, abilities, dispositions, especially in relation to his conscious problems.

What is disclosed about a present situation will often project itself into the future by way of events *that probably will happen* in consequence. But that is as far as true divination seeks to go.

USE OF THE CARDS

The general method of using the Tarot is as follows. The querent is first required to shuffle the pack. This step is vital, since the querent's subconscious mind must be allowed to operate on the pack, to put it in an order on which the reading depends. A certain number of the cards —usually less than the full pack—are laid out in a *spread.* There are many different kinds of spreads—the cartomante should experiment to find the one or two best suited to his reading ability. The spread is usually dealt by the cartomante, but any steps that depend on selection (rather than the order of the pack) are left to the querent.

The cartomante then proceeds to read the spread. Now, in some spreads, certain parts of the layout are assigned to certain aspects of the question. But even here, *all cards of the spread have a bearing on every aspect.* The task of the cartomante is to link together the meanings of the separate cards into a consistent whole.

Some who "play" fortunetelling, as a kind of parlor game, assign one card at a time to answer one question at a time. This method is a very false simplification.

REVERSED CARDS

The early Tarot cards were "one-headed," that is, each contained a single picture. The card acquired a significance for its right-side-up position that was modified in the wrong-side-up position. Modern cards are "two-headed," having identical designs on the two halves, so that (for most of them) there is no wrong side up. While cartomancy can be and has been adapted to these two-headed cards, much is thereby lost.

Therefore one narrower edge of each double-headed card should be marked so that the card may have an *upright* and a *reversed* position.

THE MAJOR TRUMPS

O. THE FOOL. Excess—immoderation, extravagant idealism, mania, intoxication, frenzy. Folly —eccentricity, mistake, failure. Inconsiderate action. *Reversed:* Nullity—absence, apathy, negligence, carelessness. Vanity.

1. THE JUGGLER. Will—mental activity, initiative, resolute pursuit of an aim. Skill—constructive power, diplomacy, address. Subtlety—craft, trickery, versatility, occult wisdom and power. *Reversed:* Disquiet—sickness, pain, loss, disaster. Enemies—opposition, snares, disgrace.

2. THE HIGH PRIESTESS. Mystery—secrets, things hidden, unrevealed future. Penetration of mysteries—knowledge, science, art, critical faculty. Tenacity—constancy, reaction. Duality. *Reversed:* Imperfect knowledge—superficiality, conceit. Passion—moral or physical ardor.

3. THE EMPRESS. Nature—creation, beauty. Production—fruitfulness. Partnership—marriage. Feminine influence. *Reversed:* Darkness—night, the unknown, the clandestine. Difficulty—ignorance, doubt, vacillation.

4. THE EMPEROR. Authority—power, control, leadership. Stability—security. Ambition—purposefulness, realization. Support—aid, protection. *Reversed:* Power not fully developed—immaturity, obstruction, confusion. Benevolence—compassion.

5. THE HIEROPHANT. Intuition—religion, occult force. Inspiration—eloquence. Alliance—marriage. *Reversed:* Captivity—servitude. Indulgence—mercy, over-kindness, weakness. Meetings—reunion, a journey.

6. THE LOVERS. Attraction—love, desire. Harmony—beauty, concord. *Reversed:* Indecision—rival interests, temptation.

7. THE CHARIOT. Progress—achievement, victory, success, conquest. *Reversed:* Trouble—dispute, quarrel, litigation, tumult. Defeat.

8. JUSTICE. Equity—rightness, probity, triumph of the deserving side. Judgment—clear perception, tolerance. *Reversed:* Legal affairs—a lawyer, a lawsuit. Bias—bigotry, severity.

9. THE HERMIT. Prudence—wisdom, moderation, economy, circumspection. Obstacles—difficulty, insufficiency. *Reversed:* Concealment—disguise, dissimulation. Corruption—roguery, treason. Caution—hesitation, fear.

10. THE WHEEL OF FORTUNE. Good fortune—success, a turn for the better, felicity. Destiny—luck, ups and downs of fortune. *Reversed:* Increase—abundance, superfluity.

11. STRENGTH. Energy—action, power, struggle. Courage—endurance. Victory. *Reversed:* Abuse of power—despotism, restriction. Discord.

12. THE HANGED MAN. Spiritual wisdom—discernment, intuition, divination. Material reverses—loss, suffering, anxiety, a victim to the spite of others. *Reversed:* Selfishness. People—the crowd, the body politic.

13. DEATH. Mortality—death, end, corruption. Change—transition, drastic alteration. *Reversed:* Inertia—lethargy, sleep. Hope destroyed.

14. TEMPERANCE. Moderation—economy, frugality. Management—adaptation, accommodation, diplomacy. *Reversed:* Disunion—opposition, obstruction, competing interests. Clerical matters—churches, sects, priesthood, a cleric.

15. THE DEVIL. Violence—blind force, vehemence, extreme effort. Evil—lack of principle, materiality, bondage. Fate—that which is predestined. *Reversed:* Weakness—pettiness, blindness, lack of understanding. Evil fate.

16. THE TOWER. Unforeseen catastrophe—sudden calamity, ruin, distress, disgrace. Danger—conflict, deception. *Reversed:* The same in lesser degree. Also, oppression—tyranny, imprisonment.

17. THE STAR. Hope—promising outlook, peace, serenity. Spiritual love—unselfishness, influence over others. *Reversed:* Privation—loss, theft. Arrogance—haughtiness. Frustration—impotence.

18. THE MOON. Deception—false friends, hidden enemies, danger. Strife—quarreling, disappointment. Darkness—error, fear, occult forces. *Reversed:* Deception in lesser degree—error, uncertainty, instability. Fickleness.

19. THE SUN. Happiness—contentment, material gain, riches, fortunate marriage. *Reversed:* The same in lesser degree.

20. THE JUDG(E)MENT. Drastic change—awakening, realization, spiritual advancement by suffering, rebirth. Outcome—decision, determination. *Reversed:* Weakness—pusillanimity. Deliberation—decision, sentence.

21. THE WORLD. Worldly success—material gain. Change of place—a move, distant traveling, a voyage, emigration, flight. Synthesis—adjustment, adaptation, co-operation, joint action. *Reversed:* Fixity—inertia, permanence, stagnation.

THE SUITS

Each suit is associated with a particular activity or sphere of life. This fact is recognized in the significations of the separate cards. It also enters as a factor in the spread as a whole—a majority or preponderance of cards of one suit indicates the activity in which the querent is the most interested or which contains the influences affecting him most vitally.

Wands signify the domain of business—livelihood, career, ambitions, business relationships with other persons.

Cups signify personal relationships, acquaintances, friends, lovers, as well as pleasure and the sources of pleasure, the arts.

Swords signify obstacles, strife, disaster, trouble, anxiety, the problems to be met in every domain.

Coins signify money, material possessions, gain and loss, and, to a lesser extent, success or failure, advantage or disadvantage, in any domain.

WANDS

KING. A dark man. An ardent and honest friend. Honesty, conscientiousness. A possible inheritance. *Reversed:* A tolerant but austere man. Advice that should be followed.

QUEEN. A dark woman. A mature woman, magnetic, friendly, loving. Good will toward the querent. Honor, chastity. Business success. *Reversed:* Takes color from the neighboring cards. May mean jealousy, deceit, even infidelity.

KNIGHT. A dark, friendly young man. Rash business projects. Impulsive action, misunderstanding. Departure, change of residence. *Reversed:* Rupture, alienation, discord. Flight, emigration.

PAGE. A dark young man. A lover. A young relative. A messenger, envoy. News, probably of family matters. *Reversed:* Bad news. Indecision, uncertainty. An announcement.

TEN. If neighboring cards are favorable, success, gain, good fortune; otherwise, difficulty, perplexity, obstacles. If adjacent to Nine of Swords, failure. A discovery. *Reversed:* Deception, disguise, perfidy, intrigue.

NINE. Strength, triumph over opposition. Delay, suspension, postponement. *Reversed:* Adversity, calamity.

EIGHT. Speed, activity, haste. Projects develop quickly and favorably. Arousal of love, promise of felicity. *Reversed:* Jealousy, quarrels, dispute. Reproaches of conscience.

SEVEN. Valor, courage in the face of difficulties. Negotiation, barter, competition. Exchange of ideas, discussion, publication. *Reversed:* A caution against indecision. Perplexities easily dispelled.

SIX. Victory after strife, expectation fulfilled. Success in the arts. Good news. *Reversed:* Apprehension, fear. Treachery, disloyalty. Indefinite delay.

FIVE. Competition for material gain. Improvement in business prospects. *Reversed:* Strife, litigation, opposition, but these may be turned to advantage.

FOUR. Prosperity, concord, peace. Completion of work, retirement. *Reversed:* The same. Also increase, embellishment.

THREE. Partnership, co-operation. An important undertaking, enterprise, effort. Established strength. *Reversed:* Cessation of troubles. A favorable outcome.

TWO. Intellectual pursuits, science. Trivial obstacles overcome. *Reversed:* Surprise, wonder, enchantment. A trivial disappointment.

ONE. Invention, creation, enterprise. A new business venture. Birth, family. *Reversed:* Decadence, decline, ruin.

CUPS

KING. A fair man. A man of business, law, or divinity. A calm exterior but subtle nature. *Reversed:* Hypocrisy, dishonesty, double-dealing. Vice, scandal. A loss.

QUEEN. A fair woman. An honest, devoted woman, a good spouse and mother. An intelligent, imaginative, poetic woman. Happiness. Success. *Reversed:* Takes color from neighboring cards. May show vice, dishonor, depravity.

KNIGHT. A fair young man. Approach—arrival, a messenger, advances, proposition, invitation. *Reversed:* Duplicity, fraud, trickery.

PAGE. A fair young man or child. A studious person. Meditation, reflection, deliberation. One who renders a service. *Reversed:* Taste, inclination. Artifice, seduction.

TEN. Contentment, friendship, happiness. Honors. A person acting in the querent's interest. *Reversed:* Sorrow. A quarrel, indignation, violence.

NINE. Good health, material success. This is the WISH card. It points to the realization of hopes. *Reversed:* Disappointment of hopes, or delay in their realization.

EIGHT. Mildness, timidity, modesty. A decline in an enterprise. Matters thought important decline to slight consequence. *Reversed:* Great joy, celebration, happiness.

SEVEN. Sentiment, contemplation, exercise of the imagination in a dream world. Illusory success. A change in domestic affairs. *Reversed:* Will, determination, strong desire.

SIX. Entrance into new relations or environment. New knowledge, new friends. A love affair. *Reversed:* The future (events read in neighboring cards lie in the future).

FIVE. Partial disappointment, a falling short of expectation. A legacy or gift. *Reversed:* Alliance, good fortune in love. Ancestry, consanguinity. News.

FOUR. Aversion, disgust, trifling vexations, weariness. Dissatisfaction. *Reversed:* Novelty, new relations, an unforeseen event.

THREE. Victorious outcome, happy issue. Reconciliation, solace, healing. Merriment. *Reversed:* Quick decision, dispatch, achievement. Sensuous pleasure.

TWO. Passion, love, natural desire, affinity,

friendship, concord, union. *Reversed:* The same.

ONE. Fertility, productiveness, abundance. One's house, abode. A letter from a friend. *Reversed:* Instability, mutation, revolution.

SWORDS

KING. A black-haired man of mature age. A distrustful, cautious man. A wise but severe counselor. A man full of ideas or ulterior designs. Care, caution, watchfulness. Authority, command. *Reversed:* One prejudicial to the querent. Perversity, cruelty, perfidy, evil intention.

QUEEN. A black-haired woman of mature age. A perceptive, subtle woman. A spiteful woman. Widowhood, mourning. *Reversed:* Malice, bigotry, artifice, deceit. Prudery.

KNIGHT. A soldier. A brave, clever, active young man. Enmity, war, destruction, opposition, resistance. Skill, address, subtlety. Controversy, debate. *Reversed:* Imprudence, extravagance. Inefficiency, incapacity.

PAGE. A treacherous person, an imposter, an eavesdropper. Secret service, vigilance, spying. Authority, overseeing. *Reversed:* Unpreparedness. Unforeseen consequences. Sickness.

TEN. Affliction, distress, sadness, tears. Loss of employment, bankruptcy. *Reversed:* Dispelling of delusion or error. Temporary advantage or success.

NINE. Failure, miscarriage, disappointment. Suffering, despair, death. *Reversed:* Doubt, suspicion. Shame, imprisonment.

EIGHT. A crisis. Bad news. Conflict. Calumny, censure. *Reversed:* What is unforeseen, accident, fatality. Opposition, treachery.

SEVEN. Risky venture, possible injury, partial success. A plan, design, attempt. *Reversed:* Good advice or instruction. Gossip, slander.

SIX. A journey by water. Emergence from difficulties, success after uncertainty. A means, route, way. *Reversed:* Declaration, confession. A proposal of love.

FIVE. Defeat, dishonor, degradation. An escape from dangers. *Reversed:* Failure, loss, destruction. Burial, obsequies.

FOUR. Retreat from strife, relief from anxiety, repose, rest. Solitude, retirement. *Reversed:* Recklessness, abandon. Desertion.

THREE. Separation, removal, rupture, divorce. Absence. Delay. *Reversed:* Mental disorder. Confusion, distraction, error. Alienation.

TWO. Balance of forces or influences. Conformity. Friendship, affection, intimacy. *Reversed:* Imposture, falsehood, duplicity.

ONE. Triumph by force, conquest. An excessive degree in everything. *Reversed:* The same. Also, augmentation, childbirth, conception.

COINS

KING. A dark man. A steady, reliable married man. Intelligence, business ability. *Reversed:* Perversity, peril. Weakness, vice.

QUEEN. A dark woman. An intelligent, charming, but moody married woman. Opulence, generosity, magnificence. Liberty. Security. *Reversed:* Mistrust, suspicion, fear. Evil. Suspense.

KNIGHT. An industrious but dull young man. Utility, a service, a useful discovery. Responsibility, rectitude, patience. *Reversed:* Inertia, laziness, stagnation, repose. Unemployment, idleness.

PAGE. A diligent, studious young man. Study, application, scholarship, reflection. Management, rule. *Reversed:* Prodigality, dissipation, a spendthrift. Luxury, liberality. Bad news.

TEN. Riches, gain. Family matters, extraction, archives, a dwelling house. *Reversed:* Inheritance, dowry, pension.

NINE. Prudence, discernment. Safety, certitude. Success, accomplishment. *Reversed:* Bad faith, roguery, deception.

EIGHT. Skill, craftsmanship. Work, employment. *Reversed:* Usury, exaction. Vanity, cupidity. Abandonment of an enterprise.

SEVEN. Business, barter. A gain of money after a journey. Delayed success. *Reversed:* An uncertain outlay of money. A bad debt.

SIX. Presents, gifts, gratification. An opportune time for action. A social gathering. *Reversed:* Desire, envy, jealousy. Illusion.

FIVE. Money troubles, insolvency, penury. Concord among friends or lovers. *Reversed:* Discord, disorder, chaos.

FOUR. Property, possessions, inheritance, a legacy. Security. *Reversed:* Delay, suspense, opposition.

THREE. Renown, glory. Financial gain, a marriage for money. *Reversed:* Mediocrity, pettiness.

TWO. Recreation, gaiety. Agitation, embroilment, trouble. *Reversed:* Simulated enjoyment. Composition, handwriting, a letter.

ONE. Great wealth, material gain, gold. Contentment, felicity, ecstasy. *Reversed:* Riches, but without perfect peace of mind.

COURT CARDS

The kings, queens, knights, and pages are to be taken as representing persons concerned in the querent's affairs. Kings and queens represent men and women of mature age, usually married.

Knights are young men, usually unmarried. Maids and young persons generally are represented by pages.

Reversal of a court card *may* but does not necessarily indicate reversal of sex. It may betoken an effeminate man or mannish woman, or a person in whom the significations of the card are displayed in diluted degree or sublimed form. Here guidance must be sought in the accompanying cards.

The person represented by a court card is generally favorable towards those persons on the side the card faces and generally unfavorable towards those on the opposite side. But this preference may apply rather to the influences at work than to the persons concerned.

THE SIGNIFICATOR

To commence a consultation, the cartomante should select one card from the Tarot to represent the querent. This card is called the Significator. It should be a court card corresponding with the sex, age and marital condition of the querent.

Whether the Significator is removed from the pack depends on the particular spread.

SHUFFLING

The cartomante should first shuffle the Tarot thoroughly. In this process, it is important to turn some of the cards around endwise, so that when they are eventually dealt it will be a matter of chance which and how many cards are reversed. If the cartomante can execute a *riffle shuffle,* so much the better, for in making this shuffle the two packets are naturally turned in opposite directions. If he uses the *overhand shuffle,* he should turn the upper packet around before amalgamating it with the lower.

The pack is then given to the querent to shuffle. This step should on no account be omitted. Since many persons are not adept at shuffling, the cartomante should adopt a procedure designed to simplify the process as much as possible. The querent first cuts the pack into three packets, using the left hand alone. Then the querent shuffles each packet separately, by his preferred method, though he should be encouraged to riffle if he can. Then he unites the three packets and shuffles the whole—by a series of cuts, if he cannot do better.

The querent should be instructed to free his mind of all other thoughts so far as possible during the shuffling. He should concentrate on the manual task and seek particularly to exclude *any thoughts of his problem.*

THE SEVEN-CARD SPREAD

This is recommended as the best spread for the beginner, since it uses the fewest cards. The neophyte should practice until he is confident that he can read the seven-card spread quickly, weighing one indication against another, before he ventures upon the larger spreads.

The Significator is first removed from the pack, before shuffling. After the shuffle, the cartomante deals the seven cards from the top of the pack in a row, right to left, below the Significator, which should lie above the middle card, as in the diagram.

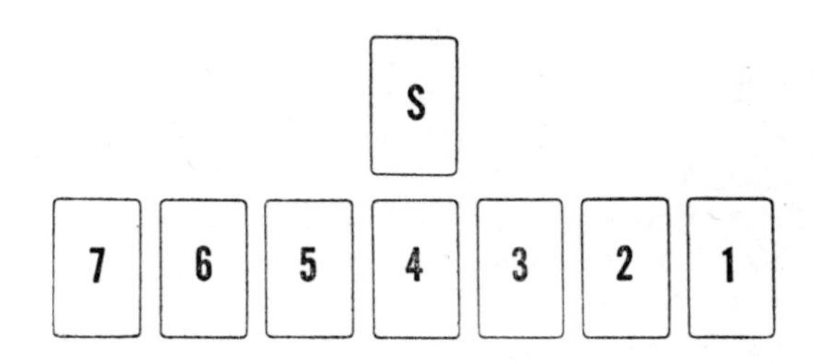

These seven cards have the following significance:

1. The past
2. The present
3. The future
4. The querent's control over the influences affecting the situation
5. The influences beyond the querent's control
6. The opposition to be expected
7. The outcome

The cartomante reads the cards in order from 1 to 7, bearing in mind that the particular card that falls in a given position has foremost influence on that aspect, but that its interpretation must be conditioned *by the other six cards.* In other words, the cartomante must read and expound the consistent "story" that lies in all seven cards together.

THE TEN-CARD SPREAD

Remove the Significator from the pack and place it face up on the table. After the pack is shuffled, deal ten cards from the top in order as shown by the diagram. The first card is placed so as partly to cover the Significator; the second card is placed crosswise on these two; the sixth is placed on the side toward which the

Significator looks (or to the left if the face on the card looks straight ahead).

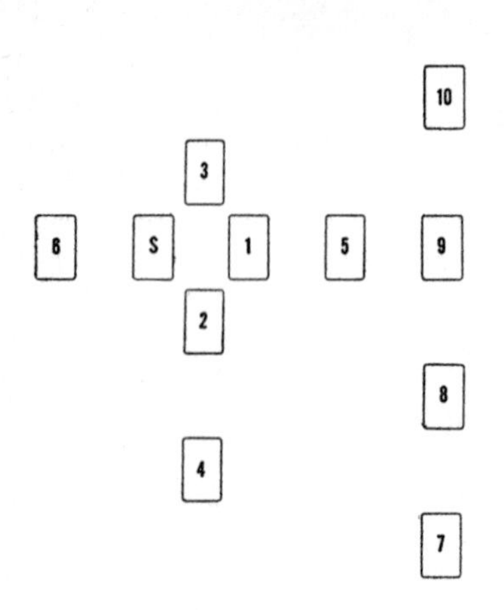

The ten cards represent:

1. What covers him; the most important influence on the querent's present situation.
2. What crosses him; the principal obstacle he has to surmount.
3. What crowns him; his aim, or the best that he can achieve.
4. What is beneath him; the foundation of the matter, or influence now operative.
5. What is behind him; the influence now waning.
6. What is before him; the influence that will presently develop.
7. Himself; the querent, his position in the matter.
8. His house; the remoter but stable influences of his environment, position in life, friends, etc.
9. His hopes and fears; the state of the querent's mind.
10. What will come; the probable outcome of all the foregoing.

Read the cards in order—always remembering that the card that lies in each position is the dominant, but not the sole, indication of that aspect. If a court card appears in the tenth position, the meaning is that the outcome is beyond the querent's control, in the hands of another person.

THE TWENTY-ONE-CARD SPREAD

Remove the Significator from the pack before shuffling. After the shuffle, lay out twenty-one cards in a pyramid, in the order shown by the diagram. Place the Significator below this layout, between cards 4 and 5.

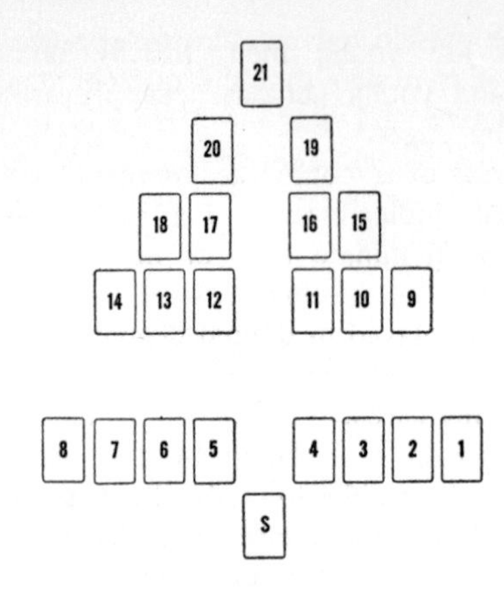

Commence by reading in order the cards in positions 5, 9, 13, 17, 21. These govern the whole situation. Then continue with the rows from left to right, bearing in mind that each card is to be read in the light of those cards immediately adjacent to it, left, right, above or below.

THE FORTY-TWO-CARD SPREAD

After shuffling, deal forty-two cards in six rows of seven cards each, from right to left. If the Significator is not among them, remove the Significator from the unused portion of the pack. If the Significator appears in the layout, remove it and replace it by a card chosen at random by the querent from the rest of the pack. Put the Significator next to the right end of the top row.

Read the cards row by row from top down, beginning first with the center card, then taking the cards on either side of this center card in pairs. Each pair, counting away from the center, is to be read as an indivisible unity, and interpreted according to the dominant influence of the center card.

THE FIFTEEN-CARD SPREAD

This is a difficult method that should be attempted only by the experienced.

After shuffling, lay out fifteen cards *face down* in three rows of five each, dealing from right to left. Then turn up and read the cards in the order shown by the diagram.

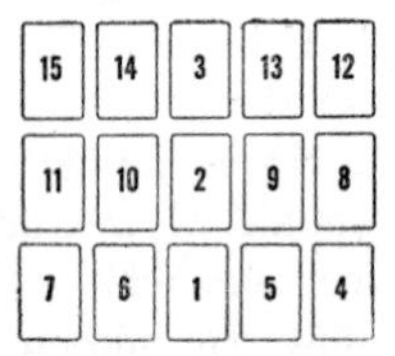

If the preselected Significator appears in the layout, it is a sign that the querent dominates the situation and will bring matters to a successful conclusion. The Significator is also read for its usual meaning in the sequence of cards. If the Significator does not appear in the layout, the outcome is uncertain.

In turning up the cards, interpret each in the light of the previous cards that have been turned. Cards 1,2,3 are dominant over all the rest, and decide the main lines of the "story" which the others can but modify.

The difficulty of this method is of course that cards turned later may seem to contradict those turned earlier. But if he can cope with it, the cartomante will find this one of the best methods.

THE QUERENT'S PROBLEM

The querent usually states his problem in full to the cartomante. But he may merely state that he has a problem, and leave it to the cartomante to find an appropriate answer in the cards. In such case, the cartomante is well advised to begin with the following deal, designed to diagnose the nature of the problem.

Remove the four aces from the pack. Direct the querent to shuffle them, then deal them in a row. Have the rest of the pack shuffled, and have the querent divide it at random into four packets, placed below the four aces. Now look through the packets for the prefixed Significator. The packet in which it is found shows the domain in which the querent's problem falls, according to the general significance of the suits (as indicated by the aces). Thus, if it is found in the ace of wands packet, the Significator betokens a question of business, livelihood, etc.; if in the ace of cups packet, a matter of personal relations, etc.

If the result of this test is wrong, the consultation should be abandoned or postponed.

A SPECIFIC QUESTION

If the querent has a specific question in mind, which he states clearly to the cartomante, time may be saved by the following spread.

After the pack is shuffled, have the querent cut it again into three packets, using his left hand. Turn up the top cards of these packets. Read the three as a unity, but with the middle card predominating, to find the answer to his question. If in doubt as to the interpretation, turn the three packets over and read the three bottom cards in the same way. *They must give the same answer as the top cards,* but may give it in plainer terms.

In this method, the Significator is not removed from the pack. If it turns up in the selected trio, the meaning is that the querent himself has control over the situation and can decide the answer. In middle position, the Significator means that the querent does not realize his own control of the situation. If at left or right, the appearance of this card is equivocal: the querent may not realize his own control of the situation, or he *may not be sincere in posing his problem.* The cartomante is thus well advised always to examine the bottom cards of the packets, even though he sees a clear answer in the top cards.

¶ *You can't always have the tarots around, of course, but fortunetelling must go on; it is traditionally a favorite boy-meets-girl diversion, though palmistry with its hand-holding opportunities may be even better. Below, Rudolf Rheinhardt tells one of the many ways in which fortunes are told with regular cards. Despite his German name he was an Englishman, and you should please forgive his use of knave instead of jack.*

Fortunetelling with Regular Cards

by RUDOLF RHEINHARDT

SORTILEGE was practiced from the earliest times. Those who believe that European cards were brought from India by Gypsies regard this as their primitive use. The first book on the subject was published at Venice in 1540. Following is a brief statement of the usual system employed in "telling fortunes" by means of cards. The following abbreviations are employed: Kg., King; Q., Queen; Kv., Knave; A., Ace; H., Hearts; D., Diamonds; C., Clubs; S., Spades.

In general, a man of very fair complexion is represented by Kg. D.; a woman by Q. D. Persons of less fair complexion by Kg. and Q. H.; a man and woman of very dark complexion by Kg. and Q. S.; while those not quite so dark are represented by C. But a widow, no matter how fair, can be represented only by Q. S. A. H. denotes the house of the person consulting the decrees of fate; A. C., a letter; A. D., a wedding ring; A. S., sickness and death; Kv. D. is a selfish and deceitful friend; Kv. H. is a sincere, unselfish friend; Kv. S. is a lawyer, a person to be avoided; Kv. C. is a sincere friend, but of very touchy temper; Kvs. also represent the thoughts of their respective Kgs. and Qs. Several D. coming together signify the receipt of money; several H. denote love; a concourse of C. foretells drunkenness and debauchery, with their consequent ill health; and a number of S. together indicate disappointment. Moreover, Kg. D. is quick to anger, but easily appeased; while Q. D. is fond of gayety and of rather a coquettish disposition. Kg. H. is slow to anger, but when put in a passion is appeased with great difficulty; he is good-natured, but obstinate; his Q. is a model of sincere affection, devotion, and prudence. Kg. S. is so ambitious that in matters of love and business he is much less scrupulous than he ought to be; while his Q. is a person not to be provoked with impunity. Kg. and Q. C. are everything that can be desired: he is honorable, true, and affectionate; she is agreeable, genteel, and witty.

Following are the interpretations of the minor cards. 10 D., wealth, honorable success in business. 9 D., roving disposition combined with successful adventures in foreign lands. 8 D., a happy marriage, though perhaps late in life. 7 D., satire, scandal. 6 D., early marriage, succeeded by widowhood. 5 D., unexpected but generally good news. 4 D., an unfaithful friend; a secret betrayed. 3 D., domestic quarrels, trouble, unhappiness. 2 D., a clandestine engagement (a card of caution). 10 H., health and happiness, with many children. 9 H., wealth and good position in society. 8 H., fine clothes; mixing in good society; invitations to balls, theaters, parties. 7 H., good friends. 6 H., honorable courtship. 5 H., a present. 4 H., domestic troubles caused by jealousy. 3 H., poverty, shame, and sorrow, the result of imprudence (a card of caution). 2 H., success in life, and a happy marriage attained by virtuous discretion. 10 S., disgrace, crime, imprisonment; death on the scaffold. 9 S., grief, ruin, sickness, death (a card of caution). 8 S., great danger from imprudence. 7 S., unexpected poverty through the death of a relative (a card of caution). 6 S., a child; to the unmarried a card of caution. 5 S., great danger from giving way to bad temper. 4 S., sickness. 3 S., tears; a journey by land (a card of caution). 2 S., a removal. 10 C., unexpected wealth, through the death of a relative. 9 C., danger through drunkenness (a card of caution). 8 S., danger from covetousness (a card of caution). 7 C., a prison; danger from opposite sex. 6 C., competence by honorable industry. 5 C., a happy though not wealthy marriage (a card of caution). 4 C., misfortune through caprice or inconstancy (a card of caution). 3 C., quarrels; it also has reference to time, signifying three years, three months, three weeks, or three days, and denotes that a person will be married more than once. 2 C., disappointment; vexation.

The manner of operation is as follows: The cards are shuffled and cut into three parts by the inquirer. The fortuneteller lays the cards, one by one, face up on the table, in rows of nine each, excepting the last. Every ninth card has an ominous import. Then the cards are read, as in the following example. The young lady being fair, but not too fair, is represented by Q. H. Sad to say, her lover (Kg. D.) is found flirting with a widow (Q. S.), rich in this world's goods (being accompanied by 10 D.). But her lover's thoughts (Kv. D.) are directed toward her home (A. H.); a letter (A. S.) and a wedding ring (A. D.) are in close combination, evidently signifying that though the lover is flirting with the widow, he is thinking of sending a letter with an offer of marriage to the young lady herself. There is a legacy (10 C.) in store for the seeker after fortune; but a lawyer (Kv. S.) stands between her and it, who will cause some vexation (2 C.) and disappointment. A sincere friend (Kv. H.) will assist to put matters right. The unfaithful friend (4 D.) will find both satire and scandal (7 D.) helpless to injure our interesting queen of hearts. A present (5 H.) will soon be received by her, honorable courtship (6 H.) will lead her to a happy marriage (2 H.), the reward of her virtuous discretion; health and happiness and troops of children (10 H.) will be her enviable lot. Do this young lady's thoughts, represented by the Kv. H., ever stray far from home? Yes, look, there they are far away with the old, hot-tempered, dark-complexioned lover (Kg. S.), who, as is plainly shown by his being accompanied by the ten of diamonds, is prosperously engaged at the Australian diggings, or elsewhere. Does he ever think of his old flame, the heart-complexioned young lady now consulting the cards in England? No. His thoughts (Kv. S.) are fixed on that very fair but rather gay and coquettish lady, (Q. D.): they are only divided by a few good hearts, one of them (6 H.) representing honorable courtship. Count now from that 6 H. to the ninth card from it, and lo! it is a wedding ring (A. D.): they will be married in less than a year.

POKER

In a card-playing poll of 1941, Contract Bridge showed up as unquestionably number one; but the pollsters made an off-the-record reservation: "It is likely that an appreciable portion of the women named Contract Bridge because to them it sounds 'more refined,' and that actually they prefer to play some other game." Similar surveys taken since World War II indicate that (a) snobbery is declining, or (b) Poker is moving up, for now Poker leads the polls. *The origin and history of nearly every card game are obscure. "Cavendish" (page 19) has shown the European background of Poker, chiefly in three- and four-card games. The first five-card expression of the Poker principle was the Persian game As Nas, with four players and twenty cards, each player receiving five cards and the only counting hands being four, three or two of a kind. Louis Coffin of the United States Playing Card Company made exhaustive researches into the history of the American game, and George Coffin (no relation) leaned heavily on these researches in his summary of the history, an excerpt from the introduction to his book* FORTUNE POKER.

from Fortune Poker

by GEORGE S. COFFIN

AMERICAN POKER probably originated in New Orleans among French inhabitants who had been in the French service in Persia circa 1800-1820. The French name was Poque, pronounced poke, and Southerners corrupted the pronunciation to two syllables, pokuh, or Poker. The original Persian game was played with twenty cards and five were dealt to each of four players. Hands were bet and shown down. The basic idea was the bluff. The game spread up river via steamboats and throughout the States. As card games were originally played extensively on river boats, playing-card companies used the common property trade name "Steamboat Playing Cards." In 1835 the game was still played with twenty cards.

By 1837 the game was adapted to the full pack of fifty-two cards. The draw feature was introduced widely during the Civil War. General Nathan Bedford Forrest, Confederate Cavalry leader, was reportedly bankrupt, until with ten dollars he won several hundred in a Draw Poker game. His wife was a very religious woman. When he brought home his winnings, he figured that she had been praying for his good luck.

Immediately after the Civil War, Stud was introduced, probably around Ohio, Indiana and

Illinois. Jackpots date from 1870, in Toledo, Ohio.

Also around this time, General Jacob Schenk* was our ambassador to the Court of St. James. A member of the royal family became interested in Poker, and the good general ended up by teaching the game to the entire court!

The first Poker game ever reported in print occurred in December 1829. An English actor, Joe Cowell, was touring the States at the time and, by his own pen, he enjoyed the distinction of being the first Poker kibitzer on record. Writes Mr. Louis Coffin:

"He [Cowell] was born in England, 7 August 1792, and, after a brief career in the English Navy, went on the stage. During a trip from Louisville to New Orleans on the steamboat Helen McGregor in December 1829, he witnessed much card playing and describes in particular three incidents connected with the games of UKER, SEVEN UP, and POKER. The last is quoted in full on the following pages, and it is perhaps the earliest description of a Poker game yet discovered.

"NOTE: In the second paragraph of the extract the author mentions 25 cards only, but the next sentence clearly proves that 20 cards only, not 25, were used."

Extract is as originally published from page 94, Volume II of a book entitled:

THIRTY YEARS
PASSED AMONG THE PLAYERS
IN
ENGLAND AND AMERICA
INTERSPERSED WITH
ANECDOTES AND REMINISENCES
of a variety of persons, directly or indirectly
connected with the drama during the
THEATRICAL LIFE OF
JOE COWELL, COMEDIAN
WRITTEN BY HIMSELF
(HARPER & BROTHERS, 82 CLIFF ST.,
NEW YORK, 1844)

One night, while I was getting instructed in the mysteries of Uker, and Sam was amusing himself by building houses with the surplus cards at the corner of the table, close by us was a party playing Poker. This was then exclusively a high-gambling Western game, founded on Brag, invented, as it is said, by Henry Clay when a youth; and if so, very humanely, for either win or lose, you are much sooner relieved of all anxiety than by the older operation.

For the sake of the uninformed, who had better know no more about it than I shall tell them, I must endeavour to describe the game when played with twenty-five cards only, and by four persons.

The aces are the highest denomination: then the kings, queens, jacks and tens; the smaller cards are not used; those I have named are all dealt out, and carefully concealed from one another; old players pack them in their hands, and peep at them as if they were afraid to trust even themselves to look. The four aces, with any other card, cannot be beat. Four kings, with an ace cannot be beat because then no one can have four aces; and four queens, or jacks, or tens, with an ace, are all inferior hands to the kings when so attended. But holding the cards I have instanced seldom occurs when they are fairly dealt; and three aces for example, or three kings, with any two of the other cards, or four queens, or jacks or tens, is called a full, and with an ace, though not invincible, are considered very good bragging hands. The dealer makes the game, or value of the beginning bet and called the anti—in this instance it was a dollar—and then everybody stakes the same amount, and says, "I'm up."

It was a foggy, wretched night. Our bell was kept tolling to warn other boats to our whereabouts or to entreat direction to a landing by a fire on the shore. Suddenly a most tremendous concussion, as if all-powerful Nature had shut his hand upon us, and crushed us all to atoms, upset our cards and calculations, and a general rush was made, over chairs and tables toward the doors . . . The cabin was entirely cleared, or, rather, all the passengers were huddled together at the entrances, with the exception of one of the Poker players; a gentleman in green spectacles, a gold guard-chain, long and thick enough to moor a dog, and a brilliant diamond breast-pin; he was, apparently, quietly shuffling and cutting the Poker deck for his own amusement. In less time than I am telling it, the swarm came laughing back, in which snags, sawyers, bolts blown out, and boilers burst, were most conspicuous. But all the harm the fracas caused was fright; the boat, in rounding to a wood-pile, had run onto the point of an island, and was high and dry among a never-ending supply of fuel to feed this peculiar navigation, which alone can combat the unceasing, serpentine, tempestuous current of the I-will-have-my-own-way, glorious Mississippi.

The hubbub formed a good excuse to end our game, which my stupidity had made desirable long before, and I took a chair beside the Poker players,

* Mr. Coffin may mean Robert Cumming Schenck, who was our minister to the Court of St. James's from 1871 to 1876. Almost until the twentieth century the United States was not considered by the British to be a nation of sufficient importance for the exchange of envoys of ambassadorial rank.

THE MISSISSIPPI RIVER-BOAT GAME

Drawing by J. Franklin Whitman, Jr. in Hoyle's *Rules of Games*

who, urged by the gentleman with the diamond pin, again resumed their seats. It was his turn to deal, and when he ended, he did not lift his cards, but sat watching quietly the countenances of the others. The man on his left had bet ten dollars; a young lawyer, son to the then Mayor of Pittsburgh, who little dreamed of what his boy was about, who had hardly recovered from his shock, bet ten more; at that time, fortunately for him, he was unconscious of the real value of his hand, and consequently did not betray by his manner, as greenhorns mostly do, his certainty of winning. My chicken* friend bet that ten dollars and five hundred dollars better!

"I must see that," said Green Spectacles, who now took up his hand with "I am sure to win," trembling at his fingers' ends; for you couldn't see his eyes through his glasses; he paused a moment in disappointed astonishment, and sighed, "I pass," and threw his cards upon the table. The left-hand man bet "that five hundred dollars and one thousand dollars better!"

The young lawyer, who had had time to calculate the power of his hand—four kings with an ace—it could not be beat! but still he hesitated at the impossibility, as if he thought it could—looked at the money staked and then at his hand again, and, lingeringly, put his wallet on the table and called. The left-hand man had four queens, with an ace; and Washington, the four jacks with an ace.

"Did you ever see the like on't!" said he, good-humourdly, as he pushed the money toward the lawyer, who, very agreeably astonished, pocketed his two thousand and twenty-three dollars clear!

The truth was, the cards had been *put up,* or *stocked,* as it is called, by the guard-chain-man while the party were off their guard, or, rather, on the guard of the boat in the fog, inquiring if the boiler had burst; but the excitement of the time had caused him to make a slight mistake in the distribution of the hand; and young "Six-and-eight-pense" got the one he had intended for himself. He was one of many who followed card playing for a living, but not properly coming under the denomination of gentleman-sportsman, who alone depends on his superior skill. But in that pursuit, as in all others, even among the players, some black-sheep and black-legs will creep in, as in the present instance.

* So called, because in an earlier anecdote he had elaborated on the technique of fighting gamecocks.—G.S.C. Not chicken by today's definition!—EDITORS

[One of the editors made a round-up of today's Poker game in this article (December, 1941) in The American Legion Magazine, *and you will find here also some of the rare anecdotes of the game. This was wartime Poker; but, as the author points out, that is when Poker booms.*

Poker? You Bet!

by OSWALD JACOBY

"NICE WORK, Ozzie," a friend congratulated me the other day. "You're making a great hit with that book of yours. Everywhere I go, they're playing more than twice as much Poker as they used to."

"It's not the book," I told him. "It's the Army. Poker's the original Old Army Game; and when the Army expands, Poker booms along with it."

I wasn't being modest; I was just stating a fact. Just think back and you'll see that it's so. Before the Civil War, Poker in this country was limited to New Orleans and a few towns along the Mississippi. The war brought millions of men together—men who wanted excitement and action when they played a game. Their answer, then as now, was Poker.

After the war, thousands of soldiers went out West to found new homes, and they took their favorite game with them. That's how Poker came to the West two or three generations ago.

The Spanish-American War caused a mild Poker boom towards the turn of the century, but the effect was much more noticeable in the World War [I]. That's when Poker became a truly national game. For the Army gave thousands of Westerners the chance to teach the game to Easterners; and after the war the Easterners went home and taught it to their friends.

Today we have ringside seats at the biggest boom of them all. Poker is still the favorite army game, and the new soldiers will fall for it just as hard as their grandfathers did.

I saw some of it during the Christmas leave. Quite a few young fellows, sons of my friends, came home on leave from camp, enthusiastic Poker fans. Enthusiasm's catching for now the girls (and boys) they left behind them are playing it. And that's just the beginning. Wait until all those boys finish their full training. There'll be a hundred thousand new Poker fans, each eager to organize a game in his circle of friends.

People who realize what's going on sometimes ask me what effect it'll have on Bridge. Very little effect, I tell them. I was a Bridge fan in 1918 (it was Auction Bridge in those days), but when I got into the Army I didn't play a dozen rubbers of Auction; it was always Poker. When I got back to civilian life, I didn't lose my taste for Poker—but I've managed to get in a little Bridge, too.

There's another curious thing about Army Poker that's as true today as it was twenty-odd years ago. They play straight Five-Card Stud and Draw—none of these fancy concoctions with weird hands and nine wild cards. When you're taking life without frills you want your games the same way.

Now, talking about Army Poker brings to mind the experience my former office boy Billy had in one of the new training camps. Billy is a good boy—too good. An only son, he'd been kept under pretty strict control at home. So he really welcomed it when he was called up. Now he was free to be one of the boys!

Soon after he arrived at camp he had a chance to get to town, and he wandered into an ice-cream parlor. There, in the back, were a bunch of the boys from the camp playing Draw Poker. Billy gulped and asked if he could sit in. And before he knew it, Bill had a chair under him and five cards in front of him on the table. Then he picked up his first hand and found four kings staring him right smack in the face!

Naturally, his first impulse was to bet every cent he had (and that wasn't very much, for nobody in the game had more than three or four dollars).

But then he remembered what his father told him about Poker games and strangers. Very clumsy of them, thought Billy, to frame him on the very first hand! They wouldn't catch him for much!

The pot was opened ahead of him while all this was going through his mind, and one of the boys gave him a good poke in the ribs to bring him back to earth. "I'll stay," said Billy hastily. Then he called himself an idiot, for the next man raised. If he'd thrown his cards away, he'd have been out of the whole mess.

Much to his surprise, the opener just called the raise; and he realized that he was expected to raise back. But Billy couldn't see any sense in digging his own grave, so he just called. He'd have tossed his cards in except that now he was curious to see what would happen.

The opener drew three cards, Billy drew one, and the raiser drew two. The opener checked, and so did Billy. Then, just as Billy thought he would, the raiser made a bet. The opener dropped, and Billy—still curious—called.

"Aces full," sang out the other fellow as he reached for the pot. Billy couldn't believe his ears; he'd been positive the other fellow would wind up with four aces or a straight flush! All of a sudden he felt a little sick. The whole business had been on the up-and-up after all his suspicion.

"Hold on," he muttered. "It's my pot." And he laid down his four kings.

"It was terrible," Billy told me, when he saw me during the Christmas leave. "They all sat there and looked at my hand, and nobody said a word. Then they sort of looked at each other and nodded. And every single one of them picked up his money, got up, and walked over to another table. The whole game just walked off and left me without saying a word!"

Billy's all right now, but he'd have been a lot better off if he hadn't been told a lot of wild tales about Poker players. When you get a bunch of young fellows together, it doesn't do them any harm to play Poker for the small amount of money they have; and there isn't one cheat in a thousand.

At that, however, it's hard to blame poor Billy, for some of the tales that are told about four kings or four aces are very wild indeed. Perhaps my young friend thought about the young Easterner who got into a tough Stud game out West in the days when western etiquette prescribed only one gun on formal occasions.

Everything went along all right for a while, although one hard-boiled old rancher swore a blue streak and threatened to kill the next so-and-so who beat him out of a pot. Even that passed off smoothly enough; but the young tenderfoot noticed that all the other players, tough though they looked, hastened to soothe the rancher. Evidently he was the local terror.

But whatever misgivings the young man had disappeared when he got the Stud player's dream. Aces back-to-back, with a raise from a player who had only a king up! On the next turn he got another ace, showing a pair of aces; and the other player got a king, showing a pair of kings. To make a long story short, he finally got four aces and his opponent got four kings!

Naturally he bet his whole pile, and only when his opponent called did he realize that he was playing against the hard-boiled rancher! "I've got four kings," snarled that worthy, turning up his hole king, "and if you've got four aces, this blankety-blank game's crooked and I'm going to plug you full of holes." Whereupon he took out his gun and slammed it down on the table.

Our hero moistened his lips, swallowed, and decided that discretion was the better part of valor. "Four kings beats my full house," he lied, as he folded his hand and threw it among the discards.

Then, raising a warning finger, "But don't think that kind of talk gets you anywhere!"

Another legendary victim fared a little better. He was dealt four aces in Draw Poker; and he was certain the game was crooked! What was he to do?

He was positive the player behind him had a four-card straight flush which would be filled whether he drew one card to his four aces or stood pat with them. Suppose he drew two cards throwing away one of the aces!

No, he reflected. These crooks were much too smart to have overlooked that. They probably had it fixed up so that he'd lose even if he drew three cards!

And the poor fellow was right, for the sharp behind him had a queen-jack-ten-nine of spades. The top card of the deck was the king of spades, the next was the eight of spades, and the next was another king. So the crook was bound to fill either a straight flush against four aces or a straight against three aces!

There was so much money in the pot that our hero hated to give up without a struggle—so he threw away his whole hand and drew five cards! The crooks hadn't thought of that one, for the five cards were the eight of spades and four kings! And, just as in the last tale, four kings won a pot that rightfully belonged to four aces!

But these are just the legends of Poker. Any time I get four kings—or even four deuces—I'm going to bet my shirt on them. It won't bother me if I'm playing with strangers, because every experienced card player knows there's about a thousand times as much talk about cheats as there is actual cheating.

As a matter of fact, it was because a young Poker player was wrongly suspected of cheating that some very remarkable things happened during the Civil War. Now, this isn't one of those wild tales about Poker players that I just complained about. It was told me by an old sergeant whose reputation for veracity was unequaled in that select company of truth-tellers.

The young fellow who started it all was a rookie who went from Tennessee in 1861 to fight in Lee's infantry. He couldn't add two and two, but he used to win all the money in the Poker game that his company held every Saturday night. Naturally that annoyed everybody else, and some of them even got suspicious about a fellow that couldn't sign his own name but could corner all the money in any Poker game that he played in.

They tried everything they could think of to catch him cheating, but the more they tried the less they found out—and the more they lost to him. Finally it began to dawn on them that they really had in their company one of the finest Poker players in the world—perhaps the finest of all.

But it didn't do them much good to arrive at this conclusion. Finding it out had cost them about a ton of the best Confederate currency, most of which was still on the cuff. They had to find some way to pay off, and after a while they hit upon a scheme.

They simply organized a Poker game in every company of the regiment. Each company was to pick its champion, and all of these were to play in a regimental championship. The idea was to back their man in the regimental game and thus win enough to pay what they owed him.

Everything went off as scheduled, and then they had another bright idea. Why stop there—why not get up a divisional championship? And so it went, until one fine day their man was champion of all the Southern armies.

In the meantime, an enterprising spy had seen what was going on. It looked pretty blame good to him, so he put the system into operation in the Northern armies.

Well you can guess what happened. After a while there was a Yank champ and a Johnny Reb champ—with no new worlds to conquer unless they played against each other. Each side was fanatically devoted to its own champion; and to most of the soldiers the war wasn't a matter of States' Rights or anything else as hifalutin' as that—it was simply a matter of licking the daylights out of those stubborn fools who thought *their* man could play Poker in the same league as the *real* champ.

That state of affairs couldn't go on forever, and eventually tension got so high that negotiations were opened between the two armies and generals on both sides. And after much wrangling it was decided to stage the long-awaited Poker match and to let the outcome settle the whole darned war!

"But that's incredible!" I objected, when the story was told to me.

"When you've played Poker as long as I have," the sergeant reassured me, "you'll believe fancier stories than this one. If I wasn't a truthful man, I c'd tell you tales that'd curl your hair right up in knots. And you'd believe 'em too. Now, d'you want me to go on—or are you gonna call a man a liar that was there and seen it all?"

Naturally, I told him that if he had seen it himself, that settled it. I had just wondered whether somebody else had told him the story. After all, there *were* people who sometimes exaggerated a trifle, just to make a story sound a little better—but of course he wasn't one of them. That soothed the old man, and he went on with the story.

The match was set for late June, 1863; and since the North had won the toss, it was to be played on Northern grounds. So the Southern champ got on a horse and rode up into Pennsylvania; and such was the excitement and the feverish flurry of betting that the entire army, General Lee and all, came up to cheer him on. The Northerners were equally het up, and there were probably as many Yanks as Rebs on the scene, generals included.

Generals aren't human beings, the sergeant assured me earnestly. Two armies were waiting for the game to start—and they had to waste time with speeches and toasts, and figuring out how many guns the Poker champs rated as a salute! But finally the match started.

It was Five-Card Stud, head-on. Each man started with ten thousand chips, and the game was table stakes, so one slip might mean the whole works. But for six hours of that fateful June 30th, the two masters worked like mad without getting anywhere. By midnight they were right back where they started!

The trouble was that too much was at stake. Neither man wanted to risk the whole war on a single hand unless he had a sure thing. And as soon as either felt sure enough to tap the other fellow for his whole pile, his opponent would realize he was beaten and refuse to call. So there were a lot of checks, small bets, hesitant calls . . . and no real action.

It got so bad that General Lee and General Meade considered calling the whole thing off. And while they were discussing that, the excitement began. Both men were betting feverishly, raising each other in larger and larger amounts.

The two generals got to the table in time to see the Southern champion shove all of his chips into the middle of the table. Without a second's hesitation the Yank called with all of his chips. The whole war hung in the balance!

Like most good Poker players, the two champs were born showmen, and they paused for a few seconds before they turned up the hole cards. It wasn't often that they played for stakes like these, and they meant to savor the excitement to the last drop.

Lee looked hurriedly at the up cards of both hands. His man had jack-nine-eight-seven showing. He'd better have a ten in the hole, or there'd be a court-martial in the morning, peace or no peace! He relaxed when he saw the Yank's hand—just ace-nine-seven-two of diamonds. The best he could have was a pair of aces! What suckers these Yanks were!

And while Lee was congratulating himself in this vein, the Yank supporters looked equally jubilant. They were quite sure their man had a diamond in the hole, while the best the Johnny Reb could have was a straight. The flush was a cinch to win—and they'd collect their bets and go home in peace.

The modern Poker player probably doesn't realize what the trouble was—why each side was so sure it had won. But old-timers remember that the flush was not always considered a legal hand—that's the way with the Tiger and the Blaze today. There were no official rule books, and local custom was all-powerful in settling disputes.

But now two local customs were about to conflict. The flush was played all over the North, but was virtually unknown in the South. No wonder the two champions had piled all their chips in the middle of the table; according to his own lights, each was betting on a sure thing!

When the two hole cards were turned up there was a deafening cheer from both sides. And even while exulting in victory, each side glowed with pride at the sportsmanship of the opponents. Listen to them cheer—even though they had just lost the war! . . . After a minute or so, each side began to realize that something was wrong. The best losers in the world couldn't cheer like that . . . And after another minute or two the argument began.

My sergeant friend didn't remember much of the argument. He remembers punching some general on the nose—he'd always wanted to sock a general—and then the first thing he knew he was hustling back to camp. The war was on again!

But this time there was no doubt what they were fighting about. They could print what they liked in the history books, but the real issue was whether or not the flush was a legal hand in Poker.

The next day saw the beginning of a terrific battle. After three days of fighting, the Southerners retreated from the scene of the Poker match—Gettysburg, Pennsylvania. And it took two more years of fighting for the flush to come into its own. All because there were no official Poker laws in those days!

"Can you prove that story?" I asked, when the sergeant paused for breath.

"Prove it!" he snorted. "You've got the proof right in your own book! Doesn't it say there that flushes count? What better proof could you have?"

There was no denying that, so I had to admit he was right. And today I often get to wondering. . . . Does that bird Hitler play Stud?

¶ *W. Somerset Maugham is a card-player himself and the whole world of card-players is proud to have so distinguished a fellow. You will admire and enjoy this Poker essay by Mr. Maugham, and you will admire also Mr. Maugham's charitable spirit; for the English do not play Poker exactly as Americans do, and each nation thinks its own way best, but Mr. Maugham here endorses one American point of view.* ¶ *Mr. Maugham's visit to Seoul was in the 1920s, before that unhappy city became a punching bag for blockbusters.*

The Code of a Gentleman

by W. SOMERSET MAUGHAM

I ARRIVED in Seoul toward evening and after dinner, tired by the long railway journey from Peking, to stretch my cramped legs I went for a walk. I wandered at random along a narrow and busy street. The Koreans in their long white gowns and their little white top-hats were amusing to look at and the open shops displayed wares that intrigued my foreign eyes. Presently I came to a second-hand bookseller's and, catching sight of shelves filled with English books, I went in to have a look at them.

I glanced at the titles and my heart sank. They were commentaries on the Old Testament, treatises on the Epistles of St. Paul, sermons and lives of divines. I supposed that this was the library of some missionary whom death had claimed in the midst of his labors.

The Japanese are astute, but I wondered who in Seoul would be found to buy a work in three volumes on the Epistle to the Corinthians. But as I was turning away, between volume two and volume three of this treatise I noticed a little book bound in paper. I do not know what induced me to take it out. It was called "The Complete Poker Player" and its cover was illustrated with a hand holding four aces. I looked at the title page. The author was Mr. John Blackbridge, actuary and counselor-at-law, and the preface was dated 1879.

I wondered how this book happened to be among the books of a deceased missionary and I looked in one or two to see if I could find his name. Perhaps it was there only by accident. It may be that it was the entire library of a stranded gambler and had found its way to those shelves when his effects were sold to pay his hotel bill; but I preferred to think that it was indeed the property of the missionary, and that when he was weary of reading divinity he rested his mind by the perusal of these lively pages.

But the owner of the shop was looking at me with disfavor so I turned to him and asked the price of the book. He gave it a contemptuous glance and told me I could have it for twenty sen.

I do not remember that for so small a sum I have ever purchased better entertainment. For Mr. John Blackbridge in these pages of his did a thing which no writer can do who deliberately tries to, but which, if done unconsciously, gives a book a rare and precious savor: he painted a complete portrait of himself.

I see him very distinctly as a man of middle age in a black frock coat and a chimney-pot hat, wearing a black satin stock; he is clean-shaven and his jaw is square; his lips are thin and his eyes are wary; his face is sallow and somewhat wrinkled. It is a countenance not without severity, but when he tells one of his stories or makes one of his dry jokes, his eyes light up and his smile is winning.

He enjoyed his bottle of Burgundy, but I cannot believe that he ever drank enough to confuse his excellent faculties. He was just rather than merciful at the card table and he was prepared to punish presumption with rigor.

He had few illusions, for here are a few of the things that life had taught him: "Men hate those whom they have injured; men love those whom they have benefited; men naturally avoid their benefactors; men are universally actuated by self-interest; gratitude is a lively sense of expected benefits; promises are never forgotten by those to whom they are made, usually by those who make them."

It may be presumed that he was a Southerner, for while speaking of jack pots, which he describes as a frivolous attempt to make the game more interesting, he remarks that they are not popular in the South. "This last fact," he says, "contains much promise, because the South is the conservative portion of the country, and may be relied on as the last resort of good sense in social matters. The revolutionary Kossuth made no progress below Richmond; neither spiritualism nor free love nor Communism has ever been received with the least favor by the Southern mind; and it is for this reason that we greatly respect the Southern verdict upon the jack pot."

It was in his day an innovation and he condemned it. "The time has arrived when all additions to the present standard combinations in Draw Poker must be worthless; the game being complete." The jack pot, he says, "was invented in Toledo, Ohio, by reckless players to compensate losses incurred by playing against cautious players; and the principle is the same as if a party should play whist for stakes, and all be obliged every few minutes to stop and purchase tickets in a lottery, or raffle."

Poker is a game for gentlemen—he does not hesitate to make frequent use of this abused word; he lived in a day when to be a gentleman had its obligations but also its privileges—and a straight flush is to be respected, not because you make money on it ("I have never seen anyone make much money upon a straight flush," he says) but "because it prevents any hand from being *absolutely* the winning hand, and thus relieves gentlemen from the necessity of betting on a certainty. Without the use of straights, and hence without the use of a straight flush, four aces would be a certainty, and no gentleman could do more than *call* on them."

This, I confess, catches me on the raw, for once in my life I had a straight flush, and I bet on it till I was called.

Mr. John Blackbridge had a sense of personal dignity, rectitude, humor and common sense. "The amusements of mankind," he says, "have not as yet received proper recognition at the hands of the makers of the civil law, and of the unwritten social law," and he had no patience with the persons who condemn the most agreeable pastime that has been invented, namely gambling, because risk is attached to it.

Every transaction in life is a risk, he truly observes, and involves the question of loss and gain. "To retire to rest at night is a practice that is fortified by countless precedents, and it is generally regarded as prudent and necessary. Yet it is surrounded by risks of every kind." He enumerates them and finally sums up his argument: "If social circles welcome the banker and merchant who live by taking fair risks for the sake of profit, there is no apparent reason why they should not at least tolerate the man who at times employs himself in giving and taking fair risks for the sake of amusement."

But here his good sense is obvious. "Twenty years of experience in the city of New York, both professionally [you must not forget that he is an actuary and counselor-at-law] and as a student of social life, satisfy me that the average American gentleman in a large city has not over three thousand dollars a year to spend upon amusements. Will it be fair to devote more than one-third of this fund to cards? I do not think that anyone will say that one-third is not ample allowance for a single amusement. Given, therefore, a thousand dollars a year for the purpose of playing Draw Poker, what should be the limit of the stakes, in order that the average American gentleman may play the game with a contented mind, and with the certainty not only that he can pay his losses, but that his winnings will be paid to him?"

Mr. Blackbridge has no doubt that the answer is two dollars and a half. "The game of Poker should be intellectual and not emotional; and it is impossible to exclude the emotions from it if the stakes are so high that the question of loss and gain penetrates to the feelings."

It may be seen that Mr. Blackbridge looked upon Poker as only on the side a game of chance. To his mind it needs as much force of character, mental ability, power of decision and insight into motive to play poker as to govern a country or lead an army.

I am tempted to quote interminably, for Mr. Blackbridge seldom writes a sentence which is other than characteristic, and his language is measured, clear and pointed. Could anything be better than this terse but adequate description of a card-sharper? "He was a very good-looking man of about forty years of age, having the appearance of one who had been leading a temperate and thoughtful life."

But I will content myself with giving a few of his aphorisms and wise saws chosen almost at random from the wealth of his book:

"Let your chips talk for you. A silent player is so far forth a mystery; and a mystery is always feared.

"In this game never do anything that you are not compelled to; while cheerfully responding to your obligations.

"At Draw Poker all statements not called for by the laws of the game, or supported by ocular demonstration, may be set down as fictitious; designed to enliven the path of truth throughout the game, as flowers in summer enliven the margins of the highway.

"Lost money is never recovered. After losing you may win, but the losing does not bring the winning.

"No gentleman will ever play any game of cards with the design of habitually winning and never losing.

"A gentleman is always willing to pay a fair price for recreation and amusement.

". . . that habit of mind which continually leads us to undervalue the mental force of other men, while we continually overvalue their good luck.

"Players usually straddle when they are in bad luck, upon the principle that bad play and bad luck united will win. A slight degree of intoxication aids to perfect this intellectual deduction.

"Euchre is a contemptible game.

"The lower cards as well as the lower classes are only useful in combination or in excess, and cannot be depended upon under any other circumstances.

"It is a hard matter to hold four aces as steadily as a pair, but the table will bear their weight with as much equanimity as a pair of deuces.

"Of good luck and bad luck: To feel emotions over such incidents is unworthy of a man; and it is much more unworthy to express them. But no words need be wasted over practices which all men despise in others and, in their reflecting moments, lament in themselves.

"Endorsing for your friends is a bad habit, but it is nothing to playing poker on credit . . . Debit and credit ought never to interfere with the fine intellectual calculations of this game."

There is a fine ring about his remarks on the player who has trained his intellect to bring logic to bear upon the principles and phenomena of the game. "He will thus feel a constant sense of security amid all possible fluctuations that occur, and he will also abstain from pressing an ignorant or an intellectually weak opponent, beyond what may be necessary either for the purpose of playing the game correctly or of punishing presumption."

I leave Mr. John Blackbridge with his last word and I can hear him saying it gently but with a tolerant smile:

"For we must take human nature as it is."

POKER IN AMERICAN FICTION

¶James Jones's book FROM HERE TO ETERNITY *has been praised for a variety of reasons, but our reason is probably unique: He has performed the miracle of describing Blackjack and Poker players as they actually act and feel. ¶The card-playing in* FROM HERE TO ETERNITY *is chiefly concentrated in Chapter 20, which we here reprint entire. The background story is this: Prewitt, the hero, aspires to win the heart (not merely the body, which can be had in varying degrees for two to ten dollars) of Lorene, the new girl at his company's favorite Honolulu whorehouse. In pursuance of his campaign he needs a stake. Typically, the only way that occurs to him to get this stake is to win it gambling. He almost makes the grade, but he suffers from the prime and immemorial plague of gamblers: He doesn't know when to quit. ¶Mr. Jones now tells his own story and we delay him only long enough to say that despite the sad ending to this chapter, Prew does get the girl a few chapters later. ¶We have not tampered with Mr. Jones's distinctive style in punctuation, capitalization, etc., not because of any restrictions but because we wouldn't want to.*

from From Here to Eternity
by JAMES JONES

YOU KNOCK OFF drill at ten o'clock on Payday. You shower, shave, brush your teeth again, dress carefully in your best inspection uniform, being careful to knot the suntan tie just right. Then, dressed, you work hard on your fingernails before you finally go outside to stand around in the sun in the company yard and wait for them to begin the paying off, being very careful all the time of the knot in the tie and of the fingernails, since all company paying officers have their little idiosyncrasies of personal inspection even if Payday is not a regular inspection day. With some it was the shoes, with others the crease of the pants, with others the haircut. With Capt. Holmes it was the knot in the tie and the fingernails and while if these did not satisfy him he did not redline you or anything like that, still you got a rigorous telling off and had to fall out to the end of the line.

You stand around in little groups on Payday and talk about it excitedly and about the half holiday it is, groups that can't stay still and break up and reform with parts of other groups into new groups, continually shifting, not able to stand still, except for the twenty per cent men who are already waiting like vultures at the kitchen door where you must emerge. Until then finally you see the guard bugler go up to the megaphone in the quad in the brilliant morning sunshine (more brilliant, oddly, than on any other morning) and sound Pay Call.

"Pay day," the bugle says to you, *"pay day. What you go na do with a drunk en sol jer? Pay day?"*

"Pay day," the bugle answers you, *"pay day. Put him in the guard house till he's so ber. Pay day. P-a-y . . . d-a-y."*

Then the shifting excitement grows much stronger (oh, the bugler plays a responsible part, a traditional, emotional, important part, a part heavy with the past, with all the past centuries of soldiering) and you see The Warden carrying a GI blanket from the orderly room to the messhall and Mazzioli following him with the Payroll like a lord chamberlain carrying the Great Seal and then the shining-booted Dynamite carrying the black satchel and grinning beneficently. It takes them quite a while to get set up, move the tables, spread the blanket, count the silver out and lay the greenbacks out in sheaves, get the jawbone list of PX checks and show checks ready for The Warden to collect, but already you begin to form the line, by rank, noncoms first, then Pfcs and Pvts in one group together, the men within each group lining up for once without argument or pushing, alphabetically.

Then, finally, they begin to pay and you can see the line moving very slowly up ahead of you, until you stand in the doorway of the dim messhall yourself while the man in front of you gets paid, until they call your last name and you answer with your first name, middle initial and serial number and step up to Dynamite and salute, standing stiffly while he looks you over and you show your fingernails and he, satisfied, pays you off, tossing you one of his pat jokes like, *"Save enough back to go to town on"* or *"Dont drink all this up in one place."* Oh, he is a soldier, Dynamite, a soldier of the old school, Dynamite. And then holding this money, (less laundry, less insurance, less allotment if any, less the $1 to the Company Fund) that it took you all month to earn and that they are giving you the rest of this day off to spend, you move down the long blanket covered table to The Warden who collects for PX checks and shows checks you have drawn during the month and that you really did not mean to draw at all (promised yourself, last Payday, you would not draw, this month) but drew somehow anyway when they came out on the 10th and the 20th. Then out through the kitchen to the porch where the heavy capital of the financial wizards of twenty per cent men like Jim O'Hayer and Turp Thornhill and, to a lesser extent that is really only a hobby, Champ Wilson, takes its toll also from the dwindling pile.

Payday. It is truly an occasion, even the feud between you and the jockstraps is in eclipse when its Payday. In the long, low ceilinged shadiness of the squadroom with the sun very bright outside men are stripping off the suntans feverishly and pulling on the civilians and you know there will not be very many for chow this noon, practically none tonight except for losing gamblers.

Out of his $30.00, after the debts were paid, Prew had exactly $12.00 and two dimes. This, which would not even buy Lorene for one all night session, he blessed and genuflected over and took over to O'Hayer's.

The sheds, across the street from the dayroom and jerrybuilt on the strip of worn near-bald earth between the street and the narrow gauge Post railroad, were already going full blast. The quarter-ton maintenance trucks had been moved to the regimental motor park, the big spools of phone wire were neatly stacked outside, the 37mm anti-tank guns (some the old short-barreled steel-wheeled that were familiar, some the new long-barreled rubber-tired looking strange and foreign like the pictures of the German arms in *Life* Magazine) had been rolled out and covered up with tarps, and the spielers hired for a buck an hour called unceasingly like circus barkers from before each shed to *"Come inside, boys. Poker, blackjack, craps, chuckaluck, all inside. Test that luck, boys."*

In O'Hayer's all five lima-bean-shaped blackjack tables were working full capacity. Under the green shaded lights green visored dealers called the cards in monotonous low voices against the hum. Both dice tables were crowded three deep with players, and the three poker tables that were dealing only stud today to take care of more players had no seats open.

Standing in the door he thought how by the middle of the month all this money would have sifted down into the hands of a few heavy winners who would be at this table where O'Hayer sat playing now, one of his hired help dealing. They would be winners from all over, from as far away as Hickam and Fort Kam and Shafter and Fort Ruger. They would make this the biggest game on the Inland Post, if not on the whole Rock. The thought made his belly flutter, how he might with luck be one of them. He had done it once before, but only once, at Myer. And the resolution to win just enough for town and quit grew dim and wavered and, but for his stiff determination bolstered by the picture of Lorene, would have fled entirely.

He worked methodically with small bets for two hours at a blackjack table (deliberately monotonously, deliberately uninspired) to run his twelve bucks up to the twenty which was the take-out at the poker tables. Then he moved over to the one where O'Hayer was to wait for an open seat, which would never be long on Payday when most of the players were just small fry like himself with a table stake wanting to bite into the big boys' capital. They were constantly going broke and dropping out. He waited without excitement, promising himself faithfully that if he won two hands he'd quit, because two wins in this game would give him plenty for tonight with enough left over for a good weekend (today was Thursday) or Saturday night and Sunday night (and maybe Sunday day, if she said okay, maybe at the beach with her) with Lorene. Just two wins. He had it all figured out.

The round green felt with a bite cut out for the dealer's seat was strewn with piles of half-dollars and cartwheels and the red plastic two-bit chips for ante-ing. They caught and threw back sardonically the greenglass-shaded light, vividly red and silver against the soft light-absorbing felt. He could see The Warden and Stark among the players. Jim O'Hayer sat relaxed with a rakish, expensive green visor cocked over the coldly rigidly mathematical eyes, constantly rolling two cartwheels one over the other with a click that ate into the nerves.

It was Stark, his hat tipped low over his eyes, who finally pushed back his four legged mess stool and gave himself the coup de grace: "Seat open."

"You aint quittin?" O'Hayer said softly.

"Not for long," Stark said, looking at him reflectively. "Just till I borry some money."

"See you then," O'Hayer grinned. "Good luck with it."

"Well now thank you, Jim," Stark said.

Stark, some kibitzer whispered, had in the

last hour dropped the whole $600 he had managed to build up since ten o'clock. Stark stared at him and he subsided, and Stark elbowed slowly out through the press, still looking reflective.

Prew slid onto the empty $600 seat wondering darkly if this was an omen and pushed his little ten and two fives over to the dealer as unobtrusively as possible. The money boys kept the takeout low on Payday, so you could get in, but they stared at your twenty bucks contemptuously, when you did. He got back a stack of 15 cartwheels, 6 halves, and 8 of the plastic chips and fingering them did not any longer mind the contempt because the old familiar alchemy, the best drug of them all against this life, spread over him as he flipped a red chip in there with the others. His heart was beating faster with louder, more emphatic thumps, echoing in his ears. The gambler's flush was spreading across his face, making it feverish. The bottom of his belly dropped away from under him leaving him standing on the edge of which the world stopped moving.

Here, he thought, just here, and only here, held in these pieces of pasteboard being tossed facedown around the table, governed by whatever Laws or fickle Goddess moved them, here lay infinity and the secret of all life and death, what the scientists were seeking, here under your hand if you could only grasp it, penetrate the unreadability. You may shortly win $1000. You may more shortly be completely broke. And any man who could just only learn to understand the reason why would be shaking hands with God. They were playing table stakes and in front of the winners lay thick piles of greenbacks weighted down with silver. The sight of all this crisp green paper that was so important in this life swept him with a greediness to take these crinkly good smelling pieces of paper to himself, not for what they would buy but for their lovely selves. All this was contained in the slow, measured, inexorable dropping of the cards, like time beating slowly but irresistibly in the ears of an old old man.

Around the table twice, twice ten cards, once down, once up. Somebody's watch beat loudly. And the known familiar faces took on new characteristics and became strange. The bright light cast strange shadows down from the impassive brows and noses, making of each man an eyeless hairlip. He did not know these men. That was not Warden there or O'Hayer there, only a pair of bodyless hands moving the top card under the holecard for a secret look, only an armless hand clicking a stack of halves down one on top of the other, then lifting all and clicking them down again, and again, perpetually, with measured thoughtfulness. An unreasoning thrill passed down his spine, and all the unpleasantness his life had become in the last two months fell away from him, dead, forgotten.

The first hand was a big one. He had hoped for a small one, his $20 would not go far in this game. But the cards were high, and the betting heavy. He had jacks backed up and by the third round he was all in, for the side pot his twenty shared, unable because this was table stakes to go into his pocket for more money if he had it which he did not. The pot he could win was shoved to one side and the betting went on in the center, and all he could do was sit and sweat it out. On the fourth card O'Hayer caught the ace to match his holecard that all of them knew he had because Jim O'Hayer never stayed for fun. He raised fifteen. Prew's belly sagged and he looked at his jacks ruefully and was very glad he was all in for the pot. But on the last card he caught another jack, making a pair showing. He felt his heart skip a beat and cursed silently because he was all in for the pot.

There was nearly a hundred and fifty in his pot. O'Hayer won the other, the smaller pot. Warden looked at O'Hayer and then at him and snorted his disgust. Prew grinned, dragging in his pot, and reminded himself that if he won the next one he would quit and check out and Warden could really snort then.

He didnt need to win the next one. What he had from the first was plenty. But he had promised himself two hands, not one, so he stayed in. But he did not win the second hand. Warden won it, and he had dropped $40 which left him only about a hundred and now he felt he needed the second win before he dropped out so he stayed in. But he did not win the third hand either, or the fourth, nor did he win the fifth. He dropped clear down to less than $50, before he finally won another one.

Raking in the money he sighed off the tenseness that had grown in him in ratio to the shrinking of his capital; he had begun to believe he would never win another one. But now though he had a real backlog to work from. The second win put him up to over two hundred. Two hundred was plenty capital. And he began to play careful, weighing each bet. He played shirtfront poker, enjoying it immensely, completely lost in loving it, in matching his brain against the disembodied brains against him. It was true poker, hard monotonous unthrilling, and he truly loved it, and played steadily, losing only a little, dropping out often, winning a small one now and then, playing now against the time when he would win that really big one and check out.

He knew of course all the time that it could not go on indefinitely this way, $200 was no reserve to put up against the capital in this game, but then all he wanted was just one more big win like the first two, one that would be bigger because now he had more money, one he could quit on and check out for good. If he had won the first two like he promised he would have quit then but he hadnt won them he had only won one and now he wanted this last one to quit on, before he finally got caught.

But before the big win he was just waiting for to quit on came they caught him, they caught him good.

He had tens backed up, a good hand. On the fourth card he drew another. On the same card Warden paired kings showing. Warden checked to the tens. Prew was cautious, they were not *trying* to play dirty poker in this game but with this much on the table anything went. Warden might have trips and he was not being sucked in, he was not that green. When the bet had checked clear around to him he raised lightly, very lightly, just a touch, a feeler, a protection bet he could afford to abandon and lose. Three men dropped out right away. Only O'Hayer and Warden called, finally. O'Hayer obviously had an ace paired to his holecard and was willing to pay for the chance to catch the third. O'Hayer was a percentage man, twenty percentage man, O'Hayer. And Warden who thought quite a while before he called looked at his holecard twice and then he almost didnt call, so he had no trips.

On the last card O'Hayer missed his ace and dropped out, indifferently. O'Hayer could always afford to drop out indifferently. Warden with his kings still high checked it to Prew, and Prew felt a salve of relief grease over him for sure now Warden had no trips. Warden had two pairs and hoped the kings would nose him out since O'Hayer had two bullets. Well, if he wanted to see them he could by god pay for seeing them, like everybody else, and Prew bet twenty-five, figuring to milk the last drop out of him, figuring he had this one clinched, figuring The Warden for his lousy pair to brace his kings. It was a legitimate bet; Warden had checked his kings twice when they were high. Warden raised him sixty dollars.

Looking at Warden's malignant grin he knew then he was caught, really hooked, right through the bag. By three big kings. Outsmarted. Sucked in like a green kid. The first time somebody checked a cinch into him. His belly flopped over sickeningly with disbelief and he made as if to drop out, but he knew he had to call.

There was too much of his money in this pot, which was a big one, to chance a bluff. And The Warden knew just how high to raise without raising too high to get a call.

The hand cost him two hundred even, he had about forty dollars left. He pushed the stool back, way back, and got up then.

"Seat open."

Warden's eyebrows quivered, then hooked up pixishly.

"I hated to do that to you, kid. I really did. If I didnt need the money so goddam bad I'd by god give it back."

The table laughed all around.

"Ah, you keep it," Prew said. "You won it, Top, its yours. Check me out," he said to the dealer, thinking why didn't you drop out you son of a bitch after that second win like you promised, thinking this is not an original lament.

"Whats wrong, kid?" Warden said. "You look positively unwell."

"Just hungry. Missed noon chow."

Warden winked at Stark who had only just come back. "Too late to catch chow now. You better stick around? Win some of this back? Forty, fifty bucks aint much take home pay."

"Enough," Prew said. "For what I need." Why didnt he let it go? Why did he have to rub it in? The son of a bitching bastard whoring bastard.

"Yeah, but you want a bottle too, dont you? Hell, we all friends here, just a friendly game for pastime. Aint that right, Jim?"

Prew could see his eyes clenching into rays of wrinkles as he looked at the gambler.

"Sure," O'Hayer said indifferently. "Long as you got the money to be friendly. Deal the cards."

Warden laughed softly, as if to himself. "You see?" he said to Prew. "No cutthroat. No hardtack. The take out's only twenty."

"Beats me," Prew said. He started to add, *"I've got a widowed mother,"* but nobody would have heard it. The cards were already riffling off the deck.

As he moved back Stark goosed him warmly in the ribs and winked, and slipped into the seat.

"Heres fifty," Stark said to the dealer.

Outside the air free of smoke and moisture of exhaled breath smote Prew like cold water and he inhaled deeply, suddenly awake again, then let it out, trying to let out with it the weary tired unrest that was urging him to go back. He could not escape the belief that he had just lost $200 of his own hard-earned money to that bastard Warden. Come on, cut it out, he told himself, you didnt lose a cent, you're twenty to the good, you got enough for tonight, lets me and you walk from this place.

The air had wakened him and he saw clearly that this was no personal feud, this was a poker game, and you cant break them all, eventually they'll break you. He walked around the sheds and down to the sidewalk. Then he walked across the street. He even got so far his hand was on the doorknob of the dayroom door and the door half open. Before he finally decided to quit kidding himself and slammed the door angrily and turned around and went irritably back to O'Hayer's.

"Well look who's here," Warden grinned. "I thought we'd be seeing you. Is there a seat open? Somebody get up and give this old gambler a seat."

"Aw can it," Prew said savagely and slipped into the seat of another loser who was checking out and grinning unhappily at The Warden with the look of a man who wants to do the right thing and be a good sport but finds it hard.

"Come on, come on," Prew said. "Whats holding things up? Lets get this show on the road."

"Man!" The Warden said. "You sound like you're itchin for a great big lick."

"I am. Look out for yourself. I'm hot. First jack bets."

But he was not hot and knew it, he was only savagely irritated, and there is a difference and it took him just fifteen minutes and three hands to lose the forty dollars, as he had known he would. Where before he had played happily, lost in loving it, savoring every second, now he played with dogged irritation, not giving a damn, angered by even the time it took to deal. You dont win at poker playing that way, and he stood up feeling a welcome sense of release that came with being broke and able to quit now.

"Now I can go home and go to bed. And sleep."

"What!" The Warden said. "At three o'clock in the afternoon?"

"Sure," Prew said. Was it only three o'clock? He had thought they'd played Tattoo already. "Why not?" he said.

The Warden snorted his disgust. "Punks wont never listen to me. I told you you should of quit when you was ahead. But would you listen? A lot you listen."

"Forgot," Prew said. "Forgot all about it. Hows for loanin me a hundred, and I'll remember." It got a laugh around the table.

"Sorry, kid. You know I'm behind myself."

"Hell. And I thought you was winnin." It got another laugh, and he felt better, but he remembered it did not put money back in his pocket. He elbowed his way out.

"What you want to awys be pickin on the kid for, First?" he heard Stark say behind him.

"Pick on him?" Warden said indignantly. "Whatever give you that idea?"

"He dont need you to pick on him," the K Co topkick, a bald fat man with drinker's hollowed eyes, said. "From what I hear."

"Thats right," Stark said. "He doin all right by himself."

Warden snorted then. "He can take it. He's a punchy. He's use to bein hit. Some of them even like it."

"If I was him," the K Co topkick said, "I'd transfer the hell out of there."

"Thats all you know," Warden said. "He cant. Dynamite wont let him."

"Come on," Jim O'Hayer's voice said nasally. "Is this a sewing circle or a card game? King is high, king bets."

"Bet five," Warden said. "You know, thats what I like about you, Jim. Your overwhelming sense of human compassion," he said quizzically. In his mind Prew could see the eyes clenching themselves into those somehow ominous rays of wrinkles.

He let the shaky door swing shut behind him, cutting off the talk, wishing he could find it in him to hate that bitchery Warden but he couldn't, and remembering suddenly he had not even in his passion thought to get a sandwich and coffee from O'Hayer's freelunch for the players. But he would not go back in there now.

He could also remember, suddenly, a lot of other things he had meant to do with part of that money before he risked it. He needed shaving cream and a new bore brush and a new Blitz rag and he had wanted to stock up some tailormades. It was lucky he had a carton of Duke's still stashed away.

Because you are through, Prewitt, he told himself, your wad is shot, your roll is gone, you're through till next month now, and there will be no Lorene for you this month. By next month she may have retired and gone back to the States already.

He jammed his hands in his pockets savagely

and found some change, a small pile of dimes and nickels, and brought it out and looked at it, wondering what it was good for. It was enough to get into a small change game in the latrine, but the hopelessness of ever running that little bit back up to two hundred and sixty bucks hit him and he threw it down into the railroad bed viciously and with satisfaction watched it spread like shot but glinting silver, then heard with satisfaction the clink of it hitting the rails. He turned back to the barracks. Lorene, or no Lorene, poker or no poker, you are not borrowing any money at no twenty percent thats for sure. You aint borrowed any twenty percent money since you been on this rock and you aint starting now, school keeps or not.

He found Turp Thornhill in his own shed next to O'Hayer's. Because there was nothing in O'Hayer, even at twenty percent, when he was playing, Turp was neither playing nor dealing. He was moving from dice table to blackjack table to poker table back to dice table, perpetually and nervously, checking up as usual on his dealers to see they were not cheating him.

The tall chinless hawknosed Mississippi peckerwood possessed all the disgusting traits of a backward people with few of the compensating good. But he did loan money, even though he lived an eternal gimlet-eyed suspicion, a grasping pinch-mouthed service pride in being *"just what he was, by god, and no hifalutin airs, take it or leave it."* He had earned the management of his gambling shed by being in the same company 17 years and ass-kissing his superiors every minute of that time, and now he was in position to compensate for it with a sadistic cruelty toward anyone he calculated he could dominate.

"Haw," Turp hawked, when Prew called him over to one side and hit him up for twenty. He doubled up his long thin frame and prodded the other slyly. "Haw," he hollered, loud enough for everybody in the humming shed to hear, "so Prewitt the Hard's a finally givin in, 'ey? Got his guts all riled over wantin a little, 'ey? So he decide to come around and see ole daddy Turp that ain't good enuf for him to talk to 'cept on Payday to borry some money, 'ey? Well, it comes to all on us, boy, it comes to all on us."

He got his wallet out, but did not open it yet, he was not through yet.

"Where you aim to go? The Service? The Ritz? The Pacific? The New Senator? The New Congress Mrs. Kipfer runs? I know em all, boy, hell I support em. Listen, now, boy. Let me give you a little tip. Ers a new job over to the Ritz. Not so hot on looks but boys! will she work you over. Hunh? What you say? Kind of gits ye, don't it? Like to have a little bit a that stuff? wunt ye? Hows about er, 'ey?"

A number of the players were looking at them now and laughing. Turp grinned back at them smugly, relishing his audience, not wanting to lose it, not just yet.

Prew was still silent but his face was reddening in spite of himself. He cursed silently at his face for reddening.

Turp laughed again, winking at his audience, get this now, this going to be a good one now, just get this. His long bony nose poked into Prewitt's face with each bob of nervous laughter. The grin pulled up the long corners of his chinless mouth making his face into a series of sharp prying Vs. The subdued murky eyes popped into bright intensity like bursting flares, filled with obscene curiosity and insulting laughter. Turp was at his best before an audience, get this now.

"Haw," Turp hawked, winking at his audience. "Why hell, boy, if you'd do it with her her way, you wunt have to borry no money. She'd give it to ye for nothin, and probly be willin to take you to raise in the bargain. Hows about that, 'ey?"

The audience roared. Old Turp was in form. Even the dice stopped rattling.

"I hear thats what she likes," Turp hawked. "Hows about it, 'ey? Man never knows till he tried it. Maybe he been missin somethin all his life. I hear them boys out in Hollywood make a lot of money that a way. Man awys use a leetle money, caint he? Might even get to like it, who knows?"

"Haw, look at im. He blushin. Look at im, boys. Laws, I do declare he blushin. You really want to borry some money now, Prewitt? Or you just pullin my leg now? Maybe you wont need it now."

Prew stayed silent but he was having trouble with it. He had to keep shut, if he aimed to get the money. And Turp had money. Turp made money. He had been running a shed from G Company when O'Hayer was just an upstart. But O'Hayer's rise had been meteoric and he had topped them all. For this Turp hated and feared the gambler with a sly longnosed implacability. Yet strangely, he took the small sums he made from his loans and the large sums he made from his shed and lost them all across O'Hayer's poker table along in the middle of the month. After the Payday gambling rush was over and his own shed was closed down, he would sit in on the winners' game, betting wildly, cursing with nervous excitability, losing steadily. It was as if the sterile contamination of his own spavined Mississippi land had gotten like clap into his blood and made even himself an object of his own ingrown suspicious hatred, so that he frantically threw away every cent he could pick up, in order to keep Turp from cheating Thornhill. And in the end the hated O'Hayer, cool and mathematical and impersonal, always collected the profits of Turp's shed in addition to his own.

Turp let him have the twenty, finally, after a pause in his Southern Ku Klux Klan brand of humor, a pause in which white lines of suspicion pinched in upon his mouth and cut down through his laughter while he attempted to divine all the thousand ways this seemingly open man might be trying to crook him, oh, he looked honest enough, but you never can tell, and Turp Thornhill knew better than to trust a man's looks. Turp Thornhill was like Diogenes, he had never seen an honest man, and he never would. After insulting him, ridiculing him, suspicioning him, torturing him by letting on he could not afford to loan it, Turp generously let him have the whole twenty dollars he had asked for, at twenty per cent, and warned him narrowly not to try to pull some wise shenanigan when it come time to pay it back.

Prew, as he dressed for town with the twenty in his pocket, felt the degradation of Turp's foul breath still on him that a shower would not wash off and wondered which was worse, to be poked by Turp's foul breathing Mississippi nose or to be sprayed with Ike Galovitch's foul smelling Slavic spit. This was sure turning out to be some outfit. A fine home, this outfit. He was also wondering, as he dressed, at the humiliations men will suffer for a woman that they will not suffer for any other thing, even for their politics.

Octavus Roy Cohen, a remarkably versatile man of letters, developed a classic theme in the following story with a Maupassant twist. This story, published in 1926, foreshadowed the "card detective" of today—such men as Michael MacDougall, John Scarne, and Sidney Radner, who have saved American tourists and servicemen many millions of dollars by exposing gambling chicaneries. Of course, these men are professional magicians, not cardsharpers real or reformed; while Roy Cohen made his hero an actual cardsharper who wasn't reformed; just for this once he turned honest—and sentimental.

The Case Ace

by OCTAVUS ROY COHEN

BEFORE his visitor was well across the threshold Roger Andrews appraised that pudgy person unerringly. "A gentleman," said Roger to himself, and proceeded to meet his caller upon that basis.

His tall well-knit figure crossed the room courteously; his fine gray eyes glanced at the card which he held; he inclined his head gravely.

"Mr. Peck?"

The stout gentleman heartily extended his hand. "Fabian Peck, sir. And I judge that this is Mr. Andrews?"

Roger answered with the faintest suggestion of a nod as he invited his guest to a chair. The face of the tall man was calm and inscrutable; his eyes, as he turned briefly away, were frosty.

Roger Andrews seated himself and waited for Peck to speak, meanwhile observing—without appearing to do so—every minutest detail of his guest's personal appearance.

He saw a man comfortably in the fifties and in that stage of physical preservation which is generally referred to as hale and hearty; a man quietly and expensively tailored; rather too ruddy of complexion and obviously well pleased with himself and his own importance. His manner seemed to say: "Well, I am Fabian Peck—*the* Fabian Peck." Roger Andrews knew the type and so accorded just that faint degree of silent deference which compelled persons of the Fabian Peck sort to like him.

Mr. Peck, on his part, was decidedly ill at ease. He experienced the fidgety sensation of being inferior, and that was a feeling to which Fabian Peck was not accustomed. Besides, it was not at all as he had planned. His bluff heartiness, his firm handshake, seemed to make very little impression upon the cold gray man opposite. Andrews was interested—but that was all. Certainly he did not seem aware of the fact that any great honor was being conferred upon him.

It was this very absence of apparent curiosity which caused Mr. Peck to lose a considerable portion of the aplomb which had accompanied him to Roger's apartment. He was embarrassed. Of course there was no reason for embarrassment. A man of this type— But Fabian Peck hemmed and hawed and talked about the weather and the latest market reports and the aromas of favorite cigars.

And Roger Andrews chatted courteously—as though a visit of this sort were the most natural thing in the world, until finally Peck could stand it no longer and burst forth with the object of his visit.

"Mr. Andrews," he boomed—with a volume of sound which served to disguise some small portion of his intense disconcertion—"Mr. Andrews, I suppose you are wondering who I am and why I have called upon you."

Andrews nodded slightly. "Naturally."

"Naturally. Of course—quite naturally. Well, as to who I am: My home is in Atlanta. I have handled considerable cotton in my time. I retired from active participation in business several years ago."

Mr. Peck paused, seeming to have run out of breath. He looked pleadingly at his host as though begging that individual to make the task more simple. But save for a ghostly little smile of amusement which flitted across Andrew's thin lips, that gentleman gave no hint of any emotion other than a thoroughly impersonal and scrupulously polite interest.

Fabian Peck mopped at a broad forehead with an immaculate linen handkerchief.

"A mutual friend of ours suggested that I call upon you, Mr. Andrews."

"Ah! I see. A mutual friend?"

"Er—a—yes. Jim Moriarty!"

It was out at last. Fabian Peck exhaled audibly with relief. He watched fearfully for some flush of anger on the face of the tall man opposite; awaited some indication of outrage. But Roger Andrews nodded quite calmly.

"Jim Moriarty? A fine chap, Jim. And a truly great detective."

"You are right, sir." Peck was tremendously relieved that Roger had put into words the declaration of Moriarty's profession. "I understand that he is one of the very best. And—er—he speaks very highly of you."

This time Roger smiled. It was a broad and illuminating smile, which for a moment rid his face of its granite austerity.

"I'm sure Jim would. He and I have been friends for a great many years."

"So he told me. Said I could trust you absolutely. Of course, Mr. Andrews, the situation is —er—peculiar; and I confess that I'm more than a trifle embarrassed."

"No necessity for that. The fact that Jim Moriarty sent you to me speaks for itself."

"Just so, just so. He told me a great deal about you. He spoke very highly—Confound it! Mr. Andrews, I'm no man to beat about the bush! He told me that you are probably the most expert card manipulator living today."

Again that peculiarly sunny smile lighted the ascetic features. "He flatters me."

"He tells me that—er—you have for a great many years made a quite excellent living playing cards; and also that—er—that you—well, it is rather difficult to put into words."

"That my hands are quicker than the eyes of the gentlemen with whom I play?"

"Yes. And thank you for saying it for me. I appreciate that sincerely."

Quite suddenly Roger Andrews elected to direct the conversation.

"You have come to me at the suggestion of Jim Moriarty because I am a famous card-sharper. Is that it?"

"Yes, sir."

"Well—why?"

Fabian Peck was more at ease. The difficult and embarrassing preliminaries had been concluded. He could now talk freely and unreservedly.

"I wish to engage you—professionally."

Andrews' eyes narrowed, concealing a flash of genuine interest. He made no comment, however, and Peck continued, gradually acquiring a measure of confidence.

"I am one of a group in Atlanta," he explained, "who happen to be very well fixed in a worldly way—so well fixed that all of us retired from business several years ago. The public is fond of referring to us as millionaires. Whether that estimate is an exaggeration doesn't particularly matter. We have been cronies for years. Originally there were six of us. We belong to the Chess and Whist Club—which happens to be a rather exclusive and old-fogyish social institution in Atlanta, and for several years the six of us have met on Wednesday nights to play Poker. I believe we are all good Poker players. Certainly we have indulged for years and we love the game. We play for rather high stakes, but it happens that a thousand or so dollars won or lost in an evening doesn't worry us. We play really for the fun of it, and the fact that the stakes are fairly high merely lends zest to our entertainment. I suppose you follow me?"

Andrews inclined his head. "I understand, of course."

"Well"—once again a hint of embarrassment returned to Peck's manner—"about six months ago one of our Poker circle died. That left us with only five; and five is not, to our way of thinking, a good game. So we looked about for a new member. It happened that there was only one man in the city who seemed to qualify. You see, we care nothing for the money, and yet for a man in moderate circumstances the game would be entirely too steep. And so eventually we hit upon Garry Anchor—Garrison P. Anchor."

Fabian Peck paused, lighted a fresh cigar and adjusted his waistcoat. It was obvious that he did not find his next words easy, nor did Andrews smooth the way for him. At length the pudgy gentleman cleared his throat and spread his fingers in an apologetic gesture.

"What I am about to say, Mr. Andrews, may sound snobbish. I assure you it is not intended so. At any rate, Mr. Anchor is a man of decidedly attractive personality about whom we know very little socially. Our group has lived in Atlanta since that prosperous city was a small town. Our family roots are deep in the soil of Georgia. Mr. Anchor came to our city only about five years ago. He seemed to be fairly well educated and wealthy. He became a member of several clubs, including the Chess and Whist. He did not appear to be exactly our type, yet we liked him. And so, when we needed a sixth member for our Poker sessions, we invited him to join. The first night he played with us he won. The second time he won again. We thought nothing of it. But when he won and won and won—almost without a single break—we could not help but notice and wonder. He has yet to miss one of our meetings, and so far as I can remember he has never lost. We are very much afraid, Mr. Andrews, that it cannot be entirely luck."

And now Fabian Peck threw his head back and met squarely the cold gray glance which Andrews bestowed upon him. Andrews was keenly interested.

"This Mr. Anchor"—he queried—"he is really wealthy?"

"Very. More so, probably, than most of us."

"And his weekly winnings average—"

"Around a thousand or fifteen hundred dollars, I should say."

"H'm! Scarcely enough to interest a millionaire."

"Exactly." Fabian Peck rose to his feet and paced the room nervously in short, mincing steps. "That is precisely the point I have been attempting to make. Mr. Anchor's winnings mean nothing to him. By the same token, the amounts that the other men lose mean nothing to them. But since we began to suspect that all was not as it should be, the weekly game has lost its interest. We are laboring under a strain, and, damn it all, we don't relish the idea that we might be playing cards with a person who is not a gentleman."

"I see. He has been winning too consistently, eh? You have never discovered anything wrong, but this steady winning has aroused your suspicions. If you are wrong in suspecting him of dishonesty you are quite content that he should go on winning, but if he's doing anything dishonorable you prefer to invite him to resign. Is that it?"

"Precisely, sir. You have put it clearly and concisely. The uncertainty is robbing us of all pleasure in our game. We dare not take action for fear that we might be doing Mr. Anchor an injustice. It is a monstrous thing, sir, to suspect an intimate acquaintance of cardsharping; but it is decidedly more monstrous to play week after week with a person who is cheating. Of all filthy, petty offenses—" Suddenly Fabian Peck stopped and his face purpled with embarrassment. "I trust, sir, that you will pardon me. I am afraid I have been rude and tactless."

"Not at all." Roger spoke with suave courtesy. "We will accept the fact that I am a professional cardsharper and let it go at that. I assure you that my feelings cannot be hurt."

"That is very fine of you, sir. And no matter how nicely you put it—I did blunder and make an ass of myself, sir. I apologize. To come back to the story, however: The situation at home is intolerable. If Anchor is a cheat, he must be invited to resign. If his winnings have been coincidence, or luck, or what not, then we each owe him a mental apology. But we have to find out—and soon. Do you understand?"

"Clearly."

"I went to Jim Moriarty and asked him for an introduction to a card manipulator who was also a gentleman." The anomaly struck him and he fidgeted nervously, but Andrews met him with level-eyed imperturbability. "He referred me to you, and, sir, if I may be permitted to say so, you fill the latter half of the bill adequately."

"Thank you," answered Andrews gravely. "I believe I can qualify in both respects. You see my field of operations has been largely transatlantic steamships—and my victims men of wealth and social position."

He made the statement calmly, unemotionally—leaving Peck somewhat aghast. He looked with renewed interest upon this person who appeared to be a gentleman and who acted like a gentleman and who yet spoke calmly and unfeelingly of the fact that he made his living by cheating at cards.

"On behalf of myself and my friends," went on Peck somewhat stiltedly, "I wish to engage you to return to Atlanta with me. Entirely at our expense, of course, and for whatever fee you consider reasonable. You will be there as a friend of mine, and as such will be given a card to the Chess and Whist Club. You will be invited to sit in our little Poker game on Wednesday evenings. Of course you will have no financial interest in the game. The money spent for your chips will be repaid you, and any winnings of yours are to be turned back to us, as, of course, we will reimburse you for any losings. Your status in the game will be that of watcher—to find out what is going on, provided, indeed, that anything is."

"And the others?"

"They will know who you are and why you are there. Except Mr. Anchor, of course."

Andrews sat motionless, staring at the other through half-closed eyes. He was more interested than he cared to admit even to himself. The prospect of a few weeks in such an atmosphere held out to him an almost irresistible allure.

He was a peculiar type of man, Andrews. Good blood flowed in his veins; he was a college graduate. But behind those cold eyes lurked a brain which was too keen and too impatient for ordinary commercial pursuits. He had tried the path of rectitude and found that it bored him; and so, because he had the ability to fathom the thoughts of others, and because his long slender fingers had been fond always of amusing themselves by card tricks, he gravitated without particular self-opposition into a profession which paid well and contained just sufficient of danger to keep him interested and amused.

But he was vastly intrigued by Peck's proposition. He liked the pudgy, fussy man with his queer combination of masculine directness, old-maid meticulousness and air of impregnable honor. He was sufficiently introspective to understand that a few weeks as a member of the Poker circle would prove interesting; a few weeks during which he would play cards with gentlemen as a gentleman.

He visioned the cobwebby Chess and Whist Club, the fusty, dusty group of retired millionaires who played for high stakes because they liked the tang of it. And the sheer drama of the situation—the outsider who won and won and won. He turned abruptly and extended his hand.

"I accept, Mr. Peck."

The fleshy palm met his own in a firm grasp.

"I am exceedingly grateful. From what Jim Moriarty has told me—"

"You need have no fear of my efficiency. Cards are instinctive with me—which is probably why I am what I am."

"I see. And when can you leave, Mr. Andrews?"

"Tonight."

"Good. I shall attend to the reservations. We will meet at the train?"

"Very well." Andrews escorted him to the door and bade him a courteous farewell.

The trip from Chicago to Atlanta proved pleasant. Andrews liked Peck. He knew the type, of course; he had fattened upon it for years; but for the first time he was cultivating one in other than a professional way. Peck was not a victim and never would be. And he was scrupulous about permitting no hint of their different positions to creep into his manner.

After all, Fabian Peck was a man who had done things. He had wrested material success from life, and had done it honestly and fairly. Roger Andrews held him in awe and regarded him with a respect which he could not conceal. After all, he represented what Roger would have preferred to be, had all other things been equal. Not that Andrews was troubled by conscience or regretful of his career, but merely that he was too innately fine strung to relish his very doubtful position in the social scheme.

They arrived in Atlanta on Tuesday shortly before noon. Peck's chauffeur met them at the Terminal Station, and Andrews was driven to one of the leading hotels, where rooms had been reserved for him. Then Peck left and Roger Andrews walked to the window, where he stared out across the treetops upon the city of Atlanta and became convinced that he was going to enjoy this brief excursion into the realm of probity.

He spent the afternoon and the day following in sight-seeing: he visited Stone Mountain and viewed with keen interest the Daughters of the Confederacy memorial; he spent an hour in thorough enjoyment of the weird cyclorama at Grant Park; he called upon two of his friends temporarily resident in the Federal prison.

Wednesday evening at six o'clock, Fabian Peck drove by for him. With Peck was another man, a man as tall as Andrews and quite as grave and dignified.

"Mr. Andrews—Mr. Grinnell."

Rogers knew that Grinnell was not the man he had come to observe, and he added Grinnell to the list of those whom he instinctively liked—a man big and rugged and self-possessed. A great architect, he was to learn later.

They chatted easily as they drove toward the Chess and Whist Club. There was no hint of superiority in Grinnell's manner, any more than there had been in the fussy officiousness of Fabian Peck. Andrews was being accepted at face value, and it was with a feeling of fitness that he alighted with his hosts before the grim gray portals of the austere Chess and Whist Club and accompanied them into the gloomy lobby.

The place was entirely too fusty to have been anything but exclusive. Three or four elderly men lounged in easy chairs, poring over the evening papers. From an adjoining room on the main floor came the click of billiard balls; Andrews glimpsed the players—graybeards both. The atmosphere was rather tomblike, but it thrilled the gaunt young soldier of fortune. For once in his life he was about to enter into a card game without being keyed to a pitch of nervous intensity.

Fabian Peck paused at the desk long enough to introduce Andrews to the secretary and to obtain a guest card for him. Another elderly man joined them and was introduced to Andrews. They went upstairs to a private card room. The chips were already arranged; two new decks of cards were on the table, their seals unbroken. Three other men were there—two of them around sixty years of age, rather of the Peck type. The third stood out in vivid relief. Roger Andrews knew him even before the introduction.

It was obvious that Garrison P. Anchor did not belong with this crowd. Perhaps fifty years of age, he was of powerful physique and virile personality. His handclasp was firm, his glance direct, and his voice boomed heartily through the dank little room.

"Mr. Andrews! Awfully glad to welcome you into the game tonight. We're a terrible crowd of old fogies, but we do enjoy ourselves."

Andrews smiled. He liked the man instinctively, but it was with a sort of liking different from that which he entertained for Peck and Grinnell and the others. Here was a man more after his own type—a man who was still of the world, who gave the impression of retaining the capacity for accomplishment.

West, of course. There was no mistaking the breezy friendliness. And Andrews was interested; not only because this was the man whom he had been brought down to watch, but also because Anchor, alone of the group, knew him only as a gentleman vouched for and introduced by Peck. As such he was accepted without question and it would have taken a keener man than Anchor to have discerned the unusual scrupulousness of the others toward their visitor.

Roger Andrews was vastly amused. He knew that he had created something of a sensation with his manner, his correct dinner coat, his soft well-modulated voice, his easy flow of conversation, his calm and unruffled acceptance of a highly bizarre situation. He knew that the others were trying to readjust their preconceived notions of a professional gambler, and that they liked him personally, yet were afraid of him. They were all so terrifically honest, so horrified by the personification of iniquity.

With Garry Anchor, however, there was none of this restraint. Anchor, bluff and hearty, liked Andrews from the first and was at no pains to conceal it.

"Golf?"

"A little."

"Great! Have to take you out to East Lake for a round. You'll be here a while?"

"Couple of weeks, I guess."

"Say! That's wonderful. What you shoot?"

"Pretty badly. In the late eighties when I'm going good."

"You can give me about two and two. I'm an awful duffer. Haven't been playing the game more than a couple of years. Fascinating thing though. Sometimes I think it beats Poker."

Andrews caught the glances which passed covertly among the others. He resolved to ask Peck about this; yet surely Peck could not object to his playing golf with Anchor. Queer situation. He liked the man. Anchor was alive and vital and wholesome, and if he was a bit noisy, that was no grave fault.

The game began. Each man started with a stack valued at one thousand dollars. They played a quiet, repressed game—with only Anchor's big voice occasionally puncturing the dignified silence.

But Andrews saw early that these men played Poker seriously. No foolishness here. They knew the game, loved it, and extracted from it every last ounce of enjoyment. They inspected their cards one by one, deliberated over the draw with all the caution of men whose very lives hung on the luck of the deck. They made a great play of attempting to size one another up, and there was little levity in the proceedings. Once in a while one would accuse another—with heavy humor—of attempting to bluff, and would be invited to raise; but aside from that they played with desperate earnestness.

Andrews enjoyed himself. He, too, liked Poker and he played earnestly and well. His own stack of chips grew larger, then smaller, then larger again. For the first time in years he played his own cards as they came to him; played with keen interest and absorbed deftness.

He knew the men. From the moment the game began the chips had lost all monetary value in their eyes; they would have played with the same absorption had the yellows represented ten cents each instead of one hundred dollars. The money value was a mere excuse; they demanded the tang of a wager, perhaps to revive from a forgotten past memory of the thrills which had been theirs in the days when a pot lost or won meant a bit of heartache or an intoxicating thrill.

Only Garry Anchor played differently from all the others. He maintained a steady flow of ponderous jocularity. He seemed to be enjoying himself thoroughly and he joked with the older men in a manner which Andrews knew they ordinarily would have liked.

It was altogether a peculiar session of card playing, and it seemed rather queer to Andrews that Anchor caught no hint of the constraint.

As the evening wore on, the stack of chips in front of Garry Anchor grew taller. There was nothing startling about it—few very large pots. But there was a steady flow in his direction. He played with enthusiasm but apparent indifference, masking with ceaseless banter whatever depth of interest he may have felt.

Andrews won too. It was not in him to play other than a fine fame. His face was immobile, his eyes expressionless. Once or twice he and Anchor were left alone in a pot.

"H'm!" would come Anchor's booming voice. "The stranger is with me, eh? Two cards, you drew. I wonder just how much you really know about this little ol' game? To kicker or not to kicker. Oh, well, let's try it once. I boost it a red chip."

The faintest suggestion of a smile from Roger as he flipped two reds into the pot. No word.

"Raises me, does he? I reckon Garry Anchor knows when to look around. What have we?"

At the conclusion of the session Anchor had won about twenty-five hundred dollars. Andrews was four hundred dollars ahead. Fabian Peck had won, and the others had lost rather heavily, Grinnell being the chief sufferer. They stood around chatting for a few moments and then strolled from the now silent building. Peck took Andrews to the hotel, Grinnell accompanying them.

Andrews' first act was to return to Peck the amount of his winnings. There was a moment of constraint, and it was obvious to Andrews that they were waiting for him to make some comment about Garry Anchor. But instead he chatted quietly of his pleasure in the evening and of certain interesting hands; then he turned his level gray eyes full on Peck.

"Mr. Anchor has invited me to play golf with him."

Peck looked up in surprise. "Yes. What about it?"

"I am down here as your agent. Do you prefer that I refuse the invitation?"

"Good Lord, no! Please accept. Glad to take you out with me some time if you wish." Fabian Peck was struggling to make Andrews feel at ease. "Of course you understand—the peculiar conditions—"

"That's quite all right, Mr. Peck. I merely didn't wish to take advantage of the fact that you vouched for me."

Peck and Grinnell drove away. As they got beyond earshot Grinnell turned to his friend.

"Fabe, I like that man."

"So do I. Queer, isn't it—how hard it is to remember that he is a criminal?"

Andrews waked at ten the following morning. The warm southern sun streamed in through the windows and played across the bed. He stretched luxuriously and reveled in the quiet comfort, the freedom from mental strain. Then he phoned for breakfast. At eleven o'clock the telephone rang.

"Mr. Andrews?"

"Yes."

"This is Garry Anchor. Get your full portion of sleep last night?"

"Plenty."

"How about a little cow-pasture pool this morning?" The voice was hearty; the humor—as usual—forced and conventional.

"Delighted. I haven't my clubs, though."

"I'll scrape you up a set. Suppose I drift by for you in an hour? We'll grab a bite at the club."

Andrews was in the lobby when Garry Anchor arrived. The man wore a rather flagrant golf suit, but he seemed more at home in it than he had in the dinner dress of the previous night. On the way out to the course Anchor was voluble.

He seemed fond of discussing himself in a hearty, boyish way which rather appealed to Roger. He told of his earlier days when things had not broken well for him; then of an oil strike. "Things been pretty soft for me since then. Too damned soft though. No excitement. I crave excitement. This crowd here's awful nice, but fearfully high hat—you know."

"Yes—I know."

"Of course they're your sort. And they're a pretty nice gang. But fossilized."

The golf game was pleasant. Anchor played badly and profanely, but with rugged abandon. He maintained an incessant fire of conversation. Andrews was puzzled; he was as yet undetermined whether the excessive volubility masked a keen brain or an empty head. He was inclined to believe the former.

The following night Anchor insisted on having Roger at his home for dinner. It was a magnificent structure, built rather more on the lines of a club than a private residence. "Meet the little wife!" was Anchor's manner of introducing his guest to Mrs. Anchor. She was a small woman of the type best described as sweet, and it was evident that she stood profoundly in awe of her massive and dominant husband. It developed during the meal that she had been a schoolteacher in Ardmore, Oklahoma. Their romance had antedated his oil strike.

Saturday night the Anchors took Roger to the regular dinner dance at one of the country clubs. Fabian Peck was there and his greeting had a rather strained note. Later in the evening Roger made it a point to take Peck aside.

"Any objection to this, Mr. Peck?"

"We-ell, no; not exactly."

"What is it?" Andrews' voice was crisp.

"You see, Mr. Andrews—your position—and the fact that the Anchors do not know—"

"I am here to take orders from you." Roger was not given to equivocation. "If you would rather I'd stay away from them—socially—"

"Not at all, not at all. I—er—it is merely a peculiar situation. You understand. But don't let me deprive you of any pleasure you may find in their society."

And so the acquaintanceship between Roger and the Anchors flourished. As for the other members of the little Poker circle, they were punctiliously polite—and carried their friendliness no further. They knew who Andrews was and what he was doing there: a hired crook engaged in detective work. They liked him, but they could not inject any warmth into their personal relationship.

But it was in his brief contacts with these other men that Andrews found his keenest interest. They were a fine sort, and he knew as he mixed with them that he belonged. What mattered it that his conscience was unfettered? Culturally he was equal to any one of them—superior, perhaps—and he delighted in their recognition of that fact.

The second Poker session was almost a duplicate of the first, even to the fact that Grinnell was again the heaviest loser. Once more Garry Anchor kept up a running fire of boisterous conversation and again the stack of chips before him grew slowly and surely. Time and again when they were playing stud he gauged the hole cards of the other men with uncanny prescience, betting his own cards on such occasions beyond all reason.

"I know what you've got, gentlemen. Garry, the little ol' mind reader, that's me. You played 'em like they were backed up, Peck, but I was positive not. So the pot comes this way."

In the next few days Roger saw more and more of Anchor and his wife. A sort of intimacy had developed between the men, and with its development Anchor dropped what faint formality had been apparent on Roger's initial visit to the house. He was inordinately proud of his material worth, and vastly impressed with the magnificence of his own home. His wife—he spoke of her as "the old lady"—was enormously in awe of him. Occasionally he touched upon the grim days in Oklahoma "when I didn't have all this floss and flubdub. Learned how to play Poker there, Roger, old man. Took guts to come out on the long end of some of those games."

More and more Roger found difficulty in understanding how Anchor had ever been taken into the Chess and Whist Club, and, that miracle accomplished, why he had been selected to take the place of the deceased member of the sacred Poker circle.

Anchor was a different sort. It happened that the obvious explanation was the correct one: The men considered that any game of less than six hands was not worthy of being played, and Garry Anchor was the only person available.

The other members of the group went out of their way to let Andrews understand that he was being accepted at face value—with, of course, natural reservations. He appreciated their deference to his feelings and liked every one of them, from the saturnine Grinnell to the pudgy and fussy Fabian Peck. And he was impressed by them. There was nothing impressive about Anchor. Roger felt superior to Anchor, and by the same token he confessed to himself the superiority of the others. But he couldn't help liking Garry Anchor, and he was genuinely fond of Garry's mousy, rather startled little wife.

On Wednesday evening next Andrews dined with Peck and Grinnell at the Chess and Whist Club. Peck brought up the subject which was nearest to them.

"You have played with us twice, Mr. Andrews. Have you reached any conclusion on the —er—matter upon which you were brought here?"

Roger met the other's eyes. "M'mm! I'd rather have one more session before turning in my report."

"Tonight will be sufficient, then?"

"I believe so."

"Good. Naturally, we are anxious to know. The situation is rather intolerable. Er—I don't suppose you care to give us any hint."

"I prefer not."

"Quite all right; quite all right. Isn't that so, Grinnell?"

"Certainly. We didn't limit Mr. Andrews' time."

Roger was sorry indeed that it was all to end so soon. The experience had been delightful. The situation satisfied a hunger which he had not known that he possessed. It would be with regret that he would turn in his report the following day. Oh, well! He shrugged. The current of his life flowed in other channels. This would become a golden memory.

Dinner ended, they adjourned to the card room. The other three arrived. Chips were assorted, cigars and cigarettes brought by an attendant. Peck seemed impatient.

"And now, as soon as Garry Anchor gets here—"

Eight o'clock, and Anchor had not arrived. The other men fidgeted; they were precise old fellows, and impatient of tardiness. At 8:15 he still had not come. They sat about the table, hesitating to begin. Then an attendant summoned Fabian Peck to the telephone.

A minute or so later Peck returned.

"Sorry, gentlemen, but Anchor won't be with us tonight."

There were exclamations of regret, and Roger Andrews experienced a sensation of thankfulness. This, then, would give him an additional week of delightful vacation. He scarcely heard Peck's explanation:

"Somebody came down to see him on business. They're closeted out at Anchor's home and liable to be there until after midnight. Awfully sorry. Guess we might as well begin."

They drew their chairs up to the table. Peck was designated as banker. He placed stacks before three of the men. "Better count 'em," he suggested. "I haven't. And here's one for you, Grinnell. I make the fifth."

A queer cold chill crept down Roger Andrews' spine. The muscles of his arms flexed, and a close observer might have seen his face twitch. Fabian Peck raised his sunny face to the countenance of his visitor. "Five-handed game is better than no game at all."

Roger nodded curtly. He could not trust himself to speak. In a second something had happened to him which he did not believe possible; he had been cut to the quick. By a single thoughtless and logical act he had been put once and for all time in his place; put there definitely and finally. He was Roger Andrews, professional gambler.

He had not believed that he could be so hurt. He had always prided himself upon his cast-iron sensibilities. Had he not discussed cold-bloodedly with Fabian Peck the illicit nature of his livelihood? And what cut him most deeply was the knowledge that the insult was unintentional. Rather than hurt him they would have invited him to join the game.

Of course they were right; it would be absurd for him to play. He would have to return his winnings or accept reimbursement for his losings. It wasn't the fact that he wasn't playing; that wasn't it at all. It was that he had been placed outside the pale, given to understand that he was not of them.

His long slender fingers interlocked until it seemed that the bones must crack. The color drained from his cheeks. His eyes were glassy. He watched the game and did not see it. They were very polite to him; occasionally one would turn to exhibit a particularly interesting hand; another would ask his advice.

If they had only said to him, "You are a professional crook; we do not care to have you play with us!" That would have been all right. He was sufficiently a man to face facts—and these were facts. But instead they treated him with courtesy and didn't know that they were inflicting a hurt. It was the very unconsciousness of it—dealing him out of their game, declaring him déclassé.

A cold fury enveloped him. He understood these men and he hated them and their smug decency. He wanted to sweep his arm across the table and send cards and chips showering to the floor, to cry aloud that he was as good as they.

But he wasn't as good, and he knew it. He wasn't as good, and they knew it. The veins in his temples were throbbing, and then—because he felt that he could stand it no longer—he spoke. His voice was crisp to curtness.

"Gentlemen, pardon me a moment."

The game stopped. They turned toward him. His lean, ascetic face was expressionless, giving no evidence of the internal seethe.

"You brought me to Atlanta on a definite mission, gentlemen. You brought me here to scrutinize the play of Mr. Garrison P. Anchor, and to report on it. I told Mr. Peck and Mr. Grinnell this evening that I preferred another night of play before making that report. I believe, however, that an additional evening will be unnecessary."

Fabian Peck swung his chair around. His face was agleam with interest.

"You're sure?"

"I never make statements until I am sure, Mr. Peck. And I prefer to make my report this evening and leave Atlanta to-morrow. Personal reasons."

"Yes, yes. If you're certain. Tell us—what have you discovered?"

Roger Andrews' colorless eyes swept the quintet of genteel faces. He spoke briefly and authoritatively.

"I have watched Mr. Anchor's play closely. I find that he plays an absolutely square game. His consistent winning is due entirely to the fact that he knows more about Poker than all of you gentlemen put together will ever know."

He rose. There was a chorus of appreciation; they were sincerely glad to learn that their friend Anchor was an honest man; they felt guilty for having suspected him; they were immensely pleased.

Five minutes later Roger Andrews left the Chess and Whist Club. He turned toward the city. The cool breeze of mid-evening fanned his fevered cheeks. He walked with long swinging strides, struggling to forget the hurt of it, to remember that nothing had occurred which was undeserved. He saw a taxicab and hailed it. He climbed in and snapped an address.

Through all the long drive to the residence of Garry Anchor out in the Druid Hills section of the city, Roger tried futilely to rid himself of bitterness. He knew he was unfair, unjust, but he had been hurt; and he had never before known how sensitive he was. He was at the Anchor residence before he knew it. He alighted and bade the driver wait.

He walked swiftly up the winding walkway with its precise sentineling of stately poplars. Anchor himself answered his ring. "Roger Andrews! Well, come on in. Delighted."

"No. I wish to speak with you a moment. Out here."

He turned and led the way to the lawn. Anchor followed.

They faced each other in the moonlight—Roger Andrews, tall and slender and with a face granite hard; Garry Anchor, big and robust and hearty and radiating good humor. Andrews spoke, and he did not mince words.

"I am leaving Atlanta tomorrow, Anchor. I have come to give you some good advice. I am giving it because you have been mighty decent to me, and because I like you. You can take my advice—or leave it. Briefly, it is this: Do not play any more Poker with Fabian Peck's crowd at the Chess and Whist Club. They're not your sort."

Anchor's face grew serious. He would have spoken, but the hand of Roger Andrews closed around his arm like a band of steel, and Roger's eyes flamed into his.

"But if you are fool enough to continue playing with them, Anchor," he said harshly, "take my advice and play straight!"

¶ *The extrinsic power of the big bill has intrigued writers of all generations, including Mark Twain in his* £1,000,000 Bank Note *(part of which appears elsewhere in this book). Booth Tarkington, in one of his finest stories, combines the theme with Poker. At least twice recently this story has inspired writers of TV dramas.*

The One-Hundred-Dollar Bill

by BOOTH TARKINGTON

THE NEW one-hundred-dollar bill, clean and green, freshening the heart with the color of springtime, slid over the glass of the teller's counter and passed under his grille to a fat hand, dingy on the knuckles, but brightened by a flawed diamond. This interesting hand was a part of one of those men who seem to have too much fattened muscle for their clothes: his shoulders distended his overcoat; his calves strained the sprightly checked cloth, a little soiled, of his trousers; his short neck bulged above the glossy collar. His hat, round and black as a pot, and appropriately small, he wore slightly obliqued; while under its curled brim his small eyes twinkled surreptitiously between those upper and nether puffs of flesh that mark the too faithful practitioner of unhallowed gaieties. Such was the first owner of the new one-hundred-dollar bill, and he at once did what might have been expected of him.

Moving away from the teller's grille, he made a cylindrical packet of bills smaller in value—"ones" and "fives"—then placed round them, as a wrapper, the beautiful one-hundred-dollar bill, snapped a rubber band over it; and the desired inference was plain: a roll all of hundred-dollar bills, inside as well as out. Something more was plain, too: obviously the man's small head had a sportive plan in it, for the twinkle between his eye-puffs hinted of liquor in the offing and lively women impressed by a show of masterly riches. Here, in brief, was a man who meant to make a night of it; who would feast, dazzle, compel deference, and be loved. He was happy, and went out of the bank believing that money is meant for joy.

So little should we be certain of our happiness in this world: the splendid one-hundred-dollar bill was taken from him untimely, before nightfall that very evening. At the corner of two busy streets he parted with it to the law, though in a mood of excruciating reluctance and only after a cold-blooded threatening on the part of the lawyer. This latter walked away thoughtfully, with the one-hundred-dollar bill, now not quite so clean, in his pocket.

Collinson was the lawyer's name, and in years he was only twenty-eight. But he already had the slightly harried appearance that marks the young husband who begins to suspect that the better part of his life has been his bachelorhood. His dark, ready-made clothes, his twice-soled shoes, and his hair, which was too long for a neat and businesslike aspect, were symptoms of necessary economy; but he did not wear the eager look of a man who saves to "get on for himself": Collinson's look was that of an employed man who only deepens his rut with his pacing of it.

An employed man he was, indeed; a lawyer without much hope of ever seeing his name on the door or on the letters of the firm that employed him, and his most important work was the collection of small debts. This one-hundred-dollar bill now in his pocket was such a collection, small to the firm and the client, though of a noble size to himself and the long-pursued debtor from whom he had just collected it.

The banks were closed; so was the office, for it was six o'clock, and Collinson was on his way home when by chance he encountered the debtor: there was nothing to do but to keep the bill over night. This was no hardship, however, as he had a faint pleasure in the unfamiliar experience of walking home with such a thing in his pocket; and he felt a little important by proxy when he thought of it.

Upon the city the November evening had come down dark and moist, holding the smoke nearer the ground and enveloping the buildings in a soiling black mist. Lighted windows and street lamps appeared and disappeared in the altering thickness of fog, but at intervals, as Collinson walked on northward, he passed a small shop, or a cluster of shops, where the light was close to him and bright, and at one of these oases of illumination he lingered a moment, with a thought to buy a toy in the window for his three-year-old little girl. The toy was a gaily colored acrobatic monkey that willingly climbed up and down a string, and he knew that the "baby," as he and his wife still called their child, would scream with delight at the sight of it. He hesitated, staring into the window rather longingly, and wondering if he ought to make such a purchase. He had twelve dollars of his own in his pocket, but the toy was marked "35 cents" and he decided he could not afford it. So he sighed and went on, turning presently into a darker street.

Here the air was like that of a busy freight-yard, thick with coal dust and at times almost unbreathable, so that Collinson was glad to get out of it even though the exchange was for the early-evening smells of the cheap apartment house where he lived.

His own kitchenette was contributing its share, he found, the baby was crying over some inward perplexity not to be explained; and his wife, pretty and a little frowzy, was as usual, and as he had expected. That is to say, he found her irritated by cooking, bored by the baby, and puzzled by the dull life she led. Other women, it appeared, had happy and luxurious homes, and, during the malnutritious dinner she had prepared, she mentioned many such women by name, laying particular stress upon the achievements of their husbands. Why should she ("alone," as she put it) lead the life she did in one room and a kitchenette, without even being able to afford to go to the movies more than once or twice a month? Mrs. Theodore Thompson's husband had bought a perfectly beautiful little sedan automobile; he gave his wife everything she wanted. Mrs. Will Gregory had merely mentioned that her old Hudson seal coat was wearing a little, and her husband had instantly said, "What'll a new one come to, girlie? Four or five hundred? Run and get it!" Why were other women's husbands like that—and why, oh, why! was hers like *this?* An eavesdropper might well have deduced from Mrs. Collinson's harangue that her husband owned somewhere a storehouse containing all the good things she wanted and that he withheld them from her out of his perverse willfulness. Moreover, he did not greatly help his case by protesting that the gratification of her wishes was beyond his powers.

"My goodness!" he said. "You talk as if I had sedans and seal coats and theater tickets *on* me! Well, I haven't; that's all!"

"Then go out and get 'em!" she said fiercely. "Go out and get 'em!"

"What with?" he inquired. "I have twelve dollars in my pocket, and a balance of seventeen dollars at the bank; that's twenty-nine. I get twenty-five from the office day after tomorrow—Saturday; that makes fifty-four; but we have to pay forty-five for rent on Monday; so that'll leave us nine dollars. Shall I buy you a sedan and a sealskin coat on Tuesday out of the nine?"

Mrs. Collinson began to weep a little. "The old, old story!" she said. "Six long, long years it's been going on now! I ask you how much you've got, and you say, 'Nine dollars,' or 'Seven dollars,' or 'Four dollars'; and once it was sixty-five cents! Sixty-five cents; that's what we have to live on! Sixty-five *cents!*"

"Oh, hush!" he said wearily.

"Hadn't you better hush a little yourself?" she retorted. "You come home with twelve dollars in your pocket and tell your wife to hush! That's nice! Why can't you do what decent men do?"

"What's that?"

"Why, give their wives something to live for. What do you give me, I'd like to know! Look at the clothes I wear, please!"

"Well, it's your own fault," he muttered.

"What did you say? Did you say it's my fault I wear clothes any woman I know wouldn't be *seen* in?"

"Yes, I did. If you hadn't made me get you that platinum ring—"

"What!" she cried, and flourished her hand at him across the table. "Look at it! It's platinum, yes; but look at the stone in it, about the size of a pin-head, so't I'm ashamed to wear it when any of my friends see me! A hundred and sixteen dollars is what this magnificent ring cost you, and how long did I have to beg before I got even *that* little out of you? And it's the best thing I own and the only thing I ever did get out of you!"

"Oh, Lordy!" he moaned.

"I wish you'd seen Charlie Loomis looking at this ring today," she said, with a desolate laugh. "He happened to notice it, and I saw him keep glancing at it, and I wish you'd seen Charlie Loomis's expression!"

Collinson's own expression became noticeable upon her introduction of this name; he stared at her gravely until he completed the mastication of one of the indigestibles she had set before him; then he put down his fork and said:

"So you saw Charlie Loomis again today. Where?"

"Oh, my!" she sighed. "Have we got to go over all that again?"

"Over all what?"

"Over all the fuss you made the last time I mentioned Charlie's name. I thought we settled it you were going to be a little more sensible about him. As if it was a crime my going to a vaudeville matinee with a man kind enough to notice that my husband never takes me anywhere!"

"Did you go to a vaudeville with him today?"

"No, I didn't!" she said. "I was talking about the time when you made such a fuss. I didn't go anywhere with him today."

"I'm glad to hear it," Collinson said. "I wouldn't have stood for it."

"Oh, you wouldn't?" she cried, and added a shrill laugh as further comment. " 'You wouldn't have stood for it!' How very, very dreadful!"

"Never mind," he returned doggedly. "We went over all that the last time, and you understand me: I'll have no more foolishness about Charlie Loomis."

"How nice of you! He's a friend of yours; you go with him yourself; but your wife mustn't even look at him because he happens to be the one man that amuses her a little. That's fine!"

"Never mind," Collinson said again. "You say you saw him today. I want to know where."

"Suppose I don't want to tell you."

"You'd better tell me, I think."

"Do you? I've got to answer for every minute of my day, do I?"

"I want to know where you saw Charlie Loomis."

She tossed her curls and laughed. "Isn't it funny!" she said. "Just because I like a man, he's the one person I can't have anything to do with! Just because he's kind and jolly and amusing and I like his jokes and his thoughtfulness towards a woman, when he's with her, I'm not allowed to see him at all! But my *husband*—Oh, that's entirely different! *He* can go out with Charlie whenever he likes and have a good time, while I stay home and wash the dishes! Oh, it's a lovely life!"

"Where did you see him today?"

Instead of answering his question, she looked at him plaintively, and allowed tears to shine along her lower eyelids. "Why do you treat me like this?" she asked in a feeble voice. "Why can't I have a man friend if I want to? I do like Charlie Loomis. I do like him—"

"Yes, that's what I noticed!"

"Well, but what's the good of always insulting me about him? He has time on his hands of afternoons, and so have I. Our janitor's wife is crazy about the baby and just adores to have me leave her in their flat—the longer the better. Why shouldn't I go to a matinee or a picture show sometimes with Charlie? Why should I just have to sit around instead of going out and having a nice time when he wants me to?"

"I want to know where you saw him today!"

Mrs. Collinson jumped up. "You make me sick!" she said, and began to clear away the dishes.

"I want to know where——"

"Oh, hush up!" she cried. "He came here to leave a note for you."

"Oh," said her husband. "I beg your pardon. That's different."

"How sweet of you!"

"Where's the note, please?"

She took it from her pocket and tossed it to him. "So long as it's a note for *you* it's all right, of course!" she said. "I wonder what you'd do if he'd written one to me!"

"Never mind," said Collinson, and read the note.

DEAR COLLIE: Dave and Smithie and Old Bill and Sammy Hoag and maybe Steinie and Sol are coming over to the shack about eight-thirt. Home brew and the old pastime. *You* know! Don't fail.

—CHARLIE.

"You've read this, of course," Collinson said. "The envelope wasn't sealed."

"I have not," his wife returned, covering the prevarication with a cold dignity. "I'm not in the habit of reading other people's correspondence, thank you! I suppose you think I do so because you'd never hesitate to read any note *I* get—but I don't do everything you do, you see!"

"Well, you can read it now," he said, and gave her the note.

Her eyes swept the writing briefly, and she made a sound of wonderment, as if amazed to find herself so true a prophet. "And the words weren't more than out of mouth! *You* can go and have a grand party right in his flat, while your wife stays home and gets the baby to bed and washes the dishes!"

"I'm not going."

"Oh, no!" she said mockingly. "I suppose not! I see you missing one of Charlie's stag parties!"

"I'll miss this one."

But it was not to Mrs. Collinson's purpose that he should miss the party; she wished him to be as intimate as possible with the debonair Charlie Loomis; and so, after carrying some dishes into the kitchenette in meditative silence, she reappeared with a changed manner. She went to her husband, gave him a shy little pat on the shoulder and laughed good-naturedly. "Of course you'll go," she said. "I do think you're silly about my never going out with him when it would give me a little innocent pleasure and when you're not home to take me, yourself; but I wasn't really in such terrible earnest, all I said. You work hard the whole time, honey, and the only pleasure you ever do have, it's when you get a chance to go to one of these little penny-ante stag parties. You haven't been to one for ever so long, and you never stay after twelve; it's really all right with me. I want you to go."

"Oh, no," said Collinson. "It's only penny ante, but I couldn't afford to lose anything at all."

"But you never do. You always win a little."

"I know," he said. "I've figured out I'm about sixteen dollars ahead at penny ante on the whole year. I cleaned up seven dollars and sixty cents at Charlie's last party; but of course my luck might change, and we couldn't afford it."

"If you did lose, it'd only be a few cents," she said. "What's the difference, if it gives you a little fun? You'll work all the better if you go out and enjoy yourself once in a while."

"Well, if you really look at it that way, I'll go."

"That's right, dear," she said, smiling. "Better

put on a fresh collar and your other suit, hadn't you?"

"I suppose so," he assented, and began to make the changes she suggested. He went about them in a leisurely way, playing with the baby at intervals, while Mrs. Collinson sang cheerfully over her work; and when he had completed his toilet, it was time for him to go. She came in from the kitchenette, kissed him, and then looked up into his eyes, letting him see a fond and brightly amiable expression.

"There, honey," she said. "Run along and have a nice time. Then maybe you'll be a little more sensible about some of *my* little pleasures."

He held the one-hundred-dollar bill, folded, in his hand, meaning to leave it with her, but as she spoke, a sudden recurrence of suspicion made him forget his purpose. "Look here," he said. "I'm not making any bargain with you. You talk as if you thought I was going to let you run around to vaudevilles with Charlie because you let me go to this party. Is that your idea?"

It was, indeed, precisely Mrs. Collinson's idea, and she was instantly angered enough to admit it in her retort. "Oh, aren't you *mean!*" she cried. "I might know better than to look for any fairness in a man like you!"

"See here——"

"Oh, hush up!" she said. "Shame on you! Go on to your party!" With that she put both hands upon his breast, and pushed him toward the door.

"I won't go. I'll stay here."

"You will, too, go!" she cried shrewishly. *"I* don't want to look at you around here all evening. It'd make me sick to look at a man without an ounce of fairness in his whole mean little body!"

"All right," said Collinson, violently, "I *will* go!"

"Yes! Get out of my sight!"

And he did, taking the one-hundred-dollar bill with him to the penny-ante Poker party.

The gay Mr. Charlie Loomis called his apartment "the shack" in jocular depreciation of its beauty and luxury, but he regarded it as a perfect thing, and in one way it was; for it was perfectly in the family likeness of a thousand such "shacks." It had a ceiling with false beams, walls of green burlap spotted with colored "coaching prints," brown shelves supporting pewter plates and mugs, "mission" chairs, a leather couch with violent cushions, silver-framed photographs of lady-friends and officer-friends, a droplight of pink-shot imitation alabaster, a papier-mâché skull tobacco jar among moving-picture magazines on the round card table; and, of course, the final Charlie Loomis touch—a Japanese manservant.

The master of all this was one of those neat, stoutish young men with fat, round heads, sleek, fair hair, immaculate, pale complexions and infirm little pink mouths—in fact, he was of the type that may suggest to the student of resemblances a fastidious and excessively clean white pig with transparent ears. Nevertheless, Charlie Loomis was of a free-handed habit in some matters, being particularly indulgent to pretty women and their children. He spoke of the latter as "the kiddies," of course, and liked to call their mothers "kiddo," or "girlie." One of his greatest pleasures was to tell a woman that she was "the dearest, bravest little girlie in the world." Naturally he was a welcome guest in many households, and would often bring a really magnificent toy to the child of some friend whose wife he was courting. Moreover, at thirty-three, he had already done well enough in business to take things easily, and he liked to give these little card parties, not for gain, but for pastime. He was cautious and disliked high stakes in a game of chance.

That is to say, he disliked the possibility of losing enough money to annoy him, though of course he set forth his principles as resting upon a more gallant and unselfish basis. "I don't consider it hospitality to have any man go out of my shack sore," he was wont to say. "Myself, I'm a bachelor and got no obligations; I'll shoot any man that can afford it for anything he wants to. Trouble is, you can never tell when a man *can't* afford it, or what harm his losin' might mean to the little girlie at home and the kiddies. No, boys, penny ante and ten cent limit is the highest we go in this ole shack. Penny ante and a few steins of the ole home brew that hasn't got a divorce in a barrel of it!"

Penny ante and the ole home brew had been in festal operation for half an hour when the morose Collinson arrived this evening. Mr. Loomis and his guests sat around the round table under the alabaster droplight; their coats were off; cigars were worn at the deliberate Poker angle; colorful chips and cards glistened on the cloth; one of the players wore a green shade over his eyes; and all in all, here was a little Poker party for a lithograph. To complete the picture, several of the players continued to concentrate upon their closely held cards, and paid no attention to the newcomer or to their host's lively greeting of him.

"Ole Collie, b'gosh!" Mr. Loomis shouted, humorously affecting the bucolic. "Here's your vacant cheer; stack all stuck out for you 'n' ever'thing'! Set daown, neighbor, an' Smithie'll deal you in, next hand. What made you so late? Helpin' the little girlie at home get the kiddy to bed? That's a great kiddy of yours, Collie. I got a little Christmas gift for her I'm goin' to bring around some day soon. Yes, sir, that's a great little kiddy Collie's got over at his place, boys."

Collinson took the chair that had been left for him, counted his chips, and then as the playing of a hand still preoccupied three of the company, he picked up a silver dollar that lay upon the table near him. "What's this?" he asked. "A side bet? Or did somebody just leave it here for me?"

"Yes; for you to look at," Mr. Loomis explained. "It's Smithie's."

"What's wrong with it?"

"Nothin'. Smithie was just showin' it to us. Look at it."

Collinson turned the coin over and saw a tiny inscription that had been lined into the silver with a point of steel. " 'Luck,' " he read. " 'Luck hurry back to me!' " Then he spoke to the owner of this marked dollar. "I suppose you put that on there, Smithie, to help make sure of getting our money tonight."

But Smithie shook his head, which was a large, gaunt head, as it happened—a head fronted with a sallow face shaped much like a coffin, but inconsistently genial in expression. "No," he said. "It just came in over my counter this afternoon, and I noticed it when I was checkin' up the day's cash. Funny, ain't it: 'Luck hurry back to me!' "

"Who do you suppose marked that on it?" Collinson said thoughtfully.

"Golly!" his host exclaimed. "It won't do you much good to wonder about that."

Collinson frowned, continuing to stare at the marked dollar. "I guess not, but I really should like to know."

"I would, too," Smithie said. "I been thinkin' about it. Might 'a been somebody in Seattle or somebody in Ipswich, Mass., or New Orleans or St. Paul. How you goin' to tell? Might 'a been a woman; might 'a been a man. The way I guess it out, this poor boob, whoever he was, well, prob'ly he'd had good times for a while, and maybe carried this dollar for a kind of pocket piece, the way some people do, you know. Then he got in trouble—or she did, whichever it was—and got flat broke and had to spend this last dollar he had—for something to eat, most likely. Well, he thought a while before he spent it, and the way I guess it out, he said to himself, he said, 'Well,' he said, 'most of the good luck I've enjoyed lately,' he said, 'it's been while I had this dollar on me. I got to kiss 'em good-by now, good luck and good dollar together; but maybe I'll get 'em both back some day, so I'll just mark the wish on the dollar, like this: Luck hurry back to me! That'll help some, maybe, and anyhow I'll *know* my luck dollar if I ever do get it back.' That's the way I guess it out, anyhow. It's funny how some people like to believe luck depends on some little thing like that."

"Yes, it is," Collinson assented, still brooding over the coin.

The philosophic Smithie extended his arm across the table, collecting the cards to deal them, for the hand was finished. "Yes, sir, it's funny," he repeated. "Nobody knows exactly what luck is, but the way I guess it out, it lays in a man's *believin'* he's in luck, and some little object like this makes him kind of concentrate his mind on thinkin' he's goin' to be lucky, because of course you often *know* you're goin' to win, and then you do win. You don't win when you *want* to win, or when you need to; you win when you *believe* you'll win. I don't know who was the dummy that said, 'Money's the root of all evil'; but I guess he didn't have *too* much sense! I suppose if some man killed some other man for a dollar, the poor fish that said that would let the man out and send the dollar to the chair. No, sir; money's just as good as it is bad; and it'll come your way if you *feel* it will; so you take this market dollar o' mine——"

But here the garrulous and discursive guest was interrupted by immoderate protest from several of his colleagues. "Cut it out!" "My Lord!" "*Do* something!" "Smithie! Are you ever goin' to *deal?*"

"I'm goin' to shuffle first," he responded, suiting the action to the word, though with deliberation, and at the same time continuing his discourse. "It's a mighty interesting thing, a piece o' money. You take this dollar, now: Who's it belonged to? Where's it been? What different kind o' funny things has it been spent for sometimes? What funny kind of secrets do you suppose it could 'a heard if it had ears? Good people have had it and bad people have had it: why, a dollar could tell more about the human race—why, it could tell *all* about it!"

"I guess it couldn't tell all about the way you're dealin' these cards," said the man with the green shade. "You're mixin' things all up."

"I'll straighten 'em all out then," said Smithie cheerfully. "I knew of a twenty-dollar bill once;

a pickpocket prob'ly threw it in the gutter to keep from havin' it found on him when they searched him, but anyway a woman I knew found it and sent it to her young sister out in Michigan to take some music lessons with, and the sister was so excited she took this bill out of the letter and kissed it. That's where they thought she got the germ she died of a couple o' weeks later, and the undertaker got the twenty-dollar bill, and got robbed of it the same night. Nobody knows where it went then. They say, 'Money talks.' Golly! If it *could* talk, what couldn't it tell? *No*body'd be safe. *I* got this dollar now, but who's it goin' to belong to next, and what'll *he* do with it? And then after *that!* Why for years and years and years it'll go on from one pocket to another, in a millionaire's house one day, in some burglar's flat the next, maybe, and in one person's hand money'll do good, likely, and in another's it'll do harm. We all *want* money; but some say it's a bad thing, like that dummy I was talkin' about. Lordy! Goodness or badness, I'll take anybody——"

He was interrupted again, and with increased vehemence. Collinson, who sat next to him, complied with the demand to "ante up," then placed the dollar near his little cylinders of chips, and looked at his cards. They proved unencouraging, and he turned to his neighbor. "I'd sort of like to have that marked dollar, Smithie," he said. "I'll give you a paper dollar and a nickel for it."

But Smithie laughed, shook his head, and slid the coin over toward his own chips. "No, sir. I'm goin' to keep it—awhile, anyway."

"So you do think it'll bring you luck, after all!"

"No. But I'll hold onto it for this evening, anyhow."

"Not if we clean you out, you won't," said Charlie Loomis. "You know the rules o' the ole shack: only cash goes in *this* game; no I.O.U. stuff ever went here or ever will. Tell you what I'll do, though, before you lose it: I'll give you a dollar and a quarter for your ole silver dollar, Smithie."

"Oh, you want it, too, do you? I guess I can spot what sort of luck *you* want it for, Charlie."

"Well, Mr. Bones, what sort of luck do I want it for?"

"*You* win, Smithie," one of the other players said. "We all know what sort o' luck ole Charlie wants your dollar for—he wants it for luck with the dames."

"Well, I might," Charlie admitted, not displeased. "I haven't been so lucky that way lately —not so dog-*gone* lucky!"

All of his guests, except one, laughed at this; but Collinson frowned, still staring at the marked dollar. For a reason he could not have put into words just then, it began to seem almost vitally important to him to own this coin if he could, and to prevent Charlie Loomis from getting possession of it. The jibe, "He wants it for luck with the dames," rankled in Collinson's mind: it seemed to refer to his wife.

"I'll tell you what I'll do, Smithie," he said. "I'll bet two dollars against that dollar of yours that I hold a higher hand next deal than you do."

"Here! Here!" Charlie remonstrated. "Shack rules! Ten-cent limit."

"That's only for the game," Collinson said, turning upon his host with a sudden sharpness. "This is an outside bet between Smithie and me. Will you do it, Smithie? Where's your sporting spirit?"

So liberal a proposal at once aroused the spirit to which it appealed. "Well, I might, if some o' the others'll come in too, and make it really worth my while."

"I'm in," the host responded with prompt inconsistency; and others of the party, it appeared, were desirous of owning the talisman. They laughed and said it was "crazy stuff," yet they all came in, and, for the first time in the history of this "shack," what Mr. Loomis called "real money" was seen upon the table as a stake. It was won, and the silver dollar with it, by the largest and oldest of the gamesters, a fat man with a walrus mustache that inevitably made him known as "Old Bill." He smiled condescendingly, and would have put the dollar in his pocket with the "real money," but Mr. Loomis protested.

"Here! What you doin'?" he shouted, catching Old Bill by the arm. "Put that dollar back on the table."

"What for?"

"What *for?* Why, we're goin' to play for it again. Here's two dollars against it I beat you on the next hand."

"No," said Old Bill calmly. "It's worth more than two dollars to me. It's worth five."

"Well, five, then," his host returned. "I want that dollar!"

"So do I," said Collinson. "I'll put in five dollars if you do."

"Anybody else in?" Old Bill inquired, dropping the coin on the table; and all of the others again came in. Old Bill won again; but once more Charlie Loomis prevented him from putting the silver dollar in his pocket.

"Come on now!" Mr. Loomis exclaimed.

"Anybody else but me in on this for five dollars next time?"

"I am," said Collinson, swallowing with a dry throat; and he set forth all that remained to him of his twelve dollars. In return he received a pair of deuces, and the jubilant Charlie won.

He was vainglorious in his triumph. "Didn't that little luck piece just keep tryin' to find the right man?" he cried, and read the inscription loudly. " 'Luck hurry back to me!' Righto! You're home where you belong, girlie! Now we'll settle down to our reg'lar little game again."

"Oh, no," said Old Bill. "You wouldn't let me keep it. Put it out there and play for it. You made Old Bill."

"I won't do it."

"Yes, you will," Collinson said, and he spoke without geniality. "You put it out there."

"Oh, yes, I will," Mr. Loomis returned mockingly. "I will for ten dollars."

"Not I," said Old Bill. "Five is foolish enough." And Smithie agreed with him. "Nor me!"

"All right, then. If you're afraid of ten, I'll keep it. I thought the ten'd scare you."

"Put that dollar on the table," Collinson said. "I'll put ten against it."

There was a little commotion among these mild gamesters; and someone said, "You're crazy, Collie. What do you want to do that for?"

"I don't care," said Collinson. "That dollar's already cost me enough, and I'm going after it."

"Well, you see, I want it, too," Charlie Loomis retorted cheerfully; and he appealed to the others. "I'm not askin' him to put up ten against it, am I?"

"Maybe not," Old Bill assented. "But how long is this thing goin' to keep on? It's already balled our game all up, and if we keep on foolin' with these side bets, why, what's the use?"

"My goodness!" the host exclaimed. "*I'm* not pushin' this thing, am I? *I* don't want to risk my good old luck piece, do I? It's Collie that's crazy to go on, ain't it?" He laughed. "He hasn't showed his money yet, though, I notice, and this ole shack is run on strickly cash principles. I don't believe he's got ten dollars more on him!"

"Oh, yes, I have."

"Let's see it then."

Collinson's nostrils distended a little; but he said nothing, fumbled in his pocket, and then tossed the one-hundred-dollar bill, rather crumpled, upon the table.

"Great heavens!" shouted Old Bill. "Call the doctor: I'm all of a swoon!"

"Look at what's spilled over our nice clean table!" another said, in an awed voice. "Did you claim he didn't have *ten* on him, Charlie?"

"Well, it's nice to look at," Smithie observed. "But I'm with Old Bill. How long are you two goin' to keep this thing goin'? If Collie wins the luck piece, I suppose Charlie'll bet him fifteen against it, and then——"

"No, I won't," Charlie interrupted. "Ten's the limit."

"Goin' to keep on bettin' ten against it all night?"

"No," said Charlie. "I tell you what I'll do with you, Collinson; we both of us seem kind o' set on this luck piece, and you're already out some on it. I'll give you a square chance at it and at catchin' even. It's twenty minutes after nine. I'll keep on these side bets with you till ten o'clock, but when my clock hits ten, we're through, and the one that's got it then keeps it and no more foolin'. You want to do that, or quit now? I'm game either way."

"Go ahead and deal," said Collinson. "Whichever one of us has it at ten o'clock, it's his, and we quit."

But when the little clock on Charlie's green-painted mantel shelf struck ten, the luck piece was Charlie's and with it an overwhelming lien on the one-hundred-dollar bill. He put both in his pocket. "Remember this ain't my fault; it was you that insisted," he said, and handed Collinson four five-dollar bills as change.

Old Bill, platonically interested, discovered that his cigar was sparkless, applied a match, and casually set forth his opinion. "Well, I guess that was about as poor a way of spendin' eighty dollars as I ever saw, but it all goes to show there's truth in the old motto that anything at all can happen in any Poker game! That was a mighty nice hundred-dollar bill you had on you, Collie; but it's like what Smithie said: a piece o' money goes hoppin' around from one person to another—*it* don't care!—and yours has gone and hopped to Charlie. The question is, Who's it goin' to hop to next?" He paused to laugh, glanced over the cards that had been dealt him, and concluded: "My guess is't some good-lookin' woman'll prob'ly get a pretty fair chunk o' that hundred-dollar bill out o' Charlie. Well, let's settle down to the ole army game."

They settled down to it, and by twelve o'clock (the invariable closing hour of these pastimes in the old shack) Collinson had lost four dollars and thirty cents more. He was commiserated by his fellow gamesters as they put on their coats and overcoats, preparing to leave the hot little room. They shook their heads, laughed ruefully in sympathy, and told him he oughtn't to carry hundred-dollar bills upon his person when he went out among friends. Old Bill made what is sometimes known as an unfortunate remark.

"Don't worry about Collie," he said jocosely. "That hundred-dollar bill prob'ly belonged to some rich client of his."

"What!" Collinson said, staring.

"Never mind, Collie; I wasn't in earnest," the joker explained. "Of course I didn't mean it."

"Well, you oughtn't to say it," Collinson protested. "People say a thing like that about a man in a joking way, but other people hear it sometimes and don't know he's joking, and a story gets started."

"My goodness, but you're serious!" Old Bill exclaimed. "You look like you had a misery in your chest, as the rubes say; and I don't blame you! Get on out in the fresh night air and you'll feel better."

He was mistaken, however; the night air failed to improve Collinson's spirits as he walked home alone through the dark and chilly streets. There was indeed a misery in his chest, where stirred a sensation vaguely nauseating; his hands were tremulous and his knees infirm as he walked. In his mind was a confusion of pictures and sounds, echoes from Charlie Loomis's shack: he could not clear his mind's eye of the one-hundred-dollar bill; and its likeness, as it lay crumpled on the green cloth under the droplight, haunted and hurt him as a face in a coffin haunts and hurts the new mourner. Bits of Smithie's discursiveness resounded in his mind's ear, keeping him from thinking. "In one person's hands money'll do good likely, and in another's it'll do harm." . . . "The dummy that said, 'Money's the root of all evil!' "

It seemed to Collinson then that money was the root of all evil and the root of all good, the root and branch of all life, indeed. With money, his wife would have been amiable, not needing gay bachelors to take her to vaudevilles. Her need of money was the true foundation of the jealousy that had sent him out morose and reckless tonight; of the jealousy that had made it seem, when he gambled with Charlie Loomis for the luck dollar, as though they really gambled for luck with her.

It still seemed to him that they had gambled for luck with her: Charlie had wanted the talisman, as Smithie said, in order to believe in his luck—his luck with women—and therefore actually be lucky with them: and Charlie had won. But as Collinson plodded homeward in the chilly midnight, his shoulders sagging and his head drooping, he began to wonder how he could have risked money that belonged to another man. What on earth had made him do what he had done? Was it the mood his wife had set him in as he went out that evening? No; he had gone out feeling like that often enough, and nothing had happened.

Something had brought this trouble on him, he thought; for it appeared to Collinson that he had been an automaton, having nothing to do with his own actions. He must bear the responsibility for them; but he had not willed them. If the one-hundred-dollar bill had not happened to be in his pocket, he'd have been "all right." The one-hundred-dollar bill had done this to him. And Smithie's romancing again came back to him: "In one person's hands money'll do good, likely; in another's it'll do harm." It was the money that did harm or good, not the person; and the money in his hands had done this harm to himself.

He had to deliver a hundred dollars at the office in the morning, somehow, for he dared not take the risk of the client's meeting the debtor. There was a balance of seventeen dollars in his hand, and he could pawn his watch for twenty-five, as he knew well enough, by experience. That would leave fifty-eight dollars to be paid, and there was only one way to get it. His wife would have to let him pawn her ring. She'd *have* to!

Without any difficulty he could guess what she would say and do when he told her of his necessity: and he knew that never in his life would she forego the advantage over him she would gain from it. He knew, too, what stipulations she would make, and he had to face the fact that he was in no position to reject them. The one-hundred-dollar bill had cost him the last vestiges of mastery in his own house; and Charlie Loomis had really won not only the bill and the luck, but the privilege of taking Collinson's wife to vaudevilles. But it all came back to the same conclusion: the one-hundred-dollar bill had done it to him. "What kind of a thing *is* this life?" Collinson mumbled to himself, finding matters wholly perplexing in a world made into tragedy at the caprice of a little oblong slip of paper.

Then, as he went on his way to wake his wife and face her with the soothing proposal to pawn her ring early the next morning, something happened to Collinson. Of itself the thing that happened was nothing, but he was aware of his folly as if it stood upon a mountain top against the sun—and so he gathered knowledge of himself and a little of the wisdom that is called better than happiness.

His way was now the same as upon the latter

stretch of his walk home from the office that evening. The smoke fog had cleared, and the air was clean with a night wind that moved briskly from the west; in all the long street there was only one window lighted, but it was sharply outlined now, and fell as a bright rhomboid upon the pavement before Collinson. When he came to it he paused at the hint of an inward impulse he did not think to trace; and, frowning, he perceived that this was the same shop window that had detained him on his homeward way, when he had thought of buying a toy for the baby.

The toy was still there in the bright window; the gay little acrobatic monkey that would climb up or down a red string slacked or straightened; but Collinson's eye fixed itself upon the card marked with the price: "35 cents."

He stared and stared. "Thirty-five cents!" he said to himself. "Thirty-five cents!"

Then suddenly he burst into loud and prolonged laughter.

The sound was startling in the quiet night, and roused the interest of a meditative policeman who stood in the darkened doorway of the next shop. He stepped out, not unfriendly.

"What *you* havin' such a good time over, this hour o' the night?" he inquired. "What's all the joke?"

Collinson pointed to the window. "It's that monkey on the string," he said. "Something about it struck me as mighty funny!"

So, with a better spirit, he turned away, still laughing, and went home to face his wife.

¶*It is enough for a man to be a supreme master of one art, and C. S. Forester is that when he writes sea stories. When he writes Poker stories he is not as breathtakingly faithful to the vernacular and the procedure as James Jones is (see the selection on page 146), but who cares when a man can tell such a superb story? This story appeared first in the* Saturday Evening Post *(July 10, 1943) and since then in book form.*

Some Kinds of Bad Luck

by C. S. FORESTER

FIREMAN Jimmy Lamb held three tens with the queen of hearts and the ace of diamonds. He looked round unobtrusively at the faces of his colleagues before he made his discard. Bill Cobbler had doubled the ante and Hank had raised again. But three tens made a good hand to draw to. Once already in the evening he had drawn two cards to a pair, and the showdown had proved that he had done so; it would do no harm if Hank thought he was doing so again. He discarded his queen and ace and the captain passed him two cards in return. Jimmy glanced at them casually before letting them fall on the three others. They were the ten of clubs and the jack of spades. He had four of a kind, four tens, and, what was more, he knew that no one could have four jacks or four queens or four aces. There was hardly a hand that could beat his.

Jimmy was a little hazy about the odds, but he guessed it was about ten thousand to one that he had the best hand at the table.

"I'll take one," said Bill Cobbler, "and it better be the right one."

His face told Jimmy nothing as he looked at the card the captain passed to him. Except that it was just a little too expressionless; Jimmy thought it might be that Bill had filled a straight.

"One for me," said Hank. He looked at the card. "Cripes, it's hot!"

His look gave nothing away either; the remark about the heat was perfectly genuine, for there was a trickle of sweat down Hank's cheek, and the little room at the back of the firehouse was hotter than the hinges.

It was immediately obvious what Slim and the captain thought about the strength of the opposition.

"I wouldn't stand against those draws," said Slim, and the captain did not even trouble to say anything, but dropped his cards into the discard with a wry smile.

Hank cocked an eyebrow across the table at Jimmy.

"Well," said Jimmy, pushing the chips forward. It was a neat tactical problem, whether the maximum or the minimum raise would be best adapted for luring the others on to their destruction. Jimmy thought it was time for the maximum.

"Feeling that way about it?" said Bill, his hand on his chips.

At that moment the alarm bell sounded sharply just behind Jimmy's ear, and the cards went abruptly down on the table. It was only five seconds after making his bet that Jimmy was in his place on the engine rig, thrusting his arms into the sleeves of his turn-out coat with the engine bellowing wildly as Slim started it.

"It's Bill's turn to bet," said Hank, hanging on beside Jimmy.

"The K.J. factory!" roared the captain over the noise of the engine. "Eighth and Broadway."

Slim stepped right on it and the rig went out through the door with a jerk which might have torn Jimmy from his handhold had he not been expecting it. It was certainly cooler tearing through the hot evening air than sitting in the firehouse. Jimmy buttoned the last button and put on his helmet. Then he had a few seconds to spare in which to contemplate the prospect of having four of a kind waiting for him when he should return to the firehouse.

Smoke was hanging thickly round the K.J. factory as they arrived; it was smoke which lay ominously low. K.J. made chemicals, and that kind of smoke was indicative of something other than ordinary combustion. A worried man in his shirt sleeves, with a green shade still over his eyes, addressed the captain as he arrived, pointing excitedly to a wing of the building beyond the courtyard. Jimmy was too busy coupling up the hose to see more than that out of the tail of his eye, but within a minute the captain called him over.

"You've got the steadiest head, Jimmy," said the captain. "I want you to take a line across that roof."

The man with the green shade began to speak and gesticulate, and the captain brushed him aside, interpreting for him, as one might say. "It's only an explosion roof," went on the captain, "so if you go through it there'll be no saving you. It's supported from corner to corner—you'll see the line you have to follow. The other side there's a scuttle hole. Get your nozzle playing into that."

"O.K., captain," said Jimmy.

He ran up the tall ladder; his youth and physical fitness, of which he was prodigally unaware, carrying him to the top without his noticing the exertion.

"Let's have that," he said to Hank, reaching for the nozzle; the captain had told him to take a "line," which in fireman's parlance means a hose.

The route he had to follow was plainly indicated—a path a foot wide across the frail explosion roof where the partition wall below supported the corrugated iron. A steady head as well as considerable physical strength would be necessary to drag sixty feet of hose along there without deviating from the true course. Jimmy made the crossing without really noticing any extra strain upon him. Sure enough, there was the scuttle hole that the captain had spoken about; the captain had a positive genius for getting the facts of the situation in the shortest possible time and then acting upon them. The fact that he had crossed an explosion roof ought to have conveyed to Jimmy that below him there were substances which, to express it in its lowest terms, might at some time explode; but even at the cost of subtracting something from his appearance of heroism, it must be pointed out that Jimmy was so preoccupied with the immediate details of the business in hand that he had no thought to spare for any broader outlook.

There was smoke from this scuttle hole, but not the chemical, rubbery smoke he had encountered at ground level. This must be the office wing containing the source of the fire which was boring its way through to the chemical factory; these old-fashioned buildings, added to piece by piece with the growth of the business, had never been sensibly planned from the fireman's point of view. Jimmy turned a cataract of water in through the scuttle hole and was gratified by the instant results obtained. Somewhere down below him, although Jimmy was not aware of it, certain drums and carboys of highly active chemicals had been on the point of disintegrating in the heat and mingling their contents in one tremendous conflagration. Jimmy's stream of water arrived just in time to prevent this happening. Playing on the actual source of the fire, it helped to bring it under control with the usual absurd rapidity with which a fire is mastered if tackled promptly and in the right way. In fact, next morning the city newspaper hardly troubled to mention the fact that there had been a fire at the K.J. factory, for no official either of the management or of the fire department troubled to tell the reporter that a delay of five more minutes would have given him a front-page story of destruction and death.

Jimmy trailed his nozzle back to the ladder, when the captain signaled him.

"Pick up the gingham and let's go home," said the captain. A hose when it is in action is a "line," but when it has to be packed up again it is "gingham" or "spaghetti" or any one of half a dozen other things, according to the whim of the fireman.

As Jimmy swung himself onto the ladder he remembered again that he had four of a kind waiting for him at the firehouse, and the dreary routine work of rolling up hoses and checking over equipment seemed to him to take even longer than usual, so anxious was he to give Bill Cobbler and Hank a lesson in Poker which would last them for the rest of their lives. In the firehouse the cards lay face downward on the table where they had left them; as they sat down, Jimmy turned his up for a reassuring peep. Four beautiful tens and the jack of spades. He remembered that no one could have four queens or four aces either.

"It's Bill's turn to bet," said Hank, exactly as he had said it standing on the rig beside Jimmy.

"I'll raise you a red one," said Bill.

"And I'll raise you a blue one," said Hank.

The maximum raise; Jimmy was still preoccupied with the problem of not scaring Bill and Hank out.

"Well, I'll just raise you one more blue," he said. He wanted to appear neither unconcerned nor eager.

"O.K. I can stick around in this company too," said Bill, pushing three blue chips into the pot.

Hank raised again without comment, and Jimmy followed his example.

"That's three raises," said Slim, who had been an interested onlooker.

"I'll stay to see you," said Bill.

Hank said nothing, but dropped in another blue.

All eyes turned toward Jimmy, and he uncovered his four tens.

"That beats me, brother," said Bill, pushing his hand into the discard. But Hank was slowly turning his cards over one by one. One king. Two kings. Three kings. Four kings. The ten-thousandth chance had come off.

"Well, aren't I the unluckiest something or other that ever climbed a ladder?" said Jimmy.

It took ten years to transform Fireman Jimmy Lamb into Maj. Gen. James Lamb; ten crowded years which included a year of peacetime training in the American Air Corps and nearly as long again of desperate fighting on each of four continents. That early fireman's training was in no sense wasted, all the same; the physical fitness and the habits of prompt thought which it instilled into him helped to save his life more than once in the battlefields of the air all over the world. It may even have had something to do with the insight into character and genius for organization which Lamb came to display, and which marked him out not merely as a superb combat pilot but also, when promotion came to him, as a general able to handle large forces both in actual battle and in the patient preparation for it.

The Supervisory Committee of International Relations was unfeignedly glad when General Lamb accepted a commission in their air force. It was not easy to attract the best type of man into the international service; many were thoroughly tired of living under discipline in their national armies and air forces, and many others withdrew, a little frightened at the prospect of endless peacetime years to be spent in service routine. The idealists who formed the majority of the committee were not enamored, on the other hand, of the prospect of employing the type that welcomes routine and red tape as an excuse for not thinking for themselves. No one could say that General Lamb did not think for himself, for he had demonstrated his ability to do so from the South Seas to the Arctic, and everyone knew that it was his word as chief staff officer which had made the Fourth Air Army the victorious instrument it had proved to be in the last year of the war. The committee was not a very military-minded body, and it was with a sigh of relief that they turned over to General Lamb the task of constructing, out of something like primeval chaos, the air force which was put at their disposal—pilots of a dozen nations and mechanics of even more, all drifted together out of the air services of innumerable armies.

The general enjoyed the work of organization. It was something more than mere office work, even though it kept him tied to a desk or a table for many more hours a day than he liked. There was room for the play of imagination, seeing that there were no precedents for the organization of an international air force and no one could be at all sure where or against whom it would be employed. The committee believed that it only had to be good to insure its never having to be employed; General Lamb listened to their lofty sentiments and did not voice his disagreement. No member of that committee had ever worked for a fire department, while the general had worked for what he still believed to be the finest organization of its kind, but the perfection of that organization had not stopped fires from breaking out.

The general was at his desk one evening after dinner—he kept a queer timetable which enabled him to devote daylight hours to more profitable uses—when Aubert, his principal staff officer, brought in a sheaf of flimsy paper covered with typewritten characters.

"There's more still coming through," said Aubert in the perfect but toneless English which characterized him. "I brought this in in case you might want to start on it at once. It's from Yanac, and he's using the reserve code."

"Is he, by golly?" said the general.

The reserve code had never before troubled the wires or the ether of the world; it had been kept for times of gravest emergency, so that any unauthorized person that wanted to decode it would have to start from scratch. Aubert opened the safe and brought out the red-bound volume that contained the reserve code. He sat down at the typewriter beside Lamb and twirled a sheet of paper into the machine with a flourish of his long white fingers. He had begun to pick out the decoded message when Lamb pushed aside the returns he was studying and turned to him. "Here, I'll help you with that," he said; "it'll take you all night by yourself."

He flipped through the pages of the key, his eyes darting from message to key and back again; the code was complicated and a misinterpretation of any symbol threw the interpretation of all the following symbols out of line. Aubert's arched eyebrows arched higher still as he typed the words dictated to him, and he looked sidelong at his chief to judge of their effect, but Lamb still read on imperturbably. When Aubert reached the foot of the second page, it was more than he could stand.

"This is damned serious," he said.

"Let's see all that Yanac has to say first," said Lamb.

The sheaf of flimsies made four typewritten pages. Aubert reached over and held down the switch of the interoffice-communication system. "Bring in the rest of that message," he said.

"Only 'arf a pige more 'as come through, sir," said a cheerful cockney voice in reply. "I'll bring it up."

That was strange, for it seemed as if Yanac's message should be much longer; and when they decoded the final half page, they found that the message broke off not merely in the middle of a sentence but in the middle of a word.

Aubert pressed the switch again. "Has any more come through?" he asked.

"No, sir, not a word."

"Call back by radio," interposed Lamb. "See if you can find out what's wrong."

Aubert closed the switch and met his chief's eyes. "Curiouser and curiouser," he said. He looked through the typewritten message and then up again. "Yanac's generally sound."

"I'd trust him before anyone I know," said Lamb simply.

Yanac was in charge of the supervision of disarmament in a part of the world where the late turmoil had taken longer than elsewhere to subside.

"This shouldn't come to us at all," said Aubert; "it ought to go direct to the committee."

"Maybe so," agreed Lamb. "I expect Yanac means to report to them as well."

"He seems to be very sure of his facts," went on Aubert, "and they ring true."

According to Yanac, someone was planning a fresh upheaval in tortured Europe. Lamb knew that to be perfectly likely, even though it was incredible to him that anyone or any body of men could be such fools as to risk starting the whole frightful business over again.

The buzzer sounded and Aubert held down the switch.

"The cable's broke, sir. I arst 'em to send the message on by wireless, but there's not much hope till tomorrow, sir, wiv all the congestion."

That in itself was confirmation of what Yanac was trying to tell them.

"Better pass this on to the committee," suggested Aubert.

Lamb looked at the clock and did a couple of sums in his head, working out what time it would be in two other places of the world. It would take hours to get a quorum of the committee together at that time of night. Not merely that, but, although the committee contained some of the best brains in the world and some of the most lofty idealism, it was not a committee that would act rapidly. It would take all day to reach a decision as vital as the one necessary, and that was just what the people Yanac was in contact with were counting on.

"I'll leave that for you to do," said Lamb. "Call Bulow and have my plane brought out—the four-motor. Roberts and Sanchez can pilot it. I'll start in twenty minutes."

While Aubert put the order through, Lamb walked up and down the room; he was ready by the time Aubert released the switch.

"These are your orders," he said. "Take them down quick, so that I can sign them before I go."

Aubert twirled a fresh sheet of paper into the typewriter and his fingers danced madly over the keys as Lamb dictated the three brief paragraphs.

"Those are my orders," said Lamb, signing the sheet. "They hold good unless countermanded by me in person; not by cable or by telephone, even if you're sure it's my voice. You'll carry them out whether I'm alive or dead. There's the plane on the runway."

General Lamb would be the first to admit that he made a poor plane passenger; he had piloted his own plane too long ever to be a good passenger. He had the sense to leave the details to the pilots, but he found it hard to compose himself to sleep while flying, and it irked his conscience to shift his position in the plane when he knew that the pilot had just got the machine leveled off and the automatic pilot in use; a trip to the stern then meant altering the whole balance. And accustomed though he was to long-distance flying, there was still something faintly unsettling in the thought of tearing through the night at three hundred miles an hour with the dawn racing six hundred miles an hour after him, trying to catch him up.

Tonight it was important that the dawn should not catch him. Man's material progress has been enormous. However, mankind still has no control over the fundamentals of nature; the wind still blows and the rivers still run and the sun still rises and sets; and the sort of coup about which Yanac had sent the warning was one which would need daylight for its execution. Lamb looked at his watch and then was mildly annoyed with himself for doing so. Looking at his watch would not increase their speed, and if the plane was ahead of schedule or behind it, he could trust Roberts or Sanchez to tell him so. He was acting just as he did when he was a rookie fireman going out on his first few calls.

The plane tore through the stratosphere, swooping down to refill, climbing up again after ten minutes' frantic work by the mechanics at the airports. It crossed half an ocean and half a continent before, finally, Roberts set it down on the last runway. Not such a good landing either; Roberts let her bounce and took her up again with a jerk.

Well, for gosh sake, said Lamb to himself, thrown back abruptly against his seat. He wanted to go forward and find out what on earth Roberts thought he was doing, but he had to resign himself philosophically to his humble role of passenger. The plane circled, its searchlights stabbing at the ground, and Lamb, peering through his window, saw the dark shape of a truck stationary on the runway. No wonder Roberts had had to take her up in a hurry. The plane circled again, and this time the runway was clear and Roberts brought her down. As the plane came to a stop, Sanchez came aft, his face working and his hands gesticulating with Latin-American excitement.

"These damn droops!" he said. "They call us down and then run a truck clean onto the runway! Somebody ought to be shot!"

Lamb entered into no discussion of the incident with him. It occurred to Lamb that there were certain people in this capital who would not be at all sorry if an accident were to incapacitate for a few hours the major general commanding the air force. If the accident were severe enough to kill him, that would be just too bad. Seeing that the interested parties could not have had more than two hours' notice of his arrival, they had got to work promptly in putting their truck on the runway.

The plane door opened, and standing at the foot of the ladder to welcome him was a figure in uniform, his right hand in a stiff salute. Lamb remembered his face, but for the life of him could not remember his name; he had been one of his comrades in arms in the last triumphant year of the war.

"Welcome, general," said the officer.

"Good evening, colonel," said Lamb—it seemed the safest bet to call him colonel—but he felt a twinge of guilt at forgetting the insignia of these old-fashioned armies. He descended the ladder and they shook hands.

"This is an unexpected pleasure," said the officer. "What can I do for you, general?"

Lamb fished in his pockets for his notes. "That's the name of the man I want to see. I must see him immediately."

He looked at his watch again, and once more felt like an idiot for doing so. By his watch it was ten in the morning, but here it was still two hours before dawn.

"He's a very important man," said the officer. "He's hard to see. And at this time of night——"

"I have to see him," said Lamb.

"He's the leader of the opposition," said the officer dubiously. There was that in his expression which told Lamb the officer did not approve of the opposition.

"That's why I want to see him," said Lamb. "We'll telephone and say I am on the way."

"Come this way then," said the officer. "I had your plane stopped at the side entrance. I thought maybe you would not want to go out through the main offices."

"What was that truck doing on the runway?" asked Lamb as they passed through the gate.

"God knows how that happened!" said the officer vehemently. "I'm not in charge here, you know. I saw it happen. The truck just ran across as you were coming in. Do you want to speak to the officer in charge of the control tower?"

"No," said Lamb, "it doesn't matter."

"Some thoughtless idiot," concluded the officer.

"Look out!" said Lamb suddenly, grabbing the officer's arm and leaping wildly for the curb. An unlighted motor-car at high speed missed them by inches.

"Lots of damn fools about tonight!" sputtered the officer wrathfully.

"It looks like it," agreed Lamb.

"That's one of the opposition cars too," went on the officer. "Did you see the badge?"

"Something like the ace of clubs?"

"That's right. It's a clover leaf really. Strictly speaking, that badge is illegal since the last proclamation."

"But it's still to be seen in the streets?"

"Yes."

The national government here was hardly strong enough to deal with a turbulent opposition; Yanac had already pointed that out. And the leader of the opposition was an able and determined man. At two hours' notice he had been able to plan and execute two attempts to achieve his apparently accidental death.

"Here's the telephone," said the officer.

"Do the speaking for me," said Lamb, motioning him in. "Say I must speak to him on a matter of life and death. Use those words or as near to them as you can get in your language."

The officer emerged three minutes later. "He'll see you," he said. "I said you'd be there in ten minutes. My car's outside."

"There may be another accident," said Lamb as they drove through the dark streets, "but I don't think it's likely."

Lamb guessed that the leader, now that he knew that Lamb wanted to see him, would be curious to hear what he had to say and would defer any further attempts on his life until afterward. His guess proved correct, for they reached the big house in the fashionable square on the top of the hill without any incident. Two men were standing like sentries outside the front door.

"That's illegal too," said the officer wryly. "Private armies are forbidden, but I don't think our premier dare risk a showdown."

The door swung open as Lamb went up the steps, and the two sentries stood at stiff salute as he walked past them. A butler in dress clothes bowed to him as he entered and led him through to a room at the back of the house. It was full of the smoke of cigars; Lamb guessed that either the two people he saw at the table had been smoking there all night or else a large conference had hastily adjourned on his arrival. At the head of the table sat the leader of the opposition; Lamb recognized him by the heavy mustache which had appeared in a good many cartoons lately. The other man was smaller and insignificant.

"Good evening," said Lamb. "Please forgive my troubling you at this time of night."

"It is nothing," said the leader. "I need very little sleep. Will you please sit down, general?"

The other man pushed a box of cigars across to Lamb, who selected one with care, cut off the end with a great deal of deliberation, and then spent several seconds lighting it. When he had finished, he looked at the leader.

"I hear you intend to disturb the peace of the world today," he said.

The leader's glance did not waver before this assault. "You may be misinformed," he said; "and if I were contemplating any action, it would be to obtain justice for my country."

"My information," said Lamb, "is that your party has planned to seize a certain border city today. That would be in violation of the decision of the Supervisory Committee of International Relations."

Lamb had used that name deliberately, just as a bullfighter flutters his cloak to induce the bull to charge.

"The SCIR!" said the leader, and the contempt in his voice was beyond description.

Lamb knew he had been making inflammatory speeches about the committee; he could guess now how effective they had been, if the leader was always able to throw that amount of contempt into his tone.

"They are the people who pay me to do my job," he said mildly.

"Did they pay you to come here?" interposed the other man.

"No," said Lamb simply. "They probably have only just heard that I have arrived."

"You are meddling in other people's business, then?" went on the other man.

"I chose to consider it my own business," said Lamb.

"And now you find there is nothing you can do," sneered the leader. "Our preparations are made and we move in three hours."

"The city will be ours," continued the other man, "and we can snap our fingers at your committee."

"You think they'll take no action?"

"Committees never do, and the SCIR least of all." The leader slapped the table with a thick hairy hand.

"Your idea is," said Lamb musingly, his eyes looking above and beyond the heads of his audience of two, "to lay hold of the city by force. You think then the committee will make the best of a bad job and leave you in possession, sooner than spill blood to turn you out."

"Then our country will have justice," said the leader.

"And your premier will be thoroughly discredited when the people compare his record with yours. At the next election he will be out and you will be in. You will be in power. But that power will be founded on an act of violence. The pattern will be established again. You will demand more concessions, and then more, with violence or the threat of violence as your argument. And when violence is successful, your people will agree to rearmament. I can foresee war throughout the world in ten years' time. Are you still going to do this thing?"

It was a long speech, and his audience moved a little restlessly in their seats before the other man spoke. "If your committee foresees this, why do they not render us justice now and prevent all this happening?"

"Justice," said Jimmy, keyed up by now to almost epigrammatic eloquence, "is what you think is right. Injustice is what the other man thinks is right."

As nobody seemed inclined to answer, Jimmy plunged into another speech.

"I was a fireman once," he said. "I know how fires start. They have small beginnings, but if those beginnings are not dealt with at once, they grow bigger and bigger and they take a firmer and firmer hold, and before you know where you are, the thing that a man could deal with in five seconds with a hand extinguisher has become a three-alarm fire and an all-night job. I believe in stopping these things before they have taken hold."

The leader suddenly broke into laughter, showing white teeth beneath the heavy mustache. "That's a pretty speech, general. It's a pity that you are entirely wrong. You are wrong in more ways than I can count offhand. No world is a good world where injustice flourishes. That's the first point. And I promise my people peace and not war; I make that promise to the whole world. What I propose to do today will be a salutary medicine to a sick world languishing under the blundering ministrations of these incompetent committees of yours. They debate and we act. You understand, general, we act."

"The political existence of our party," supplemented the other man, "hinges on today's doings. If we draw back now, we are discredited. It would be simple suicide for us."

Jimmy could see that this last speech was directed as much to the leader as to himself; it was the prick of the goad.

"We shall march," said the leader.

"You see, you are helpless," said the other man, "and as you realize that we shall be very busy from now on, I am sure you will not take up any more of the leader's time. Unless, general, you are attracted by the prospects of our success. We could offer a distinguished position and a princely salary to a good air-force officer—one, for instance, who is tired of his own discredited service. We shall have a large air force to put under his command soon."

Jimmy hardly noticed the bribe that was offered him; he was merely patiently waiting for the man to finish speaking. With the leader's decision to march, the time had come for the mailed fist to make itself felt through the velvet glove.

"Listen," he said a trifle more loudly, and then he restrained himself and paused to knock off the ash from his cigar. He could not hope to outshout the leader, who, notoriously, could shout louder than anyone else in public life. "Before I left my headquarters I gave some orders to my chief of staff. That's Aubert. Do you remember what Aubert did in the south of France? I don't think there is a man on earth with less pity than Aubert when he starts fighting. That's curious, considering what a sissy manner he has."

Jimmy waited deliberately, to force a reply from the men he was speaking to.

"What orders did you give him?" asked the leader thickly.

"He is to carry out one of the schemes we have drawn up on paper for exercises. He won't be able to assemble a thousand planes at the decisive point. I admit that; these movements call for time and organization. But he will be coming with five hundred. I know all about the twenty planes you have hidden away, but those old fighters won't last a minute before ours, as you know. Aubert has orders to destroy every military column on any road leading to the city. He'll do it, all right; Aubert's not the man for half measures."

There was a very curious train of thought at the back of Jimmy's mind as he finished speaking; a nearly forgotten memory was stirring. Once he had laid down four tens in the certainty that it was the best hand at the table, and four kings had beaten him. This was a pretty good hand that he was laying down now. He could not imagine that the leader had a royal flush, but it might happen. One could never be quite positive of anything. He watched the leader's face while doing his best not to appear to be doing so.

"It would be political suicide not to march," prodded the other man.

"It'll be real suicide if you do march," said Jimmy.

The other man stirred in his chair again, and for some reason Jimmy took his eyes from the leader's face and looked across at him. He was holding an automatic pistol, his hand steadied on the table and the muzzle pointed at Jimmy. The sight of it brought him a great wave of relief—he was in too exalted a mood to think of his own personal danger—because it was clear to him at once that the threat of personal violence was in itself an admission of defeat.

"Put that thing away," said Jimmy. "It won't help you at all if you kill me."

The leader and the other man sat passive.

"I'm telling you the truth," went on Jimmy. "Aubert has his orders, and almost my last words to him were that he should carry them out whether I was dead or alive. And if I am dead, Aubert will not rest until he's seen the man who's killed me hanged."

"Put it away," said the leader. He would not have risen to his present position if he had not been a good judge of humanity. He could see that Jimmy meant what he said. Moreover, he had the tact to admit defeat gracefully. "The committee is to be congratulated on the zeal and efficiency of its servant. You are worth the salary they pay you, general."

"You wouldn't think so if you were to read some of the papers back at home," grinned Jimmy. "State taxes and Federal taxes used to be bad enough, and now there's an international tax on top of that, and, by golly, you ought to hear 'em howl. But I've saved 'em a war today; it's just the old fire-department tradition."

"One throw?" asked Aubert, his elbow on the bar and the dice box in his hand.

"One throw," said Jimmy.

Aubert rolled the dice out onto the bar. "Four fours," he announced.

Jimmy rattled the dice and rolled them out. "Threes," he said. "Aren't I the unluckiest something or other that ever walked the earth?"

Until the 1870s playing cards did not have the index markings in their corners. While a player was looking at the full face of every card in his hand, other players could peek. Cards with index markings, called "squeezers," permitted a player to read his hand from the corners of the cards. The cards shown were made in 1881.

¶[This is the most moral story in the book, and fittingly we have selected it from among the masterpieces of O. Henry; for he himself tasted of all the degradation and frustration to which the compulsive gambler's life must lead. ¶[The story is about a card-player, not about card-playing. Though O. Henry often wrote about players of games, he almost never touched on the games themselves, though he knew them well. Also, the title of the story requires one brief comment: The game is Poker; the "Blackjack" of the title was a mountain, not a game.

A Blackjack Bargainer

by O. HENRY

THE MOST disreputable thing in Yancey Goree's law office was Goree himself, sprawled in his creaky old armchair. The rickety little office, built of red brick, was set flush with the street—the main street of the town of Bethel.

Bethel rested upon the foothills of the Blue Ridge. Above it the mountains were piled to the sky. Far below it the turbid Catawba gleamed yellow along its disconsolate valley.

The June day was at its sultriest hour. Trade was not. Bethel dozed in the tepid shade. It was so still that Goree, reclining in his chair, distinctly heard the clicking of the chips in the grand-jury room, where the "courthouse gang" was playing Poker. From the open back door of the office a well-worn path meandered across the grassy lot to the courthouse. The treading out of that path had cost Goree all he ever had—first, inheritance of a few thousand dollars, next, the old family home, and, latterly, the last shreds of his self-respect and manhood. The "gang" had cleaned him out. The broken gambler had turned drunkard and parasite; he had lived to see this day come when the men who had stripped him denied him a seat at the game. His word was no longer to be taken. The daily bout at cards had arranged itself accordingly, and to him was assigned the ignoble part of the onlooker. The sheriff, the county clerk, a sportive deputy, a gay attorney, and a chalk-faced man hailing "from the valley," sat at table, and the sheared one was thus tacitly advised to go and grow more wool.

Soon wearying of his ostracism, Goree had departed for his office, muttering to himself as he unsteadily traversed the unlucky pathway. After a drink of corn whisky from a demijohn under the table, he had flung himself into the chair, staring, in a sort of maudlin apathy, out at the mountains immersed in the summer haze. The little white patch he saw away up on the side of Blackjack was Laurel, the village near which he had been born and bred. There, also, was the birthplace of the feud between the Gorees and the Coltranes. Now no direct heir of the Gorees survived except this plucked and singed bird of misfortune. To the Coltranes, also, but one male supporter was left—Colonel Abner Coltrane—a man of substance and standing, a member of the State Legislature, and a contemporary with Goree's father. The feud had been a typical one of the region; it had left a red record of hate, wrong, and slaughter.

But Yancey Goree was not thinking of feuds. His befuddled brain was hopelessly attacking the problem of the future maintenance of himself and his favorite follies. Of late, old friends of the family had seen to it that he had whereof to eat and a place to sleep, but whisky they would not buy for him, and he must have whisky. His law business was extinct; no case had been intrusted to him in two years. He had been a borrower and a sponge, and it seemed that if he fell no lower it would be from lack of opportunity. One more chance—he was saying to himself—if he had one more stake at the game, he thought he could win; but he had nothing left to sell, and his credit was more than exhausted.

He could not help smiling, even in his misery, as he thought of the man to whom, six months before, he had sold the old Goree homestead. There had come from "back yan' " in the mountains two of the strangest creatures, a man named Pike Garvey and his wife. "Back yan'," with a wave of the hand toward the hills, was understood among the mountaineers to designate the remotest fastnesses, the unplumbed gorges, the haunts of lawbreakers, the wolf's den, and the boudoir of the bear. In the cabin far up on Blackjack's shoulder, in the wildest part of these retreats, this odd couple had lived for twenty years. They had neither dog nor children to mitigate the heavy silence of the hills. Pike Garvey was little known in the settlement, but all who had dealt with him pronounced him "crazy as a loon." He acknowledged no occupation save that of a squirrel hunter, but he "moonshined" occasionally by way of diversion. Once the "revenues" had dragged him from his lair, fighting silently and desperately like a terrier, and he had been sent to state's prison for two

* "Revenuers," to us today.

years. Released, he popped back into his hole like an angry weasel.

Fortune, passing over many anxious wooers, made a freakish flight into Blackjack's bosky pockets to smile upon Pike and his faithful partner.

One day a party of spectacled, knickerbockered, and altogether absurd prospectors invaded the vicinity of the Garveys' cabin. Pike lifted his squirrel rifle off the hook and took a shot at them at long range on the chance of their being revenues.* Happily he missed, and the unconscious agents of good luck drew nearer, disclosing their innocence of anything resembling law or justice. Later on, they offered the Garveys an enormous quantity of ready, green, crisp money for their thirty-acre patch of cleared land, mentioning, as an excuse for such a mad action, some irrelevant and inadequate nonsense about a bed of mica underlying the said property.

When the Garveys became possessed of so many dollars that they faltered in computing them, the deficiencies of life on Blackjack began to grow prominent. Pike began to talk of new shoes, a hogshead of tobacco to set in the corner, a new lock to his rifle; and, leading Martella to a certain spot on the mountainside, he pointed out to her how a small cannon—doubtless a thing not beyond the scope of their fortune in price—might be planted so as to command and defend the sole accessible trail to the cabin, to the confusion of revenues and meddling strangers forever.

But Adam reckoned without his Eve. These things represented to him the applied power of wealth, but there slumbered in his dingy cabin an ambition that soared far above his primitive wants. Somewhere in Mrs. Garvey's bosom still survived a spot of femininity unstarved by twenty years of Blackjack. For so long a time the sounds in her ears had been the scaly-barks dropping in the woods at noon, and the wolves singing among the rocks at night, and it was enough to have purged her vanities. She had grown fat and sad and yellow and dull. But when the means came, she felt a rekindled desire to assume the perquisites of her sex—to sit at tea tables; to buy inutile things; to whitewash the hideous veracity of life with a little form and ceremony. So she coldly vetoed Pike's proposed system of fortifications, and announced that they would descend upon the world and gyrate socially.

And thus, at length, it was decided, and the thing done. The village of Laurel was their compromise between Mrs. Garvey's preference for one of the large valley towns and Pike's hankering for primeval solitudes. Laurel yielded a halting round of feeble social distractions comportable with Martella's ambitions, and was not entirely without recommendation to Pike, its contiguity to the mountains presenting advantages for sudden retreat in case fashionable society should make it advisable.

Their descent upon Laurel had been coincident with Yancey Goree's feverish desire to convert property into cash, and they bought the old Goree homestead, paying four thousand dollars ready money into the spendthrift's shaking hand.

Thus it happened that while the disreputable last of the Gorees sprawled in his disreputable office, at the end of his row, spurned by the cronies whom he had gorged, strangers dwelt in the halls of his fathers.

A cloud of dust was rolling slowly up the parched street, with something traveling in the midst of it. A little breeze wafted the cloud to one side, and a new, brightly painted carryall, drawn by a slothful gray horse, became visible. The vehicle deflected from the middle of the street as it neared Goree's office, and stopped in the gutter directly in front of his door.

On the front seat sat a gaunt, tall man, dressed in black broadcloth, his right hands incarcerated in yellow kid gloves. On the back seat was a lady who triumphed over the June heat. Her stout form was armored in a skin-tight silk dress of the description known as "changeable," being a gorgeous combination of shifting hues. She sat erect, waving a much-ornamented fan, with her eyes fixed stonily far down the street. However Martella Garvey's heart might be rejoicing at the pleasures of her new life, Blackjack had done his work with her exterior. He had carved her countenance to the image of emptiness and inanity; had imbued her with the stolidity of his crags and the reserve of his hushed interiors. She always seemed to hear, whatever her surroundings were, the scaly-barks falling and pattering down the mountainside. She could always hear the awful silence of Blackjack sounding through the stillest of nights.

Goree watched this solemn equipage, as it drove to his door, with only faint interest; but when the lank driver wrapped the reins about his whip, and awkwardly descended, and stepped into the office, he rose unsteadily to receive him, recognizing Pike Garvey, the new, the transformed, the recently civilized.

The mountaineer took the chair Goree offered him. They who cast doubts upon Garvey's soundness of mind had a strong witness in the man's countenance. His face was too long, a dull saffron in hue, and immobile as a statue's. Pale blue, unwinking round eyes without lashes added to the singularity of his gruesome visage. Goree was at a loss to account for the visit.

"Everything all right at Laurel, Mr. Garvey?" he inquired.

"Everything all right, sir, and mighty pleased is Missis Garvey and me with the property. Missis Garvey likes yo' old place, and she likes the neighborhood. Society is what she 'lows she wants, and she is gettin' it. The Rogerses, the Hapgoods, the Pratts, and the Troys hev been to see Missis Garvey, and she hev et meals to most of thar houses. The best folks hev axed her to differ'nt kinds of doin's. I cyan't say, Mr. Goree, that sech things suits me—fur me, give me them thar." Garvey's huge yellow-gloved hand flourished in the direction of the mountains. "That's whar I b'long, 'mongst the wild honeybees and the b'ars. But that ain't what I come fur to say, Mr. Goree. Thar's somethin' you got what me and Missis Garvey wants to buy."

"Buy!" echoed Goree. "From me?" Then he laughed hoarsely. "I reckon you are mistaken about that. I sold out to you, as you yourself expressed it, 'lock, stock, and barrel.' There isn't even a ramrod left to sell."

"You've got it; and we 'uns want it. 'Take the money,' says Missis Garvey, 'and buy it fa'r and squa'r.' "

Goree shook his head. "The cupboard's bare," he said.

"We've riz," pursued the mountaineer, undeflected from his object, "a heap. We was pore as possums, and now we could hev folks to dinner every day. We been reco'nized, Missis Garvey says, by the best society. But there's somethin' we need we ain't got. She says it ought to been put in the 'ventory ov the sale, but it 'tain't thar. Take the money, then,' she says, 'and buy it fa'r and squa'r.' "

"Out with it," said Goree, his racked nerves growing impatient.

Garvey threw his slouch hat upon the table and leaned forward, fixing his unblinking eyes upon Goree's.

"There's a old feud," he said, distinctly and slowly, " 'tween you 'uns and the Coltranes."

Goree frowned ominously. To speak of his feud to a feudist is a serious breach of the mountain etiquette. The man from "back yan' " knew it as well as the lawyer did.

"No offense," he went on, "but purely in the way of business. Missis Garvey hev studied all about feuds. Most of the quality folks in the mountains hev 'em. The Settles and the Goforths, the Rankins and the Boyds, the Silers and the Galloways, hev all been cyarin' on feuds from twenty to a hundred year. The last man to drap was when yo' uncle, Judge Paisley Goree, 'journed co't and shot Len Coltrane f'om the bench. Missis Garvey and me, we come f'om the po' white trash. Nobody wouldn't pick a feud with we 'uns, no mo'n with a fam'ly of tree toads. Quality people everywhar, says Missis Garvey, has feuds. We'uns ain't quality, but we're buyin' into it as fur as we can. 'Take the money, then,' says Missis Garvey, 'and buy Mr. Goree's feud, fa'r and squa'r.' "

The squirrel hunter straightened a leg half across the room, drew a roll of bills from his pocket, and threw them on the table.

"Thar's two hundred dollars, Mr. Goree; what you would call a fa'r price for a feud that's been 'lowed to run down like yourn hev. Thar's only you left to cyar' on yo' side of it, and you'd make mighty po' killin. I'll take it off yo' hands, and it'll set me and Missis Garvey up among the quality. Thar's the money."

The little roll of currency on the table slowly untwisted itself, writhing and jumping as its folds relaxed. In the silence that followed Garvey's last speech, the rattling of the Poker chips in the courthouse could be plainly heard. Goree knew that the sheriff had just won a pot, for the subdued whoop with which he always greeted a victory floated across the square upon the crinkly heat waves. Beads of moisture stood on Goree's brow. Stooping, he drew the wicker-covered demijohn from under the table and filled a tumbler from it.

"A little corn liquor, Mr. Garvey? Of course you are joking about—what you spoke of? Opens quite a new market, doesn't it? Feuds, prime, two-fifty to three. Feuds, slightly damaged—two hundred, I believe you said, Mr. Garvey?"

Goree laughed self-consciously.

The mountaineer took the glass Goree handed him and drank the whisky without a tremor of the lids of his staring eyes. The lawyer applauded the feat by a look of envious admiration. He poured his own drink and took it like a drunkard, by gulps, and with shudders at the smell and taste.

"Two hundred," repeated Garvey. "Thar's the money."

A sudden passion flared up in Goree's brain. He struck the table with his fist. One of the bills flipped over and touched his hand. He flinched as if something had stung him.

"Do you come to me," he shouted, "seriously with such a ridiculous, insulting, darned-fool proposition?"

"It's fa'r and squa'r," said the squirrel hunter, but he reached out his hand as if to take back the money; and then Goree knew that his own flurry of rage had not been from pride or resentment, but from anger at himself, knowing that he would set foot in the deeper depths that were being opened to him. He turned in an instant from an outraged gentleman to an anxious chafferer recommending his goods.

"Don't be in a hurry, Garvey," he said, his face crimson and his speech thick. "I accept your p-p-proposition, though it's dirt cheap at two hundred. A trade's all right when both p-purchaser and b-buyer are s-satisfied. Shall I w-wrap it up for you, Mr. Garvey?"

Garvey rose, and shook out his broadcloth. "Missis Garvey will be pleased. You air out of it, and it stands Coltrane and Garvey. Just a scrap of writin', Mr. Goree, you bein' a lawyer, to show we traded."

Goree seized a sheet of paper and a pen. The money was clutched in his moist hand. Everything else suddenly seemed to grow trivial and light.

"Bill of sale, by all means. 'Right, title, and interest in and to' . . . 'forever warrant and——' No, Garvey, we'll have to leave out that 'defend,' " said Goree, with a loud laugh. "You'll have to defend this title yourself."

The mountaineer received the amazing screed that the lawyer handed him, folded it with immense labor, and placed it carefully in his pocket.

Goree was standing near the window. "Step here," he said, raising his finger, "and I'll show you your recently purchased enemy. There he goes, down the other side of the street."

The mountaineer crooked his long frame to look through the window in the direction indicated by the other. Colonel Coltrane, an erect, portly gentleman of about fifty, wearing the inevitable long, double-breasted frock coat of the Southern lawmaker, and an old high silk hat, was passing on the opposite sidewalk. As Garvey looked, Goree glanced at his face. If there be such a thing as a yellow wolf, here was its counterpart. Garvey snarled as his unhuman eyes followed the moving figure, disclosing long amber-colored fangs.

"Is that him? Why, that's the man who sent me to the pen'tentiary once!"

"He used to be district attorney," said Goree, carelessly. "And, by the way, he's a first-class shot."

"I kin hit a squirrel's eye at a hundred yard," said Garvey. "So that thar's Coltrane! I made a better trade than I was thinkin'. I'll take keer of this feud, Mr. Goree, better'n you ever did!"

He moved toward the door, but lingered there, betraying a slight perplexity.

"Anything else today?" inquired Goree, with frothy sarcasm. "Any family traditions, ancestral ghosts, or skeletons in the closet? Prices as low as the lowest."

"Thar was another thing," replied the unmoved squirrel hunter, "that Missis Garvey was thinkin' of. 'Taint so much in my line as t'other, but she wanted partic'lar that I should inquire, and ef you was willin', 'pay fur it,' she says, 'fa'r and squa'r.' Thar's a buryin' groun', as you know, Mr. Goree, in the yard of yo' old place, under the cedars. Them that lies thar is yo' folks what was killed by the Coltranes. The monyments has the names on 'em. Missis Garvey says a fam'ly buryin' groun' is a sho' sign of quality. She says ef we git the feud, thar's somethin' else ought to go with it. The names on them monyments is 'Goree,' but they can be changed to ourn by——"

"Go!" screamed Goree, his face turning purple. He stretched out both hands toward the mountaineer, his fingers hooked and shaking. "Go, you ghoul! Even a Ch-Chinaman protects the graves of his ancestors. —Go."

The squirrel hunter slouched out of the door to his carryall. While he was climbing over the wheel Goree was collecting, with feverish celerity, the money that had fallen from his hand to the floor. As the vehicle slowly turned about, the sheep, with a coat of newly grown wool, was hurrying, in indecent haste, along the path to the courthouse.

At three o'clock in the morning they brought him back to his office, shorn and unconscious. The sheriff, the sportive deputy, the county clerk, and the gay attorney carried him, the chalk-faced man "from the valley" acting as escort.

"On the table," said one of them, and they deposited him there among the litter of his unprofitable books and papers.

"Yance thinks a lot of a pair of deuces when he's liquored up," sighed the sheriff, reflectively.

"Too much," said the gay attorney. "A man had not business to play Poker who drinks as much as he does. I wonder how much he dropped tonight?"

"Close to two hundred. What I wonder is

whar he got it. Yance ain't had a cent fur over a month, I know."

"Struck a client, maybe. Well, let's get home before daylight. He'll be all right when he wakes up, except for a sort of beehive about the cranium."

The gang slipped away through the early morning twilight. The next eye to gaze upon the miserable Goree was the orb of day. He peered through the uncurtained window, first deluging the sleeper in a flood of faint gold, but soon pouring upon the mottled red of his flesh a searching, white, summer heat. Goree stirred, half unconsciously, among the table's debris, and turned his face from the window. His movement dislodged a heavy law book, which crashed upon the floor. Opening his eyes, he saw, bending over him, a man in a black frock coat. Looking higher, he discovered a well-worn silk hat, and beneath it the kindly smooth face of Colonel Abner Coltrane.

A little uncertain of the outcome, the colonel waited for the other to make some sign of recognition. Not in twenty years had male members of these two families faced each other in peace. Goree's eyelids puckered as he strained his blurred sight toward the visitor, and then he smiled serenely.

"Have you brought Stella and Lucy over to play?" he said, calmly.

"Do you know me, Yancey?" asked Coltrane.

"Of course I do. You brought me a whip with a whistle in the end."

So he had—twenty-four years ago, when Yancey's father was his best friend.

Goree's eyes wandered about the room. The colonel understood. "Lie still, and I'll bring you some," said he. There was a pump in the yard at the rear, and Goree closed his eyes, listening with rapture to the click of the handle and the bubbling of the falling stream. Coltrane brought a pitcher of the cool water and held it for him to drink. Presently Goree sat up—a most forlorn object, his summer suit of flax soiled and crumpled, his discreditable head tousled and unsteady. He tried to wave one of his hands toward the colonel.

"Ex-excuse—everything, will you?" he said. "I must have drunk too much whisky last night, and gone to bed on the table." His brows knitted into a puzzled frown.

"Out with the boys a while?" asked Coltrane, kindly.

"No, I went nowhere. I haven't had a dollar to spend in the last two months. Struck the demijohn too often, I reckon, as usual."

Coltrane touched him on the shoulder.

"A little while ago, Yancey," he began, "you asked me if I had brought Stella and Lucy over to play. You weren't quite awake then, and must have been dreaming you were a boy again. You are awake now, and I want you to listen to me. I have come from Stella and Lucy to their old playmate, and to my old friend's son. They know that I am going to bring you home with me, and you will find them as ready with a welcome as they were in the old days. I want you to come to my house and stay until you are yourself again, and as much longer as you will. We heard of your being down in the world, and in the midst of temptation, and we agreed that you should come over and play at our house once more. Will you come, my boy? Will you drop our old family trouble and come with me?"

"Trouble!" said Goree, opening his eyes wide. "There was never any trouble between us that I know of. I'm sure we've always been the best of friends. But, good lord, Colonel, how could I go to your home as I am—a drunken wretch, a miserable, degraded spendthrift and gambler—"

He lurched from the table to his armchair, and began to weep maudlin tears, mingled with genuine drops of remorse and shame. Coltrane talked to him persistently and reasonably, reminding him of the simple mountain pleasures of which he had once been so fond, and insisting upon the genuineness of the invitation.

Finally he landed Goree by telling him he was counting upon his help in the engineering and transportation of a large amount of felled timber from a high mountainside to a waterway. He knew that Goree had once invented a device for this purpose—a series of slides and chutes—upon which he had justly prided himself. In an instant the poor fellow, delighted at the idea of his being of use to anyone, had paper spread upon the table, and was drawing rapid but pitifully shaky lines in demonstration of what he could and would do.

The man was sickened of the husks; his prodigal heart was turning again toward the mountains. His mind was yet strangely clogged, and his thoughts and memories were returning to his brain one by one, like carrier pigeons over a stormy sea. But Coltrane was satisfied with the progress he had made.

Bethel received the surprise of its existence that afternoon when a Coltrane and a Goree rode amicably together through the town. Side by side they rode, out from the dusty streets and gaping townspeople, down across the creek bridge, and up toward the mountain. The prodigal had brushed and washed and combed himself to a more decent figure, but he was unsteady in the saddle, and he seemed to be deep in the contemplation of some vexing problem. Coltrane left him in his mood, relying upon the influence of changed surroundings to restore his equilibrium.

Once Goree was seized with a shaking fit, and almost came to a collapse. He had to dismount and rest at the side of the road. The colonel, foreseeing such a condition, had provided a small flask of whisky for the journey, but when it was offered to him Goree refused it almost with violence, declaring he would never touch it again. By and by he recovered and went quietly enough for a mile or two. Then he pulled up his horse suddenly and said:

"I lost two hundred dollars last night, playing Poker. Now, where did I get that money?"

"Take it easy, Yancey. The mountain air will soon clear it up. We'll go fishing, first thing, at the Pinnacle Falls. The trout are jumping there like bullfrogs. We'll take Stella and Lucy along and have a picnic on Eagle Rock. Have you forgotten how a hickory-cured ham sandwich tastes, Yancey, to a hungry fisherman?"

Evidently the colonel did not believe the story of his lost wealth; so Goree retired again into brooding silence.

By late afternoon they had traveled ten of the twelve miles between Bethel and Laurel. Half a mile this side of Laurel lay the old Goree place; a mile or two beyond the village lived the Coltranes. The road was now steep and laborious, but the compensations were manv The tilted aisles of the forest were opulent with leaf and bird and bloom. The tonic air put to shame the pharmacopaeia. The glades were dark with mossy shade, and bright with shy rivulets winking from the ferns and laurels. On the lower side they viewed, framed in the near foliage, exquisite sketches of the far valley swooning in its opal haze.

Coltrane was pleased to see that his companion was yielding to the spell of the hills and woods. For now they had but to skirt the base of Painter's Cliff; to cross Elder Branch and mount the hill beyond; and Goree would have to face the squandered home of his fathers. Every rock he passed, every tree, every foot of the roadway, was familiar to him. Though he had forgotten the woods, they thrilled him like the music of "Home, Sweet Home."

They rounded the cliff, descended into Elder Branch, and paused there to let the horses drink and splash in the swift water. On the right there was a rail fence that cornered there and followed the road and stream. Inclosed by it was the old apple orchard of the home place; the house was yet concealed by the brow of the steep hill. Inside and along the fence, pokeberries, elders, sassafras, and sumac grew high and dense. At a rustle of their branches, both Goree and Coltrane glanced up, and saw a long, yellow, wolfish face above the fence, staring at them with pale, unwinking eyes. The head quickly disappeared; there was a violent swaying of the bushes, and an ungainly figure ran up through the apple orchard in the direction of the house, zigzagging among the trees.

"That's Garvey," said Coltrane; "the man you sold out to. There's no doubt but he's considerably cracked. I had to send him up for moonshining once, several years ago, in spite of the fact that I believed him irresponsible. Why, what's the matter, Yancey?"

Goree was wiping his forehead, and his face had lost its color. "Do I look queer, too?" he asked, trying to smile. "I'm just remembering a few more things." Some of the alcohol had evaporated from his brain. "I recollect now where I got that two hundred dollars."

"Don't think of it," said Coltrane, cheerfully. "Later on we'll figure it all out together."

They rode out of the branch, and when they reached the foot of the hill Goree stopped again.

"Did you ever suspect I was a very vain kind of fellow, Colonel?" he asked. "Sort of foolish proud about appearances?"

The colonel's eyes refused to wander to the soiled, sagging suit of flax and the faded slouch hat.

"It seems to me," he replied, mystified, but humoring him, "I remember a young buck about twenty, with the tightest coat, the sleekest hair, and the prancingest saddle horse in the Blue Ridge."

"Right you are," said Goree, eagerly. "And it's in me yet, though it don't show. Oh, I'm as vain as a turkey gobbler, and as proud as Lucifer. I'm going to ask you to indulge this weakness of mine in a little matter."

"Speak out, Yancey. We'll create you Duke of Laurel and Baron of Blue Ridge, if you choose; and you shall have a feather out of Stella's peacock's tail to wear in your hat."

"I'm in earnest. In a few minutes we'll pass the house up there on the hill where I was born, and where my people lived for nearly a century. Strangers live there now—and look at me! I am about to show myself to them ragged and poverty-stricken, a wastrel and a beggar. Colonel Coltrane, I'm ashamed to do it. I want you to let me wear your coat and hat until we are out of sight beyond. I know you think it a foolish pride, but I want to make as good a showing as I can when I pass the old place."

"Now, what does this mean?" said Coltrane to himself, as he compared his companion's sane looks and quiet demeanor with his strange request. But he was already unbuttoning the coat, assenting readily, as if the fancy were in nowise to be considered strange.

The coat and hat fitted Goree well. He buttoned the former about him with a look of satisfaction and dignity. He and Coltrane were nearly the same size—rather tall, portly, and erect. Twenty-five years were between them, but in appearance they might have been brothers. Goree looked older than his age; his face was puffy and lined; the colonel had the smooth, fresh complexion of a temperate liver. He put on Goree's disreputable old flax coat and faded slouch hat.

"Now," said Goree, taking up the reins. "I'm all right. I want you to ride about ten feet in the rear as we go by, Colonel, so that they can get a good look at me. They'll see I'm no back number yet, by any means. I guess I'll show up pretty well to them once more, anyhow. Let's ride on."

He set out up the hill at a smart trot, the colonel following as he had been requested.

Goree sat straight in the saddle, with head erect, but his eyes were turned to the right, sharply scanning every shrub and fence and hiding-place in the old homestead yard. Once he muttered to himself, "Will the crazy fool try it, or did I dream half of it?"

It was when he came opposite the little family burying ground that he saw what he had been looking for—a puff of white smoke, coming from the thick cedars in one corner. He toppled so slowly to the left that Coltrane had time to urge his horse to that side, and catch him with one arm.

The squirrel hunter had not overpraised his aim. He had sent the bullet where he intended, and where Goree had expected that it would pass—through the breast of Colonel Abner Coltrane's black frock coat.

Goree leaned heavily against Coltrane, but he did not fall. The horses kept pace, side by side, and the colonel's arm kept him steady. The little white houses on Laurel shone through the trees, half a mile away. Goree reached out one hand and groped until it rested upon Coltrane's fingers, which held his bridle.

"Good friend," he said, and that was all.

Thus did Yancey Goree, as he rode past his old home, make, considering all things, the best showing that was in his power.

¶*[In this story Poker gives Leslie Charteris the theme for as good a Saint story as ever he wrote, with a double (no, a triple) twist at the finish. We fear that it was stretching too far to have a man "with only a pair of sevens bluff recklessly for a couple of rounds"; a man may bet recklessly but he never bluffs recklessly, and even for a fall guy one bluff per hand is par for the course. But everyone plays badly now and then, while we don't know anyone who ever wrote a better Poker story than this one.*

The Mug's Game

by LESLIE CHARTERIS

THE STOUT jovial gentleman in the shapeless suit pulled a card out of his wallet and pushed it across the table. The printing on it said:

MR. J. J. NASKILL.

The Saint looked at it, and offered his cigarette case.

"I'm afraid I don't carry any cards," he said. "But my name is Simon Templar."

Mr. Naskill beamed, held out a large moist hand to be shaken, took a cigarette, mopped his glistening forehead, and beamed again.

"Well, it's a pleasure to talk to you, Mr. Templar," he said heartily. "I get bored with my own company on these long journeys, and it hurts my eyes to read on a train. Hate traveling, anyway. It's a good thing my business keeps me in one place most of the time. What's your job, by the way?"

Simon took a pull at his cigarette while he gave a moment's consideration to his answer. It was one of the few questions that ever embarrassed him. It wasn't that he had any real objection to telling the truth, but that the truth tended to disturb the tranquil flow of ordinary casual conversation.

Without causing a certain amount of commotion, he couldn't say to a perfect stranger:

"I'm a sort of benevolent brigand. I raise hell for crooks and racketeers of all kinds, and make life miserable for policemen, and rescue damsels in distress, and all that sort of thing."

The Saint had often thought of it as a deplorable commentary on the stodgy unadventurousness of the average mortal's mind, but he knew that it was beyond his power to alter.

He said apologetically, "I'm just one of those lazy people. I believe they call it 'independent means.'"

That was true enough for an idle moment. The Saint could have exhibited a bank account that would have dazzled many men who called themselves wealthy, but it was on the subject of how that wealth had been accumulated that several persons who lived by what they had previously called their wits were inclined to wax profane.

Mr. Naskill sighed.

"I don't blame you," he said. "Why work if you don't have to? Wish I was in your shoes myself. Wasn't born lucky, that's all. Still, I've got a good business now, so I shouldn't complain. Expect you recognize the name."

"Naskill?" The Saint frowned slightly. When he repeated it, it did have a faintly familiar ring. "It sounds as if I ought to know it——"

The other nodded.

"Some people call it 'No-skill,'" he said. "They're about right, too. That's what it is. Magic for amateurs. Look."

He flicked a card out of his pocket on to the table between them. It was the ace of diamonds. He turned it over and immediately faced it again. It was the nine of clubs. He turned it over again, and it was the queen of hearts.

He left it lying face down on the cloth, and Simon picked it up curiously and examined it. It was the three of spades, but there was nothing else remarkable about it.

"Used to be a conjuror, myself," Naskill explained. "Then I got rheumatism in my hands, and I was on the rocks. Didn't know any other job, so I had to make a living teaching other people tricks.

"Most of 'em haven't the patience to practice sleight of hand, so I made it easy for 'em. Got a fine trade now, and a two-hundred-page catalogue. I can make anybody into just as good a magician as the money they like to spend, and they needn't practice for five minutes. Look."

He took the card that the Saint was still holding, tore it into small pieces, folded his plump fingers on them for a moment and spread out his hands—empty. Then he broke open the cigarette he was smoking, and inside it was a three of spades rolled into a tight cylinder, crumpled but intact.

"You can buy that for a dollar and a half," he said. "The first one I showed you is two dollars. It's daylight robbery, really, but some people like to show off at parties, and they give me a living."

Simon slid back his sleeve from his wrist watch, and glanced out of the window at the speeding landscape. There was still about an hour to go before they would be in Miami, and he had nothing else to take up his time.

Besides, Mr. Naskill was something novel and interesting in his experience, and it was part of the Saint's creed that a modern brigand could never know too much about the queerer things that went on in the world.

He caught the eye of the waiter at the other end of the dining car, and beckoned him over.

"Could you stand a drink?" he suggested.

"Scotch for me," said Mr. Naskill gratefully. He wiped his face again while Simon duplicated the order. "But I'm still talking about myself. If I'm boring you——"

"Not a bit of it." The Saint was perfectly sincere. "I don't often meet anyone with an unusual job like yours. Do you know any more tricks?"

Mr. Naskill polished a pair of horn-rimmed spectacles, fitted them on his nose and hitched himself forward.

"Look," he said eagerly.

He was like a child with a new collection of toys. He dug into another of his sagging pockets, which Simon was now deciding were probably loaded with enough portable equipment to stage a complete show, and hauled out a pack of cards which he pushed over to the Saint.

"You take 'em. Look 'em over as much as you like. See if you can find anything wrong with 'em.

"All right. Now shuffle 'em. Shuffle 'em all you want."

He waited.

"Now spread 'em out on the table. You're doing this trick, not me. Take any card you like. Look at it—don't let me see it.

"All right. Now, I haven't touched the cards at all, have I, except to give 'em to you? You shuffled 'em, and you picked a card without me helping you. I couldn't have forced it on you or anything. Eh? All right.

"Well, I could put any trimmings I wanted on this trick—any fancy stunts I could think up to make it look more mysterious. They'd all be easy because I know what card you've got all the time. You've got the six of diamonds."

Simon turned the card over. It was the six of diamonds.

"How's that?" Naskill demanded gleefully.

The Saint grinned. He drew a handful of cards toward him, face downward as they lay, and pored over the backs for two or three minutes before he sat back again with a rueful shrug.

Mr. Naskill chortled.

"There's nothing wrong with your eyes," he said. "You could go over 'em with a microscope, and not find anything. All the same, I'll tell you what you've got. The king of spades, the two of spades, the ten of hearts——"

"I'll take your word for it," said the Saint resignedly, "but how on earth do you do it?"

Naskill glowed delightedly.

"Look," he said.

He took off his glasses and passed them over. Under the flat lenses, Simon could see the notations clearly printed in the corners of each card —KS, 2S, 10H. They vanished as soon as he moved the glasses, and it was impossible to find a trace of them with the naked eye.

"I've heard of that being done with colored glasses," said the Saint slowly, "but I noticed yours weren't colored."

Naskill shook his head.

"Colored glasses are old stuff. Too crude. Used to be used a lot by sharpers but too many people got to hear about 'em. You couldn't get into a card game with colored glasses these days. No good for conjuring, either.

"But this is good. Invented it myself. Special ink, and special kind of glass. There is a tint in it, of course, but it's too faint to notice."

He shoved the cards over the cloth.

"Here, keep the lot for a souvenir. You can have some fun with your friends. But don't go asking 'em in for a game of Poker, mind."

Simon gathered the cards together.

"It would be rather a temptation," he admitted. "But don't you get a lot of customers who buy them just for that?"

"Sure. A lot of professionals use my stuff. I know 'em all. Often see 'em in the shop. Good customers—they buy by the dozen. Can't refuse to serve 'em—they'd only get 'em some other way, or buy somewhere else.

"I call it a compliment to the goods I sell. Never bothers my conscience. Anybody who plays cards with strangers is asking for trouble, anyway. It isn't only professionals, either. You'd be surprised at some of the people I've had come in and ask for a deck of 'readers'—that's the trade name for 'em. I remember one fellow . . ."

He launched into a series of anecdotes that filled up the time until they had to separate to their compartments to collect their luggage. Mr. Naskill's pining for company was understandable after only a few minutes' acquaintance. It was clear that he was constitutionally incapable of surviving for long without an audience.

Simon Templar was not bored. He had already had his money's worth. Whether his friends would allow him to get very far with a program of card tricks if he appeared before them in an unaccustomed set of horn-rimmed glasses was highly doubtful, but the trick was worth knowing, just the same.

Almost every kind of craftsman has specialized journals to inform him of the latest inventions and discoveries and technical advances in his trade, but there is as yet no publication called *The Grafter's Gazette and Weekly Skulldugger* to keep a professional freebooter abreast of the newest devices for separating the sucker from his dough.

Mr. Naskill's conversation had yielded a scrap of information that would be filed away in the Saint's well-stocked memory against the day when it would be useful. It might lie fallow for a month, a year, five years, before it produced its harvest. The Saint was in no hurry. In the fullness of time, he would collect his dividend—it was one of the cardinal articles of his faith that nothing of that kind ever crossed his path without a rendezvous for the future, however distant that future might be. But one of the things that always gave the Saint a particular affection for this story was the promptness with which his expectations were fulfilled.

There were some episodes in Simon Templar's life when all the component parts of a perfectly rounded diagram fell into place one by one with such a sweetly definitive succession of crisp clicks that mere coincidence was too pallid and anemic a theory with which to account for them —when he almost felt as if he were reclining passively in an armchair, and watching the oiled wheels of Fate roll smoothly through the convolutions of a supernaturally engineered machine.

Two days later, he was relaxing his long lean body on the private beach of the Roney Plaza, reveling in the sharp clean bite of the sun on his brown skin, and lazily debating the comparative attractions of iced beer or a tinkling highball as a noon refresher, when two voices reached him sufficiently clearly to force themselves into his drowsy consciousness.

They belonged to a man and a girl, and it was obvious that they were quarreling.

Simon wasn't interested. He was at peace with the world. He concentrated on digging up a small sand castle with his toes, and tried to shut them out. And then he heard the girl say:

"My God, are you so dumb that you can't see that they must be crooks?"

It was the word "crooks" that did it.

When the Saint heard that word, he could no more have concentrated on sand castles than a rabid Egyptologist could have remained aloof while gossip of scarabs and sarcophagi shuttled across his head.

A private squabble was one thing, but this was something else that to the Saint made eavesdropping not only pardonable, but almost a moral obligation.

He rolled over and looked at the girl. She was only a few feet from him, and even at that range it was easier to go on looking than to look away. From her loose raven hair down to her daintily enameled toenails there wasn't an inch of her that didn't make its own demoralizing demands on the eye, and the clinging silk swimsuit she wore left very few inches any secrets.

"Why must they be crooks?" asked the man stubbornly. He was young and tow-headed, but the Saint's keen survey traced hard and haggard lines in his face. "Just because I've been out of luck——"

"Luck!" The girl's voice was scornful and impatient. "You were out of luck when you met them. Two men that you know nothing about, who pick you up in a bar and suddenly discover that you're the bosom pal they've been looking for all their lives—who want to take you out to dinner every night, and take you out fishing every day, and buy you drinks and show you the town—and you talk about luck!

"D'you think they'd do all that if they didn't know they could get you to play cards with them every night, and make you lose enough to pay them back a hundred times over?"

"I won plenty from them to begin with."

"Of course you did! They let you win—just to encourage you to play higher. And now you've lost all that back, and a lot more that you can't afford to lose. And you're still going on, making it worse and worse."

She caught his arm impulsively, and her voice softened.

"Oh, Eddie, I hate fighting with you like this, but can't you see what a fool you're being?"

"Well, why don't you leave me alone if you hate fighting? Anyone might think I was a kid straight out of school."

He shrugged himself angrily away from her, and as he turned he looked straight into the Saint's eyes. Simon was so interested that the movement caught him unprepared, still watching them as if he had been hiding behind a curtain, and it had been abruptly torn down.

It was so much too late for Simon to switch his eyes away without looking even guiltier that he had to go on watching, and the young man went on scowling at him, and said uncomfortably:

"We aren't really going to cut each other's throats, but there are some things that women can't understand."

"If a man told him that elephants lay eggs, he'd believe it, just because it was a man who told him," said the girl petulantly, and she also looked at the Saint. "Perhaps if *you* told him——"

"The trouble is, she won't give me credit for having any sense——"

"He's such a baby——"

"If she didn't read so many detective stories——"

"He's so damned pig-headed——"

The Saint held up his hands.

"Wait a minute," he pleaded. "Don't shoot the referee—he doesn't know what it's all about. I couldn't help hearing what you were saying, but it isn't my fight."

The young man rubbed his head shamefacedly, and the girl bit her lip.

Then she said quickly: "Well, please, won't you *be* a referee? Perhaps he'd listen to you. He's lost fifteen thousand dollars already, and it isn't all his own money——"

"For God's sake," the man burst out savagely, "are you trying to make me look like a complete heel?"

The girl caught her breath, and her lip trembled. And then, with a sort of sob, she picked herself up and walked away quickly without another word.

The young man gazed after her in silence, and his fist clenched on a handful of sand as if he would have liked to hurt it.

"Oh, hell," he said expressively.

Simon drew a cigarette out of the packet beside him and tapped it meditatively on his thumbnail while the awkward hiatus made itself at home. His eyes seemed to be intent on following the movements of a small fishing cruiser far out on the emerald waters of the Gulf Stream.

"It's none of my damn business," he remarked at length, "but isn't there just a chance that the girl friend might be right? It's happened before, and a resort like this is rather a happy hunting ground for all kinds of crooks."

"I know it is," said the other sourly. He turned and looked at the Saint again miserably. "But I *am* pig-headed, and I can't bear to admit to her that I could have been such a mug. She's my fiancée—I suppose you guessed that. My name's Mercer."

"Simon Templar is mine."

The name had a significance for Mercer that it apparently had not had for Mr. Naskill. His eyes opened wide.

"Good God, you don't mean— You're not the Saint?"

Simon smiled. He was still immodest enough to enjoy the sensation that his name could sometimes cause.

"That's what they call me."

"Of course I've read about you, but—well, it sort of . . ." The young man petered out incoherently. "And I'd have argued with you about crooks! But—well, you ought to know. Do *you* think I've been a mug?"

The Saint's brows slanted sympathetically.

"If you took my advice," he answered, "you'd let those birds find someone else to play with. Write it off to experience, and don't do it again."

"But I can't!" Mercer's response was desperate. "She—she was telling the truth. I've lost money that wasn't mine. I've only got a job in an advertising agency that doesn't pay very much, but her people are pretty well off.

"They've found me a better job here, starting in a couple of months, and they sent us down here to find a home, and they gave us twenty thousand dollars to buy it and furnish it, and that's the money I've been playing with. Don't you see?

"I've *got* to go on and win it back!"

"Or go on and lose the rest."

"Oh, I know. But I thought the luck must change before that. And yet—but everybody who plays cards isn't a crook, is he? And I don't see how they could have done it. After she started talking about it, I watched them. I've been looking for it. And I couldn't catch them making a single move that wasn't aboveboard.

"Then I began to think about marked cards—we've always played with their cards. I sneaked away one of the packs we were using last night, and I've been looking at it this morning. I'll swear there isn't a mark on it. Here, I can show you."

He fumbled feverishly in a pocket of his beach robe, and pulled out a pack of cards. Simon glanced through them. There was nothing wrong with them that he could see—and it was then that he remembered Mr. J. J. Naskill.

"Does either of these birds wear glasses?" he asked.

"One of them wears pince-nez," replied the mystified young man. "But——"

"I'm afraid," said the Saint thoughtfully, "that it looks as if you are a mug."

Mercer swallowed.

"If I am," he said helplessly, "what on earth am I going to do?"

Simon hitched himself up.

"Personally, I'm going to have a dip in the pool. And you're going to be so busy apologizing to your fiancée, and making friends again, that you won't have time to think about anything else. I'll keep these cards and make sure about them. Then suppose we meet in the bar for a cocktail about six o'clock, and maybe I'll be able to tell you something."

When he returned to his own room, the Saint put on Mr. Naskill's horn-rimmed glasses and examined the cards again. Every one of them was clearly marked in the diagonally opposite corners with the value of the card and the initial of the suit, exactly like the one Naskill had given him. And it was then that the Saint knew that his faith in destiny was justified again.

Shortly after six o'clock, he strolled into the bar and saw that Mercer and the girl were already there. It was clear that they had buried their quarrel.

Mercer introduced her.

"Miss Grange—or you can just call her Josephine."

She said: "We're both ashamed of ourselves for having a scene in front of you this afternoon, but I'm glad we did. You've done Eddie a lot of good."

"I hadn't any right to blurt out all my troubles like that," Mercer said sheepishly. "You were damned nice about it."

The Saint grinned.

"I'm a pretty nice guy," he murmured. "And now I've got something to show you. Here are your cards."

He spread the deck out on the table, and then he took the horn-rimmed glasses out of his pocket and held them over the cards so that the other two could look through them. He slid the cards under the lenses one by one, face downwards, and turned them over afterwards, and for a little while, they stared in breathless silence.

The girl gasped.

"I told you so!"

Mercer's fists clenched.

"By God, if I don't murder those——"

She caught his wrists as he almost jumped from the table.

"Eddie, that won't do you any good."

"It won't do them any good, either! When I've finished with them——"

"But that won't get any of the money back."

"I'll beat it out of them!"

"But that'll only get you in trouble with the police. That wouldn't help. Wait!"

She clung to him frantically.

"I've got it. You could borrow Mr. Templar's glasses, and play them at their own game. You could break Yoring's glasses—sort of accidentally. They wouldn't dare stop playing on account of that. They'd just have to trust to luck—like you've been doing, and anyway, they'd feel sure they were going to get it all back later.

"And you could win everything back and never see them again." She shook his arm in her excitement. "Go on, Eddie. It'd serve them right. I'll let you play just once more if you'll do that!"

Mercer's eyes turned to the Saint, and Simon pushed the glasses across the table to him.

The young man picked them up slowly, looked at the cards through them again. His mouth twitched. And then, with a sudden hopeless gesture, he thrust them away and passed a shaky hand over his eyes.

"It's no good," he said wretchedly. "I couldn't do it. They know I don't wear glasses. And I—I've never done anything like that before. I'd only make a mess of it. They'd spot me in five minutes. And then there wouldn't be anything I could say. I—I wouldn't have the nerve. I suppose I'm just a mug after all——"

The Saint leaned back and put a light to a cigarette. In all his life he had never missed a cue, and it seemed that this was very much like a cue. He had come to Miami to bask in the sun and be good, but it wasn't his fault if business was thrust upon him.

"Maybe someone with a bit of experience could do it better," he said. "Suppose you let me meet your friends."

Mercer looked at him, first blankly, then incredulously. And the girl's dark eyes slowly lighted up.

Her slim fingers reached impetuously for the Saint's hand.

"You wouldn't really do that—help Eddie win back what he's lost——"

"What would you expect Robin Hood to do?" asked the Saint quizzically. "I've got a reputation to keep up—and I might even pay my expenses while I'm doing it." He drew the revealing glasses toward him and tucked them back in his pocket. "Let's go and have some dinner, and organize the details."

But actually, there were hardly any details left to organize, for Josephine Grange's inspiration had been practically complete in its first outline.

He felt like a star actor waiting for the curtain to rise on the third act of an obviously triumphant first night when they left the girl at the Roney Plaza and walked over to the Riptide. "That's where we usually meet," Mercer explained. And a few minutes later, he was being introduced to the other two members of the cast.

Mr. Yoring, who wore the pince-nez, was a small, pear-shaped man in a crumpled linen suit, with white hair and bloodhound jowls and a pathetically frustrated expression. He looked like a retired businessman whose wife took him to the opera.

Mr. Kilgarry, his partner, was somewhat taller and younger, with a wide mouth and a rich nose and a raffish manner. He looked like the kind of man that men like Mr. Yoring wish they could be. Both of them welcomed Mercer with an exuberant bonhomie that was readily expanded to include the Saint.

Mr. Kilgarry ordered a round of drinks.

"Having a good time here, Mr. Templar?"

"Pretty good."

"Aren't we all having a good time?" crowed Mr. Yoring. "I'm gonna buy a drink."

"I've just ordered a drink," said Mr. Kilgarry.

"Well, I'm gonna order another," said Mr. Yoring defiantly. No wife was going to take him to the opera tonight. "Who said there was a depression? What do you think, Mr. Templar?"

"I haven't found any in my affairs lately," Simon answered truthfully.

"You in business, Mr. Templar?" asked Mr. Kilgarry interestedly.

The Saint smiled.

"My business is letting other people make money for me," he said, continuing strictly in the vein of truth. He patted his pockets significantly. "The market's been doing pretty well these days."

Mr. Kilgarry and Mr. Yoring exchanged glances, while the Saint picked up his drink. It wasn't his fault if they misunderstood him. But it had been rather obvious that the conversation was doomed to launch some tactful feelers into his financial status, and Simon saw no need to add to their coming troubles by making them work hard for their information.

"Well, that's fine," said Mr. Yoring, happily. "I'm gonna buy another drink."

"You can't," said Mr. Kilgarry. "It's my turn."

Mr. Yoring looked wistful, like a small boy who has been told that he can't go out and play with his new air gun. Then he wrapped an arm around Mercer's shoulders.

"You gonna play tonight, Eddie?"

"I don't know," Mercer said hesitantly. "I've just been having some dinner with Mr. Templar——"

"Bring him along," boomed Mr. Kilgarry heartily. "What's the difference? Four's better than three, any day. D'you play cards, Mr. Templar?"

"Most games," said the Saint cheerfully.

"That's fine," said Mr. Kilgarry. "Fine," he repeated, as if he wanted to leave no doubt that it was fine.

Mr. Yoring looked dubious.

"I dunno. We play rather high stakes, Mr. Templar."

"They can't be too high for me," said the Saint boastfully.

"Fine," said Mr. Kilgarry again, removing the last vestige of uncertainty about his personal opinion. "Then that's settled. What's holding us back?"

There was really nothing holding them back except the drinks that were lined up on the bar, and that deterrent was eliminated with a discreetly persuasive briskness.

Under Mr. Kilgarry's breezy leadership, they piled into a taxi and headed for one of the smaller hotels on Ocean Drive, where Mr. Yoring proclaimed that he had a bottle of Scotch that would save them from the agonies of thirst while they were playing. As they rode up in the elevator he hooked his arm affectionately through the Saint's.

"Say, you're awright, ole man," he announced. "I like to meet a young feller like you. You oughta come out fishing with us. Got our own boat here, hired for the season, and we just take out fellers we like. You like fishin'?"

"I like catching sharks," said the Saint with unblinking innocence.

"You ought to come out with us," said Mr. Kilgarry hospitably.

The room was large and comfortable. In the center was a card table already set up, looking as if it belonged there. There were bottles and a pail of ice on a pea-green and old-rose butterfly table.

Mr. Kilgarry brought up chairs, and Mr. Yoring patted Mercer on the shoulder.

"You fix a drink, Eddie," he said. "Let's all make ourselves at home."

He lowered himself into a place at the table, took off his pince-nez, breathed on them and began to polish them with his handkerchief.

Mercer's tense gaze caught the Saint's for an instant. Simon nodded imperceptibly and settled his own glasses more firmly on the bridge of his nose.

"How's the luck going to be tonight, Eddie?" chaffed Kilgarry, opening two new decks of cards, and spilling them on the cloth.

"You'll be surprised," retorted the young man. "I'm going to give you two gasbags a beautiful beating tonight."

"Attaboy," chirped Yoring encouragingly.

Simon had taken one glance at the cards, and that had been enough to assure him that Mr. Naskill would have been proud to claim them as his product.

After that, he had been watching Mercer's back as he worked over the drinks. Yoring was still polishing his pince-nez when Mercer turned to the table with a glass in each hand. He put one glass down beside Yoring, and as he reached over to place the other glass in front of the Saint, the cuff of his coat sleeve flicked the pince-nez out of Yoring's fingers and sent them spinning.

The Saint made a dive to catch them, missed, stumbled, and brought his heel down on the exact spot where they were in the act of hitting the carpet. There was a dull crunching sound, and after that, there was a thick and stifling silence.

Yoring blinked as if he were going to burst into tears.

"I'm terribly sorry," said the Saint.

He bent down to gather up some of the debris. Only the gold bridge of the pince-nez remained in one piece, and that was bent. He put it on the table, started to collect the scraps of glass and then gave up the hopeless task.

"I'll pay for them, of course," he said.

"I'll split it with you," Mercer said. "It was my fault. We'll take it out of my winnings."

Yoring looked from one to another with watery eyes.

"I—I don't think I can play without my glasses," he mumbled.

Mercer flopped into the vacant chair and raked in the cards.

"Come on," he said callously. "It isn't as bad as all that. You can show us your hand and we'll tell you what you've got."

"Can't you manage?" urged the Saint. "I was going to enjoy this game, and it won't be nearly so much fun with only three."

The silence came back, thicker than before. Yoring's eyes shifted despairingly from side to side. And then Kilgarry crushed his cigar violently into an ash tray.

"You can't back out now," he said, and there was an audible growl in the fruity tones of his voice. "Straight Poker—with the joker wild. Let's go."

To Simon Templar, the game had the same dizzy unreality that it would have had if he had been supernaturally endowed with a genuine gift of clairvoyance. He knew the value of every card as it was dealt, knew what was in his own hand before he picked it up.

Even though there was nothing mysterious about it, the effect of the glasses he was wearing gave him a sensation of weirdness that was too instinctive to overcome. It was mechanically childish, and yet it was an unforgettable experience. When he was out of the game, watching the others bet against each other, it was like being a cat watching two blind men looking for each other in the dark.

For nearly an hour, curiously enough, the play was fairly even. When he counted his chips he had only a couple of hundred dollars more than when he started.

Mercer, throwing in his hand whenever the Saint warned him by a pressure of his foot under the table that the opposition was too strong, had done slightly better. But there was nothing sensational in their advantage.

Even Mr. Naskill's magic lenses had no influence over the run of the cards, and the luck of the deals slightly favored Yoring and Kilgarry. The Saint's clairoyant knowledge saved him from making any disastrous errors, but now and again he had to bet out a hopeless hand to avoid giving too crude an impression of infallibility.

He played a steadily aggressive game, waiting patiently for the change that he knew must come as soon as the basis of the play had had time to settle down and establish itself. His nerves were cool and serene, and he smiled often with an air of faint amusement. But something inside him was poised and gathered like a panther crouched for a spring.

Presently Kilgarry called Mercer on the third raise, and lost a small jackpot to three nines. Mercer scowled as he stacked the handful of chips.

"Hell, what's the matter with this game?" he protested. "This isn't the way we usually play. Let's get some life into it."

"It does seem a bit slow," Simon agreed. "How about raising the ante?"

"Make it a hundred dollars," Mercer said sharply. "I'm getting tired of this. Just because my luck's changed, we don't have to start playing for peanuts."

Simon drew his cigarette to a bright glow.

"It suits me."

Yoring plucked at his lower lip with fingers that were still shaky.

"I dunno, ole man—"

"O.K." Kilgarry pushed out two fifty-dollar chips with a kind of fierce restraint. "I'll play for a hundred."

He had been playing all the time with grim concentration, his shoulders hunched as if he had to give some outlet to a seethe of violence in his muscles, his jaw thrust out and tightly clamped. And as the time went by, he seemed to have been regaining confidence. "Maybe the game is on the level," was the idea expressed by every line of his body, "but I can still take a couple of mugs like this in any game."

He said, almost with a resumption of his former heartiness:

"Are you staying long, Mr. Templar?"

"I expect I'll be here for quite a while."

"That's fine! Then after Mr. Yoring's got some new glasses, we might have a better game."

"I shouldn't be surprised," said the Saint amiably.

He was holding two pairs. He took a card, and still had two pairs. Kilgarry stood pat on three kings. Mercer drew three cards to a pair, and was no better off afterwards. Yoring took two cards and filled a flush.

"One hundred," said Yoring nervously.

Mercer hesitated, threw in his hand.

"And two hundred," snapped Kilgarry.

"And five," said the Saint.

Yoring looked at them blearily. He took a long time to make up his mind. And then, with a sigh, he pushed his hand into the discard.

"See you," said Kilgarry.

With a wry grin, the Saint faced his hand. Kilgarry grinned also, with a sudden triumph, and faced his.

Yoring made a noise like a faint groan.

"Fix us another drink, Eddie," he said, huskily.

He took the pack and shuffled it clumsily. His fingers were like sausages strung together. Kilgarry's mouth opened on one side, and he nudged the Saint as he made the cut.

"Lost his nerve," he said. "See what happens when they get old?"

"Who's old?" said Mr. Yoring plaintively. "There ain't more'n three years—"

"But you've got old ideas," Kilgarry jeered. "You could have beaten both of us."

"You never had to wear glasses—"

"Who said you wanted glasses to play Poker?

It isn't always the cards that win," said Kilgarry. He was smiling, but his eyes were almost glaring at Yoring as he spoke. Yoring avoided his gaze guiltily and squinted at the hand he had dealt himself. It contained the six, seven, eight and nine of diamonds, and the queen of spades.

Simon held two pairs again, but the card he drew made it a full house.

He watched while Yoring discarded the queen of spades, and felt again that sensation of supernatural omniscience as he saw that the top card of the pack, the card Yoring had to take, was the ten of hearts.

Yoring took it, fumbled his hand to the edge of the table, and turned up the corners to peep at them. For a second, he sat quite still, with only his mouth working. And then, as if the accumulation of all his misfortunes had at last stung him to a wild and fearful reaction like the turning of a worm, a change seemed to come over him. He let the cards flatten out again with a defiant click and drew himself up. He began to count off hundred-dollar chips.

Mercer, with only a pair of sevens, bluffed recklessly for two rounds before he fell out in response to the Saint's kick under the table.

There were five thousand dollars in the pot before Kilgarry, with a straight, shrugged surrenderingly, and dropped his hand in the discard.

The Saint counted two stacks of chips and pushed them in.

"Make it another two grand," he said.

Yoring looked at him waveringly. Then he pushed in two stacks of his own. "There's your two grand." He counted the chips he had left, and swept them with a sudden splash into the pile. "And twenty-nine hundred more," he said.

Simon had twelve hundred left in chips. He pushed them in, opened his wallet, and added crisp new bills.

"Making three thousand more than that for you to see me," he said coolly.

Mercer sucked in his breath and whispered: "Oh, boy!"

Kilgarry said nothing, hunching tensely over the table.

Yoring blinked at him.

"Len' me some chips, ole man."

"Do you know what you're doing?" Kilgarry asked in a harsh, strained voice.

Yoring picked up his glass, and half emptied it. His hand wobbled so that some of it ran down his chin.

"I know," he snapped.

He reached out and raked Kilgarry's chips into the pile.

"Eighteen hunnerd," he said. "I gotta buy some more. I'll write you a check——"

Simon shook his head.

"I'm sorry," he said quietly. "I'm playing table stakes. We agreed on that when we started."

Yoring peered at him.

"You meanin' something insultin' about my check?"

"I don't mean that," Simon replied evenly. "It's just a matter of principle. I believe in sticking to the rules. I'll play you a credit game some other time. Tonight we're putting it on the line."

He made a slight gesture toward the cigar box where they had each deposited five one-thousand-dollar bills when they bought their chips.

"Now look here," Kilgarry said menacingly.

The Saint's clear-blue eyes met his with sapphire smoothness.

"I said cash, brother. Is that clear?"

Yoring groped through his pockets. One by one he untangled crumpled bills from various hiding places until he had built his bet up to thirty-two hundred and fifty dollars. Then he glared at Kilgarry.

"Len' me what you've got."

"But——"

"All of it!"

Reluctantly, Kilgarry passed over a roll. Yoring licked his thumb, and numbered it through. It produced a total raise of four thousand one hundred and fifty dollars. He gulped down the rest of his drink, and dribbled some more down his chin.

"Go on," he said thickly, staring at the Saint, "raise that."

Simon counted out four thousand-dollar bills. He had one more, and he held it poised. Then he smiled. "What's the use?" he said. "You couldn't meet it. I'll take the change and see you."

Yoring's hand went to his mouth. He didn't move for a moment, except for the wild swerve of his eyes.

Then he picked up his cards. With trembling slowness, he turned them over one by one. The six, seven, eight, nine—and ten *of diamonds*.

Nobody spoke. And for some seconds, the Saint sat quite still. He was summarizing the whole scenario for himself, in all its inspired ingenuity and mathematical precision. He was aware that Mercer was shaking him inarticulately, and that Yoring's rheumy eyes were opening wider on him with a flame of triumph.

And suddenly Kilgarry guffawed, and thumped the table.

"Go to it," he said. "Pick it up, Yoring. I take it all back. You're not so old, either!"

Yoring opened both arms to embrace the pool.

"Just a minute," said the Saint.

His voice was softer and gentler than ever, but it stunned the room to another immeasurable silence. Yoring froze as he moved, with his arms almost shaped into a ring. And the Saint smiled very kindly.

Certainly, it had been a good trick, and an education, but the Saint didn't want the others to fall too hard. He had those moments of sympathy for the ungodly in their downfall.

He turned over his own cards, one by one. Aces. Four of them. Simon thought they looked pretty. He had collected them with considerable care, which may have prejudiced him. And the joker.

"My pot, I think," he remarked apologetically.

Kilgarry's chair was the first to grate back.

"Here," he snarled, "that's not——"

"The hand he dealt me?" The texture of Simon's mockery was like gossamer. "And he wasn't playing the hand I thought he had, either. I thought he'd have some fun when he got used to being without his glasses," he added cryptically.

He tipped up the cigar box and added its contents to the stack of currency in front of him, and stacked it into a neat sheaf.

"Well, I'm afraid that sort of kills the game for tonight," he murmured, and his hand was in his side pocket before Kilgarry's movement was half started. Otherwise, he gave no sign of perturbation, and his languid self-possession was as smooth as velvet. "I suppose we'd better call it a day," he said without any superfluous emphasis.

Mercer recovered his voice first.

"That's right," he said jerkily. "You two have won plenty from me other nights. Now, we've got some of it back. Let's get out of here, Templar."

They walked along Ocean Drive with the rustle of the surf in their ears.

"How much did you win on that last hand?" asked the young man.

"About fourteen thousand dollars," said the Saint contentedly.

Mercer said awkwardly: "That's just about what I'd lost to them before. I don't know how I can ever thank you for getting it back. I'd never have had the nerve to do it alone. And then when Yoring turned up that straight flush—I don't know why—I had an awful moment thinking you'd made a mistake."

The Saint put a cigarette in his mouth and struck his lighter.

"I don't make a lot of mistakes," he said, calmly. "That's where a lot of people go wrong. It makes me rather tired, sometimes. I suppose it's just professional pride, but I hate to be taken for a mug.

"And the funny thing is that with my reputation, there are always people trying it. I suppose they think that my reactions are so easy to predict that it makes me quite a set-up for any smart business."

The Saint sighed, deploring the inexplicable optimism of those who should know better.

"Of course, I knew that a switch like that was coming—the whole idea was to make me feel so confident of the advantage I had with those glasses that I'd be an easy victim for any card-sharping.

"And then, of course, I wasn't supposed to be able to make any complaint because that would have meant admitting that I was cheating, too. It was a grand idea, Eddie—at least you can say that for it."

Mercer had taken several steps before all the implications of what the Saint had said really hit him. "But wait a minute," he got out. "How do you mean they knew you were wearing trick glasses?"

"Why else do you imagine they planted that guy on the train to pretend he was J. J. Naskill?" asked the Saint patiently.

"That isn't very bright of you, Eddie. Now, I'm nearly always bright. I was so bright that I smelt a rat directly you lugged that pack of marked cards out of your beach robe—that was really carrying it a bit too far, to have them all ready to produce after you'd got me to listen in on your little act with Josephine.

"I must say you all played your parts beautifully, otherwise. But it's little details like that that spoil the effect. I told you at the time you were a mug," said the Saint reprovingly.

"Now, why don't you paddle off and try to comfort Yoring and Kilgarry? I'm afraid they're going to be rather hurt when they hear that you didn't manage at least to make the best of a bad job, and get me to hand you my winnings."

But Mercer did not paddle off at once.

He stared at the Saint for quite a long time, understanding why so many other men who had once thought themselves clever had learned to regard that cool and smiling privateer as something closely allied to the devil himself.

And wondering, as they had, why the death penalty for murder had ever been invented.

SOMETHING IS ALWAYS TAKING THE JOY OUT OF LIFE

Cartoon by Clare A. Briggs, 1927; courtesy of The New York *Herald Tribune*

ABOUT PEOPLE WHO PLAY POKER

It may have been the most noteworthy Poker group in American history, the assemblage of wits and eccentric geniuses that lunched at the Algonquin in the years just after World War I. Judging from the members still encountered around New York's Poker tables, they played a remarkably tough game besides. Their official historian, Margaret Case Harriman (daughter of the Algonquin's "genial host"), gives the anecdotal record in her delightful book of Algonquin reminiscences, THE VICIOUS CIRCLE.

AS THE GIRL SAID TO THE SAILOR

from The Vicious Circle

by MARGARET CASE HARRIMAN

SATURDAY was always a big day at the Algonquin Round Table, since it marked the weekly meeting of the Thanatopsis Literary and Inside Straight Club. This group of impassioned Poker players would assemble after lunch, in a room Father had given them on the second floor of the hotel, and would play all afternoon and evening, generally all night, and frequently throughout the entire weekend. Sometimes one member or another would give up and go home before the game ended, pleading extreme fatigue—a condition which F.P.A. once described as "winner's sleeping sickness," lamenting that he himself was far more subject to loser's insomnia, or "Broun's disease."

F.P.A had founded the Thanatopsis in Paris during the war, when he and his colleagues on the *Stars and Stripes* used to play at a bistro called Nini's. Stakes were modest in those days and even later when the players resumed the game in New York; but as the boys became more and more successful, and as new blood was admitted to the game, the stakes grew picturesque. Harpo Marx joined, bringing with him a zany shrewdness and a Hollywood idea of money; Raoul Fleischmann came and went, often leaving with a noticeable nick in the baking fortune; and Herbert Bayard Swope, then executive editor of the [New York] *World,* was, by nature, a man who would bet five thousand dollars on the first name of the next girl with knockknees to get out of a crowded elevator. Five hundred dollars was a normal table stake at the Thanatopsis, subject to the usual fluctuations. It has been said that Harpo won thirty thousand dollars one night, but he has always denied this, maintaining that he never won more than "a few thousand dollars" at one sitting. It is a fact, however, that the Thanatopsis in one evening took from Johnny Weaver a sum amounting to his entire royalties from *In American.*

Women were not encouraged to play, with the exception of Viola Toohey, who was a good, tough Poker player, and was also the wife of John Peter Toohey, a man so largely instrumental in reviving the Thanatopsis in New York that he was referred to by the other members as "Our Founder." Each time they called him "Our Founder" Toohey would rise gravely, and bow. Neysa McMein, Jane Grant, and Beatrice Kaufman occasionally sat in, but it was only for a little while, the way you would let a child have one piece of candy before dinner. Solvent male newcomers were usually welcome, as long as they were prepared to expect no mercy.

"I hope you boys won't be too hard on me. I'm the worst Poker player in the world," a first-timer might say as the game started.

"We shall see," the boys would mutter grimly, and then proceed to prove, if possible, that his statement was correct.

Sometimes a stranger would turn out to be something of a surprise. One night Woollcott brought Michael Arlen, the Armenian-born writer who was New York's current glory-boy because of *The Green Hat,* in which Katharine Cornell was then starring. Though born in Armenia and christened Dikran Koujoumian, Arlen was excessively British in manner, with a kind of frosty elegance. Airily he set about violating every rule of Poker, drawing to inside straights and committing other crimes, and to the boys' amazed disgust, won every round. As the chips mounted in front of Arlen, H. L. Mankiewicz finally spoke.

"I move," he said wearily, "that next round, we kitty out for the Turks."

The Thanatopsis became a popular hangout with friends of the Vicious Circle who would drop in to kibitz after the theater, and on nearly every Saturday night the crowd would include Ina Claire, Beatrice Lillie, Gertrude Lawrence, Roland Young, Alfred Lunt, Lynn Fontanne, and other theater people who were playing in town at the time. Sometimes these friends brought other friends of their own, who were always plainly fascinated by the strange customs of the Thanatopsis. One such rite was to rise in unison around the table whenever anyone made a foolish play and, to the tune of Gilbert and Sullivan's "He Remains an Englishman," solemnly warble:

"He rema-AINS a god-dam fool."

Another tradition was the phrase, "As the girl said to the sailor." This splendidly meaningless tag line was used as a comment on any and every remark that seemed to require no other answer. If Connelly complained of a losing streak, if Kaufman said he was hungry, if Woollcott remarked that they needed new cards . . . "As the girl said to the sailor" was considered adequate reply. Its origin was lost in some forgotten, bawdy A.E.F. joke, but its use at the Thanatopsis was mainly pure, until the night somebody brought along a young Southern actress who became increasingly mystified by the catchword as the evening wore on.

"My!" she said finally to F.P.A. "You certainly seem to be crazy about that ol' monkey business!"

"I never tire of that ol' monkey business," growled Adams.

"As the girl said to the sailor," a chorus of voices around the table instantly intoned.

On one occasion Adams had reason to suffer on account of the Thanatopsis Literary and Inside Straight Club. When he married Esther Root, in 1925, the Thanatopsis voted to give him—as a wedding present, for home use—the handsomest Poker set obtainable, with ivory chips and all . . . on one condition: After his wedding in the afternoon, he must return and play Poker with them that night. Adams agreed, and brought the bride along to kibitz, and both of them behaved so prettily that the boys let them go home around 2 A.M.

Each of the Thanatopsis players had idiosyncrasies of his own. George Kaufman was a great one for betting on low cards—or perhaps, as his fellow players sometimes surmised, a great one for thinking that a ten is a high card. He would bet on a pair of tens and take it calmly when someone came up with jacks or better, merely remarking, "I will now fold my tens like the Arabs, and as silently steal away." Kaufman's collaborator, Marc Connelly, was a fierier sort.

He once tore up his cards in a temper, after a ruinous run of losses.

Marc's outburst is mainly remembered by former Thanatopsis men as one of the few occasions when Ring Lardner, who often sat in on the game and was playing that night, ever said anything.

"Childish!" said Lardner.

Ring Lardner was the most silent man in the world, and he looked even more mournful than most professional humorists. It is said that he once stared so long in silence at a man who came to interview him that the interviewer nervously came back twice in the five minutes after he had left, to see if Lardner was really there. This tale is apocryphal. The truth is that Lardner never looked like a man who might vanish; he merely looked like a man who knew some secret way of making everybody else vanish.

At the Thanatopsis, where everybody loved him for what he wrote as well as for his wordless and strangely appealing personality, Lardner was comfortably allowed to say nothing, except "Hello," "I raise," "I'm out," "Good night," and other technical expressions of good will. About the only other time he ever volunteered a remark, according to Thanatopsis members, was the night David Wallace turned up for an impromptu game wearing an Army shirt with the Infantry insignia on its collar tabs. Wallace, at that time publicity agent for William Harris, Jr., had been a first lieutenant during World War I. The reason he wore the Army shirt, he says now, was that his laundry hadn't come back when the Thanatopsis pulled him out of bed to play Poker, and he had to put on the first shirt that came to hand.

Woollcott began baiting him the minute he came in the door.

"I didn't know we were entertaining General Pershing," he said bitterly; and, "Do tell us all about your war experiences in the front trenches." Later, he said, "Tell me, are you related to General Lew Wallace, who wrote *Ben Hur?"*

It was Woollcott at his nastiest, but everybody in the room, including Dave Wallace, realized that it was also the Woollcott who had wanted to go to the war and had been turned down by the Army, Navy, and Marines as being nearsighted, flatfooted, and overweight, and had ended up as a kind of publicity man for the Medical Corps and a contributing editor of the *Stars and Stripes*. It was natural for Woollcott to hate an Infantry man, and, since he always took everything personally, it was natural for him to consider Dave Wallace's Army shirt a deliberate, personal insult.

The Thanatopsis went on playing Poker, with Dave Wallace taking a hand. But Woollcott was still simmering.

"It's too bad you're sitting down, General Wallace," he said presently, "or you might show us your battle scars."

At this, Dave Wallace lost his temper and threw down his cards. He glared across the table at Woollcott.

"At least I'm not a writing soldier!" he shouted.

There was a silence. And again Ring Lardner made his only remark of the evening.

"You sure swept the table that time, Dave," he said quietly.

Wallace followed Lardner's lazy glance around the table. The circle of Poker players included almost every "writing" soldier who had been on the staff of the *Stars and Stripes* in France.

There are those who maintain that Lardner made two remarks that night, and that his next one was immediate and tactful.

"Roodles?" he said.

Dave Wallace was the most prominent of what might be called the "cushion" membership of the Vicious Circle. Like one or two other regular lunchers in the group who were themselves neither conspicuous nor famous, he was a good audience. He was usually the first to arrive at the Round Table, ready to laugh at the first thing Woollcott, or Adams, or Benchley, or Ross, or any of the other great men said. Dave's laughter was genuine, if overprompt, and one thing about him made it seem even more spontaneous; Dave had dimples. Somehow, a man with dimples can be a stooge and never look like one.

The Vicious Circle needed an audience like Dave and his one or two fellow claquers; it got to be a strain, sharpening their wits only on one another. Besides, they cherished Dave for another reason. As a theatrical press agent he knew many beautiful actresses, and nobody at the Round Table, or at the Thanatopsis, was ever averse to having a pretty actress at his side. The Vicious Circle treasured Dave for his wide acquaintance among beauties, for his ready laughter, and for his patent hero-worshiping—but they treated him, mostly, like a bunch of little boys kicking around a mud turtle to make it lie on its back.

One reason for this was that Dave, unfortunately, was an incurable social snob, the kind that dearly loves a Vanderbilt. Social snobbery was one of the things the Vicious Circle condemned—at least, until some time later, when they themselves began to meet a few Vanderbilts. They never let Dave forget a remark he made the time a friend got married and Dave inquired about the bride.

"Who was she?" he wanted to know.

"Oh, just plain folks," they told him. "Her father was a grocer."

"Wholesale, of course?" Dave asked anxiously.

The Vicious Circle's bland distaste for pretentiousness once provoked one of George Kaufman's most-quoted sallies. A stranger, sitting in at the Poker game, took to bragging of his ancestry back to the time of the Crusades. Finally Kaufman gave him a proud retort.

"I had an ancestor, too," he said. "Sir Roderick Kaufman. He also went on the Crusades! . . . As a spy, of course," George added thoughtfully.

Racial gags never caused any ill feeling in the small, perfect democracy of the Round Table and Thanatopsis circle, perhaps because they were usually volunteered by someone belonging to the race or creed in question and were nearly always at the expense of something else—snobbery, pretentiousness, phoniness, or any of the other qualities the boys derided.

"Did you fellows know that I have a little Jewish blood?" Herbert Bayard Swope inquired, one evening at Poker.

"And did you all know that I'se got a tinge of the tarbrush?" asked Paul Robeson, who was sitting in.

Another night, Raoul Fleischmann happened to remark that he was fourteen years old before he knew that he was a Jew.

"That's nothing," said Kaufman. "I was sixteen before I knew I was a boy."

Sometimes these mild ribaldries shocked Dave Wallace's notions of old-world decorum. Dave, a sedate and simple soul, took a fairly constant ribbing from the crowd anyway. For example, Kaufman, as banker of the Thanatopsis, handled all the checks and so knew that Dave's middle initial was H, and that he was for some reason fiercely secretive about it. After hazarding many uncouth guesses which Dave, no master of repartee, bore with patience, his cronies took to sending in squibs to *The New Yorker,* all credited to the well-known wit, David H. Wallace. These were either corny or perfectly pointless, and Ross gleefully published every one. "It," quoth Dave Wallace, " 'never rains but it pours' " would appear at the bottom of a page; or, "As David H. Wallace says, 'Tea and coffee are good to drink, but tennis is livelier.' "; or, "David H. Wallace, the monologist, convulsed his set with a good one the other evening. 'It seems there were two Irishmen,' Mr. Wallace began, but could not go on for laughing." Only once did they let him have a real joke, and he now recalls it with a shudder. "It raised my hair," says Dave, who is nearly bald. The joke went like this: " 'Once there were two Jews,' David H. Wallace related at a recent soiree, 'and now look!' " The authors of this line were later revealed to be George S. Kaufman and Raoul H. Fleischmann.

Naturally, Wallace was not the Vicious Circle's only target; a pleasant mockery tinged most of the remarks the boys exchanged with one another. One night Woollcott arrived wearing a bearskin coat he had bought for $200, before the war. "This coat was a smart investment," he boasted, preening himself. "I can sell it any day for as much as I paid for it."

F.P.A. glanced across the table at Heywood Broun, slumped in his usual rumpled and spotty heap.

"You couldn't get that much for your entire wardrobe, Heywood," he surmised, "unless it was from a costumer."

Broun merely smiled his angelic smile. "Poor old Broun," he murmured. But it was easygoing, softspoken "poor old Broun" nevertheless who was partly responsible for the only fist fight the Thanatopsis remembers. This was a battle between Broun and Joe Brooks, a stockbroker and member of the Thanatopsis, and it did not take place in the Thanatopsis clubroom; it took place chiefly in an even more interesting chamber, namely Heywood Broun's mind.

Thanatopsis members are not sure how it began. Some say that Joe Brooks refused to sell chips to Dorothy Parker; others say Mrs. Parker never played Poker and the argument was about something else entirely. Mrs. Parker, interrogated, says "Ooh!" At any rate, one thing led to another and many questions were involved, including American womanhood, the Socialist Party, the Right to Strike, Censorship in the Theater versus Decency in the Theater, How to Make Ravioli, and Where Do you Get Your Suits Made, You Monster? Both men quit the Poker game in a fury and went home separately at about two in the morning. A couple of hours later, Broun, tossing in his bed and unable to sleep, suddenly sat up and addressed his wife, Ruth Hale.

"I'm going down and beat hell out of that son of a bitch," he announced.

Ruth tried to dissuade him, pointing out the lateness of the hour and the fact that Joe Brooks was a trained athlete and a former All-American football player, but it was no use. Broun pulled on a pair of trousers and a coat, taxied dangerously from his house on West 85th Street to East 10th Street, where Brooks lived, and kept his finger on the bell until Brooks opened the door. He then pasted Brooks on the jaw.

There were no eyewitnesses to that battle, which raged all over the Brooks apartment, but it was later disclosed that Broun took a life-sized beating in which even his garments were ripped to shreds, and that he taxied home in the dawn with two black eyes and wearing a suit of gentleman's evening clothes lent to him by his recent adversary.

The final victory was Broun's, however. When he took off Brooks's coat he found in a pocket a fat address book crammed with the addresses and telephone numbers of innumerable fair women. Serenely, as the sun came up, Heywood sat at his window tearing up the pages of the address book, and watching the fragments drift away on the early morning breeze.

Although fisticuffs were not a general diversion of the Thanatopsis, the clubroom in the Algonquin usually looked, after a Poker session, as though carnage had taken place there. Sandwich crusts, mayonnaise, cigar butts and fruit peelings were strewn everywhere, there were a dozen new cigarette burns in the carpet, and several chairs had come apart at the seams from too much tilting back to scrutinize the table. These damages represented a pure loss to Father, since the Thanatopsis was charged nothing for the room and never spent anything on food in the hotel on Poker nights. When they got hungry one of the members would go down to a Sixth Avenue delicatessen and come back with a paper bag full of sandwiches and fruit. One hot summer night they ordered in from a neighboring caterer a whole ice-cream freezerful of strawberry and pistachio ice cream, which melted and ran all over the carpet. It was after that incident that Father caused a large sign to be hung in the clubroom in time for the next session. The sign read simply:

BASKET PARTIES WELCOME

The boys got a good laugh out of it, and even found it a handy thing to jot down telephone numbers on.

Not all of the Poker games were held in the Algonquin, although that became the club's best-known meeting place. Sometimes one of the members would play host in his own apartment, and they would all "kitty out" for the refreshments; occasionally a literati-struck actress would invite them to meet in her penthouse or duplex and they would feast freely on a superb buffet and gratefully allow their hostess to sit in on the game. This was truly a courteous gesture, for they did not enjoy taking money from a woman. One time, Alice Brady, whom they had met through Dave Wallace—then press agent for her father, William A. Brady—asked them to come and play at her house in the Fifties, fed them royally on pheasant and champagne and took a jovial hand in the Poker game. She was so stimulated by the company that she made reckless bets all over the place, and was soon seriously in the red. One of the boys took Wallace aside.

"Listen, for godsakes," he said, "tell her to go easy. Or better still, you sit beside her and tell her how to play her hand."

"If you insist," said Dave. "It made them feel more comfortable," he explains now. "My first instinct was to tell them the truth—that Alice could afford to lose more than all of 'em put together at that particular time. She had just signed a contract with Famous Players for forty weeks at four thousand a week, on a rising scale."

Many people who ought to know say that what finally ruined the Thanatopsis was the fact that the stakes became too high; they rose from one hundred dollars to two hundred and fifty, then to five hundred, and too often the sky was the limit. Too much money was involved, and the game degenerated into a cutthroat project rather than a friendly gathering. At least once the members tried to curb their own skyrocketing bets—they cut the value of the chips by fifty per cent so that, although a chip was still called a dollar, it was worth only fifty cents. However, their minds remained geared to think in terms of fat round figures. One night, soon after the devaluation, Ross won $450.00 in real dollars. "Just think," said Toohey mournfully, "last week that would have been nine hundred dollars!"

What you gain on the swings you lose on the roundabouts, and the Thanatopsis boys proceeded to gamble on other games the money they saved by cutting the chips at Poker. They never played any game except for money—anagrams, craps, Cribbage, croquet. One or two of them grew peevish when they lost—Marc Connelly often flew into a temper, and Woollcott was a great one for kicking the Cribbage board across the room—but mostly, they took their ups and downs philosophically. "None but the brave chemin de fer," sighed Bob Sherwood one evening, after losing a monumental sum at that sport, at Swope's.

As the Thanatopsis grew richer (and some of its members poorer), it moved its headquarters from the Algonquin to the Colony Restaurant, where its wealthy new members such as Swope and Joe and Gerald Brooks had been long and favorably known. Father did not grieve over its departure. His true love was the Round Table, and the Round Table still met at the Algonquin. As for Gene Cavallero, that other master of diplomacy, who owns the Colony, he has only one comment to make on the Thanatopsis.

"It was an honor to have them," he says. With a shrug.

¶*The "dead man's hand" has the most celebrated name and most uncertain composition of any known to Poker. All the legend of Western lore and ballad agrees that Wild Bill Hickok was playing Poker when he was shot and killed; but was his final Poker hand the two black aces and the two black eights? Or aces and eights of indeterminate suits? Or jacks and eights? Or unknown? Here is the most reliable account we have been able to find.*

The Dead Man's Hand

from Wild Bill Hickok

by FRANK JENNINGS WILBACH

DEADWOOD was an outlaw town in 1874. As the land belonged to the Indians the Government could not recognize it as a settlement. It was not so recognized until June 1877. But when Wild Bill arrived there it was a free and easy place, everybody carrying a bag of gold nuggets as well as a brace of pistols. Doc Pierce was there at the time and in a letter to the writer dated October 18, 1925, he gives a minute description of the town and its people.

"Deadwood," he wrote, "had only one narrow street, filled with stumps, boulders, lumber, and logs, with hundreds of men surging from saloon to saloon—so you had to get acquainted with a majority of them, and have a speaking acquaintance. Whenever a gunman came to the gulch the word was passed along as quickly as it would be at a ladies' sewing society."

Harry Young, the barkeeper of Carl Mann's saloon, has furnished a picturesque description of Wild Bill's arrival at Deadwood. We have already seen that Young had been befriended by Wild Bill when he was a resident of Hays City.

"About the middle of June," wrote Young, "there arrived in Deadwood my old friend Wild Bill. Accompanying him was Charlie Utter, commonly known as Colorado Charlie. They were mounted, and a more picturesque sight could not be imagined than Wild Bill on horseback. This character had never been north of Cheyenne before this. Many in Deadwood knew him; many knew him only by reputation, particularly those who came from Montana. Among these Montana people were a good many men of note. I mean by that, gunmen, and the arrival of this character in town caused quite a commotion.

"They rode up to the saloon where I was working, both of them having known Carl Mann before. He being a great friend of Bill's they naturally called on him first. They dismounted and walked into the saloon, great crowds following them, until the room was packed. Mann cordially received them, asking them to make his saloon their headquarters, which they agreed to do. This meant money to Mann, as Bill would be a great drawing card. After the excitement of Bill's arrival had subsided a little, Bill looked at me a few moments, then said:

"Kid, here you are again, like the bad penny, but I am awfully glad to see you." And turning to Carl Mann, he remarked, "I first met this kid in Hays City, Kansas, and wherever I go he seems to precede me, but he is a good boy and you can trust him. Take my word for that."

It has frequently been stated that Bill went to the hills merely as a gambler and with no idea of prospecting for gold. This is not true. In the Deadwood *Telegram* of November 13, 1922, the writer finds: "Wild Bill sought to accumulate gold by manipulating the picture cards rather than by digging in the earth for it."

Buel, however, makes the positive statement that "Bill established himself in Deadwood to watch for an opportunity to make a profitable strike. He had located several claims." This would not indicate that his sole interest in the Black Hills was the picture cards of Deadwood, although when not otherwise occupied it is pretty certain that he spent his spare time playing his favorite game, Poker.

Had it not been for Bill's courage he might very well have met with a tragic fate even earlier than he did. There were a number of Montana gun fighters in Deadwood at the time of his arrival. Bill was envied by these men, for it appears that his reputation was much the same as that of a prize fighter who has sent all his opponents down to defeat. He was the champion. Gun fighters at that time aspired to kill any one of their number who had a superior record, and thus lay claim to the championship. One night in the Montana saloon, six gun fighters, envious of Bill's prowess, were criticizing him and openly threatening that they would get rid of him. A friend of Bill's overheard this talk and reported it to him. Bill immediately put his revolvers in order, and going straight to the Montana saloon, walked up to the crowd.

"I understand that you cheap, would-be gun fighters from Montana have been making remarks about me," he said. "I want you to understand unless they are stopped there will shortly be a number of cheap funerals in Deadwood. I have come to this town, not to court notoriety, but to live in peace, and do not propose to stand for your insults."

Whereupon Bill ordered the six men to stand against the wall and deliver up their guns. This they did in a sheepish manner. He then backed out of the saloon, and it was the last he heard of the Montana crowd aspiring to the championship.

Wild Bill was now living in peace with everyone in Deadwood, as he had traveled far from his former conflicts with the bad men of Hays and Abilene. O. W. Coursey, the historian of the Black Hills, now a resident of Mitchell, South Dakota, has made a searching investigation of those wild times. He learned that Bill had a premonition when he entered Deadwood Gulch that his end was near. When the party reached the top of the upland divide (Break Neck Hill) and looked over into Deadwood Gulch for the first time, he said to Colorado Charlie Utter, "I have a hunch that I am in my camp and will never leave this gulch alive."

"Quit dreaming," retorted Utter.

"No, I am not dreaming," replied Wild Bill. "Something tells me that my time is up, but where it is coming from I do not know, as I cannot think of one living enemy who would wish to kill me."

On the evening before he was killed he was standing up leaning against the jamb of the door to the building in which he was to be assassinated the next day, looking downcast.

"Bill, why are you looking so dumpy tonight?" Tom Dosier asked him.

"Tom, I have a presentiment that my time is up and that I am soon going to be killed," Bill replied.

"Oh, pooh, pooh!" said Tom. "Don't get to seeing things; you're all right."

A letter written by Wild Bill to his wife on that same evening lends reality to this legend:

AGNES DARLING:

If such should be we never meet again, while firing my last shot, I will gently breathe the name of my wife—Agnes—and with wishes even for my enemies I will make the plunge and try to swim to the other shore.

J. B. HICKOK.

On the following afternoon, Wednesday, August 2, 1876, he was engaged in a game of Poker in a saloon owned by Carl Mann and Jerry Lewis.

Those sitting at the table beside Wild Bill were Carl Mann, Charles Rich, and Captain Massey, the latter a former Missouri River pilot. As the game progressed the quartet were joking and laughing.

For the first time known, Wild Bill was sitting with his back to a door. While he was facing the front door, a rear door was standing open. Charlie Rich had taken Bill's seat next to the wall, just to plague him, and kept it, though several times Bill asked Charlie to exchange places. Rich said afterward that he was the cause of Bill's murder.

Jack McCall, the assassin, entered the saloon in a careless manner, not giving the least hint of his cowardly purpose. He walked up to the bar, at which Harry Young was officiating, and then sauntered around to a point a few yards behind Wild Bill. He then swiftly drew a 45-calibre Colt and fired. The bullet passed through Bill's head, issued beneath his right cheek bone, and before it had spent its course, pierced Captain Massey's left arm. The time was 4:10 P.M.

In his letter to the writer Mr. Peirce gives several details that have not heretofore been revealed. Doc Peirce was the impromptu undertaker who took charge of the remains and looked after the details of the burial:

"Now, in regard to the position of Bill's body," writes Mr. Peirce, "when they unlocked the door for me to get his body, he was lying on his side, with his knees drawn up just as he slid off his stool. We had no chairs in those days—and his fingers were still crimped from holding his Poker hand. Charlie Rich, who sat beside him, said he never saw a muscle move. Bill's hand read 'aces and eights'—two pair, and since that day aces and eights have been known as 'the dead man's hand' in the Western country. It seemed like fate, Bill's taking off. Of the murderer's big Colt's 45 six-gun, every chamber loaded, the cartridge that killed Bill was the only one that would fire. What would have been McCall's chances if he had snapped one of the other cartridges when he sneaked up and held his gun to Bill's head? He would now be known as No. 37 on the file list of Mr. Hickok."

Doc Peirce states that Bill was living in a tent, a wagon cover stretched over a pole. Colorado Charlie Utter was his tent mate. It was to this tent that the body was taken by Doc Peirce to prepare it for burial.

In a formal statement Doc Peirce said: "When Bill was shot through the head he bled out quickly, and when he was laid out he looked like a wax figure. I have seen many dead men on the field of battle and in civil life, but Wild Bill was the prettiest corpse I have ever seen. His long mustache was attractive, even in death, and his long tapering fingers looked like marble."

The following funeral notice was printed and distributed among the miners of the district:

FUNERAL NOTICE

Died in Deadwood, Black Hills, August 2, 1876, from the effects of a pistol shot, J. B. Hickok (Wild Bill) formerly of Cheyenne, Wyoming. Funeral services will be held at Charlie Utter's camp on Thursday afternoon, August 3rd, 1876, at three o'clock P.M.

All are respectfully invited to attend.

The body of Wild Bill was enclosed in a coffin made from rough boards. Mr. Peirce had deftly closed the wound in his cheek so that it was scarcely noticeable. Bill's countenance was one of perfect peace, while his long beautiful light brown hair fell gracefully down to his broad shoulders and lay parted evenly across his forehead. According to an eyewitness, an expression of calm contentment crossed his features; the lips were slightly parted as if still smiling at the last joke that was passed around the table when the fatal shot was fired. Colorado Charlie had placed beside him in the coffin the Sharps rifle that Bill had carried for many years.

A grave had been dug at Ingleside, then a romantic spot on the mountain slope. A clergyman read the funeral service and on a large stump at the head of the grave was rudely carved the following inscription:

A BRAVE MAN, THE VICTIM OF AN ASSASSIN, J. B. HICKOK (WILD BILL) AGE 39 YEARS; MURDERED BY JACK MCCALL, AUGUST 2, 1876.

Within three years Deadwood had grown so rapidly that it was found necessary to remove the bodies in the old graveyard where Wild Bill lay. On August 3, 1879, Charlie Utter and Lewis Shoenfield, old friends of Bill's, arranged for the removal of the remains to Mount Moriah cemetery. Upon removing the coffin lid, it was found that few changes had taken place in the features. In short, Wild Bill lay after three years as if he had been merely asleep. The same smile lingered on his lips, as if the sleeper was in a pleasant dream.

An account of the exhumation of the remains was published in the Deadwood *Telegram* of November 13, 1922, in which it was stated that those who assisted the undertaker "were astounded to find that by some natural embalming process of the soil, accomplished by water which had percolated through the coffin, the body of Wild Bill had been so well embalmed as to preserve even the outlines of his features and the lines of the manifold pleatings of the dress shirt which he wore. This preservation of the body gave rise to the report that it had been petrified, but Mr. McClintock states that from his examination he would call it an embalming, rather than a petrification, by the deposition of minerals in the tissues of the body."

This lot and grave had been prepared by Colorado Charlie Utter, who had given the remains their second burial. A marble headstone was placed at the head of the grave inscribed as follows:

WILD BILL

J. B. HICKOK

KILLED BY THE ASSASSIN

JACK MCCALL

DEADWOOD CITY

BLACK HILLS

AUGUST 2, 1876

PARD, WE WILL MEET AGAIN IN THE HAPPY HUNTING GROUNDS TO PART NO MORE.

GOODBYE

COLORADO CHARLIE

C. H. UTTER.

Bluffing Stories

[Somehow the best Poker stories seem to be bluffing stories. Often the best bluff is an innocent one. For example:

A YOUNG man was playing no-limit Poker and picked up the ace-king-queen-jack-ten of spades. The betting was hot and heavy and eventually the young man ran out of money. He asked permission to get more money from his father and permission was granted. The hands and the remainder of the pack were placed in sealed envelopes and the young man went to his father.

The father was willing. In fact, he was so anxious that he brought the money himself. It was enough to call the last bet and add a big raise. The opponent, who held four nines, realized that this could not be a bluff and threw his hand away.

The envelopes were then unsealed. Out of curiosity the father looked at the hand his son held—and discovered that the young man had misread the hand. The ace of spades was a club!

THIS bluff was not innocent but it couldn't have been more effective. The game was on the deck of a Mississippi River steamboat. There was much betting before the draw, but one player stayed in on a four-flush and drew one card.

As this card was flipped toward him, the wind caught it and blew it overboard—but not before the player got a flash of its face. Without a moment's hesitation he stuck his other four cards in his pocket and dived overboard after the card.

The steamboat had to stop, back up, and launch a small boat to pick up the "man overboard"—but he triumphantly showed that he had the card. The game was resumed and the player bet heavily on his five river-soaked cards. Needless to say, no one called him. But when the wet cards were tossed out with the rest of the pack, they were seen to be four spades and one heart.

A STORY of a one-card draw is told about an Englishman and an American who were playing a game of two-handed Euchre in which only twenty-four cards are used, aces down to nines, and five cards are dealt to each player. Upon picking up a hand, the Englishman exclaimed: "If we were only playing your American game of Poker, I would have an excellent betting hand, just as it stands!"

"You mean a pat hand," returned the American, studying his own cards. "Well, mine is rather good, too. I might be willing to bet it against yours—provided I could draw just one card."

"Fair enough," returned the Englishman, "since a draw is customary in Poker. Shall we wager fifty dollars?"

The American shook his head.

"Since you're so sure of your pat hand," he said, "maybe you should give me odds—like two to one."

"Put up twenty-five, then," agreed the Englishman. "No, make it thirty. After all, you're only drawing one card, you know."

So the American put up his thirty dollars, discarded one card and picked up the card that the Englishman had dealt him, adding it to his hand. Promptly, they had the showdown. Triumphantly, the Englishman spread three kings and a pair of queens with one hand while he reached for the money with the other.

The American meanwhile tossed his hand on the table and pointed to four aces and the ten of spades. Frozen with amazement, the Englishman was still studying the winning hand while the American picked up the money. After deep calculation, the Englishman turned up the card that the American had discarded. It was the jack of hearts.

"Why!" exclaimed the Englishman. "You had those four aces all along!"

The American nodded. "That's right."

Silence while the Englishman's bewilderment increased. At last, his patience gave out.

"Then tell me," the Englishman pleaded. "Why in the world did you insist upon drawing one card?"

SIDNEY H. RADNER
from *Poker to Win*

[There has been a disappointingly small number of card-players among Presidents of the United States. Taft played Bridge—badly, by all accounts. Coolidge and Hoover tried it; Hoover "didn't care much for it" and Coolidge characteristically said nothing (but after the first few efforts he did not choose to play). Franklin D. Roosevelt played Whist at Harvard and Solitaire (the version called Spider) as Governor and President, and frequently he took a pencil and worked out the Bridge hands in the newspapers.

[There are three bright spots. Eisenhower is an

enthusiastic Bridge player—and a very good one. Harding was a Poker addict and Truman almost as much of one.

President Harding and Poker

SINCE his youth, Harding had loved the Poker table. Now in the White House the games went on—regular men's sessions with the players in their shirtsleeves and Mrs. Harding (whom they called "Ma" or "Duchess") eventually making her housewifely appearance with sandwiches and beer. The Poker cabinet of Harding's administration became almost as celebrated as the kitchen cabinet of Jackson's; its regular members were Edward B. McLean, Jesse Smith, Charles R. Forbes, Harry Daugherty and Albert Fall.

Daugherty once admired Harding's pearl tie-pin. Harding boasted that he had won it at Poker.

A drop-in member of one of the White House sessions recalled that after brisk betting Harding announced "Three kings." Daugherty, who had been betting against him, said, "They're good" and tossed his hand in—but the visitor had happened to glance over Daugherty's shoulder and knew he held three aces. He observed proper Poker etiquette and said nothing at the time, but on the way out, after the game broke up, he began to say to Daugherty, "What . . . ?" "Sh-h-h," cautioned Daugherty. "The boss likes to win."

based on *The Incredible Era*
by SAMUEL HOPKINS ADAMS

How Truman Played Poker

A SHARP wind whipped the cruiser *Augusta* as she steamed Westward across the Atlantic carrying the biggest secret of World War II—that the first atom bomb was about to be dropped on Japan.

James F. Byrnes, then Secretary of State, braced himself against a gun mount aboard the venerable warship, and yelled at me above the wind.

"Why in the world don't you men leave the President alone?" he shouted. "Give him time to do something besides play Poker."

"Let him alone?" I yelled back. "We don't start those games. He does."

I learned many interesting things about Mr. Truman from the Poker sessions aboard the *Augusta,* and later.

For one thing, Mr. Truman was not a true gambler. Poker was his safety valve. (President finds his off-duty release in golf, bridge, or painting.) No athlete or artist, Mr. Truman turned to Poker or reading history. Because of poor eyesight, however, he chose Poker many times when he would have preferred reading.

Another thing I learned was that Mr. Truman had a basic streak of kindness. Playing with comparatively low-salaried reporters, he became quite embarrassed when he won heavily. Consequently he would stay on utterly impossible hands in an effort to plow his winnings back into the game.

He did not hesitate to take calculated risks. He played a forthright hard-hitting game and seemed to bluff only out of playful mischief or boredom resulting from a long run of mediocre cards.

His game was based more on analysis of the other players than strictly on the cards themselves.

Major General Harry Vaughan, Mr. Truman's highly controversial military aide, was by far the President's favorite Poker companion. Next was either the late Charles G. Ross, the scholarly, erudite and easygoing press secretary, or George E. Allen, the ample-waisted quipster and shrewd judge of politics.

Mr. Truman introduced us to an assortment of hair-raising games using wild cards. One of his favorites was Seven Card High-Low, with the lowest of the three hole, or down, cards wild. The pots were divided by the highest and lowest hands.

A perfect hand was five aces and/or seven, five, four, three, deuce of mixed suits. It is possible in this game to win both high and low if the lucky player has the right sort of wild cards.

In this game, three cards are dealt before the betting begins, two down and one up. The last or seventh card is also dealt down, and of the three down cards the lowest and all like it are wild. It is played like regular Seven-Card Stud, except that some players tend to go a little mad after a few hands.

This game came to be known as GOG—short for Grand Old Game, as it was christened one dawn at Niagara Falls aboard the Presidential train. Ross had spent a profitable night cleaning out the press car (Mr. Truman did not participate) and as dawn broke, he raked in another pot and murmured:

"It's a grand old game."

from *How Truman Played Poker*
by MERRIMAN SMITH

GIN RUMMY

As Graham Baker says in the historical note below, the game really is Gin and not Gin Rummy; but in the names of games the public rules and even the inventor of the game can be overruled. *Gin Rummy became a fad in 1940 and 1941, chiefly because it was adopted by a lot of motion-picture stars who got their names in the papers. It has had a surprisingly long life for a fad game and is unquestionably the principal two-handed card game played in the United States, with nothing in sight to challenge its position.*

The Birth of Gin

by GRAHAM BAKER

WHEN the news of my connection with Gin got around, I was accused over a coast-to-coast radio program of being partly responsible for a staggering number of lost man-hours of work in the United States.

I guess it's true. I participated in the invention of Gin Rummy, or Gin, as it should be known.

Once I read an article in a magazine in which the writer, attempting to trace back the origin of the game, hinted that it had emerged from the dim obscurity of Tibet. This much his research had disclosed—that the real name of the game was "Djinn," or something like that.

That's a lie. The name came from a liquid refreshment of the same name.

An ignominious name, too, for it was tacked on the game at a time when the best people shuddered at the mention of Gin as a beverage. It was fit only for lowlifes. This was, of course, before Prohibition and the bathtub gave it its present social recognition.

Gin really owes its conception to the fact that my father was an impatient man when he played cards.

He was very impatient. Let me give you an illustration. We were playing Bridge one night. I stopped in the middle of the hand, trying to count trumps and figure out who held the queen of diamonds. My father glared at me.

"What're you doing?"

"I'm thinking," I replied.

"Well, stop it," he said. "You're keeping three people waiting."

To get back to the topic—Gin. It was back in 1910, when we were living in Brooklyn. My father and I were playing Rum or Rummy. More than likely this happened on a Sunday, for card playing was one of the ways the Bakers kept the Sabbath.

Not to digress, but here's another instance of my father's impatience. My brother-in-law, Fred Hackstaff (he plays on the Cornell Club Bridge Team), is a thoughtful player, but he holds no record for speed. Often, while my father was playing with him, Fred would pause to ponder, whereupon my father would deliberately permit his eyes to close, his head to fall forward on his chest, and the cards to fall out of his hand all over the floor.

But to get back to this Rum game. We kept drawing card after card, trying to meld all the cards in our hands. My father got more and more impatient.

"This game's no good," he said.

"No?"

"It takes too long. It's too slow."

This was rather strange, coming from him. Or was it? He had been playing checkers with a perfect stranger in Scotland. My father had got his name out of a checker magazine and had mailed a postcard, challenging the Scotsman to a game of what the latter called "draughts."

Weeks later, a postcard arrived from Scotland, accepting the challenge. It was my father's first move.

He got out the checkerboard, studied it for several days, and mailed a postcard to Scotland, telling that he had moved his man, 11 to 15.

The postcard ambled its way across the Atlantic and finally reached Scotland. Now the Scotsman got out his board, made a quick decision after three or four days of concentration, mailed back a card, telling of his play, 23 to 19.

The game went on in this fashion until the postcards thundered down the homestretch a year and half later. It was certainly not a game for an impatient man.

But to get back to that Sunday we were playing Rum.

"It's too slow," my father repeated. "Let's experiment a bit."

Right here, I might mention that my father liked to experiment. Years ago he used to play Whist with a group in Chicago. Always there were the usual post-mortems and beefs—"If I had held those cards, what couldn't I have done with them!"

It came to a head. They sorted out their hands, marked envelopes with names and compass points, and put them carefully away in a safe until their memories got dim.

Then the envelopes were brought out, the hands switched and played, and the difference in scores duly noted.

"There should be a shorter way of playing this game," said my father.

We messed around with it. We tried playing with fewer cards. No good. We tried making "wild" cards. Worse. We tried using the ace to complete a sequence of queen-king-ace.

Then we got around to the way it is today—without, naturally, the gambling bonuses and penalties which have been added.

"It's a good game," said my father.

"Yes."

"It isn't Rum."

"No."

"It needs a name. What'll we call it?"

Here's where I confound that writer who said that the Tibetans used to call it "Djinn."

"Rum," I ventured, for I was much younger in those days, "is the name of an alcoholic beverage which plays havoc with one's liver."

"You can shorten that, too," said my father. "Rum is the name of a drink."

"Then let's give it a drinking name. How about champagne?"

"No."

"Scotch?"

"No." I suspected that the Scotsman had beaten him in that game of draughts.

"Gin?"

My father rolled it around his tongue. "Gin. It's a drink. It's short. That's it!"

And that's how the game got its name.

We played it around the house. We even taught a few visitors, who weren't particularly impressed.

My father was then playing Bridge at the Knickerbocker Whist Club on 40th or 41st Street, New York. He played it there while waiting for enough Bridge players to fill a table. It became known as "Baker's Gin."

From my knowledge, the game had been played only in our house and at the Knickerbocker Whist Club. Then, with the death of my father, "Baker's Gin" became a dim memory.

Then suddenly, out of nowhere, everybody in this country started to play it. Nobody knows who dug it up and revived it. I didn't, and none of my family did.

I used to smile to myself when fellows came around telling of this new game. I ought to learn it, they said. I said nothing. Why should anyone believe me if I claimed credit—or assumed blame—for this epidemic?

Then, one day, while I was working at the RKO studios in Hollywood, the local librarian called me on the phone.

"Is your father's name Elwood T. Baker?" she asked. I admitted that it was. "His name's in the Encyclopaedia Britannica," she went on. "He invented Gin."

That was different. I had proof. So, in a very subtle way, by telling my few friends and my many acquaintances, I let the news leak out.

Eventually it reached the ears of Ozzie Jacoby. He asked me to write an article for his book describing the birth of this monster. He even went further and said, "Why don't you give your theories on the game?"

There I must draw the line. I am one of the few men in Hollywood who are not Gin experts. I am not the inventive genius my father was. I am only good at thinking up alcoholic names.

One of the outstanding features of Gin Rummy is that almost no two groups play exactly the same rules and yet any two players can get together and play without difficulty or misunderstanding. The following excerpts from Oswald Jacoby's book GIN RUMMY (1947) *tell how Gin is played at two leading clubs.*

Gin at the Fort Worth Club

by EDWIN A. LANDRETH

WHEN Jake asked me to write this article, I protested that I wasn't a Gin expert and felt sure that I never would be one.

He replied that all Gin players were equally qualified as experts, and that all he really wanted was an article about the club and how they play Gin there, although any comments I wanted to make on the game itself would be right welcome.

So I will start by giving a simple rule. If you follow it you will be sure to win at Gin. Just go down fustest with the fewest points. Of course the problem of how to go down fustest is up to you.

Prior to the advent of Gin the members of the Fort Worth Club who frequented the game room belonged to three definite groups. The first group was the Bridge players; the second, the domino players; and the third and largest, the *sweaters.*

The sweaters played no games at all. They merely sat, watched, and sweated when the man they happened to be watching got into serious difficulties.

After five years of steady watching, a sweater became a senior sweater; and five more years would qualify him as a chief sweater. A sweater could play out a hand or game for a player without suffering any loss of seniority, but let him play for himself just once and he automatically lost all his hard-earned perquisites.

Special high chairs are provided for chief sweaters to help them follow the play. At dominoes they have the right to announce all counts, grab a man's arm if they disapprove of his play, and even reach over and play for him if he is thinking too long. At Bridge they have the right to double any contract (once the declarer is sure to be set), redouble (if it is sure to be made), review the bidding at any time, and claim the bonus for any unbid slam.

A senior sweater possesses most of the rights of a chief sweater except that he may occupy one of the high chairs only when there is no chief sweater to claim it.

An ordinary sweater is not allowed the use of a high chair on any occasion. He may talk to senior sweaters or even to chief sweaters but is never allowed to argue with them, although he may engage in free argument and discussion with other sweaters of equally low stature. Of course he is entitled to say anything he wishes to a mere player.

The rules at the Fort Worth Club evidently differ from the rules of some of the Bridge clubs in the East. The hierarchy in those clubs rank kibitzer (highest), dorbitzer, and ts-ts-maker (lowest).

The advent of Gin Rummy really changed these groups. The domino players shifted to the new game almost immediately; most of the Bridge players followed suit; and as for the sweaters, there just aren't any left.

Gin at the Commonwealth Club

by PETER O. MILLER

WHEN Jake said, "Write me a few words on how you play the game here," my first inclination was to give him the well-known reply of Punch to the young man who asked advice on matrimony—"Don't!"

My next step, after asking myself the natural question, "Why in hell did you ever let yourself in for anything like that!" was to take a look at Mr. Webster's large dictionary. Mr. Webster defines "gin" as "a snare, or trap, for game; an engine of torture." And, using the word as a verb, you might think that gentleman had visited the Commonwealth! He says it means "to catch in a gin; to snare." And there, gentlemen, you have it!

At Richmond's Commonwealth Club (that rendezvous of males so well known for its food and for its celebrated major-domo, Rush, who brought tears to the eyes of his listeners with his rendition of Lee's Farewell Address, whose waiters invariably reply to the telephone inquiry "Is my husband there?" with "Lady, ain't nobody's husband here!")—at this club, I say, I doubt that any invitation to Gin Rummy has not been backed up by the intention that for the invitee it would be, as Mr. Webster says, "a snare; an engine of torture" and that the inviter certainly intended to catch his opponent in a gin!

At the club the usual game is two-handed, though occasionally three play with one "in the box" betting both his opponent and the outsider. Stakes vary from a minimum of half a pint* a point upwards, with the usual bet one cent.

As played at the Commonwealth in Richmond, Gin is a simple game—without variations—and all that is required is the ordinary deck of fifty-two cards, a healthy bankroll, lots of luck, a memory good enough to recall the birthdays and wedding anniversaries on both sides of the family for at least two generations, an extremely snug-fitting pair of earmuffs, and a jerkin of mail (or at least well padded) to absorb the nudges of kibitzers.

[Gin Rummy may not be an engine of torture, as Pete Miller jocularly called it in the preceding paragraphs; yet in more serious vein Ernest Lehman, a master of the short story, presents it as a surprisingly effective weapon of revenge.

You Can't Have Everything

by ERNEST LEHMAN

SHE CLUNG to my arm tightly, as though somehow that would show the others in the living room that *I* cared for *her.*

"Don't you want to dance?" she asked.

"I'm tired," I said.

"Is anything wrong, Roy?"

* The intended word is "cent," but we couldn't bring ourselves to correct the typographical error.

I turned to her, gazing at the plain, unbeautiful face that seemed to have been made for slapping. "I told you, Marsha," I said, "I'm tired. I've been working hard all week."

"Gee, I'm sorry, dear. I do want you to enjoy yourself. It's only for you that I have parties like this."

"For me? Why for me?" I demanded. "You know I don't go for these people."

She gave a little giggle. "I'm proud of you, silly. I like to have them look at you while I say to myself, 'He's mine. All mine.' "

I pulled my arm free.

"Roy—isn't that the way you feel when people look at *me?*"

I didn't answer.

"Roy?" Her eyes had me trapped.

"All this talk, honey," I said, looking away. "I'm worn out. It's Saturday night. Can't you let me relax?"

But she had already stopped listening. Sometimes not listening was the only protection she had. She drifted away to the kitchen, holding her quivering lips in a meaningless little smile, and I started breathing again. I stood there in the crowded, noisy room, playing with my drink and wondering to myself, as I had wondered so many times in the past six months, how much longer I would be able to go on keeping Marsha Cornell dangling on the string while I played the field.

I glanced around the enormous room at the old masters on the walls, at the magnificent furnishings that had been brought over, piece by piece, from the finest establishments in Europe during the first hot flush of Mr. Cornell's newly attained affluence. The old guy had it all right—plenty of it—and a lot of it would be mine someday, just as soon as I popped the proper question. The only trouble was, it would be a package deal, and Marsha came in the package.

But what the hell—I shrugged and headed for the bar. You can't have everything.

Halfway across the room I made the big mistake. I never should have turned my head. Because when I did, I saw the girl. She was on the powder-blue love seat beneath the Gainsborough. She had on a black, off-the-shoulder affair and she wasn't bothering to look even politely amused. I walked right over and sat down next to her.

"You mind?"

She turned cold gray eyes on me. "It's too early to tell." Then she smiled, and she was almost beautiful.

"Finish your drink," I said, "and I'll show you how to dance. Are you alone?"

"Practically. I came with Henry De Witt." She got rid of the glass. "He's out like a mazda in the guest room—on three drinks."

I laughed. "You sure pick 'em." Henry De Witt had gone straight from Harvard to a shiny desk at National City and his grandfather had left him a small fortune to play around with in his spare time, but he still was a terrible bust. He was too shy to talk and when he did talk no one liked what he said, and because he couldn't stand that, he'd pass out at parties as rapidly as the power of alcohol would permit. Everything he touched turned to lead. But this girl was definitely not lead. . . .

Someone had stacked oldies on the hi-fi and Tommy Dorsey was giving out with "You're a Sweetheart." We got up and she moved into my arms and we started a smooth slow-foxtrot and I knew right away that I wasn't going to show her how to dance. I wasn't going to show *her* anything.

"Tell me about you and Henry," I murmured to the scent of Jungle Gardenia in her hair.

"Must I?"

I thought it over for a moment. "No," I smiled, holding her a little closer. "By all means, no."

"What's your name?"

"Roy," I said. "Roy Samson."

"Oh." She took her face from my shoulder and looked at me. "You're—Marsha's . . ."

She winced as my hand dug into her back.

"Don't say that," I muttered harshly.

She hid her face. "I'm—I'm sorry. I must have confused you with—"

"You didn't confuse me with anyone. Just don't say it—that way."

We danced for a while, nursing the strained silence, until finally she asked, "What do you do, Roy?"

"I'm a junior customer's man at Harris, Upjohn and Company, down in the Street, if that means anything to you. I make a lot of money for some people and practically nothing for myself." And then, because I felt I had to, I added, "Marsha's father is my one big account."

"I see," she said simply, and I had an idea she did see.

"Now what about you?"

"Ursula Wynant," she said.

"Pretty."

"I model for—ha ha—a living." She kept talking, and I kept staring at her lips.

"Look," I broke in, "I don't suppose you'd care to do an off-to-Buffalo?"

She didn't answer for a long time. Then she said, "What about Marsha?"

"Let me do the worrying."

"And Henry?"

"Let him do the worrying." I eased her toward the foyer.

We got away without being too obvious. Marsha was still in the kitchen.

Outside, the cold night air was intoxicating. Or maybe it was the strange new hand held tightly in mine. We went to a small bar where the lights were kind, and we talked and drank and drank and talked, and occasionally the truth crept through the banter, and that was when the part that was the drinking suddenly seemed terribly necessary.

I kept staring at her pale, angular face, trying to decide what it was that made me feel she'd never do too well as a model, and it wasn't easy to figure out, because she wasn't far from being beautiful. She was a girl sitting at a bar in midtown Manhattan with a strange young man on a Saturday night and the future lay ahead, bright with promise and mystery. But as she talked, none of that seemed to mean as much to her as the dull years of poverty in a small Midwestern town that lay behind. And it was then, as she told me of the grubby jobs she had held before coming to New York, that I decided it was the eyes that were wrong, out of key with the rest of her. It was more than too much eye-shadow that gave them the faintly lurking sadness.

Suddenly the eyes made me uneasy. "Let's get out of here," I said.

We walked aimlessly for a couple of blocks, holding hands and not saying anything, and every now and then I could feel her looking at me, but I didn't mind the eyes in the darkness. I felt good walking at her side, better than I had felt in a long time, and I began to wonder what it would be like to feel that way for a lifetime—or at least a whole night, anyway.

Waiting at the curb for the light to change, I glanced at her and our eyes met and then I moved close and took her face in my hands.

"I don't know what the hell this is all about," I murmured, kissing her softly on the lips.

She didn't resist. "Don't you think we ought to be getting back to the party now?"

"Ursula, I want to be alone with you."

"Oh, Roy . . ." She shook her head and sighed a small, hopeless sigh.

"Please, honey."

We stood there at the curb and let the people stare at us. I didn't give a damn. I kissed her again. "Where do you live?" I said heavily.

"Well—I have a little place on Sixty-eighth just off Lexington. But—but the heat goes off at eleven."

"Shall we walk it?"

She gazed into my eyes until I had to look away. And then I heard her say, "It's later than you think, Roy."

And looking back on it now, I remember that I thought she meant the hour. We took a cab.

Her apartment was in one of those old private houses. It was small and poorly furnished. She hung up my hat and coat and brought drinks from the kitchenette.

"To us," I said. It wasn't Canadian Club and there were no canapés with it and the hooked rug beneath my feet wasn't wall-to-wall carpeting. But what the hell—you can't have everything.

"Don't go away," she said. "I'll be right back."

I didn't go away. Not then, I didn't.

But later, the blackness outside her windows started turning to gray and I was down to my last cigarette and I knew it was time to leave, but I wasn't sure just what it was I wanted to say.

"Ursula—honey—"

She covered my mouth quickly with her lips. "Don't, darling," she said. "Let's not talk about love."

I gazed at her for a moment. "Okay," I shrugged. "Okay by me."

When I came back from the closet with my hat and coat, her eyes searched mine anxiously. "But I *am* glad you sat down beside me tonight," she said. "Are you, Roy?"

I took her face in my hands. "What do you think?" It was late. I was tired. And she had said, "Let's not talk about love." So I said, "What do you think?"

It wasn't very clever.

Ma had roast beef for Sunday dinner, served with brown gravy and the usual questions: How was Marsha? Why did I stay out so late? How was Marsha? And how was Marsha?

"Please pass the potatoes, Pop."

"Why do you change the subject?" my mother asked.

"I'm not changing the subject. I happen to be rather hungry today."

"Marsha is a nice girl. She comes from a fine family. I don't know what you're waiting for."

"I'd rather not talk about it. Do you mind?" Not today I didn't want to talk about it. I wanted to go on remembering last night.

"How are you fixed for money these days?" my father said.

I glanced at him sharply. "Why do you ask?"

"Well, yesterday I got a bill from Tripler's for four hundred and twenty dollars for an overcoat, two suits and a dozen ties."

"Damn it!" I shouted, reddening. "I told them to send it to the office!"

"Roy!" my mother cried.

"I'll pay for it by the first of the month," I muttered to the plate.

"I wasn't worrying about that," my father said quietly. "I just wanted to know what it was all about. It seems to me that for a boy who is earning a hundred dollars a week, you have very expensive tastes. I hope you can afford them."

"Don't worry about it." I threw my napkin down and left the table.

I didn't want to have to tell them about the gin games with Mr. Cornell. At first, during the early weeks, I had gone around feeling good because I thought I was a guy who could play better Gin than a man who smoked dollar cigars. I had even boasted about it a little. And then, slowly, I had become aware of the fact that he was throwing the games to me, and I knew then how very much the Cornells wanted me for Marsha, how high Mr. C. was prepared to go to keep me visiting their home and leaving contented. That gave me an even nicer feeling, cozy and secure—but it was nothing I cared to talk about.

So far, it had cost Mr. Cornell plenty. The latest figures on the cover of our score-sheet showed that he owed me twenty-three hundred dollars, and though neither of us had ever put it in so many words, we both knew under what happy circumstances payment in full would be made. . . .

I took a bus downtown and went window shopping along the avenues, looking at the women and seeing only their mink coats, and looking at the Cadillacs and Lincolns and seeing only their price tags. It was then that I had to start thinking about Ursula Wynant again. But thinking about her didn't seem to be enough, so I went into a drugstore and dialed her number.

No answer.

I wasn't going to call Marsha Cornell. But I caught a glimpse of myself in the mirror behind the fountain and something that I saw there made me change my mind. It was one of the new suits from Tripler's. It looked damned good on me.

She answered on the third ring.

"Oh . . . Roy . . ." her voice wavered uncertainly.

"Are you angry, Marsha?"

She didn't say anything for a moment. "Why should I be angry?" I could almost see her pale lips trembling.

"About last night," I said. "About my leaving so early."

"You're—you're perfectly free—" she struggled with the words. "Free to do as you please."

"I was awfully tired, honey."

"I—I know. You told me several times. I—"

"What's the matter with your voice?"

"I have a cold," she blurted out. "Oh, Roy, couldn't you at least have said good night to me? Couldn't you—?"

"You were busy, honey, and I didn't want to start anything with all those people there. You know how you get."

"No, Roy, I don't know. Tell me how I get."

"Well, you sort of . . . complain."

She gave a little moan. "Is that what I do? I complain. I must learn to stop, mustn't I—"

"Oh, it's not so bad."

"Thank you, Roy," she said weakly.

"Did Henry De Witt get home all right?" I made it sound casual.

"Two of the boys took him home. He's a sensitive boy. That's why he has to drink so much —to deaden the pain. Liquor makes me sick. That's the only reason I don't touch it. She was so lovely, wasn't she?"

"Who?"

"Ursula Wynant. The girl Henry brought."

"Oh."

"The girl you left with."

I swallowed, groping for words. "Now, Marsha . . ."

"Do I sound complaining, Roy?" Her voice quivered. "I don't mean to."

"Look, honey, she asked me to drop her off on the way—"

"There's no need to explain."

"You know how a girl feels when she's left alone at a party."

"I do, Roy, don't I?" I could hardly hear her.

"Now if I wasn't all tied up tonight I'd come over and take you to a movie and in no time at all you'd get over any foolish notions about—"

"I don't feel well." Her voice broke. "I have to hang up now."

"Wait a minute, honey, you're not angry now, are you?"

"Good-by, Roy."

"I'll see you early in the week. Okay?"

"Will you?" It was a small moan. "Shall I wait at the telephone?"

"Now, Marsha. . . . Hello?"

But she had hung up. I stumbled from the booth, mopping my forehead. I was going to have to warm her up again the next time I saw her. I'd have to tell her I loved her. Maybe I'd even have to kiss her.

The trouble you could get into for only a dime . . .

Monday was a nightmare downtown. The tape was late from the opening and stocks were off one to five by noon. The boardroom was a madhouse and faces were long. But I was wearing a smile. I had put five hundred shares of Steel out on the short side for Mr. Cornell a few days before and now he was cleaning up, and the way I was smiling, you'd think it was my dough. You'd think it was mine already.

I phoned him after the close.

"See what I mean, Mr. Cornell? Four thousand dollars on a three-day trade. Not bad, not bad."

He grunted wordlessly.

I said, "You don't sound very excited."

"All right—four thousand dollars," he said in a flat voice. "It's only money."

"Only money. Hah! You bet it's only money."

"There are other things more important in life than money, Roy."

I had to laugh. *He* was the one to talk. "Like what, Mr. Cornell?"

Bitterness crept into his voice. "Like my daughter's happiness," he said. "But I don't have to tell *you* that, do I, Roy?"

"Of course not."

"I've told you many times that she's the only thing that means anything to me."

I was smiling to myself. I knew what he was getting around to.

"Certainly," I said.

"Are you doing anything tonight, Roy?"

"Why do you ask?" As though I didn't know.

"I thought . . . I thought maybe you'd come up and play a little Gin."

"Gee, Mr. Cornell," I said, "I don't know if I'll be free tonight."

Worry him a little.

"You're busy these nights, Roy, aren't you?" There was a strange note in his voice.

"Not so very. It's just that—"

"How would you like it if we raise the stakes to fifty cents a point?"

"It's just that sometimes things come up unexpectedly and I'm never sure what I'm going to be doing, but I'll tell you what. I'll push everything aside and make it my business to see you tonight. How is Marsha feeling?"

"Say around eight-thirty, Roy?"

"Eight-thirty. Right." I grinned as I hung up. Fifty cents a point! I punched my open palm with my fist. Oh, brother!

The only trouble was, I'd have to put off seeing Ursula until tomorrow. But what the hell—you can't have everything.

Downstairs, the streets were jammed with people rushing for subways, people like myself, who couldn't wait to get away from the places in which they spent most of their waking lives. The difference between them and me was: someday soon, I'd get away for good.

I saw him standing there on the sidewalk in front of the entrance, but I didn't duck away fast enough. Henry De Witt caught up with me.

"Hello, Roy," he said in that soft, weary voice of his. "I knew if I waited, I'd find you."

"What's up, Henry?" I kept moving in the direction of Broad.

He cleared his throat as he fell in step with me. "It's—it's about Ursula. You know—the girl at the party."

"What about her?" I walked faster.

"Well, nothing really." He hesitated. "I just wanted to . . . that is, Marsha told me you . . . Well, I mean, thanks for being such a good sport."

"Forget it."

"It was awfully decent of you to come through for me in a pinch and take her home the way you did."

"I said forget it!" I felt like slugging him.

"She wasn't angry with me, was she?" His eyes blinked with anxiety.

I stared at the pale face. "Why? Haven't you spoken to her?"

"I . . . I'm afraid to call." He grinned sheepishly. "I thought I'd give her time to cool off first."

I had to laugh to myself. I was never going to let her cool off.

"No," I said, "she wasn't angry."

He sighed gratefully. "You've got to let me buy you a drink."

I shrugged. "If you insist."

We went into Schuyler's and stood at the bar. The martini felt good going down, but I had to listen to Henry with it. He was gabbing about Ursula, stammering out the details of his first date with her, and I tried not to hear him but he kept moving closer. Then he lowered his voice confidentially.

"You can keep a secret, can't you?"

I looked at my watch, bored. "Anytime—anyplace."

"She didn't . . . I mean . . ." He lowered his eyes in confusion. "Ursula didn't tell you, did she?"

"Tell me what?" I picked idly at the olive in my glass.

"That . . . well, about our getting married next week."

The bartender jumped forward with the rag. "Oops! Here, let me get you another."

"No," I said hoarsely, "that's all right."

He wiped up the drink. "Don't be silly. It'll only take—"

"I said no!" I turned. "I've got to run, Henry."

"Wait a minute," Henry said, "I haven't even—"

"I'm getting out of here." I moved for the door and he ran after me.

"You'll keep it under your hat, won't you?" He held my arm.

"Let go, will you?"

He followed me to the sidewalk, talking fast. "She doesn't wear the ring at parties. It's a week from Saturday. No ceremony. Mother doesn't know yet. She wouldn't approve, so we're not going to tell her until it's too late for her to do anything about it. You won't say anything?" He clung to me. "Roy . . . ?"

"Don't worry," I snapped, brushing him aside. "Now will you lay off? I have to get uptown."

But fast. Suddenly I felt as though I'd stop breathing if I didn't see her right away, laugh about all this right away . . .

He said, "Can I give you a ride in my car?"

I turned to him with a sick look. "Your . . . car?"

"Yes. I just got it. A Caddy. Come on, it's just up the block."

"No," I said quickly. "No, thanks." And I fled up the street. A great kidder, that Henry. *He* was going to marry Ursula Wynant a week from Saturday. Ha!

Uptown, I ran the two blocks from the subway station. I pushed her bell and banged on the door for five minutes, but it was no use. She wasn't home.

There was a restaurant on the corner, and because it was dinnertime, I went in and ordered a meal, but all I could do was stare at the food and watch the clock. It was almost eight o'clock when I returned.

The light was on in her window and my heart leaped.

"Who is it?" I heard her voice, muffled behind the closed door.

"Roy," I sang out.

"Who?"

"Roy Samson." Was she kidding?

The door swung open and I choked up at the sight of her loveliness.

"Hello," I said airily. "May I?"

"This *is* a surprise." She wasn't smiling. "Come in."

The living room wasn't quite the way I had remembered it. Somehow, it seemed just a little smaller and a little plainer. I threw my hat and coat on the sofa and took her hands in mine.

"Ursula, honey." I examined her face. Then I kissed it. Her lips were cold. "Baby," I said, "how I've missed you. It's been almost two whole days."

She looked at me uncertainly. "Would you like a drink?"

"Yes," I said. "I sure would." All at once I needed one desperately. The coldness of her lips . . . the look on her face . . .

She came back and I took the glass eagerly. "I called you so many times yesterday," I said.

She nodded. "I know."

"You know?"

"I heard the phone ringing."

I set the glass down. "But, honey, why didn't you answer?"

"Because—" She averted her eyes. "Because I knew it would be you."

I stepped to her quickly and took her arm. "Ursula, look at me."

"Please, Roy." She pulled away.

But I wouldn't let go. "Honey," I said softly. I drew her to me and held my lips to hers, feeling her stiffen, then relax in my arms. "Why didn't you want it to be me?"

She didn't answer.

My voice rose to a shout. "Why didn't you want it to be me?"

She broke away and went to the window. "Please go, Roy. Please. I don't . . . I don't want . . ."

"You don't want what?" I cried out.

She turned and I saw the anguish on her face. "I don't want to fall in love with you!"

The words hit me in the pit of my stomach—*I don't want to fall in love with you*—and all I could do was stand there dumbly as the truth crept over me like a sickness, knowing all at once that that was what I had wanted, really, more than anything else in the world.

"Jesus, honey," I groaned, "but what about—what about the other night?"

"It was wonderful . . . a treasure . . ." I heard her voice. Her face was turned to the window again. "I'll always remember it. Don't spoil it, Roy."

And the bitterness was upon me. "He was right, then," I sneered. "He wasn't kidding." I grabbed the glass from the table.

She turned. "Who?"

"I saw Henry this afternoon." I drained the glass. "He told me everything. You are to be congratulated." My face twisted. "Congratulations. Here comes the bride—all dressed in a Cadillac."

She came over to me. "Please, please don't be angry."

"I'm not angry," I snapped, shoving her hand away. "What have I got to be angry about? I hardly know you. I've got no claims. You said it yourself, didn't you? Let's not talk about love, that's what you said. Okay. Let's not talk about love." I moved for my hat and coat. "Let's not talk about anything. Let's especially not talk about Henry De Witt."

"Roy—wait a minute!" She held on to my arm, and something in her voice cried out to me.

"All right." My lips trembled. "I'm waiting."

She buried her face on my chest, and I knew then that she was crying. "I'm so sorry, Roy, but please try to forgive me. I guess I was hoping you'd be as casual as most men are. Maybe I was selfish, but when you feel you're going under the waves for the last time you want to take one last look around at all that you'll never have again. . . ."

"What do you mean?" I pulled her face up angrily. "Why never again? Why does it have to be a lifetime with Henry De Witt? Why?"

"Look at me," she pleaded. "Can't you see it written all over my face? Look around at this shabby apartment. Can't you understand how it can be that there are too many things I want too much because I never had them at all? They're the things that money can buy, Roy—not love—and I can't help myself any more for wanting them. Didn't you ever want the things that money can buy?"

"What's that got to do with it?" I cried out in sudden fury. "Never mind what *I* want!" Knowing that my anger had betrayed me.

She regarded me for a moment. "We're so much alike, aren't we? We'd never have been right for each other anyway. We need the Henrys—and the Marshas . . ."

"Marsha?" I grabbed her wrist. "What's she got to do with this?"

"They're always there waiting for us," Ursula went on. "The submissive, who have to buy what they want, waiting for the dominant to come along and swallow them up. It's something like your Stock Exchange, Roy. Always sell in a rising market, before you get too old or too unattractive to find a buyer."

"No," I cried, turning away. "It's not true." The words sounded hollow to my ears. "That isn't the way it is."

"It is for me, Roy," she said quietly.

"No." I shook my head weakly, trying not to see the clock on the bookcase, silent reminder of a waiting card table, a hopeful father and a girl who wanted me to gaze into her wounded eyes for the rest of our natural lives.

"I know what I want out of life," Ursula was saying, "and I'm not going to trade it in for love."

"Honey, please!" I took her in my arms.

"It's no use." She struggled. "I could love you—much too easily, Roy. But it's too late."

"You've got to listen to me!" I pleaded with her, holding her close and seeking her lips as though to still her protests, knowing that I wasn't really fighting for her—I was fighting for myself. "Listen to me now!" I shouted.

"No!" She broke away with a desperate cry and ran to the door. "Oh, God, please get out, Roy!"

"Honey—"

"Get out!" She tore open the door and stood there tensely. "Can't you see?" she implored. "It's got to be good-by."

I stared at her. I watched her until the crumbling face was no longer beautiful, and a sneer managed to find its way to my lips. She was just another girl, that was all—a girl who couldn't stop knowing what she wanted out of life long enough to give me a reprieve—a stay of execution.

"Okay, baby," I said quietly. "Anything you say." I went past her and took up my hat and coat.

"You're not angry, Roy?" Her voice reached out to me hopefully.

"Angry? No." I smiled a crooked little smile. "Just bored."

"Roy—"

I sauntered out without even looking back.

What the hell—you can't have everything. Maybe it was time I stopped trying. I glanced at my watch. I was late. The old man would be fretting and Marsha would be sitting there on the sofa biting her stubby fingernails. Maybe it was time to get down on one knee, mouth a few pretty words and begin to cash in on a lifetime of ease. The field was getting dull, anyway.

"The field is for suckers," I said to myself in the darkness of the cab. I stopped off on the way and bought a box of candy.

And then I was strolling through the lobby, past the gold-braided doorman and the plush, unused furniture and the picture windows that looked out upon useless, well-manicured gardens. I caught sight of myself in the mirror-lined walls of the elevator, and I saw that my face was pale and thin. I had been trying too hard. The rest would do me good. A nice long lifetime of rest. . . .

Mr. Cornell answered the door.

"I'm late," I said, breezing past him into the foyer.

He shuffled the unlit cigar to the other side of his mouth. "Give me your hat and coat, Roy."

"Candy, too." I put the package on the sideboard. "Sweets for the sweet. And where *is* my little sweetie?"

I went into the living room, drinking in the soft, rich glow of its dimly lighted splendor. It was a beautiful room, the kind of room that made you wonder what you could have been seeking in the tawdry flats of the Ursula Wynants. This was it. This was what I wanted and this was what I was going to have.

I sang out, "Marsha?" waiting for the archway to spew her into my arms.

Mr. Cornell came in. "Have a drink, Roy?"

"No, thanks," I said. "Where's everybody?"

"Mrs. Cornell is in her bedroom. She doesn't feel well."

"I'm sorry to hear that." I sank comfortably into a club chair. "You want to tell Marsha I'm here? Tell my little—"

"Marsha is out."

I looked up at him, blinking. "Marsha? Out?" I laughed.

"She is out . . . with a young man. . . ." He picked the words carefully. "Out for the evening . . . on a date . . . with a boy from my office . . . who . . . who is very much interested in her."

I chuckled. "Really?"

"Is there a joke, Roy?" His lips began to quiver. "Is it so strange and humorous that men should be interested in a lovely . . . charming young creature . . ." He sounded as though he were going to cry. "A sweet . . . intelligent girl who . . . who . . ."

I got up from the chair and went right past him. I went down the long hallway straight to her bedroom and tried the door. It was locked.

"Marsha?" I rattled the knob.

I heard the muffled sob on the other side.

"Honey," I called out, "come on now—stop acting foolish."

No answer.

"Marsha!" I shouted, pounding on the door. "Do you hear me?"

I went back to the living room, to the old man. "What's this all about?" I demanded.

He looked at me with haggard eyes. "My daughter is out for the evening," he said in a proud, hollow voice. "She is out on a date. . . ."

"Yeah, yeah."

"She asked me to give you a message." He seemed to straighten up as he spoke. "She doesn't care to have you call her any more. She doesn't want to see you. That was what she told me to tell you before she went out with the boy from my office."

I licked my dry lips. "We'll see about that." I started for the foyer.

He came after me. "Wait a minute—"

I stopped and looked down at his hand on my arm. A smile came to my face. "You didn't let me get very far, did you?"

"Where are you going, Roy?" he asked quietly.

"You said she was out."

"That's right." He began to lead me back. "But you came to see *me,* remember? We're going to play a little Gin Rummy tonight. No?"

He led me across the living-room carpet.

"Fifty cents a point, Roy."

"But, Mr. Cornell—"

"Isn't that what we agreed?" His grip tightened.

I nodded dumbly. "Yes, but—"

"All right, then." He opened the library door. The card table was all set up, waiting for me. "Take off your jacket, Roy. Make yourself comfortable."

He sat down at the table and began to shuffle the cards with swift, practiced skill.

I stood there, feeling my hands growing cold.

"Mr. Cornell—" I began in a feeble voice.

He was gazing at the score sheet. "Twenty-three hundred dollars," he said softly. "And all I ever wanted for her was happiness."

"Mr. Cornell—can't we—?" I swallowed.

"Sit down, Roy." He brought a flame to his cigar.

"Can't we talk this over?"

He looked up at me.

"Sit down," he said, "and cut the cards."

From RIPLEY'S BELIEVE IT OR NOT,

THE GAMBLERS' GAMES

ÉCARTÉ

¶Vicente Blasco Ibáñez did not confine his thrillers to swashbucklers who risked their lives in swordplay. Many of his protagonists were content to risk their gold in card games, an arena in which the novelist himself had often been an expert contestant. ¶In the following story, Blasco Ibáñez supplies a different twist to an eternal theme. Many real gamblers have killed themselves because they were not winning: Blasco Ibáñez's fictional hero killed himself because he was. ¶The game was Écarté. It is a very simple game. A 32-card pack is used; there are two players (though onlookers bet on the result); five cards are dealt to each player; a card is turned to establish the trump; and the player who wins three out of five tricks scores one point (two points if he wins all five tricks). Because the game is so simple, it has virtually been analyzed out of existence. Any moron can memorize the tables of correct plays.

Compassion

by

VICENTE BLASCO IBÁÑEZ

AT TEN o'clock in the evening Count de Sagreda walked into his club on the Boulevard des Capucins. There was a bustle among the servants to relieve him of his cane, his highly polished hat, and his costly fur coat; which, as it left his shoulders, revealed a shirt bosom of immaculate neatness, a gardenia in his lapel, and all the attire of black and white, dignified yet brilliant, that belongs to a gentleman who has just dined.

The story of his ruin was known by every member of the club. His fortune, which fifteen years before had caused a certain commotion in Paris, having been ostentatiously cast to the four winds, was exhausted. The count was now living on the remains of his opulence, like those shipwrecked seamen who live upon the debris of the vessel, postponing in anguish the arrival of the last hour. The very servants who danced attendance upon him, like slaves in dress suits, knew of his misfortune and discussed his shameful plight; but not even the slightest suggestion of insolence disturbed the colorless glance of their eyes, petrified by servitude. He was such a nobleman! He had scattered his money with such majesty! . . . Besides, he was a genuine member of the nobility, a nobility that dated back for centuries, whose musty odor inspired a certain ceremonious gravity in many of the citizens whose forebears had helped bring about the revolution. He was not one of those Polish counts who permit themselves to be entertained by women, nor an Italian marquis who winds up by cheating at cards, nor a Russian personage of consequence who often draws his pay from the police; he was a genuine *hidalgo,* a grandee of Spain. Perhaps one of his ancestors figured in the *Cid,* in *Ruy Blas* or some other of the heroic pieces in the repertory of the *Comédie Française.*

The count entered the salons of the club with head erect and a proud gait, greeting his friends with a barely discernible smile, a mixture of hauteur and light-heartedness.

He was approaching his fortieth year, but he was still the *beau Sagreda,* as he had long been nicknamed by the noctambulous women of Maxim's and the early-rising Amazons of the Bois. A few gray hairs at his temples and a triangle of faint wrinkles at the corner of his brows betrayed the effects of an existence that had been lived at too rapid a pace, with the vital machinery running at full speed. But his eyes were still youthful, intense and melancholy—eyes that caused him to be called "the Moor" by his men and women friends. The Viconte de la Tresminière, crowned by the Academy as the author of a study on one of his ancestors who had been a companion of Condé, and highly appreciated by the antique dealers on the left bank of the Seine, who sold him all the bad canvases they had in store, called him Velazquez, satisfied that the swarthy, somewhat olive complexion of the count, his black, heavy mustache, and his grave eyes gave him the right to display his thorough acquaintance with Spanish art.

All the members of the club spoke of Sagreda's ruin with discreet compassion. The poor count! Not to fall heir to some new legacy. Not to meet some American millionairess who would be smitten with him and his titles! . . . They must do something to save him.

And he walked amid this mute and smiling pity without being at all aware of it, encased in his pride, receiving as admiration that which was really compassionate sympathy, forced to have recourse to painful simulations in order to surround himself with as much luxury as before, thinking that he was deceiving others and deceiving only himself.

Sagreda cherished no illusions as to the future. All the relatives that might come to his rescue with a timely legacy had done so many years before, upon making their exit from the world's stage. None that might recall his name was left beyond the mountains. In Spain he had only some distant relatives, personages of the nobility united to him more by historic bonds than by ties of blood. They addressed him familiarly, but he could expect from them no help other than good advice and admonitions against his wild extravagance. . . . It was all over. Fifteen years of dazzling display had consumed the supply of wealth with which Sagreda one day arrived in Paris. The granges of Andalusia, with their droves of cattle and horses, had changed hands without ever having made the acquaintance of this owner, devoted to luxury and always absent. After them, the vast wheat fields of Castilla and the rice fields of Valencia, and the villages of the northern provinces, had gone into strange hands—all the princely possessions of the ancient counts of Sagreda, plus the inheritances from various pious spinster aunts and the considerable legacies of other relatives who had died of old age in their ancient country houses.

Paris and the elegant summer seasons had in a few years devoured this fortune of centuries. The recollection of a few noisy love affairs with two actresses in vogue; the nostalgic smile of a dozen costly women of the world; the forgotten fame of several duels; a certain prestige as a rash, calm gambler, and a reputation as knightly swordsman, intransigent in matters of honor, were all that remained to the *beau Sagreda* after his downfall.

He lived upon his past, contracting new debts with certain providers who, recalling other financial crises, trusted to a re-establishment of his fortune. "His fate was settled," according to the count's own words. When he could do no more, he would resort to a final course. Kill himself? —Never. Men like him committed suicide only because of gambling debts or debts of honor. Ancestors of his, noble and glorious, had owed huge sums to persons who were not their equals, without for a moment considering suicide on this account. When the creditors should shut their doors to him, and the money lenders should threaten him with a public court scandal, Count de Sagreda, making a heroic effort, would wrench himself away from the sweet Parisian life. His ancestors had been soldiers and colonizers. He would join the foreign legion of

Algeria, or would take passage for that America which had been conquered by his forefathers, becoming a mounted shepherd in the solitudes of southern Chile or upon the boundless plains of Patagonia.

Until the dreaded moment should arrive, this hazardous, cruel existence that forced him to live a continuous lie was the best period of his career. From his last trip to Spain, made for the purpose of liquidating certain remnants of his patrimony, he had returned with a woman, a maiden of the provinces who had been captivated by the prestige of the nobleman; in his affection, ardent and submissive at the same time, there was almost as much admiration as love. A woman! . . . Sagreda for the first time realized the full significance of this word, as if up to then he had not understood it. His present companion was a woman; the nervous, dissatisfied females who had filled his previous existence, with their painted smiles and voluptuous artifices, belonged to another species.

And now that the real woman had arrived, his money was departing forever! And when misfortune appeared, love came with it! Sagreda, lamenting his lost fortune, struggled hard to maintain his pompous outward show. He lived as before, in the same house, without retrenching his budget, making his companion presents of value equal to those that he had lavished upon his former women friends, enjoying an almost paternal satisfaction before the childish surprise and the ingenious happiness of the poor girl, who was overwhelmed by the brilliant life of Paris.

Sagreda was drowning—drowning!—but with a smile on his lips, content with himself, with his present life, with this sweet dream, which was to be the final one and which was lasting miraculously long. Fate, which had maltreated him in the past few years, consuming the remainders of his wealth at Monte Carlo, at Ostend and in the notable clubs of the Boulevard, seemed now to stretch out a helping hand, touched by his new existence. Every night, after dining with his companion at a fashionable restaurant, he would leave her at the theater and go to his club, the only place where luck awaited him. He did not plunge heavily. Simple games of Écarté with intimate friends, chums of his youth, who continued their happy career with the aid of great fortunes, or who had settled down after marrying wealth, retaining among their former habits the custom of visiting the honorable circle.

Scarcely did the count take his seat, with his cards in his hand, opposite one of these friends, when Fortune seemed to hover over his head, and his friends did not tire of playing, inviting him to a game every night, as if they stood in line awaiting their turn. His winnings were hardly enough to grow wealthy upon; some nights ten *louis;* others twenty-five; on special occasions Sagreda would retire with as many as forty gold coins in his pocket. But thanks to this almost daily gain he was able to fill the gaps of his lordly existence, which threatened to topple down upon his head, and he maintained his lady companion in surroundings of loving comfort, at the same time recovering confidence in his immediate future. Who could tell what was in store for him? . . .

Noticing Vicomte de la Tresminière in one of the salons, he smiled at him with an expression of friendly challenge.

"What do you say to a game?"

"As you wish, my dear Velazquez."

"Seven francs per five points will be sufficient. I'm sure to win. Luck is with me."

The game commenced under the soft light of the electric bulbs, amid the soothing silence of soft carpets and thick curtains.

Sagreda kept winning, as if his kind fate was pleased to extricate him from the most difficult passes. He won without half trying. It made no difference that he lacked trumps and that he held bad cards; those of his rival were always worse, and the result would be miraculously in harmony with his previous games.

Already, twenty-five golden *louis* lay before him. A club companion, who was wandering from one salon to the other with a bored expression, stopped near the players interested in the game. At first he remained standing near Sagreda; then he took up his position behind the Vicomte, who seemed to be rendered nervous and perturbed at the fellow's proximity.

"But that's awful silly of you!" the inquisitive newcomer soon exclaimed. "You're not playing a good game, my dear Vicomte. You're laying aside your trumps and using only your bad cards. How stupid of you!"

He could say no more. Sagreda threw his cards upon the table. He had grown terribly white, with a greenish pallor. His eyes, opened extraordinarily wide, stared at the Vicomte. Then he rose.

"I understand," he said coldly. "Allow me to withdraw."

Then, with a quivering hand, he thrust the heap of gold coins toward his friend.

"This belongs to you."

"But, my dear Velazquez. . . . Why, Sagreda! . . . Permit me to explain, dear count! . . ."

"Enough, sir. I repeat that I understand."

His eyes flashed with a strange gleam, the selfsame gleam that his friends had seen upon various occasions, when after a brief dispute or an insulting word he raised his glove in a gesture of challenge.

But this hostile glance lasted only a moment. Then he smiled with glacial affability.

"Many thanks, Vicomte. These are favors that are never forgotten. I repeat my gratitude."

And he saluted, like a true noble, walking off proudly erect, the same as in the most smiling days of his opulence.

With his fur coat open, displaying his immaculate shirt bosom, Count de Sagreda promenades along the boulevard. The crowds are issuing from the theaters; the women are crossing from one sidewalk to the other; automobiles with lighted interiors roll by, affording a momentary glimpse of plumes, jewels and white bosoms; the news vendors shout their wares; at the top of the buildings huge electrical advertisements blaze forth and go out in rapid succession.

The Spanish grandee, the *hidalgo,* the descendant of the noble knights of the *Cid* and *Ruy Blas,* walks against the current, elbowing his way through the crowd, desiring to hasten as fast as possible, without any particular objective in view.

To contract debts! Very well. Debts do not dishonor a nobleman. But to receive alms? In his hours of blackest thoughts he had never trembled before the idea of incurring scorn through his ruin, of seeing his friends desert him, of descending to the lowest depths, being lost in the social substratum. But to arouse compassion. . . .

The comedy was useless. The intimate friends who smiled at him in former times had penetrated the secret of his poverty and had been moved by pity to get together and take turns at giving him alms under the pretext of gambling with him. And likewise his other friends, and even the servants who bowed to him with their accustomed respect as he passed by, were in the secret. And he, the poor dupe, was going about with his lordly airs, stiff and solemn in his extinct grandeur like the corpse of the legendary chieftain, which, after his death, was mounted on horseback and sallied forth to win battles.

Farewell, Count de Sagreda! The heir of governors and viceroys can become a nameless soldier in a legion of desperadoes and bandits; he can begin life anew as an adventurer in virgin lands, killing that he may live; he can even watch with impassive countenance the wreck of his name and his family history, before the bench of a tribunal— But to live upon the compassion of his friends! . . .

Farewell forever, final illusions! The count has forgotten his companion, who is waiting for him at a night restaurant. He does not think of her; it is as if he never had seen her; as if she had never existed. He thinks not at all of that which but a few hours before had made life worth living. He walks along, alone with his disgrace, and each step of his seems to draw from the earth a dead thing; an ancestral influence, a racial prejudice, a family boast, dormant hauteur, honor, and fierce pride; and as these awake, they oppress his breast and cloud his thoughts.

How they must have laughed at him behind his back, with condescending pity! . . . Now he walks along more hurriedly than ever, as if he has at last made up his mind just where he is going, and his emotion leads him unconsciously to murmur with irony, as if he is speaking to somebody who is at his heels and whom he desires to flee.

"Many thanks! Many thanks!"

Just before dawn two revolver shots astound the guests of a hotel in the vicinity of the Gare Saint-Lazare—one of those ambiguous establishments that offer a safe shelter for amorous acquaintances begun on the thoroughfare.

The attendants find in one of the rooms a gentleman dressed in evening clothes, with a hole in his head, through which escape bloody strips of flesh. The man writhes like a worm upon the threadbare carpet.

His eyes, of a dull black, still glitter with life. There is nothing left in them of the image of his sweet companion. His last thought, interrupted by death, is of friendship, terrible in its pity; of the fraternal insult of a generous, light-hearted compassion.

¶*William Makepeace Thackeray was only one of the great novelists who wrote with complete authority on the card games of his times (he lived 1811-63). Like Balzac, Dostoevski, and perhaps too many others, he experienced the passions and frustrations of the amateur gambler and consorted with the professionals, whose passions were perhaps less but whose frustrations were even greater. The gambling card games then, in the early-to-middlin' nineteenth century, were Écarté, Faro and its variants Lans-*

quenet (*French*) or Landsknecht (*German*), *Baccarat, and the relatively new* Rouge et Noir *or* Trente et Quarante (*synonymous names for the same game, which still is much played*). ¶*Gambling at card games is a thread that runs all along Thackeray's most famous novel,* VANITY FAIR; *his most famous heroine, Becky Sharp, in that same novel, became a gambler-for-gain and her husband, Rawdon Crawley, was already one when she married him; and the most famous chapter of that novel, "How to Live Well on Nothing a Year," includes card-playing as one of the prime methods. The following passages from that chapter and elsewhere in* VANITY FAIR *are an accurate description of card-playing in Napoleonic times.*

from Vanity Fair

by WILLIAM MAKEPEACE THACKERAY

ON NOTHING per annum then, and during the course of some two or three years, Crawley and his wife lived very happily and comfortably at Paris. It was in this period that he quitted the Guards, and sold out of the army. When we find him again, his mustachios and the title of Colonel on his card are the only relics of his military profession.

It has been mentioned that Rebecca, soon after her arrival in Paris, took a very smart and leading position in the society of that capital and was welcomed at some of the most distinguished houses of the restored French nobility. The English men of fashion in Paris courted her, too, to the disgust of the ladies their wives, who could not bear the parvenue. For some months the salons of the Faubourg St. Germain, in which her place was secured, and the splendors of the new Court, where she was received with much distinction, delighted and perhaps a little intoxicated Mrs. Crawley, who may have been disposed during this period of elation to slight the people—honest young military men mostly—who formed her husband's chief society.

But the colonel yawned sadly among the duchesses and great ladies of the Court. The old women who played Écarté made such a noise about a five-franc piece that it was not worth Colonel Crawley's while to sit down at a card table. The wit of their conversation he could not appreciate, being ignorant of their language. And what good could his wife get, he urged, by making curtsies every night to a whole circle of princesses? He left Rebecca presently to frequent these parties alone, resuming his own simple pursuits and amusements amongst the amiable friends of his own choice.

The truth is, when we say of a gentleman that he lives elegantly on nothing a year, we use the word "nothing" to signify something unknown—meaning, simply, that we don't know how the gentleman in question defrays the expenses of his establishment. Now, our friend the colonel had a great aptitude for all games of chance; and exercising himself, as he continually did, with the cards, the dice-box, or the cue, it is natural to suppose that he attained a much greater skill in the use of these articles than men can possess who only occasionally handle them. To use a cue at billiards well is like using a pencil, or a German flute, or a small-sword; you cannot master any one of these implements at first, and it is only by repeated study and perseverance, joined to a natural taste, that a man can excel in the handling of either. Now Crawley, from being only a brilliant amateur, had grown to be a consummate master of billiards. Like a great general, his genius used to rise with the danger; and when the luck had been unfavorable to him for a whole game, and the bets were consequently against him, he would, with consummate skill and boldness, make some prodigious hits which would restore the battle, and come in a victor at the end, to the astonishment of everybody—of everybody, that is, who was a stranger to his play. Those who were accustomed to see it were cautious how they staked their money against a man of such sudden resources and brilliant and overpowering skill.

At games of cards he was equally skillful; for though he would constantly lose money at the commencement of an evening, playing so carelessly and making such blunders that newcomers were often inclined to think meanly of his talent, yet when roused to action, and awakened to caution by repeated small losses, it was remarked that Crawley's play became quite different, and that he was pretty sure of beating his enemy thoroughly before the night was over. Indeed, very few men could say that they ever had the better of him.

His successes were so repeated that no wonder the envious and the vanquished spoke sometimes with bitterness regarding them. And as the French say of the Duke of Wellington, who never suffered a defeat, that only an astonishing series of lucky accidents enabled him to be an invariable winner—yet even they allow that he cheated at Waterloo, and was enabled to win the last great trick—so it was hinted at headquarters in England that some foul play must have taken place in order to account for the continued success of Colonel Crawley.

Though Frascati's and the Salon were open at that time in Paris, the mania for play was so widely spread that the public gambling rooms did not suffice for the general ardor, and gambling went on in private houses as much as if there had been no public means for gratifying the passion. At Crawley's charming little reunions of an evening this fatal amusement commonly was practiced, much to good-natured little Mrs. Crawley's annoyance. She spoke about her husband's passion for dice with the deepest grief; she bewailed it to everybody who came to her house. She besought the young fellows never, never to touch a box; and when young Green of the Rifles lost a very considerable sum of money, Rebecca passed a whole night in tears, as the servant told the unfortunate gentleman, and actually went on her knees to her husband to beseech him to remit the debt and burn the acknowledgment. How could he? He had lost just as much himself to Blackstone of the Hussars and Count Punter of the Hanoverian Cavalry. Green might have any decent time; but pay? of course he must pay; to talk of burning IOU's was child's play.

Other officers, chiefly young—for the young fellows gathered round Mrs. Crawley—came from her parties with long faces, having dropped more or less money at her fatal card tables. Her house began to have an unfortunate reputation. The old hands warned the less experienced of their danger. Colonel O'Dowd, of the ——th regiment, one of those occupying Paris, warned Lieutenant Spooney of that corps. A loud and violent fracas took place between the infantry colonel and his lady, who were dining at the Café de Paris, and Colonel and Mrs. Crawley, who were also taking their meal there. The ladies engaged on both sides. Mrs. O'Dowd snapped her fingers in Mrs. Crawley's face, and called her husband "no better than a blackleg." Colonel Crawley challenged Colonel O'Dowd, C.B. The commander-in-chief, hearing of the dispute, sent for Colonel Crawley, who was getting ready the same pistols with "which he shot Captain Marker," and had such a conversation with him that no duel took place. If Rebecca had not gone on her knees to General Tufto, Crawley would have been sent back to England, and he did not play, except with civilians, for some weeks after.

But in spite of Rawdon's undoubted skill and constant successes, it became evident to Rebecca, considering these things, that their position was but a precarious one, and that, even although they paid scarcely anybody, their little capital would end one day by dwindling into zero. "Gambling," she would say, "dear, is good to help your income, but not as an income itself. Some day people may be tired of play, and then where are we?" Rawdon acquiesced in the justice of her opinion; and in truth he had remarked that after a few nights of his little suppers, etc., gentlemen were tired of play with him, and, in spite of Rebecca's charms, did not present themselves very eagerly.

¶*Some years pass; we are still in* VANITY FAIR, *but Becky is now a continental adventuress, the place is a small German capital, and the game is* Trente et Quarante (*or, if you will,* Rouge et Noir). ¶*In this game the dealer lays out two rows of cards, stopping his deal of each row when the count of the cards (aces 1, face-cards 10, other cards their index value) reaches 31 or more. The row counting closer to 31 is the winning row, and the color of the first card of that row determines the winning color. One may bet on either row or either color to win or lose.*

CROWDS of foreigners arrived for the fêtes; and of English, of course. Besides the Court balls, public balls were given at the Town Hall and the Redoute; and in the former place there was a room for *Trente et Quarante* and roulette established, for the week of the festivities only, and by one of the great German companies from Ems or Aix-la-Chapelle. The officers or inhabitants of the town were not allowed to play at these games, but strangers, peasants, ladies were admitted, and any one who chose to lose or win money.

That little scapegrace Georgy Osborne amongst others, whose pockets were always full of dollars, and whose relations were away at the grand festival of the Court, came to the Stadthaus ball in company of his uncle's courier, Mr. Kirsch; and having only peeped into a playroom at Baden-Baden when he hung on Dobbin's arm, and where, of course, he was not permitted to gamble, came eagerly to this part of the entertainment and hankered round the tables where the croupiers and the punters were at work. Women were playing; they were masked, some of them; this licence was allowed in these wild times of carnival.

A woman with light hair, in a low dress, by no means so fresh as it had been, and with a black mask on, through the eyelets of which her eyes twinkled strangely, was seated at one of the roulette tables with a card and a pin, and a couple of florins before her. As the croupier called out the color and number, she pricked on the card with great care and regularity, and only ventured her money on the colors after the red or black had come up a certain number of times. It was strange to look at her.

But in spite of her care and assiduity she guessed wrong, and the last two florins followed each other under the croupier's rake as he cried out with his inexorable voice the winning color and number. She gave a sigh, a shrug with her shoulders, which were already too much out of her gown, and dashing the pin through the card on to the table, sat thrumming it for a while. Then she looked round her, and saw Georgy's honest face staring at the scene. The little scamp! what business had he to be there?

When she saw the boy, at whose face she looked hard through her shining eyes and mask, she said, *"Monsieur n'est pas joueur?"*

"Non, Madame," said the boy; but she must have known from his accent of what country he was, for she answered him with a slight foreign tone, "You have nevare played; will you do me a littl' favor?"

"What is it?" said Georgy, blushing again. Mr. Kirsch was at work, for his part, at the *Rouge et Noir,* and did not see his young master.

"Play this for me, if you please; put it on any number—any number." And she took from her bosom a purse, and out of it a gold piece, the only coin there, and she put it into Georgy's hand. The boy laughed, and did as he was bid.

The number came up sure enough. There is a power that arranges that, they say, for beginners.

"Thank you," said she, pulling the money towards her; "thank you. What is your name?"

"My name's Osborne," said Georgy, and was fingering in his own pockets for dollars and just about to make a trial, when the major, in his uniform, and Jos, *en Marquis,* from the Court ball, made their appearance. Other people finding the entertainment stupid and preferring the fun at the Stadthaus had quitted the Palace ball earlier; but it is probable the major and Jos had gone home and found the boy's absence, for the former instantly went up to him, and taking him by the shoulder pulled him briskly back from the place of temptation. Then looking round the room, he saw Kirsch employed as we have said and, going up to him, asked how he dared to bring Mr. George to such a place.

"Laissez-moi tranquille," said Mr. Kirsch, very much excited by play and wine. *"Il faut s'amuser, parbleu. Je ne suis pas au service de Monsieur."*

Seeing his condition, the major did not choose to argue with the man but contented himself with drawing away George and asking Jos if he would come away. He was standing close by the lady in the mask, who was playing with pretty good luck now; and looking on much interested at the game.

"Hadn't you better come, Jos," the major said, "with George and me?"

"I'll stop and go home with that rascal Kirsch," Jos said; and for the same reason of modesty which he thought ought to be preserved before the boy, Dobbin did not care to remonstrate with Jos, but left him and walked home with Georgy.

"Did you play?" asked the major, when they were out and on their way home.

The boy said "No."

"Give me your word of honor as a gentleman that you never will."

"Why?" said the boy. "It seems very good fun." And in a very eloquent and impressive manner the major showed him why he shouldn't, and would have enforced his precepts by the example of Georgy's own father, had he liked to say anything that should reflect on the other's memory. When he had housed him, he went to bed, and saw his light, in the little room outside of Amelia's, presently disappear. Amelia's followed half an hour afterwards. I don't know what made the major note it so accurately.

Jos, however, remained behind over the play table; he was no gambler, but not averse to the little excitement of the sport now and then, and he had some napoleons chinking in the embroidered pockets of his court waistcoat. He put down one over the fair shoulder of the little gambler before him, and they won. She made a little movement to make room for him by her side, and just took the skirt of her gown from a vacant chair there.

"Come and give me good luck," she said, still in a foreign accent, quite different from that frank and perfectly English "Thank you" with which she had saluted Georgy's coup in her favor. The portly gentleman, looking round to see that nobody of rank observed him, sat down; he muttered, "Ah, really, well now, God bless my soul. I'm very fortunate; I'm sure to give you good fortune," and other words of compliment and confusion.

"Do you play much?" the foreign mask said.

"I put a nap or two down," said Jos with a superb air, flinging down a gold piece.

"Yes; ay, nap after dinner," said the mask archly. But Jos looking frightened, she continued in her pretty French accent, "You do not play to win. No more do I. I play to forget, but I cannot. I cannot forget the old times, Monsieur. Your little nephew is the image of his father; and you—you are not changed—but yes, you are. Everybody changes, everybody forgets—nobody has any heart."

"Good God, who is it?" asked Jos, in a flutter.

"Can't you guess, Joseph Sedley?" said the little woman, in a sad voice; and undoing her mask, she looked at him. "You have forgotten me."

"Good heavens! Mrs. Crawley!" gasped out Jos.

"Rebecca," said the other, putting her hand on his; but she followed the game still, all the time she was looking at him.

"I am stopping at the Elephant," she continued. "Ask for Madame de Raudon. I saw my dear Amelia today; how pretty she looked, and how happy! So do you! Everybody but me, who am wretched, Joseph Sedley." And she put her money over from the red to the black, as if by a chance movement of her hand, and while she was wiping her eyes with a pocket-handkerchief fringed with torn lace. The red came up again, and she lost the whole of that stake. "Come away," she said. "Come with me a little; we are old friends, are we not, dear Mr. Sedley?"

And Mr. Kirsch, having lost all his money by this time, followed his master out into the moonlight, where the illuminations were winking out, and the transparency over our mission was scarcely visible.

¶*[Anthologies bristle with accounts of Thackeray's prototypical gamblers, Mr. (sometimes Lord) Deuceace and Jack Attwood; but in one of the Thackeray novels,* Barry Lyndon, *the title character himself was an adventurer and professional gambler. In the following passage, Barry Lyndon (pro Thackeray) philosophizes on cheating at cards and incidentally gives some hints on cheating methods of the 1850s. At this juncture in the novel Barry was posing as the valet of his uncle, who in turn was posing as a French nobleman. The game was Écarté.*

from Barry Lyndon

by WILLIAM MAKEPEACE THACKERAY

It was agreed that I should keep my character of valet; that in the presence of strangers I should not know a word of English; that I should keep a good lookout on the trumps when I was serving the champagne and punch about; and, having a remarkably fine eyesight and a great natural aptitude, I was speedily able to give my uncle much assistance against his opponents at the green table. Some prudish persons may affect indignation at the frankness of these confessions, but heaven pity them! Do you suppose that any man who has lost or won a hundred thousand pounds at play will not take the advantages which his neighbor enjoys? They are all the same. But it is only the clumsy fool who cheats; who resorts to the vulgar expedients of cogged dice and cut cards. Such a man is sure to go wrong some time or other, and is not fit to play in the society of gallant gentlemen; and my advice to people who see such a vulgar person at his pranks is, of course, to back him while he plays,* but never—never to have anything to do with him. Play grandly, honorably. Be not, of course, cast down at losing; but above all, be not eager at winning, as mean souls are. And, indeed, with all one's skill and advantages, winning is often problematical; I have seen a sheer ignoramus that knows no more of play than of Hebrew blunder you out of five thousand pounds in a few turns of the cards. I have seen a gentleman and his confederate play against another and his confederate. One never is secure in these cases; and when one considers the time and labor spent, the genius, the anxiety, the outlay of money required, the multiplicity of bad debts that one meets with (for dishonorable rascals are to be found at the play table, as everywhere else in the world), I say, for my part, the profession is a bad one; and, indeed, have scarcely ever met a man who, in the end, profited by it. I am writing now with the experience of a man of the world. At the time I speak of I was a lad, dazzled by the idea of wealth, and respecting, certainly too much, my uncle's superior age and station in life.

There is no need to particularize here the lit-

* A famous rejoinder, first attributed to Richard Brinsley Sheridan: "What would *you* do, if you detected a man cheating at cards?"—"Back him, of course."

tle arrangements made between us; the play-men of the present day want [need] no instruction, I take it, and the public have little interest in the matter. But simplicity was our secret. Everything successful is simple. If, for instance, I wiped the dust off a chair with my napkin, it was to show that the enemy was strong in diamonds; if I pushed it, he had ace, king; if I said, "Punch or wine, my lord?" hearts was meant; if "Wine or punch?" clubs. If I blew my nose, it was to indicate that there was another confederate employed by the adversary; and then, I warrant you, some pretty trials of skill would take place. My Lord Deuceace, although so young, had a very great skill and cleverness with the cards in every way; and it was only from hearing Frank Punter, who came with him, yawn three times when the chevalier had the ace of trumps, that I knew we were Greek to Greek,* as it were.

* Into the early twentieth century, cardsharpers were called Greeks. The Greeks did not earn this derogatory association by cheating more (or less) than persons of other nationalities, but only by winning more than gamblers of other nations, by their astute practice of pooling or syndicating their stakes, appointing a single representative to bet for them, and so entering every game with more capital than their adversaries. Today the cardsharper is called either a mechanic or a thief, both of which are titles proudly borne by those who deserve them.

BACCARAT

¶*Baccarat, a game almost unknown in the United States, has (with its variant, Chemin-de-fer) for many years been the principal gambling card game of Europe. It belongs to the same family as Blackjack or Twenty-one, but in Baccarat the object is to reach a count of 9, with face cards and tens each counting ten and other cards their spot value; but multiples of ten are always dropped, so 3, 13 and 23 all count as 3.* ¶*In European casinos the banker is not the house but the player who, in an auction, bids willingness to put up the most money as the "bank." Players may then bet against the bank, which is obligated to pay off bets only to the amount of money remaining in the bank. Unless some mad millionaire happens to be present, a representative of the Greek syndicate always bids in the bank.* ¶*The following story about Baccarat was Ely Culbertson's favorite and has appeared in print many times. This version is the one he would have selected himself, for it appeared in his autobiography,* THE STRANGE LIVES OF ONE MAN. *The setting is Paris in 1922.*

from The Strange Lives of One Man

by ELY CULBERTSON

I BREAK A BANK

I DRANK more and more, and soon reached the next-to-lowest rung of the ladder to nowhere. All my life I had resolutely resisted self-pity. But now I let it come in, and with each new drink the stream increased.

One by one I surrendered all my ambitions and plans. I now had left only a few rags of cynical, defeatist philosophy and an illusion that any time I really wanted to I could be stronger than anyone. And even this illusion crumbled during my few sober moments. In order to fortify it I made sporadic efforts to do something "significant."

To that end, I puttered around with the Russian Social Revolutionists who, now united with the monarchists, were developing innumerable plots to defeat the steel of Lenin with the croissants† of the Parisian cafés. We held many secret sessions but, except for General Gurko, the former commander in chief of the South Russian armies, and a few other practical Russians, we merely talked, talked, and talked. Everyone was preoccupied with making long speeches in which his philosophico-ethical position would be delineated to the finest nuance. These children, lost in yesterday, naïvely hoped that somehow, somewhere, through some mysterious operation of "forces" in Russia, they would be lifted up again to the heights from which they had been so unceremoniously hurled by an insignificant and unwashed minority. A few of us wanted action—wanted to fight. I obscurely felt that there, perhaps, lay my best hope of escape from myself.

I now was completely penniless, and agreed with a friend of mine, a former officer of the Russian Guard, to accompany him at his expense to Riga and enlist, if possible, against the Bolsheviks. I had no hatred for the Bolsheviks, but

† Crescent-shaped, semisweet pastries, eaten with coffee.

felt that their leaders, though sincerely idealistic, were deceiving themselves and drawing the Russian people into one of the most tragic morasses of history.

These considerations were but a faint echo of my old self; I had little faith in what I was doing, having come to believe that the laws of history were cruel and inexorable. I simply hoped to escape the gutters of Paris. Everything was arranged, and the day of our departure rapidly approached. The night before we were to leave I wrote letters to Elvina and Father, went to the Luxembourg Gardens for a last look, and visited my adopted daughter. I did not want to say good-by to anyone else.

Then I dropped in at a well-known club on Rue Volnay, a couple of blocks from the Café de la Paix. This was the place of my former triumphs where, as a banker in Écarté, I had won thousands. Now I had only twenty francs in my pocket. I stood diffidently, watching the agonized features of system players around a Baccarat table—the hopelessly damned and the helplessly hopeful—who childishly tried to conquer future events with past events. Nonchalantly I placed my twenty francs against the bank. I already counted it as lost, for I decided if I won the first time to let it ride until I could accumulate a few hundred francs for a gorgeous binge. Maybe there is a special God for drunks. If not, I'll walk home, I thought. It's more exciting to be absolutely penniless.

Having placed my bet, I humbly retreated from the table to make room for bigger players. Suddenly I felt a sharp pain in my right foot. Someone had not only stepped on my toes but had crushed them with his heel. "Ouch!" I cried. The offender turned around as if to apologize, but, recognizing me, said nothing. He was a Rumanian *bon vivant* whom I had once cleaned out at Écarté. He fancied himself as a great player and apparently had never forgiven me.

"You stepped on my toes," I said, controlling my anger.

"So I did," he rejoined with studied insolence.

"Don't they apologize in your country?"

"Not to you."

"In that case you'll be glad to know that you're a pig, a Rumanian pig."

"You call me a pig?" he asked menacingly.

"Yes, you," I insisted with arrogant calm, ready to ward off a possible blow.

All this was said quietly, though the words were charged with sibilant hatred. No one observed us, for all were intent on watching the coup that was being played.

The dark face of the Rumanian grew livid as he said, "If you will give me your card, my friends will make all the necessary arrangements. Right away!" He was an ex-officer, and in those days duels were still fought, though rarely, and usually with harmless results.

"Don't be a fool, in addition to being a pig," I sneered. "All I am debating is whether to punch your nose now or wait until we get outside."

"We'll see about that," said the Rumanian and, again stepping on my toes, he walked to the door. I limped after him.

Rue Volnay is rather a small street with a few dozing cabmen, and occasional customers walking into the Chatham Bar and Henri's. No sooner had we stepped on the pavement than I punched my Rumanian in the face. I was never a skilled boxer, but he knew even less about the manly art of self-defense and apparently had nothing but contempt for the Queensberry rules. Muttering with rage, he closed in and, throwing an arm around my neck, caught hold of my right hand and bit it fiercely. We rolled on the pavement. And then began the most ludicrous exhibition of wrestling, pummeling, and kicking ever witnessed on the sedate Rue Volnay. The fracas lasted quite a while, and even the cabbies' horses displayed mild curiosity. Finally the Rumanian's muscles seemed to become less tense and he stopped fighting. We both got up.

He went away without saying a word, and when I shouted at his back, "Pig! Pig!" he didn't answer.

I re-entered the club to wash up. In the mirror I saw a fearful picture. My left eye was swollen, my nose was bleeding. Little bunches of torn-out hair were sticking to my perspiring face. I felt pain all over my body, and my torn shirt was black-gray with dust. I washed hurriedly for fear someone might come in—my swollen lips would not permit a lucid explanation. Just as I was fixing up my collar and tie, I heard loud voices in the gaming room outside. I listened. The voices—there were many of them—grew to an indecorous pitch, and there were vague sounds of many shuffling feet. I sneaked out to see what the excitement was about. A tense group of players were pressing around the gaming table. At the table itself the play had stopped—an unheard-of event.

Monsieur Vardell, the pudgy manager of the club, was running excitedly from group to group, repeating, *"Mais, c'est impossible! C'est impossible!"*

I heard the stentorian voice of the croupier as

he pointed to a mound of thousand-franc notes and mother-of-pearl chips occupying a large corner of the table. *"Messieurs! Messieurs! A qui est cet argent? Enlevez-le donc."* (Whose money is this? Take it away, please!)

No one answered. As I approached the table, all heads turned toward me. I thought my black eye and swollen features were the cause, but then I heard one of the players saying, pointing toward me, "Maybe it's his." In a flash everything became clear to me. I remembered that when I had put up my twenty francs I had not waited to see whether I lost or won. It was now evident that while I was being beaten up in the street, acquiring a black eye and a bloody nose, my bet of twenty francs had been automatically doubling until it had finally reached the limit and broken the bank!

It isn't possible, I thought. And my heart, which only a few minutes before had been beating violently, now seemed to stop beating altogether.

Again the croupier shouted, "Take away this money, please! Whose money is this?"

This time I answered firmly, "The money is mine."

"Yours, monsieur? But, then, where were you?"

"I'm sorry," I said. "I was having a little fistic exercise." I made a pitiful attempt to smile nonchalantly through my swollen lips.

No one contested my claim. Two or three players remembered my placing the twenty-franc bet on that particular spot. A few recognized me.

"C'est l'Américain! We know him. He's all right!"

Upon an order from the manager, the croupier pushed over the little mountain of money, while the players around me, disgruntled at the delay in their game and as envious as prima donnas, exchanged observations:

"Everybody knows that Americans are crazy."

"Fancy going out for a boxing match in the middle of a game!"

"At that rate, I'd have a fight too."

Everywhere I heard the incredible words: "Eleven times!"

I counted the banknotes as I shoved them into every available pocket. As I finished, the croupier remarked, "Forty thousand, nine hundred sixty francs, monsieur. Exact?"

I gave him a royal tip and answered, "Exact." A little calculation showed me that my insignificant twenty francs had multiplied in geometrical progression eleven times. Though relatively rare, such a run in Baccarat is a weekly occurrence, while runs of seven, eight, or nine happen nightly in every self-respecting gambling house. The truly remarkable part was that had I been present during this cancerous proliferation of my twenty-franc note I would have called a halt long before the eleventh time, and either I would have lost my money or gone on a glorious drunk.

CUTTING CARDS

¶Is it true that big gamblers bet thousands of dollars on the winner of a cockroach race, the next license plate to pass the corner, the serial number on money—or a cut of the cards? Yes, it is true. The following excerpt tells of one entirely credible case. ¶The murder of Arnold Rothstein, New York boss gangster, in 1928, was one of the most lurid events of the turbulent Twenties. The police never found out (or at least never told) who killed him, but most of the theories were tied up with card games and a favorite conjecture was that he welshed on a Poker debt and suffered gangland's invariable form of retribution. ¶No slur on the New York police is intended. In the greatest of all mysteries connected with card games, the murder of Joseph Elwell in 1920, the New York police soon learned and still know who was guilty; but since they could not give the District Attorney enough courtworthy evidence to make a case, they were never safely able to make an arrest or voice an accusation. The same may have been true in the Rothstein case.

from In the Reign of Rothstein *by* DONALD HENDERSON CLARKE

ROTHSTEIN went out into Broadway and met Jimmy Meehan, in whose apartment on the northeast corner of Fifty-fourth Street and Seventh Avenue the last great card game in which Rothstein ever took part was played on September 8 and 9.

It was in this card game, which Rothstein entered late, that he borrowed $19,000 in cash from Nate Raymond, and lost $200,000 to Raymond, and more thousands to "Titanic" Thompson, whose real name is Alvin C. Thomas. Rothstein and "Titanic" cut the cards at $40,000 a cut after the stud was finished.

Meehan testified before the Grand Jury that it was between 10:30 and 11 o'clock that Rothstein handed him a loaded revolver outside Lindy's and said:

"Hold this for me. George McManus wants to see me, and I'm going up to his room. I'll be back in half an hour."

The Park Central* Hotel in Seventh Avenue, between Fifty-fifth and Fifty-sixth Streets, is about six blocks from Lindy's in Broadway at Fiftieth Street.

It was about 10:50 when Rothstein was next seen. He was crumpled against the wall in the entrance to the servants' quarters of the hotel on the Fifty-sixth Street side, about twenty feet inside the street door.

* Now the Park Sheraton.

BLACKJACK OR TWENTY-ONE

¶Since the decline of Faro, Blackjack (or Twenty-one) has become the only card game that is played in all American gambling houses, and it is a favorite of Army and home players; but since its current popularity dates only from the time of World War I, few know how ancient a game it really is. The fact is, few games, if any, have so long a history in which they have remained virtually unchanged. A French book of the 1760s describes Twenty-one as "an old game that used to be played in the provinces." ¶The following dramatic episode from THE GENTLEMAN, *a historical novel by Edison Marshall, displays Twenty-one as a popular American game more than a century ago. The story's action takes place in Charleston, South Carolina, about 1850. The narrator and hero is a young professional gambler. Mate is a gentleman of weak character who is being victimized by Memphis (also a professional gambler). The hero is violating gambling ethics when he tries to get some of Memphis' money for himself, but the heroine has asked him to do so and in historical novels love conquers all. ¶The game of Twenty-one as played by them was not much different, except in minor details, from what we play today. Aces counted one or eleven, picture cards ten, and other cards the number of spots. The player would make his bet and the dealer would give him two cards face down. The player could take more cards, face up and one at a time, until he either was satisfied or broke by totaling over 21. If the player broke he lost. Otherwise the dealer would give himself two cards face up and then either stand or draw until satisfied or over 21. A tie would be no decision. Like most authors of card stories, Mr. Marshall has endowed his hero with at least one impossible advantage. He remembers what the next four cards will be from watching the villain shuffle. Some expert players in some card games do try to remember cards from the previous deal or deals, but they can do so only when the cards are not thoroughly shuffled. It is hard to imagine that a professional gambler such as Memphis would ever be that careless or clumsy. The final coup, when the hero shows Memphis a three and then deals him a five, is standard sleight of hand. Again, it is remarkable that Memphis did not spot it.*

from The Gentleman

by EDISON MARSHALL

BACK in our rooms I asked Faro Jack for the evening off.

"You can have it," he said, "but I'm a little worried about how you'll spend it."

"How is that?"

"I can add two and two. One of the figgers is

that a young Charleston blood named Hudson, the son of Mason Hudson who lent you the books, has been hooked by Clara Day and is being fed in pieces to Memphis. The other is, your dressing up today in your best tucker and driving up to Summerville, where gamblers are usually as welcome as the smallpox. I think you've had a message from Mason Hudson, maybe a meeting with him. I think you intend to try to send the boy home. I wouldn't blame you—the debts we make when we're real young, before we find out that most of the cards are stacked, and to hell with it anyhow, well, those debts won't let us be. Memphis plays his cards well. He has only one weakness that I know of—in trying to recoup losses, he takes reckless chances. He's a bad enemy, so if you win for God's sake do it politely. And Clara—well, she knifed a man in Mobile, and she's not from a good family like she makes out when she's drunk but up out of the piney woods, and she's hellish proud."

"Thanks for the tips, boss."

I knocked on Memphis' door—he had flashy rooms on McIntyre Street—about nine o'clock. A Negro named Julius, who had a long memory for faces, and whose deft hands when removing cloaks were peculiarly talented at locating concealed weapons, peered at me through a small glass, grew wide-eyed, and admitted me with a handsome bow.

"Mister Memphis, he will sho' be glad to see you, suh," Julius informed me.

"I've come to pay my respects to an old acquaintance from Charleston, Mr. Mate Hudson. Is he playing?"

"Him and Miss Clara, they just playin' Casino for quarters."

Only now, with my meeting with Mate only a few seconds away, did I realize the large insufficiency of my own plans. My vague idea of taking all his ready money quickly and neatly, to return it later to a sadder, wiser man, had left out human equations. But the pulse of panic, chill in my veins, did not last long. As I charged myself, such an ambitious and calculating man, with failure to plot the game beforehand at once I perceived its impossibility. There were too many factors that I did not know. My play would have to depend upon the deal.

My confidence was instantly restored. I felt the same feeling that had crept through me, alerting all my nerves, before previous big games; I called it excitement, but it was cold instead of warm. It could not be called pleasurable. It was lonely and somehow desolate. I wondered if booze hounds felt something the same as they looked at and toyed with the first glass ere they started their strange journey to their special hell on earth. All the great vices are allied with Death. I did not know how, but the old gamblers and drunkards and whoremasters perceived the fact; and someday I might find the answer.

I almost lost heart again as I paused in the doorway of the card room. I saw Mate long and plain without his noticing my entrance, and I wished to God it was somebody else who had to stand this gaff. I remembered that he was two years older than I: he looked five years younger. I had seen the same boyish freshness of complexion in a country cracker, then watched him lose his meager month's pay without much remorse. On the other hand, Mate was the archetype of the Charleston aristocrat—his body at once strong and graceful, his face of fine molding. There was no lack of maleness in either. Then why in hell, I asked myself, didn't he grow up?

He saw me, leaped to his feet, and almost ran to meet me. He held out his hand and his face lighted up.

"Why, Edward! I was hoping to see you! And how damned grand you are—"

"I came here to see you, Mate."

"Did you indeed! I'm so pleased. We must have a drink. But, first, you must meet my lovely companion. Clara, my sweet, may I present a boyhood friend, Edward Stono? Edward, this is Miss Clara Day."

It is bad manners in the underworld for two of its inmates to reveal their acquaintance when being introduced by a "mark"—in Jack's rougher language, a sucker. Either might be playing a little game that the revelation might ruin. Clara's eyes only glimmered a little as she gave me a bow fit for a Legare Street parlor, for she remembered we had often danced to the playing of mughouse musicians and once came close to dancing to another piper. Those who knew Clara's ways would expect her to be cold-eyed and hard-mouthed; instead she had big, soft eyes and a tender-looking mouth with a shy smile. Her form was fine, slender and tall. She hardly missed being a beauty. She dressed modestly. But there is an ancient law, the poor man's *noblesse oblige,* that the pot must not call the kettle black. . . .

"Isn't she wonderful, Edward?" Mate asked with glowing eyes. "Clara, you must tell him the story you told me—of how you came to be here. He'll treat it in the strictest confidence, and he's one who'll understand."

"I'll tell him some time, perhaps, but not now," Clara replied hastily.

There came to me the stunning thought that Mate was being swindled far worse than I had perceived. By great cunning, Clara had chosen for her act that of an unstained rose blooming among brambles, had made Mate believe it, and he was paying the piper without even getting to dance. If so, she had gone too far. My immoral indignation grew and grew until it turned to an anger almost fine. I could play now. My brain felt whetted; I saw more clearly, as though in a wonderful glass; my hands felt light and free.

I needed them this way, for Memphis had not taken kindly to my coming. He did not waste a thought that I might have come in peace. He approached with his light, silent step, a thin-looking man, with sky-blue eyes, a short nose and a long jaw and a fine flow of ashen hair. He had no eyebrows that I could see, and no eyelashes, and he had been a great power on the Memphis waterfront, until the son of an old friend of the Blount family drowned himself for his losses in the blond man's rooms, and he had had to flee the state. He had never recovered that eminence, but he was still deadly.

"Well, Stono, this is the first time you've honored us with a visit," he remarked.

"I dropped in to see an old friend," I answered.

"I told you, Memphis, that when I took a notion to try my luck, I intended to play with Edward," Mate said, with his natural courtesy. "My only reluctance was that, if the cards went against me, he might throw some good ones my way. He was out of town—so I came here—and have had a good run for my money—winning many pots and failing to win a whole lot more by just a pip or two. Wasn't it remarkable, Memphis, how many times you beat me by a nose?"

"The cards have been running high as the Mississippi in June," Memphis said, turning to me. "Mr. Mate's hands were not quite up to mine, by and large, but the way he played 'em —man, I had my work cut out for me."

"Coming from Memphis, that's a great compliment, Mate," I said.

"I know it is. And I still expect to win back all I've lost and a bit more. That is, of course, with a little help from my Lady Luck." He turned to grin at Clara.

"Mr. Stono, what can I offer you in the way of entertainment?" Memphis said handsomely as though business was done. "I'm sure you and your old friend would enjoy a drink together—"

"That, and a few hands of cards in your good company," I answered.

At most expecting me to try to inveigle Mate to Faro Jack's room—and this kind of piracy was greatly disparaged in the gambler's world—he could hardly believe that I meant to meet him head on in his own joint. True, this would be almost certain protection against physical attack. Bloodshed here would close him out and bring him before the unbribable and severe judge of the Richmond court. But by what conceit did I imagine I could win?

I was counted a good player, but too young a hand to match that of seasoned, cunning, clever Memphis. Faro Jack and I had purposely encouraged this report, to draw trade away from him. Memphis believed it utterly. So he solved the mystery by the gambler's way of thinking—either that I was enjoying a run of luck, or getting too big for my breeches. He believed he knew the right medicine for both.

"A social game, I suppose," he remarked blandly.

"I thought we might put out two hundred each, and declare a reasonable sum." The latter would represent the most any player could draw upon, and hence, plus table stakes, the most he could lose.

"Why, that would make a nice game. There'll be no crowd tonight—the middle of the week and almost the end of the month—and we wouldn't be interrupted. What do you say, Mr. Mate?"

"Clara, do you think I can win tonight?" Mate asked.

"I think your luck has hit the bottom and tonight will turn back."

"Then I'd enjoy it very much."

"What game would you choose, Mr. Mate?" Memphis asked.

"I'll leave that to Edward."

"Then I'll say Twenty-one. Then both luck and skill will tell. And I'll declare two hundred above table stakes of the same sum." And Memphis made the same declaration.

"I'm with you, but if I lose you boys will have to stake me to bed and board until I can draw on my long-suffering banker," Mate said with his wistful smile. Then he turned to Clara and took both her hands.

"Memphis, do you agree to a head-to-head game?" I asked in an undertone. Clara was talking so gaily there was no danger of my being overheard.

"I wouldn't sink to any other kind, tonight," he answered, his placid blue eyes on mine. And I could take that any way I liked.

In a minute or two we were seated at a cloth-covered table, Memphis and I opposite each other, Clara perched on a low stool beside Mate. The table stakes were stacked in bills in front of each player. Whisky and glasses stood in easy reach.

The play began—and I became aware of an old haunting. I wondered if anyone enjoyed gambling—taking real pleasure in it—and at my choosing it as a road to fortune. At best it was a most melancholy road. It was more lonesome than the path the mountain men took in the Far West to gain their pelf in pelts. The mountain man climbed mountains. He saw scenes of grandeur, forests and waterfalls and deer drinking and the herds of buffaloes, firelight at night instead of the monotonous lamps and the strained mirthless faces of his opponents and cards shuffling and falling. The cards were time-eaters. In most games, for most players, that was all they were good for. They did not make for human sociability as did the long silences of chess, but for withdrawal from one's kind. There remained a strange, unpleasant passion, a kind of lust, that could not brook the least delay in the fall of the cards. The dealer must pick them up quickly and get on with the game. The winner must play fast, while his luck was in him. The loser must play fast, for his luck to change.

No luck was running in this game tonight, except Mate's bad luck in contesting such players as Memphis and I. The deck was cold, and the cards fell about as the laws of chance would decree, when Chance herself had turned her back on the play. Such hands as Memphis and I drew we played with caution. Our stakes of bills grew slowly, fed from Mate's dwindling stacks, but one was hardly higher than the other. Actually neither Memphis nor I was gaming in the true sense of the word. We were playing expertly but with no brilliance; perhaps we were both waiting for the coast to clear.

That would not be long. Midway through our second hour of play, Mate lost the last bill of his table stakes and drew upon the sum he had declared.

"My luck doesn't seem to be getting any better," he said with a weary smile.

"It will now," Clara mouthed. "You mark my words. Memphis could tell you how many times he's seen it turn when a player has to dig down."

But she did not look at him as she talked nor did she bother to throw any false conviction into her voice. He was hooked for what else he had; and her jaybird-sharp attention had become fixed on the play between Memphis and me. A thought had struck her that she could not credit but which brought a flush of excitement to her cheeks and a fascinating sheen on her eyes. Memphis and I were playing about even. Neither of us was crowding the other or burning up the deck, but she had thought to see Memphis far ahead by now. And so far, as no one knew better than she, we had played head-to-head. Was it possible he had met his match?

I grinned to myself and thought, "Has he met a sharper worthy of his steal?"

But I did not tarry long over the bad pun, nor with Clara's foxy mind and carnivorous nature. I was arrested by Mate's somewhat delayed reply to her hollow words of encouragement. Evidently he had considered them well and they had thrown a kind of shadow on the wall.

"No, my lovely little girl," he said quietly. "My luck's not going to change tonight and I doubt if it will ever change. I'm one of those fellows. You've seen some of us before. Fairies come to our borning. They bring us every gift man could desire. Fortune—rank—love—beauty in many forms. But we want none of them. We throw them all away. There's only one thing that we want. Do you know what it is?"

"A drink, I reckon," Clara answered pertly.

Mate paid no heed to the dreadful insolence. He never looked for anything like that or recognized it when it came. My hand quivered to slap her and refrained, not from the amount of gentlemanly training I had managed to absorb but because the end would be tragicomedy beyond bearing.

"Do you know, Edward?" Mate answered.

"Yes, sir, I think I do."

"Well, we get it sooner or later, every damned one of us." Falling silent, he looked at the two cards Memphis had dealt him, one of them a face card and the other, I thought, a seven, judging from my last glimpse of the shuffle. "Memphis, hit me again."

Almost all high-ranking card sharps can predict, roughly or with amazing exactitude, the run of the cards as they deal. It is a matter of keeping track of them during the shuffle, recognizing many of them, predicting the position of many more. A highly expert gambler may appear to look you straight in the eyes as he shuffles, let you cut, and still know most of the cards he deals you. However, it requires intense concentration and an amount of mental labor which most gamblers cannot force themselves to exert, except during high and exciting play.

In an odd way it was comparable to rifle and pistol shooting, at which many of the Low Country aristocrats excelled. Good enough shooting, even fine shooting can be pleasurable; but to achieve a great shot—holding with immeasurable closeness and touching off in the right thousandth part of a second—demands an expenditure of nervous energy and puts a strain on body and brain that few riflemen can endure.

A few gamblers can keep track of the cards while an opponent shuffles. The feat is far more difficult and rare, requiring vision and what seems an almost psychic interpretation of things seen. Often such players know where cards are without awareness of having seen them, either through a kind of unconscious vision or some mental process even more mysterious. I had demonstrated some such gift on my last visit to Faro Jack's rooms in Charleston. Since then it had undergone cultivation and enhancement. Sometimes, usually late at night, when my nerves were alive and tingling like those of a hunting wolf, I knew the positions of the fifty-two cards in a shuffled deck almost as well as a pianist knows the eighty-eight keys on his board.

Tonight I had proposed that we play Twenty-one because it would employ only a small part of the deck and hence lend itself to the uses of this special skill. About two o'clock in the morning, when Mate lost the last of his declared money and withdrew from the game, the iron was almost hot enough for me to strike. Memphis' ordinarily pale face had darkened from smoldering anger that he had not downed me yet; his eyes had a sullen look and his voice had coarsened. At my next deal he raised his bet from ten to twenty dollars. I took that hand, he the next two, I the fourth, having won by Blackjack. As it was again my turn to deal, he laid down a crisp fifty-dollar note. The air in the ugly garish room seemed to swirl from some unknown force. Mate sat brooding, hardly watching. But on Clara's face was a flush of excitement as red as her lips.

Luck gave me an easy victory with two face cards. But as I picked up the cards to deal again I had a feeling they were not right—perhaps a hunch, as a gambler would say—and I employed a little trick—actually nothing more than a free-hand lighting of a cheroot—that suggested confidence in a run of luck. Taking the strange bait, Memphis bet only ten. My hunch, or whatever it was, proved true; the first two cards I dealt him were a ten and a jack.

It was now again Memphis' turn to deal, and his fury at his puny winning brought out his old weakness, and I knew by his eyes that he had turned reckless. I laid down a hundred dollars which he matched with a quick, pugnacious gesture. I watched his deal with all the eyes in my head and did not cut. He dealt me an eight and a three. The next card—I knew it past all doubting—was a six, but close to it, perhaps adjacent, were a face card and, I thought, a seven or a nine. Also there was an ace somewhere near the top. Yet I felt fairly certain there was a red four between. I asked to be hit, got the six, and then was faced with one of the hardest problems I had ever met with in the dens.

Eight and three and six made seventeen. Another four—if it were really there—would make twenty-one. If Memphis got it, then was hit with a face card and a seven, he would have twenty-one. If the supposed seven proved to be a nine, he would break his hand. If the four was not there—if my vision failed me—his first two cards would give him a count of seventeen or nineteen, tying or beating me. Then if he were in the mood to deal himself another card, I thought it would be an ace.

My confidence grew that the top card was the four of diamonds. If Memphis knew it, he dared not palm or shift it, for my eye was on him. More likely he thought I had seen the ace, the most quickly visible of all cards, which he knew was on or near the top. So I let him sweat a few seconds more. I could have sixteen, more likely seventeen or eighteen, he thought. Call on sixteen, stand on seventeen—that rule-of-thumb was ancient as the game itself. The beads came out on his big bald brow and his pale wicked smile was a cheat. And he had settled it with himself—except for one cold little draft blowing on his heart—that I would stand when, replying to his smile, I asked to be hit again.

He had no choice but to deal me the card, and there it lay, face up on the table. When he saw it was not an ace and instead a four, his eyes bulged, and Clara uttered a stifled shriek.

The last play of the hand was bound to be anticlimactic, but I enjoyed it, sitting there with an unbeatable score of twenty-one. Memphis dealt himself two cards, which I felt sure were a black face card and neither a nine nor a seven, but a ten. Now only an ace would improve his score; any other would break his hand, yet he feared to the depths of what served him for a soul that I had twenty-one. But I might have twenty, to tie him, or, fishing for the ace, I might have broken my hand.

He decided to stand—perfectly good twenty-one in any safe and sane play—and to his great bitterness and chagrin lost his last chance. This changed to wormwood, unspittable from his mouth, when he stole a look at the next card—the one he would have drawn if he had not stood—and it was an ace.

Memphis wondered if luck were running against him, for he still would not believe that I could outplay him. He bet only twenty dollars on the next hand, which I lost, but I placed forty on the following hand and won it by sheer luck on blackjack. Now he was growing rabid and restless, as was his wont when cards ran against him, but I did not expect him to break his given word, for that is the gambler's pride. There is honor among thieves and this, besides his skill, is his only pride, for his diamonds and fine dress are mockery before God and man, as he knows full well in his heart. But Memphis did break it. As he picked up the cards to hand to me, he palmed the ace. When, having shuffled, I let him cut, he slid it to the top of the deck.

It was a wonderfully deft maneuver—I had never given Memphis his full due as a sharper, but he was the least bit afraid I had seen him. Perhaps he was becoming suspicious of the sharpness of my eyes or that Luck, that fickle goddess of the dens, had turned her back on him. But his confidence was instantly restored as he looked at his second card. Color came back to his face and triumph to his soul. Even if I had not placed it for him, I would have known that it was a face card, giving him twenty-one.

Dealing myself a face card and an eight, I stood on them and lost. And now I was facing an entirely different opponent. He could take me, his hunch told him, any time he liked. What he had thought might have been card-reading was a piece of folly shot full of luck. To strengthen his illusions, I cut my next bet from forty to ten dollars, which I won on blackjack.

"I'll play you only one more hand," I told him. "You began the deal, and I'll end it. I intend it to be the *coup de grâce.*"

"What does that mean?" he asked contemptuously.

"It's a French term. My mother is of French descent. It might be said to mean the satisfactory end of a conflict."

Then Mate, who knew perfectly well the meaning of *coup de grâce,* started up out of his lonely reverie and stared at me.

"So you're an educated fellow!" Memphis mocked in polite tones. "Why, I'm glad to know it. And if this is to be our last hand, with you dealing, I'd like your opinion as to suitable stakes. My own idea would be to make it worth while." For Memphis felt the power and the luck within him, and did not remember that the same feeling had set many a man on a course to ruin and despair.

"Thanks. Suppose you lay your bet, giving me the privilege of halving it or doubling it."

"Then I say two hundred dollars."

He smiled his strange, foxy smile into my eyes.

"Well, it's late—and I'm playing a good part with Mate's money, so I'll double it."

He stared, but remembered I was a fool and took heart. When I shuffled, I let him cut. That did not stop me from dealing him eighteen points; I was too vengeful to let him off with an easy defeat. I wanted it to sting. I planned to have it rankle many a night. I had only to look at Mate's drawn face to be encouraged in this resolve.

As I dealt him the second card, I gave him a peek at the next, and it was a three.

"Hit me again," he said.

As I did so, my hand moved a little, too quickly for him to see, and the top card that fell was a five. I dealt myself a ten and a seven, stood on them, and won. I did not flatter myself that the grim game was over. There might or might not be an aftermath of the duel with Memphis. I had taken him for more than four hundred dollars, about two hundred of which he had won from Mate, and that left a festering wound; but, like most gamblers, he knew a good beating when it came to him, he could read cards however they fell, and wharf rats avoid the company of other wharf rats whose fangs they fear. For the nonce he controlled his temper and even attempted a heartiness that must have hurt him like working a rheumatic arm. Only his high color and hot, dry eyes betrayed his fury.

The next hand, if it were played, would be the most crucial of the night. I had not thought of proposing it until close to the end of my game with Memphis; when I was drunk on cold excitement, when the brilliant interplay of hand and eye with the most powerful working of my mind had demanded too-long concentration, at the fringes of which lay half-madness as from a potent drug. Certainly the idea was wild in the extreme. I could not have entertained it in a sane moment. It might prove the *coup de main,* for in it was a genius of great gambling, or a stunning disaster. The fact remained that Mate was not yet free of Memphis' and Clara's toils—he was only shocked and devaluated and left to lie awhile; and since I had undertaken the half-mad mission, I must not shrink from half-mad measures if they bid fair to win.

The time was now. The excitement in the air had not yet died away. Memphis was too badly beaten to act swiftly and boldly; Mate was deeply depressed and amenable to being led; and Clara, hardly believing what she had seen, felt cold and lost and ugly. Her eyes followed my winnings from the table to my hand to my wallet. The hunger in them was forlorn instead of fierce, like a child's whose belly aches in vain, for there seemed nothing for her tonight except an unearned cursing from Memphis and a dreary rewooing of Mate, the gains from which, if any, lay in a dismal future. The money made me, however, the central figure of her present world.

"I'd like to play one more hand, with Mate alone," I told Memphis.

"What for?" And this was a sensible question for a gambler to ask.

"That's the point. He's lost his money. Still, I think I should give him a chance for a consolation pot." I turned to him, and spoke in a voice as casual and commonplace as I could make it, for this was the most dangerous instant of the undertaking. "Suppose I put up a hundred against—well, let's say Clara's favor for the rest of the night."

At first he was not sure he had heard me correctly. By the time he had reviewed the statement, a chill doubt of everything he held by slaked his fire. He got to his feet, but not in one angry bound, nor did his eyes blaze. He was disoriented and estranged by tonight's events and quite possibly he had made a great mistake. . . .

"What do you mean by that, Edward?" he asked, in a low, shaking voice. "As far as I know, Clara is a lady. If you've insulted her, you'll have to answer for it."

"Oh, sit down, dearie," Clara broke in before I could speak. "I'm not in the least insulted—Edward and I are old friends—and if he needs his face slapped, I'll tend to it myself. Anyway, you can use that hundred, and I feel in my bones you'll win it."

Clara spoke quietly, as she had carefully learned to do, but she could not keep a blitheness from out of her tone, and I did not think she tried. She had been suddenly revitalized. Her big soft eyes glowed quite beautifully and her breast was high and she seemed to stand on tiptoe. Mate looked from her to me, and there was sorrow in his eyes, but behind the darkness was a glimmer that I thought might be hope. Hope of what? Perhaps he himself did not know.

"I won't play such a hand," he said, as he resumed his seat. "I wouldn't think of it."

"Then I'll play it for you, pard. Put out your hundred, Edward." And when I had done so she asked with a faked cunning, "Will you let me deal?"

"Surely."

"I'll deal honestly, but you might as well kiss those bills goodbye."

One of them, a ten, took its departure in Memphis' resolute hand before the play began. Half of it represented the house's rake-off when patrons play among themselves. This the old sharper was never known to forget or to forgive, and I thought that he found a little satisfaction, a small sop to his injured vanity, in the present strict attention to his business. The other five dollars was presumably room rent, soon to be owed by the victor. I wondered if Mate presumed the same, and whether his now numbed face could feel the smack.

In her countless hours of loafing about Memphis' rooms, Clara had learned cascade shuffling. It was considered a pretty thing to see, but Mate took no joy in the sight, for it evidenced that his stainless rose growing among brambles had been in blossom a good while. Her next maneuver was not so pretty. I saw it perfectly plain, Memphis could have seen it had he not drawn off by himself to mope; and since it was unadroit, I was not sure that Mate did not see it. At least he might suspect it from her rapid talk as she played the trick, and that could be the dregs of his bitter cup.

As she toyed with the cards, she managed to pick four and place them on top of the deck. In descending order they were an ace, a jack, a ten, and a nine.

"You don't want to cut, do you?" she asked me gaily. "I know you trust me."

Perhaps for my soul's sake, more likely to palliate a turning stomach, I started to answer, "I'll cut for luck." I started to let Fate decide the sorry game. But if I did, the luck might be bad; and Clara, supposedly playing for Mate, might win. I could not imagine a more lame and impotent conclusion. I myself had intended to cheat if it were necessary to win, to fulfill some kind of a tacit pledge made to Salley and myself. Why should I blame Clara when the rich smell of money was in her nostrils?

Still I could not trust my mind or hardly my heart, and I turned to Mate.

"Will you cut, sir?"

"I wouldn't consider it, sir," he answered, his eyes on mine.

That was the real end of the game. The fall of the cards—the ace and the jack to me, the ten and the nine to her. We went through the motions of standing, and then showing our cards. Mate would not glance at them. I said nothing; and a look, perhaps of fear, perhaps of remorse, crept into Clara's face. Whatever it was, its stay was not long. I saw her pull herself together and turn with faked earnestness to Mate.

"Edward won, dearie. And he won fair, 'cause I dealt the cards myself. When the luck's with a fellow, it seems like he can't lose."

"Very well, and I'll be on my way."

"I hope I'll see you again before long."

"I'll see you in hell, I expect."

"Why, that's no way to talk—"

"Be still, Clara, and go on up," I ordered. "I'll join you in a moment."

She started to protest, but the cheapness went out of her face, God knew where, and she rose and walked with irrefutable grace to the stairs. These were white and broad and beautifully curved and had a mahogany banister, and belles had descended and brides had ascended in years gone by, when this house was a home instead of a pit of heartbreak. No bride ever mounted with a more queenly air. And the devil was in Mate, too, for he stood in a kind of attendance upon her departure, and did not move until she vanished from sight.

"Mate, I don't expect you to speak to me," I said. "But will you wait in your hotel room for a communication from me? I'll dispatch it in a few minutes."

He nodded and went out the door. I had Julius bring me pen and ink and sealing wax, and going into an anteroom I wrote rapidly and briefly:

DEAR MATE:

Once you stayed away from a party for my sake. I came to this one tonight for yours. I am returning the four hundred dollars that you lost. I most earnestly request that you keep the sum and return to Charleston; and you will deprive me of a great satisfaction if you refuse.

EDWARD

Putting four one-hundred-dollar bills with the letter, I sealed and addressed the envelope and, going into the street, put it into the trusty black hands of a cabdriver I knew well. He promised to deliver it personally to Mas' Hudson at the Planter's Hotel within twenty minutes. Then I returned to the rooms to the desolate duty of winding up the game.

When I had climbed the stairs, a door opened in the hall. I entered it to find Clara ensconced in an easy chair, a drink at her elbow. Her eyes were alight and she could not wait to tell me something.

"It wasn't fair to Mate," she said, "but I stacked that deck."

"It's no news to me," I answered.

"Was I that clumsy? I hope Mate didn't see, because it would hurt his feelings, and I'd hate to do that." She paused and looked at me sharply. "You don't seem very grateful."

"I am, though. It saved me from rigging a deck against an old acquaintance. Now he's left the joint and you are free to go."

She echoed the last word—"go"—without emphasis. Then her breast rose and I thought she was going to burst out with something; instead she let go her breath slowly and in silence. She turned a little so I couldn't get a full view of her face. And suddenly I felt no longer vengeful for Mate's wrongs, and only a desolate emptiness was in me and I was alone as on a desert island, and yet somehow Clara was with me there, and we had both arrived there in the same boat. It was like a bleak dream from which I yearned to waken.

"Let me get this straight," Clara went on, after a long pause. "You said I was free to go."

"Yes."

"I'm always free to go, or free to come. That's the one thing I get out of it—the life, I mean—perhaps I should say the only thing I've kept. I was born free and I'll die free. But what I want to know is—and pardon my curiosity—do you want me to go? It doesn't seem quite in keeping with the job you put up on Mate."

"I put it up on you too. I had to. I was paying off a debt. At first I didn't mind jobbing you—Mate would have gotten kinder treatment from a bitch jackal—but now I'm sorry it was necessary. You're not to blame for what you are. The fact remains I never intended to collect that bet, it would be a physical impossibility, and if you'll take twenty dollars and get the hell out, I'll be greatly relieved."

She walked aimlessly about the room. She was pale except for a high flush on her cheekbones and her prettiness was so marked that it would be mistaken for beauty. After a moment she stopped and looked at me.

"You're not to blame for what you are, either."

"I don't know about that."

"Do you know what you are? A tin-horn aristocrat. A card sharp trying to be a gentleman. Well, you'll never make it as long as you live."

"Well, if Mate goes home—and I think he will—and you'd better not do anything to keep him, and I mean that, Clara—"

"What would you do, kill me? I think you might kill me. I'd about as soon have you do it as what you did."

"Will you leave him alone?"

"Yes, I'll leave him alone. I'm truly afraid not to. Now what did you say would happen when he goes home?"

"I'll feel like a gentleman—for a little while."

"You never can. That's the joke of it. If you can feel like one, you are one, but you never can. The white and the black sheep are separated before they shed their milk teeth, and all the king's horses—and all the king's men—"

"Do you want me to go down first, or will you?"

"I will, but will you do a gentlemanly thing for me before we go?"

"If I can."

"There's a book on the table. Somebody left it here. Will you read it awhile? I won't disturb you."

My head swam and I did not catch her meaning.

"You fool," she said in bitter scorn of my amazement. "Do you think I want Memphis to know you've kicked me out? He'd cut my percentage tomorrow."

"I'll be glad to read the book a little while."

The book was a slender volume of tales by a little known Virginian named Poe, and I soon lost myself in it. Before long, Clara rose and spoke.

"I'm going now," she said distinctly, "and I want the twenty dollars you promised."

"Here it is." I handed her the bill.

"You poor bastard." And with that, with her graceful carriage, she walked out of the room.

THE ANNIE OAKLEY

¶*Everyone knows what an Annie Oakley is—a free pass to a show, so called because it is punched; and everyone who saw* Annie Get Your Gun *knows who Annie Oakley was. Not so many know that there is an Annie Oakley museum in her birthplace, Greenville, Ohio, conducted by her niece and biographer, Miss Annie Fern Swartwout. Miss Swartwout says, "Neither Annie nor Frank [Butler, her husband] ever played cards, even a social game, for in their time cards were used mostly for gambling and they never took a chance." Apparently Annie was taking no chances in her favorite display of marksmanship, for it is not on record that she ever missed. Here it is described in a passage from Courtney Riley Cooper's biography of the sharpshooter.*

THE FEAT was to place a playing card, the ace of hearts, at a distance of 25 yards. Then, firing 25 shots in 27 seconds, she would obliterate that ace of hearts in the center, leaving only bullet holes in its place. A card thus shot by Annie Oakley formed quite a souvenir in the eighties.

—COURTNEY RILEY COOPER
in *Annie Oakley: Woman at Arms*

FARO

Men may gamble on what they choose, and they have chosen everything from cockroach races to life and death. Card games are a conspicuously fertile field for the gambler, yet only a few card games have ever achieved the gambling glamour enjoyed by roulette and horse-racing and craps, and only one card game, Faro, ever made the grade in America. In the following brief excerpt from George Fort Milton's scholarly biography of Andrew Jackson there is comment on the part played by Faro in any metropolis of Civil War times.

from The Age of Hate

by GEORGE FORT MILTON

WARTIME Washington was a very paradise of gamblers. In August 1863, Provost Marshal Baker formally reported to Secretary Stanton that "no less than 163 of these establishments were in full blast"; most of them were on or close to Pennsylvania Avenue and some of them were sumptuously furnished. The heavily curtained windows, the general air of silence and mystery and the brightly lighted halls were significant features. A typical establishment, in which many of Thad Stevens' lighter moments were spent, was fitted up in "a magnificence which is princely." "The floor was thickly carpeted, the walls and ceilings exquisitely frescoed and adorned with choice works of art." Chandeliers with scores of gas jets shining through cut-glass globes shed a brilliant glare on costly furniture. Negro attendants in splendid livery "attended your every want with a grace and courtesy positively enchanting." The table groaned under a cold collation, and at stated hours a banquet was served. Food and wine were free to all without obligation to engage in the games of chance, although few accepted this hospitality without playing a little by way of payment. The proprietor was, "as gamblers understand the term," a gentleman of the bluest blood. "If you did not know his trade," a visitor remarked, "you would take him for one of the high officials of the republic, so courtly are his manners, and so lofty his bearing."

In such "first class" establishments, "square" games alone were played, the principal one being Faro. Money was seldom seen on the tables, for ivory counters were generally used. Thousands of dollars changed hands in a single night. The patrons were drawn "largely from members of Congress." The great men of the country could be seen at the principal Faro banks on the nights when no official reception was scheduled. The proprietors told great tales of the nation's statesmen; and in 1864, and for many years later, "the greatest men" frequented these parlors of chance. Nine in every ten of the defalcations by paymasters and others in the employment of the government "were occasioned by losses at the card tables." But these were by no means the only gambling houses. There were many "of a lower and viler character," some with "female dealers to lure the unwary to their fates." Decoys for these houses haunted the Capitol and the hotels. The unwitting visitor was made drunk, forced to play and swindled out of his last cent.

¶*Herbert Asbury put Faro first in his history of American gambling,* SUCKER'S PROGRESS; *those unfamiliar with the game (and there will be many, for only in Nevada is it still played) may find a complete description in section 3 of Mr. Asbury's chapter.*

from Sucker's Progress

by HERBERT ASBURY

1

DESPITE the proverbial ingenuity of the Yankee, he has never created a gambling game of the first rank; in this particular field his inventiveness has been confined to variation and adaptation. All of the famous short card, dice and banking games upon which the American gambler has relied for his big killings, even such traditionally American institutions as Faro, Poker, and craps, are of foreign origin, and only a few were known in the United States before the beginning of the nineteenth century.

2

THE GENESIS of Faro, for nearly three hundred years one of the most popular of all banking games, is uncertain, and is quite likely to remain so. It appears, however, to have been derived by French gamblers from the Venetian game of *Basetta* and the Italian *Hocca,* both of which, in turn, were adaptations of the German *Landsquenet,* played in the camps of the Teutonic foot soldiers as early as 1400. Faro was a popular game in Paris before the middle of the seventeenth century, and under the name of *Pharao* or *Pharaon*—so called because the backs* of the early French cards bore a picture of an Egyptian king—it was played extensively in France until 1691, when Louis XIV prohibited it by royal decree. The game was revived during the latter part of that monarch's reign, and was once more in full favor during the Regency of the Duke of Orléans, who gained control of the French throne upon the death of Louis XIV in 1715. The revival was due principally to John Law, the celebrated Scottish adventurer, whose phenomenal success at the gaming tables of Brussels, Vienna and other European capitals had earned him the nickname of King of the Gamblers. Law arrived in Paris in 1708, set up a Faro bank at the home of the actress Duclos, and won 67,000 pounds sterling before the French police concluded that he was a suspicious character and ordered him to leave the country. He returned in 1715, and the Duke of Orléans, as Regent of France, adopted his famous financial and colonization schemes, with Louisiana as the bait, which threw all France into an orgy of gambling and speculation. French historians record that nothing went on in Paris "except eating, drinking and gambling with fearful stakes." Fortunate speculators in the shares of the Mississippi Company, believing their sources of income to be limitless, gambled at Piquet with bank notes of 100,000 livres "as if they were only ten-sou pieces"; and in one night the Duchess of Berry lost the incredible sum of 1,700,000 livres at Faro, and apparently thought nothing of it.

Faro was played in England soon after it had become popular in France, and was probably in-

* Not the backs, but one of the faces. The backs of the cards were unprinted. The Pharaoh pictured on the card was equivalent to our king of hearts.

troduced by the roistering blades who had shared the French exile of Charles II. The change in spelling, from the French *Pharaon* to the English corruption Faro, occurred soon afterward,* when the game began to make headway among the common people. Throughout the reign of Charles II Faro was one of the favorite diversions of the ladies and gentlemen of his court, who gambled for huge stakes; it is recorded that Lady Castlemaine, one of Charles's mistresses, won 15,000 pounds in a single night, and on another occasion, in February, 1667, lost 25,000 pounds in a similar length of time. Faro retained its hold upon the affections of English gamesters until it was specifically prohibited by Act of Parliament in 1738. The game then declined rapidly, and Edmond Hoyle, in his famous book on games published a few years before his death in 1769, remarked that Faro was "played but little in England," and that it was purely a game for winning and losing money.† A new period of popularity for Faro began about 1785, when the gambling houses of London installed the game, and a Faro bank became the principal attraction at the routs and other entertainments of the English nobility. For more than two decades around the turn of the nineteenth century advertisements such as this, from the London *Courier* of March 5, 1794, were not uncommon:

> "As Faro is now the most fashionable circular game in the *haut ton,* in exclusion of melancholy Whist, and to prevent a company being cantoned into separate parties, a gentleman, of unexceptionable character, will, on invitation, do himself the honor to attend the rout of any lady, nobleman, or gentleman, with a Faro Bank and Fund, adequate to the style of play, from 500 to 2,000 guineas.
>
> "Address G. A., by letter, to be left at Mr. Harding's, Piccadilly, nearly opposite Bond-Street.
>
> "N.B. This advertisement will not appear again."

It seems certain, although no documentary proof exists, that Faro was brought to America by the French colonists—among them many professional and amateur gamblers—who settled Alabama and Louisiana early in the eighteenth century; and the first game in what is now the United States was probably played either in Mobile, or in New Orleans, which was destined to become the port of entry for many other famous card and dice games. From the French possessions in the South, Faro was spread eastward and northward by sailors and travelers, and later by the peripatetic gamblers who worked the early flatboats and steamboats, and by the sharpers who traveled the wilderness trails on foot or horseback and found their suckers in the roadside taverns or the cabins of the lonely settlers. In New York, Boston, Philadelphia and other Eastern cities—with the exception of Charleston, where it was a favorite gambling game among the French Huguenots and the refugees from Acadia—Faro was little known, if at all, before the American Revolution. It is said to have been introduced into New York by camp followers of the British Army, but it is more probable that it was brought to the East by visitors from New Orleans or Charleston, or by the French soldiers of Lafayette and Rochambeau.

The dissemination of Faro was quickened by the Louisiana Purchase, and within a decade after that historic event it had become the most widely played game in the United States, and had gained a foothold from which it was not dislodged for more than a hundred years. Today* Faro is seldom heard of, and it is doubtful if a dozen Faro banks are in regular operation between the Atlantic and the Pacific; but until the early years of the twentieth century, when it began to succumb to a changing public taste, Faro was the mainstay of every important gambling house north of the Rio Grande River, and the ruin of thousands who tried to beat it. No other card or dice game, not even Poker or craps, has ever achieved the popularity in this country that Faro once enjoyed, and it is extremely doubtful if any has equaled Faro's influence upon American gambling or bred such a host of unprincipled sharpers. It was the medium of the first extensive cheating at cards ever seen in the United States, and the rock upon which were reared the elaborate gambling houses and the wolf-traps of the early and middle nineteenth century; while around it developed the system of cappers and ropers-in which is still used effectively by American gaming resorts.

3

MANY CHANGES and improvements have been made in dealing and betting at Faro since the first Frenchman "called the turn," but the basic structure of the game remains unchanged, and essentially it is the same as when Hoyle† first collated the rules almost two hundred years ago.

* Yes, in 1713 if not earlier.

† Hoyle himself never mentioned Faro; Mr. Asbury's citation is evidently from one of the dozens of extensions of Hoyle's books. See page 26.

* 1938.

† Again: It was not Hoyle but one of his unauthorized successors. See the footnote on page 24.

Briefly, the cards are drawn one at a time from a full pack, and alternately win and lose for the bank and the player, the denomination only being considered. In greater detail, this is the way Faro was played in the United States during the golden age of the game:

The dealer sat at a table, and at his right was an assistant who paid and collected the bets, and watched for trickery among the players. In front of the dealers was the dealing box, and the layout, the latter a suit of thirteen cards, usually spades, pasted or painted on a large square of enameled oilcloth. On the left of the dealer was another assistant who manipulated the case-keeper, a small box containing a miniature layout, with four buttons running along a steel rod opposite each card. The buttons were moved along, as on a billiard counter, as the cards were played, so that the players could tell at a glance what cards remained to be dealt. In some houses the progress of the game was also kept by the players on small printed sheets. The use of these sheets, however, was not general.

The cards in the layout were arranged in two parallel rows, with the ace on the dealer's left and the odd card, the seven, on his extreme right. Sufficient space was left between the rows for the players to place their bets. In the row nearest the players were the king, queen and jack, called the "big figure," and the ten, nine and eight. In the row nearest the dealer were the ace, deuce and trey, called the "little figure," and the four, five and six. The six, seven and eight were called the "pot." The king, queen, ace and deuce formed the "grand square"; the jack, three, four and ten were the "jack square," and the nine, eight, six and five were the "nine square."

All preliminaries having been arranged, the dealer shuffled and cut the cards, and then placed them face upward in the dealing box, the top of which was open. The card thus exposed was dead, as was the last card in the box, although as originally played, and in some sections of the country until comparatively recent times, both counted for the bank. When play began the cards were drawn through a slit in the box, a spring pushing the remainder of the pack into position. They were placed in two piles, one close to the box and the other about six inches away. The dead card began the farthest pile, on which all winning cards were placed.

The first card exposed in the box when the dead card had been withdrawn was a "loser" and counted for the bank. It began the pile nearest the box. The next card was a "winner," and counted for the players. Every two cards drawn in this manner were called a "turn," and the game thus proceeded until twenty-five turns had been made, in each of which there was a "winner" and a "loser." If two cards of the same denomination appeared on a single turn, it was called a "split," and the bank took half of all money which had been bet on the card. When the last turn was reached, with a "winner," a "loser," and a dead card remaining in the box, the players were invited to make bets on the order in which they would appear. To the correct guesser the bank paid four to one. If, however, two of the cards were of the same denomination, the odds were only two to one. On all turns before the last, even money was paid.

To avoid the confusion of betting upon a dead card, wagers were not placed until the pack had been cut and placed in the dealing box. In the early days of Faro bets could be made only upon the figures, the squares, the pot and single cards, but as the game developed they were allowed on innumerable combinations; for example, by using systems called "heeling" and "stringing along," it was possible to bet on twenty-one different groups of cards, all playing a single card to win.

The limit of a Faro game was determined by the prosperity of the banker, who announced before bets were made the amount for which he would play. The top limit was allowed when two, three or four cards, commonly called doubles, triples and quadruples, of a particular denomination remained in the box. When only a single, or case, card remained, thus giving the bank no chance of a split, the limit was halved. The banker also announced whether the limit would be open or running. If the former, a player was permitted to bet only a stipulated amount, but he could bet it as often as he pleased. If the latter, a gambler was given the privilege of "going paroli," a phrase which, incidentally, has been corrupted into parlay and is in common usage on the race tracks. In other words, a Faro player could parlay his winnings, if any, to a sum previously agreed upon as the extreme running limit, and then, if he wished, bet the whole upon a single card or combination. The running game was popular for many years, especially in New York and the East, but it was so obviously advantageous to the bank that eventually it fell into disfavor. By the beginning of the Civil War it had been abandoned everywhere except in the skinning-houses, where the best luck the player could expect in any event was a split.

For a hundred years after Faro had been transplanted to America, the game was dealt from a pack held face downward in the dealer's left hand. Dealing boxes were an American innovation, and made their appearance about 1822, when a Virginia gambler named Bayley constructed the first one and put it into a game at Richmond. It was of brass, about half an inch wider than a pack of cards and a little longer, and was covered over the top except for an oblong hole in the center, just large enough to enable the dealer to insert a single finger and push the top card through a slit in the side of the box, in which the pack had been placed face downward. Bayley attempted to market his invention, but it was not generally well received because it concealed the pack. The gambling houses in New Orleans refused to install it, and Faro continued to be dealt from the left hand until 1825, when a Cincinnati watchmaker named Graves invented and introduced an open dealing box which quickly caught the public fancy. Within a few years it was in use throughout the country, and with minor alterations and improvements has remained the standard. With the adoption of Graves's box, a change in the method of dealing was made—the pack was placed in the box face upward, and the top card was always exposed.

4

IN THE HANDS of a square dealer, Faro as played in the United States sixty or seventy years ago was the fairest banking game ever devised. In no other was the percentage against the player so small; many experts of the period, indeed, declared that with the first and last cards dead the bank had no advantage at all except what might be found in the splits, and that this was so slight as to make the game almost pure chance. Others estimated the percentage in favor of the bank at from one and one-half to three, still others held that it could not be precisely calculated; and some contended that if "heeling" and "stringing along" were permitted the percentage was actually in favor of the player. Said an old-time gambler in 1873:

"Faro is the only banking game of chance known to us whose percentage cannot be clearly defined. The best algebraists among the gambling community of this country have been unable to show us that Faro has one and three-fourths per cent in its favor. . . . Many mathematicians have set their brains to work to discover the exact percentage on Faro, but in every instance they have ignominiously failed. They have told us that on one thousand deals of the game, the splits on each deal will average one and one-half. Some of these astute calculators have told us that two splits per deal is a fair average, but it seems that none of them, as yet, have come to any definite conclusion on that or any of these points. They have also told us that a pack of cards in twenty-five turns, counting the 'soda' and 'hock' [the first and last cards] as dead cards, can come six hundred and two different ways, counting among that number, twenty-five splits which may take place. They have calculated the chances of quadruple, triple and double cards splitting at any stage of a deal. Still these clear heads are unable to arrive at the exact percentage on the game. Some think it will reach two and one-half per cent, while a majority of the most intelligent gamblers in the country believe it will not exceed one and one-half."

An almost conclusive argument for the theory that the percentage at honest Faro is virtually nonexistent is the fact that the canny management of Monte Carlo has never permitted the game to be played at that celebrated resort. "At Monte Carlo," wrote R. F. Foster, the foremost American authority on games for many years before the World War, "everything is perfectly fair and straightforward, but no games are played except those in which the percentage in favor of the bank is evident, and is openly acknowledged. In Faro there is no such advantage, and no honest Faro bank can live. It is for that reason that the game is not played at Monte Carlo, in spite of the many thousands of Americans who have begged the management to introduce it. The so-called percentage of splits at Faro is a mere sham, and any candid dealer will admit that they do not pay for the gas."

Foster estimated that in an honest game of Faro splits should occur about three times in two deals. But an honest game has always been a great rarity; Faro was a cheating business almost from the time of its invention. The earliest of the great Faro bankers of whom much is known, John Law and de Chalabre, were notorious cheats, and so, in the main, were their predecessors and successors. As early as 1731 the *Gentleman's Magazine,* of London, publishing a list of the employees of a first-class gambling house, referred to "a cheating game called Faro." Swindling at Faro on a large scale in the United States began soon after the introduction of the open dealing box, which also marked the beginning of the game's period of greatest popularity. Crooked boxes were in use within a few months after the invention of the watchmaker Graves had been placed on the market, and for years there was a steady stream of dishonest appliances bearing such impressive names as gaff, tongue-tell, sand-tell, top-sight tell, end squeeze, screw box, needle squeeze, lever movement, coffee-mill, and horse-box. They were all dealing boxes with the exception of the gaff, which was a small instrument shaped like a shoemaker's awl and worn attached to a finger ring. Occasionally one of the gadgets got out of order and caused considerable embarrassment to the unlucky sharper who owned it, but as a rule they worked perfectly in the hands of competent operators, although some of them were intricate contrivances of springs, levers, sliding plates, thumb screws, and needle-like steel rods. Many were devised and manufactured by Graves himself, and others were invented by Louis David of Natchez, also a watchmaker, who made a fortune in the 1840s selling German silver tongue-tell boxes at from $125 to $175 each.

These artifices were accompanied and followed by a flood of prepared cards. Some were strippers, which meant that the sides and ends of certain cards in each suit had been trimmed; others were readers, marked on the backs; while the backs of still others had been sanded or otherwise roughened—the best process was perfected by Graves—so that any two could be made to stick together. Strippers were cut in various ways, the most popular being hollows, rounds, rakes, wedges, and concave and convex, also known as "both ends against the middle." Any variety could be bought ready for use, but the careful gambler purchased shears, knives and trimming plates, and prepared his own stock. The portion shaved from each card was so slight—about one-thirty-second of an inch—as to be unnoticeable to the ordinary player, but it was large enough for the gambler to tell where the stripped cards lay in the pack. With the marked, stripped and sanded cards the sharper could stack the pack as he wished, and by using them in the crooked boxes he could make splits appear at his pleasure, deal two cards at a time, deal a card to lose when there was a heavy play on it to win, and arrange the last turn in a way that would mean most to the bank.

The advantages thus given the dealer were so widely used that cheating soon became as much a part of Faro in America as a pack of cards. The fundamental fairness of the game made such a situation well-nigh inevitable. A gambler who operated a Faro bank was put to considerable expense to provide quarters and the necessary apparatus, and he wasn't in the business for fun. "To justify this expenditure," wrote Foster, "he must have some permanent advantage, and if no such advantage or 'percentage' is inherent in the principles of the game, any person playing against such a banker is probably being cheated."

¶ *Mr. Asbury closes his chapter with some more quotations from R. F. Foster; but since we intend next to let Mr. Foster speak for himself, we will pass over that portion and say a few words about Mr. Foster.* ¶ *Robert Frederick Foster undoubtedly knew more about the rules and history of games, and wrote more books and articles about them, than any other man who ever lived. He was Scottish born (in 1853) but came to the United States as a very young man and spent most of the rest of his life here, though he punctuated it with much travel and dabbling in the most heterogeneous occupations, ranging from gold-prospecting to lecturing on Pelmanism. His first love always was games, and his major opus,* FOSTER'S COMPLETE HOYLE *(1897), was the best of its kind ever compiled and was the standard authority for thirty years. It is a commentary on the rapid change in games, and not on Foster's competency, when we observe that not one game still popularly played is correctly described in current editions of that book. It is a shame that the publishers of Foster's book persist in printing and selling new editions, which they misrepresent as "authoritative," to the detriment of Foster's reputation.* ¶ *R. F. Foster was a tiny man, perhaps five-two and 100 pounds, but his full beard, especially as it gradually grayed, gave him a distinguished look. Strangely enough, Foster never played any game even passably well. He was living testimony for the Shavian apothegm, "He who can, does. He who cannot, teaches." Because he played so poorly, and also because of his overfertile imagination that put all his anecdotes in disrepute, he was not highly respected by the card-playing fraternity. When he died in 1945, in his ninety-third year, no one took the trouble to be present at his interment except the gravediggers, an impatient undertaker's man, and one of the editors of this volume and his wife, who said one last prayer for the soul of Robert Frederick Foster.* ¶ *In his description of Faro, Mr. Foster grants the prevalence of dishonest dealers in the old Faro games, but—correctly—he does not say, as Mr. Asbury did, that the house must cheat to win. The few Faro banks still running (chiefly in Nevada) are nearly all honest. In fact, the house percentage is slightly larger in Faro than in craps; the profit, as in any business, depends on the turnover—plus other factors, as Mr. Foster will now point out.*

Faro Bank

by R. F. FOSTER

FIFTY or sixty years ago, there were no laws enforced against open gambling houses, which were the closest approach to a men's club in many large cities.

Faro and Keno were the most popular games, and even today Faro is still ranked by the professional gambler as the most interesting banking game in the world, on account of the variety of "systems" that have been devised to beat it. Society still plays Keno, or Bingo.

Faro is usually called Faro bank because it is played against a banker, who is assumed to have unlimited capital. No one ever broke a Faro bank. When one "breaks the bank" at Monte Carlo, it means only that the capital allotted to that particular table has been exhausted, and it is closed for the day. Thirty or more other tables are still in play.

An elementary description of Faro would be; a layout of the thirteen cards of the spade suit enameled on a green cloth, with spaces between for players to bet their chips. Behind this layout a dealer shuffles and places a pack of 52 cards, face up, in a dealing box, open at the top. A spring under the pack keeps it pushed up level with the top of the box as cards are withdrawn through a slit on the right, which is level with the top and visible card. This slit is just wide enough to permit the passage of only one card at a time.

A variation called "Stuss" can be played in any society gathering by dispensing with the dealing box, the banker holding the pack in his left hand. The thirteen spades can be spread on any ordinary table. A good supply of chips is the only extra equipment necessary.

The card showing on the top of the box is called "soda" and has no value. When the dealer pushes it off and lays it aside, the next card withdrawn and placed beside the box will be the "loser" on that turn, while the one now left exposed in the box will be the "winner." This process is followed until all cards have been withdrawn, two at a time. The cards in the layout represent denominations only; not suits.

The players arrange or change their bets before each turn, and the game is to guess whether the denomination they bet on will win or lose the first time it appears. A checker placed on the top of the chips indicates a bet to lose. Such bets are called "coppered" as coppers were originally used for that purpose.

If two of the same denomination come on the same turn, it is a "split," and the dealer takes half of all the money on that card, win or lose. This is popularly supposed to be the bank's only percentage in the game, and in a square game splits are due about three times in two deals. Greater frequency suggests something crooked.

The dealer takes and pays all bets after each turn, and waits for players to arrange, increase, or withdraw their bets for the next turn. The usual limit in a two-dollar game, one in which a stack of 20 white chips costs $2, is $50 on "open cards," and $25 on "cases"—denominations of which only one remains in the box, which of course cannot be split. On the last turn, when only three cards are left in the box, the dealer will bet 4 to 1 against any player's guessing their order. If two of them are of the same denomination, such as two 8's and a queen, it is called a "cat-hop," and the bank will bet only 2 to 1 against guessing it. The last card left in the box is called "hockelty" [and is said to be] "in hock."* In Stuss the dealer takes any bet left on this card; but not when dealing with a box.

A lookout, representing the capital backing the bank, sits on a high chair on the dealer's right, to see that bets are properly taken and paid from the check-rack on the dealer's right; red chips being worth 5 whites, and blue chips 5 reds. The lookout also protects the bank from possible collusion between the dealer and a player.

In order that players may know how many of each denomination are still to come, and to prevent them from betting on cards that have all been withdrawn, a record is kept by one of the players on a sort of abacus. In addition to this, printed slips are provided for the "system" players, to record the way each card came out.

Any bet left on a dead card, and apparently forgotten by its owner, becomes a "sleeper," and any player may take it as soon as the next turn is being made. "First come, first served." Many a tin-horn gambler has made a living sitting in a game as "case-keeper," and having a keen eye and a ready hand for sleepers. Good-natured dealers usually give such poor devils a chance; while others will reach for the sleeper them-

* From which, of course, the expression as ordinarily used is derived.

selves, just as they put their fingers on the top card to make the next turn.

CANFIELD'S HONEST CARDS

FARO CARDS [were] of the best linen, and the jacks [had] legs, to distinguish them from kings. The cards [had] square corners, and in crooked games the edges [were] sometimes trimmed for "wedges" or "strippers" [cards for cheating]. When District Attorney Jerome raided Canfield's place, he consulted me as a possible witness and pointed out a quantity of thin strips of card which he imagined might be the remains of cutting wedges. I assured him they were nothing but the dirty edges of used packs, as they were of unequal lengths. Faro cards are too expensive to throw away, and a very keen knife, such as the ones photographers use, can trim an infinitesimal strip, leaving the cards as good as new. Even after two or three such trimmings, the smallness of the reduction in the size of the pack detracts nothing from its usefulness.

HOW THE BANK WINS

To start a Faro bank, three professional dealers are required to take turns at the box, while the capital is invariably supplied by some rich man who has sufficient confidence that the dealers are honest, and that the investment will pay. I had an opportunity to examine the books of a Faro bank in Houston, Tex., more than sixty years ago,* and the record showed the average profit on a $2-a-stack bank, after deducting all running expenses, rent and salaries (police protection and racketeers being then unknown), was about $50 a day. This was evidently not all made on splits.

It is not so many years ago that a dealer named Vogel, or Fogley, was paid a salary of $150 a week and 25 per cent of the profits, by a Faro bank on Clark Street, in Chicago. That any person should be paid such an amount for pulling cards out of a box, two at a time, naturally arouses one's curiosity. To pay and take bets, with a lookout to help one, is a simple matter; an occasional mistake not being expensive. Fogley's dealing beat one man out of $80,000.

Once when a famous Faro-bank proprietor at Long Branch was explaining to some visitors who were curious to see a gambling house in daytime what a perfectly fair game it was, I ventured to suggest that as any bright typewriter girl could pull cards out of a box and settle the bets on a layout, he might allow me to put some such girl in as dealer for a month, with his own lookout.

If he agreed to allow me to advertise the arrangement for a few weeks in advance, I was sure I could get him a guarantee of $2,000 a week for the privilege. Of course every gambler in the United States would have wanted a seat at that table to take advantage of such an unheard-of snap. The professional gambler knows perfectly well that splits do not pay for modern electric lighting, any more than they used to pay for the gas.

A VALUABLE DEALER

THE SKILL of a professional Faro dealer is not acquired in a day. In Marshall, Texas, I had a room mate who called himself Pet Caffey. He had been an editor on a first-class New York daily; but had the misfortune to kill a man who had been too friendly with Caffey's sister. I never learned his real name; but he had taken to gambling and dealing Faro. He used to sit at a table for an hour at a time, with a shade over his eyes and a looking-glass exactly halfway across the table. This gave him the exact picture that a person sitting opposite him would have of his hands while shuffling a pack of cards. What he could do with a pack of Faro cards without even looking at them was beyond belief.

There is not the slightest danger of meeting any such skillful dealing in a social game of stuss, and in that form of the game the chances are at least as equal for the players as in shooting craps.

THE BANK'S ADVANTAGE

THE FIRST great advantage of the bank was that "a sucker will not sit and win as much as he will sit and lose." The other matter in the bank's favor was that nine men out of ten had a system; and once the dealer knew that system, he could beat it.

That they were right about the first item I already knew, as I had seen numerous examples during my two weeks at the Faro table. A leading town barber came in one night and lost about $600. He repeatedly asked the dealer to change the cards, which was always promptly done. Finally, he sent out and got a 5¢ pack of "steamboat" cards, and the dealer gladly used them, remarking to the interested spectators that "luck attaches to individuals; not to seats or cards."

Next day the barber came in with 50¢ in his pocket. He spent 25¢ of it on a sandwich and a glass of beer. The other 25¢ he threw down

* This was published in 1945.

in the "pot," a bet to take in the four cards at the end of the layout (queen-king-ace-deuce), to win. It won four times cumulative, and he had four dollars. By scattering his bets all over the place he ran this up to about eighty dollars, and was so afraid his luck would change that he cashed in and quit. The dealer ordered drinks for the house, and relieved his feelings by observing:

"That fellow backed his bad luck last night for six hundred. If he stayed with his good luck today he might have won six thousand."

NO FARO AT MONTE CARLO

I WAS ALWAYS curious to know why they did not deal Faro at Monte Carlo; but could never get any light on the subject until I went there. The explanation given me by one of the managers was simple enough. He said their principle was to depend entirely on percentages, however small, and they were satisfied there was no system, *as a system,* that would beat roulette; but there were systems that would beat Faro, if honestly dealt, and they would never allow a shadow of suspicion to fall on the honesty of their methods at Monte Carlo.

He pointed out that they had only one zero and had cut down the percentage against the players at roulette to the lowest point, letting them put their bets "in prison" if zero came up when they were betting on any of the even chances, and returning their money if they were correct on the next roll. They welcomed any system, all systems, confident that the percentage of the game and the limits to the bets would and must win out in the end. They could not see any such advantages in Faro.

¶ *In 1803, when the action of Tolstoy's* WAR AND PEACE *opens, Faro was the favored gambling game of the* haut monde *in France; and since the Russian nobility aped the French, Faro was necessarily the Russian favorite too.* ¶ *The game of Faro as Tolstoy describes it in the following passage required no such elaborate paraphernalia as the casino game. The dealer, or banker, held a pack of cards in his hand. Anyone betting against him might name a card, or draw a card from the dealer's pack, or draw a card from a "still" or unused pack. Each player having chosen his card and placed his bet, the dealer proceeded to expose the cards, two at a time, the first going on a "win" pile and the second on a "lose" pile. Suits did not count; when first the card of a player's rank showed up, the bet was settled. The player won if his card fell on the "win" pile and lost to the dealer if his card fell on the "lose" pile. The dealer had no mathematical advantage, for a split or pair called off the bet.* ¶ *The protagonists of the following excerpt are the young Count Nikolai Rostof and his former friend Dolokhof, who is in love with Rostof's cousin Sonya. Dolokhof has proposed to Sonya and has been refused because (as Dolokhof knows, though she did not say so) she is in love with Nikolai. Dolokhof has determined on revenge. Tolstoy does not say that Dolokhof can cheat when he wishes to, but the implication is quite clear.* ¶ *This is a powerful scene, one of the most powerful in a novel whose stature demands no comment here. Tolstoy shows how well he understands the process whereby the compulsive gambler is drawn farther and farther into the pit of heavy loss. The excerpt has been condensed somewhat to avoid unexplained allusions. The translation is that of Nathan Haskins Dole, edited by Princess Alexandra Kropotkin.*

from War and Peace

PART 9, CHAPTERS 13-15

by LEO TOLSTOY

FOR two days, Rostof had not seen Dolokhof at his house, or found him at home; on the third day he received a note from him:

"As I intend never to visit your house again, for reasons which you may appreciate, and as I am about to rejoin my regiment, I am going to give a farewell supper this evening to my friends. Come to the English Hotel."

At ten o'clock that evening, after the theater, where he had been with Denisof and his family, Rostof repaired to the place Dolokhof had designated. He was immediately shown into the handsomest room of the hotel, which Dolokhof had engaged for the occasion. A score of men were gathered around the table, at the head of which sat Dolokhof between two candles. There was a pile of gold and bills on the table, and Dolokhof was keeping the bank.

Since Dolokhof's proposal and Sonya's refusal, Nikolai had not seen him, and he felt a slight sense of confusion at the thought of their meeting. Dolokhof's keen, cold eyes met Nikolai's the moment he entered the room, as if he had been waiting for him for some time.

"We have not met for several days," said Dolokhof. "Thank you for coming. Here, I will only finish this hand. Ilyushka and his chorus are coming."

"I have called at your house," said Rostof, reddening.

Dolokhof made no answer.

"You may bet," he said.

Rostof recalled a strange conversation which he had once had with Dolokhof. "Only fools play on chance," had been Dolokhof's remark at the time.

"But perhaps you are afraid to play with me," said Dolokhof now, as if he read Rostof's thoughts, and he smiled.

By his smile Rostof could plainly see that he was in the same frame of mind as he had been at the time of the dinner at the club, or, one might say, at any of those times when Dolokhof, bored by the monotony of life, felt the necessity of escaping from it by some strange and outrageous action. Rostof felt ill at ease. He racked his brain but was unable to find an appropriate repartee for Dolokhof's words. But before he had a chance to reply, Dolokhof, looking straight into Rostof's face, said slowly, with deliberate intervals between the words, so that all might hear:

"Do you remember you and I were talking once about gambling? 'It's a fool, who is willing to play on chance. One ought to play a sure hand,' but I am going to try it."

Try the chance or the sure thing—I wonder which, thought Rostof.

"Well, you'd better not play," Dolokhof added, and springing the freshly opened pack of cards, he cried:

"Bank, gentlemen!"

Pushing the money forward, Dolokhof prepared to start the bank. Rostof took a seat near him and at first did not play. Dolokhof glanced at him.

"What? Won't you take a hand?" And strangely enough Nikolai felt it incumbent upon him to select a card and stake an insignificant sum on it, and thus begin to play.

"I have no money with me," he said.

"I will trust you."

Rostof staked five rubles on his card and lost; he staked again, and again he lost. Dolokhof took Rostof's stake ten times running.

"Gentlemen," said he, after he had been keeping the bank some time, "I beg of you to lay your stakes on the cards, otherwise I may become confused in the accounts."

One of the players ventured the hope that he was to be trusted.

"I trust you, certainly, but I am afraid of getting the accounts mixed. I beg of you to lay your money on the cards," replied Dolokhof. "Don't *you* worry, you and I will settle our accounts afterwards," he added, turning to Rostof.

The game went on; the servant kept filling their glasses with champagne.

All Rostof's cards failed to be matched, and his losses amounted to eight hundred rubles. He was just writing down on the back of a card "eight hundred rubles" but, as it happened that at that moment a glass of champagne was handed him, he hesitated, and once more staked the sum that he had been risking all along, that is, twenty rubles.

"Make it that," said Dolokhof, though he was apparently not looking at Rostof. "You'll win it back all the quicker. The others win but you keep losing. Or are you afraid of me?" he insisted.

Rostof acquiesced, staked the eight hundred which he had written down on a seven of hearts with a bent corner, which he had picked up from the floor. He remembered it well enough afterwards. He laid down this seven of hearts, after writing on the broken part the figures "eight hundred" in large, distinct characters; he drank the glass of foaming champagne handed to him by the waiter, smiled at Dolokhof's words, and, with a sinking at the heart, while hoping that a seven would turn up, watched the pack of cards in Dolokhof's hands.

The gain or loss dependent on this seven of hearts would have very serious consequences for Rostof. On the preceding Sunday, Count Ilya Andreyitch [Rostof] had given his son two thousand rubles, and, although he generally disliked to speak of his pecuniary difficulties, had told him that he could not have any more till May, and therefore begged him, for this once, to be rather economical. Nikolai had told him that two thousand rubles would be amply sufficient, and gave him his word of honor not to ask for any money till spring.

And now, out of that sum, only twelve hundred rubles were left. Of course, that seven of hearts, if he lost on it, would signify not only the loss of sixteen hundred rubles, but also the necessity of breaking his word to his father. With a sinking heart, therefore, he watched Dolokhof's hands, and said to himself:

Now let him hurry up and give me this card, and I will put on my cap and go home to supper with Denisof, Natasha, and Sonya, and truly I will never, as long as I live, take a card into my hands again.

At that instant his home life, his romps with

Petya, his talks with Sonya, his duets with Natasha, his game of Piquet with his father, and even his peaceful bed in his home on the Povarskaya, came to him with such force and vividness and attraction that it seemed to him like an inestimable bliss which had passed and been destroyed forever. He could not bring himself to believe that stupid chance, by throwing the seven of hearts to the right rather than to the left, might deprive him of all this just comprehended and just appreciated happiness and plunge him into the abyss of a wretchedness never before experienced, and of which he had no adequate idea. It could not be so, and yet, with a fever of expectation, he watched every motion of Dolokhof's hands. Those coarse reddish hands, with heavy knuckles and hairy wrists showing from under his shirt cuffs, laid down the pack of cards, took up the champagne glass that had been handed him, and put his pipe in his mouth.

"And so you are not afraid to play with me?" repeated Dolokhof, and, as if for the purpose of telling some humorous story, he laid down the cards, leaned back in his chair, and with a smile deliberately began to speak:

"Yes, gentlemen, I have been told that there is a report current in Moscow that I am a sharper, and so I advise you to be on your guard against me."

"Come now, deal ahead!" said Rostof.

"Oh! These Moscow old ladies!" exclaimed Dolokhof, and with a smile he took up the cards.

"O-o-o-oh!" almost screamed Rostof, clasping his head with both hands. The seven which he needed already lay on top, the very first card in the pack. He had lost more than he could pay.

"Now, don't ruin yourself!" said Dolokhof, giving Rostof a passing glance; and proceeded to deal the cards.

During the next hour and a half the majority of the gamblers watched their own play with only casual interest.

The whole game centered on Rostof alone. Instead of the sixteen hundred rubles against him there was already a long column of figures which he had reckoned to be at least ten thousand rubles, and which he now vaguely imagined to be perhaps fifteen thousand. In reality the sums added up to more than twenty thousand rubles. Dolokhof no longer listened to stories or told them himself; he watched each motion of Rostof's hands, and occasionally cast hasty glances at the paper containing Rostof's indebtedness. He had made up his mind to keep him playing until his losses should reach forty-three thousand rubles. He had selected this number because forty-three represented the sum of his and Sonya's ages. Rostof, supporting his head in both hands, sat in front of the table, now all written over, wet with wine, and littered with cards. One painful impression filled his mind; those wide-jointed, red hands with the hairy wrists, those hands which he loved and which he also hated, held him in their power.

Six hundred rubles, ace, quarter-stakes, nine-spot, impossible to win it back, and how gay it would be at home!—Knave on five—it cannot be.—And why is he treating me so?" said Rostof to himself, mingling his thoughts and recollections.

Sometimes he staked on a card a large sum, but Dolokhof refused to accept it and himself named the stake. Nikolai would submit, and then pray God, just as he prayed on the battlefield; then it would occur to him that perhaps the first card that he might draw from the pile of rejected cards on the table would save him; then he would count up the number of buttons on his jacket and select a card with the same number on which to stake the double of what he had already lost; then, again, he would look for aid to the other players, or glance into Dolokhof's face, now so cold, and try to read what was passing in his mind.

Of course he knows what this loss means for me. It cannot be that he desires me to lose like this. For he was my friend. For I loved him. But of course it isn't his fault; how can he help it if luck favors him? And neither am I to blame, said he to himself. I have done nothing wrong. Have I killed anyone, or insulted anyone, or wished anyone evil? Why, then, this horrible misfortune? And when did it begin? It was only such a short time ago that I came to the table with the idea of winning a hundred rubles so as to buy for mamma's birthday that jewel box, and then go home. I was so happy, so free from care, so gay! And I did not realize then how happy I was! When did it all end, and when did this new, this horrible state of things begin? What does this change signify? And here I am, just the same as before, sitting in the same place at this table, choosing and moving the same cards, and looking at those heavy-knuckled, dexterous hands. When did this take place and what is it that has taken place? I am well, strong, and just the same as I was, in the selfsame place! No, it cannot be! Surely this cannot end in such a way! His face was flushed, he was in a perspiration, in spite of the fact that it was not warm in the room. And his face was terrible and pitiable, especially because of his futile efforts to seem composed.

The list of his losses was nearing the fatal number of forty-three thousand. Rostof had in readiness a card with the corner turned down as the quarter-stakes for three thousand rubles, which he had just won, when Dolokhof, rapping with the pack, flung it down, and taking the lump of chalk began swiftly to reckon up the sum total of Rostof's losses with his firm, legible figures, breaking the chalk as he did so.

"Supper, it's time for supper, and here are the gypsies!"

It was a fact; at that moment a number of dark-skinned men and women came in, bringing with them a gust of cold air and saying something in their gypsy accent. Nikolai realized that all was over; but he said, in an indifferent tone, "What, can't we play any more? Ah, but I had a splendid little card all ready!"

Just as if the mere amusement of the game was what interested him the most!

All is over! I have lost! was what he thought. Now a bullet through my brains—that's all that's left. And yet he said, in a jocund tone, "Come now, just this one card!"

"Very well," replied Dolokhof, completing the sum total. "Very good! Make it twenty-one rubles then," said he, pointing to the figure twenty-one, which was over and above the round sum of forty-three thousand; and, taking up the pack of cards, he began to shuffle them. Rostof obediently turned back the corner and, instead of the six thousand which he was going to wager, carefully wrote twenty-one.

"It's all the same to me!" said he. "All I wanted to know was whether you would give me the ten or not."

Dolokhof gravely began to deal. Oh, how Rostof at that moment hated those red hands, with the short fingers and the hairy wrists emerging from the shirt cuffs, those hands that had him in their grasp!

The ten-spot fell to him.

"Well, you owe me just forty-three thousand, Count," said Dolokhof, getting up from the table and stretching himself. "One gets tired sitting still so long," he added.

"Yes, I am worn out, too," said Rostof.

Dolokhof, as if to remind him that it was not seemly to jest, interrupted him:

"When do you propose to pay me this money, Count?"

Rostof, coloring with shame, drew Dolokhof into another room. "I cannot pay you at such short notice, you must take my note," said he.

"Listen, Rostof," said Dolokhof, with a frank smile and looking into Nikolai's eyes, "you know the proverb: 'Lucky in love, unlucky at cards.' Your cousin is in love with you, I know."

"Oh! how horrible it is to be in this man's power," thought Rostof. He realized what a blow it would be to his father, to his mother, to learn that he had been gambling and had lost so much. He realized what happiness it would be if he could only have avoided doing it, or could escape confessing it, and he realized that Dolokhof knew how easily he might save him from this shame and pain, and yet here he was playing with him as a cat plays with a mouse.

"Your cousin," Dolokhof started to say, but Nikolai interrupted him.

"My cousin has nothing to do with this, and there is no need to bring her in," he cried, in a fury.

"Then when will you pay me?" demanded Dolokhof.

"Tomorrow," replied Rostof, and he left the room.

To say "tomorrow," and to preserve the conventional tone of decorum, was not hard; but to go home alone, to see his brother and sisters, his father and mother, to confess his fault and ask for money to which he had no right, after giving his word of honor, was horrible.

When Nikolai reached home the family were still up. The young people on their return from the theater had had supper and were now sitting at the clavichord. As soon as he entered the music room he felt himself surrounded by that romantic atmosphere of love which had reigned all winter in his home, and which now seemed to hang breathlessly around Sonya and Natasha, like the air before a thunderstorm.

Sonya sat at the clavichord playing the introduction to the barcarole which was Denisof's especial favorite. Natasha was getting ready to sing. Denisof gazed at her with ecstatic eyes.

Nikolai began to pace up and down the room.

Now, why should they want to make her sing? What can she sing? There's nothing here to make a fellow feel happy! said Nikolai to himself.

Sonya struck the first chord of the prelude.

My God, I am a ruined, dishonorable man! A bullet through my brain, that is the only thing left for me, and not singing! his thoughts went on. Go away? But where? Very well, let them sing!

Nikolai continued to stride up and down the room, glancing at Denisof and the girls, but avoiding their eyes.

Nikolenka, what is the matter? Sonya's eyes, fixed on him, seemed to ask. She had immediately seen that something unusual had happened to him.

Nikolai turned away from her. Natasha also, with her quickness of perception, had instantly noticed her brother's preoccupation. She had observed it, but she felt so gay at that time, her mood was so far removed from grief, melancholy, and reproaches, that (as often happens in the case of young girls) she purposely deceived herself. No, I'm too happy now to disturb my joy by trying to sympathize with the unhappiness of another, was her feeling, and she said to herself: No, of course I am mistaken. It must be that he is as happy as I am myself.

Natasha this winter had for the first time begun to take singing seriously; that was really because Denisof had been so enthusiastic about her voice. In it there was a girlish sensitivity, an unconsciousness of its own power, and an untrained velvet tone, combined with the lack of knowledge of the art of singing in such a way that it seemed as if it would be impossible to change anything in that voice without ruining it.

"What does this mean?" queried Nikolai, as he listened to her voice and opened his eyes wide. What has come over her? How she sings tonight! he said to himself. And suddenly all the world for him was concentrated on the expectation of the following note, the succeeding phrase, and everything in the world was divided into those three beats: *"Oh mio crudele affetto"* . . . one, two, three; one . . . two . . . three; one . . .

It was long since Rostof had experienced such delight from music as he did that night. But as soon as Natasha had finished her barcarole, grim reality again came back to him. Without saying a word to anyone, he left the room and went up to his own chamber. A quarter of an hour later the old count came in from the club, cheerful and satisfied. Nikolai, finding that his father had returned, went to his room.

"Well, have you had a pleasant day?" asked Ilya Andreyitch, smiling gaily and proudly at his son. Nikolai wanted to say yes, but he found it impossible; it was as much as he could do to keep from bursting into tears. The count began to puff at his pipe, and did not perceive his son's state of mind.

Well, it can't be avoided, said Nikolai to himself, for the first and last time. And suddenly, in a negligent tone which seemed to him utterly shameful, he said to his father, just as if he were asking for the carriage to drive downtown, "Papa, I came to speak to you about business. I had forgotten all about it. I need some money."

"What's that?" said the father, who had come home in a peculiarly good-natured frame of mind. "I told you that you wouldn't have enough. Do you need much?"

"Ever so much," said Nikolai, reddening, and with a stupid, careless smile which he could not for a long time pardon himself for. "I have been losing a little; that is, considerably; I might say a great deal—forty-three thousand."

"What? To whom? You are joking!" cried the count, flushing just as elderly men are apt to flush, with an apoplectic rush of blood coloring his neck and the back of his head.

"I promised to pay it tomorrow," continued Nikolai.

"Well!" said the old count, spreading his hands and falling helplessly back upon the divan.

"What's to be done? It's what might happen to anyone!" said the son, in a free and easy tone of banter, while all the time in his heart he was calling himself a worthless coward who could not atone by his whole life for such an act. He felt an impulse to kiss his father's hands, to fall on his knees and beg his forgiveness, but still he assured his father in that careless and even coarse tone that this was a thing likely to happen to anyone!

Count Ilya Andreyitch dropped his eyes when he heard his son's words, and fidgeted about as if he were trying to find something.

"Yes, yes," he murmured, "it'll be hard work, I am afraid . . . hard work to raise so much. . . . It happens to everyone, yes, yes, it happens to everyone."

And the count, with a swift glance at his son's face, rose to leave the room.

Nikolai was prepared for a refusal, but he had never expected this.

"Papa! Papa dear!" he cried, hastening after him with a sob. "Forgive me!" And, seizing his father's hand, he pressed it to his lips and burst into tears.

¶*Tolstoy wrote about Faro without naming it, on the assumption that his readers would recognize the game; another great Russian novelist, Dostoevski, writing about the times in Russia more than a generation later, saw fit to name the game. The novel, Dostoevski's (and one of the world's) most famous, is* THE BROTHERS

KARAMAZOV. *The eldest brother, Dmitri (or Mitya) is on a final wild fling prior to his inevitable arrest and trial for the murder of his father. With him are his light o' love, the femme fatale Grushenka, whom our teenagers would call a* KMUK *(crazy mixed-up kid), and whose rôle in drama Marilyn Monroe has rather publicly aspired to play; and two Polish adventurers who are intent chiefly on separating Dmitri from his money and who come eventually to a bad end in the best traditions of the motion-picture and television codes.* ¶*In contrast to the eighteen translations of* WAR AND PEACE, *there is only one direct translation of* THE BROTHERS KARAMAZOV *from the Russian to English. It was made by an Englishwoman, Constance Garnett, some fifty years ago. By coincidence, Prince Pyotr Kropotkin, then living in exile in England, was Miss Garnett's chief consultant at the time; and his daughter, Princess Alexandra Kropotkin, an American since the middle 'twenties, has edited and condensed this excerpt for us.* ¶*Dostoevski's insight into the psychology of the gambler is not subject to question. He ruined himself time after time by irresponsible gambling.* ¶*Pan means sir, Mr., gentleman.*

from The Brothers Karamazov
by FEODOR DOSTOEVSKI

WITH HIS long, rapid stride, Mitya walked straight up to the table.

"Gentlemen," he said in a loud voice, almost shouting, yet stammering at every word, "I . . . I'm all right! Don't be afraid!" he exclaimed, "I —there's nothing the matter." He turned suddenly to Grushenka, who had shrunk back in her chair toward Kalganov and clasped his hand tightly. "I . . . I'm coming along too. I'm here till morning. Gentlemen, may I stay with you till morning? Only till morning, for the last time, in this room?"

So he finished, turning to the fat little man, with the pipe, sitting on the sofa. The latter removed his pipe from his lips with dignity and observed severely, "Sir, we're here in private. There are other rooms."

"Why, it's you, Dmitri Fyodorovitch! What do you mean?" answered Kalganov suddenly. "Sit down with us. How are you?"

"Delighted to see you, my dear man—and my dear boys, I always thought a lot of you," Mitya responded, joyfully and eagerly, at once holding out his hand across the table.

"Aie! What a strong handshake you have! You've quite broken my fingers," laughed Kalganov.

"He always squeezes like that, always," Grushenka put in gaily, with a timid smile, suddenly convinced from Mitya's expression that he was not going to make a scene. She was watching him with intense curiosity and still some uneasiness. She was impressed by something about him, and indeed the last thing she expected of him was that he would come in and speak like this at such a moment.

"Good evening," Maximov ventured blandly, on the left. Mitya rushed up to him too.

"Good evening. You're here too! How glad I am to find you here too! Gentlemen, gentlemen, I . . ." (He addressed the Polish gentleman with the pipe again, evidently taking him for the most important person present.) "I rushed here . . . I wanted to spend my last day, my last hour in this room, in this very room . . . when I too adored . . . my queen . . . Forgive me, sir," he cried wildly, "I rushed here and vowed . . . Oh, don't be afraid, it's my last night! Let's drink to our good understanding. They'll bring the wine at once . . . I brought this with me." (Something made him pull out his bundle of notes.) "Allow me, sir! I want to have music, singing, a revel, as we had before. But the worm, the unnecessary worm, will crawl away, and there'll be no more of him. I will commemorate my day of joy and my last night."

He was almost choking. There was so much, so much he wanted to say, but strange exclamations were all that came from his lips. The Pole gazed fixedly at him, at the bundle of notes in his hand; looked at Grushenka, and was evidently perplexed.

"If my suverin lady is permitting——" he began.

"What does 'suverin' mean? 'Sovereign,' I suppose?" interrupted Grushenka. "I can't help laughing at you, the way you pronounce your words. Sit down, Mitya, what are you talking about? Don't frighten us, please. You won't frighten us, will you? If you won't, I am glad to see you . . ."

"Me, me frighten you?" cried Mitya, flinging up his hands. "Oh, forget about me, go your way, I won't hinder you!"

And suddenly he surprised them all, and no doubt himself as well, by flinging himself on a chair and bursting into tears, turning his face away to the opposite wall, while his arms clasped the back of the chair tight, as though embracing it.

"Come, come, what a fellow you are!" cried Grushenka reproachfully. "That's just how he comes to see me—he begins talking, and I can't make out what he means. He cried like that once before, and now he's crying again! It's shameful! Why are you crying? As though you had anything to cry for!" she added enigmatically, emphasizing each word with some irritability.

"I'm not crying . . . Well, good evening!" He instantly turned round in his chair, and suddenly laughed, not his abrupt, wooden laugh but a long, quivering, inaudible, nervous laugh.

"There you go again. Come, cheer up, cheer up," Grushenka said to him persuasively. "I'm very glad you've come, very glad. Mitya, do you hear, I'm very glad! I want him to stay here with us," she said peremptorily, addressing the whole company, though her words were obviously meant for the man sitting on the sofa. "I wish it, I wish it! And if he leaves I shall go too!" she added.

"What my queen commands is law!" pronounced the Pole, gallantly kissing Grushenka's hand. "I beg you, sir, to join our company," he added politely, addressing Mitya.

Mitya jumped up with the obvious intention of delivering another tirade, but the words did not come.

"Let's drink, sirs," he blurted out, instead of making a speech. Everyone laughed.

"Good heavens! I thought he was going to begin again!" Grushenka exclaimed nervously. "Do you hear, Mitya?" she went on insistently. "Don't prance about, but it's nice you've brought the champagne. I want some myself, and I can't bear liqueurs. And best of all, you've come yourself. We were fearfully dull here—You've come for a spree again, I suppose? But put your money in your pocket. Where did you get such a lot?"

Mitya all this time had been holding in his hand the crumpled bundle of notes on which the eyes of all, especially the Poles, were fixed. In confusion he thrust the notes hurriedly into his pockets. He flushed. At that moment the innkeeper brought in an uncorked bottle of champagne, and glasses on a tray. Mitya snatched up the bottle, but he was so bewildered that he did not know what to do with it. Kalganov took it from him and poured out the champagne.

"Another! Another bottle!" Mitya cried to the innkeeper, and, forgetting to clink glasses with the Pole whom he had solemnly invited to drink to their good understanding, he downed his glass without waiting for anyone. His whole countenance suddenly changed. The solemn and tragic expression with which he had entered vanished completely, and a childlike expression irradiated his face. He seemed to become suddenly gentle and subdued. He looked shyly and happily at everyone, with a continual nervous little laugh, and the blissful expression of a dog who has done wrong, been punished, and forgiven. He seemed to have forgotten everything, and looked round at everyone with a childlike smile of delight. He gazed at Grushenka, laughing continually, and brought his chair close up to her. By degrees he had gained some idea of the two Poles, though he had formed no definite conception of them yet.

The Pole on the sofa struck him by his dignified demeanor and his Polish accent; and above all, by his pipe. Well what of it? It's a good thing he's smoking a pipe, he reflected. The Pole's puffy, middle-aged face, with its tiny nose and two very thin, pointed, dyed and impudent-looking mustaches, had not so far roused the faintest doubts in Mitya. He was not even particularly struck by the Pole's absurd wig made in Siberia, with lovelocks foolishly combed forward over the temples. I suppose it's all right for him to wear a wig, he mused blissfully. The other, younger Pole, who was staring insolently and defiantly at the company and listening to the conversation with silent contempt, still only impressed Mitya by his great height, which was in striking contrast to the Pole on the sofa. If he stood up, he'd be six foot three—the thought flitted through Mitya's mind. It occurred to him, too, that this Pole must be the friend of the other, as it were, a "bodyguard," and no doubt the big Pole got his orders from the little Pole with the pipe. But this all seemed to Mitya perfectly natural and not to be questioned. In his state of doglike submissiveness all feeling of rivalry had died away.

Grushenka's mood and the enigmatic tone of some of her words he completely failed to grasp. All he understood, with a fast-beating heart, was that she was being kind to him, that she had forgiven him and made him sit by her. He was beside himself with delight, watching her sip her glass of champagne. The silence of the company seemed somehow to strike him, however, and he looked around at everyone with expectant eyes.

Why are we sitting here though, gentlemen? Why don't you begin doing something? his smiling eyes seemed to ask.

"He keeps talking nonsense, and we were all laughing," Kalganov began suddenly, as though divining his thoughts, and pointing to Maximov.

Mitya immediately stared at Kalganov and then at Maximov.

"Oh, it's certainly anything but amusing!" Kalganov mumbled.

"Let's play Faro again, as we did just now," Maximov tittered suddenly.

"Begin, gentlemen," Mitya assented, pulling his notes out of his pocket, and laying two hundred-ruble notes on the table. "I want to lose a lot to you. Take your cards. Make the bank."

"We'll have cards from the landlord, gentlemen," said the little Pole, gravely and emphatically.

"That's much the best way," chimed in Pan Vrublevsky.

"From the landlord? Very good, I understand, let's get them from him. Cards!" Mitya shouted to the landlord.

The landlord brought in a new, unopened pack, and informed Mitya that the girls were getting ready, and that the Jews with the cymbals would most likely be here soon; but the cart with the provisions had not yet arrived.

"Take your places, gentlemen," cried Pan Vrublevsky.

"No, I'm not going to play any more," observed Kalganov. "I've lost fifty rubles to them just now."

"The Polish gentleman had no luck, perhaps he'll be lucky this time," the Pole on the sofa observed in his direction.

"How much in the bank? To correspond?" asked Mitya.

"That's according, sirs, maybe a hundred, maybe two hundred, as much as you will stake."

"A million!" laughed Mitya.

"The Sir Captain has heard of Pan Podvysotsky, perhaps?"

"What Podvysotsky?"

"In Warsaw there is a bank and anyone comes and stakes against it. Podvysotsky comes, sees a thousand gold pieces, stakes against the bank. The banker says 'Podvysotsky, are you laying down the gold, or must we trust to your honor?' 'To my honor, pan,' says Podvysotsky. 'So much the better.' The banker throws the dice. Podvysotsky wins. 'Take it, Pan,' says the banker, and pulling out the drawer gives him a million. 'Take it, Pan, this is what you won.' There was a million in the bank. 'I didn't know that,' says Podvysotsky. 'Pan Podvysotsky,' said the banker, 'you pledged your honor and we pledged ours.' Podvysotsky took the million."

"That's not true," said Kalganov.

"Pan Kalganov, in gentlemanly society one doesn't say such things."

"As if a Polish gambler would give away a million!" cried Mitya, but checked himself at once. "Forgive me, gentlemen, it's my fault again, he would give away a million, for honor, for Polish honor. You see how I talk Polish, ha-ha! Here, I stake ten rubles, the jack leads."

"And I put a ruble on the queen, the queen of hearts, the pretty little panienotchka, he-he!" laughed Maximov, pulling out his queen; and, as though trying to conceal it from everyone, he moved right up and crossed himself hurriedly under the table. Mitya won. The ruble won too.

"A corner!" cried Mitya.

"I'll bet another ruble, a 'single' stake," Maximov muttered gleefully, hugely delighted at having won a ruble.

"Lost!" shouted Mitya. "A 'double' on the seven!"

The seven too was trumped [lost].

"Stop!" cried Kalganov suddenly.

"Double! Double!" Mitya doubled his stakes, and each time he doubled the stake, the card he doubled was trumped by the Poles. The ruble stakes kept winning.

"On the double!" shouted Mitya furiously.

"You've lost two hundred, sir. Will you stake another hundred?" the Pole on the sofa inquired.

"What? Lost two hundred already? Then another two hundred! All doubles!"

And pulling his money out of his pocket, Mitya was about to fling two hundred rubles on the queen, but Kalganov covered it with his hand.

"That's enough!" he shouted in his ringing voice.

"What's the matter?" Mitya stared at him.

"That's enough! I don't want to play any more. Don't!"

"Why?"

"Because I don't. Hang it, come away. That's why. I won't let you go on playing."

Mitya gazed at him in astonishment.

"Give it up, Mitya. He may be right. You've lost a lot as it is," said Grushenka, with a curious note in her voice. Both the Poles rose from their seats with a deeply offended air.

"Are you joking?" said the short man, looking severely at Kalganov.

"How dare you!" Pan Vrublevsky, too, growled at Kalganov.

"Don't dare to shout like that," cried Grushenka. "Ah, you turkey cocks!"

Mitya looked at each of them in turn. But something in Grushenka's face suddenly struck him, and at the same instant something new flashed into his mind—a strange new thought!

"Madame Agrippina," the little Pole began, crimson with anger, when Mitya suddenly went up to him and slapped him on the shoulder.

"Sir, two words with you."

"What do you want?"

"In the next room. I've two words to say to you, something pleasant, very pleasant. You'll be glad to hear it."

The little Pole was taken aback, and looked apprehensively at Mitya. He agreed at once, however, on condition that Pan Vrublevsky went with them.

"The bodyguard? Let him come, and I want him, too. I must have him!" cried Mitya. "March, gentlemen!"

"Where are you going?" asked Grushenka, anxiously.

"We'll be back in one moment," answered Mitya.

There was a sort of boldness, a sudden confidence shining in his eyes. His face had looked very different when he entered the room an hour before.

He led the Poles, not into the large room where the chorus of girls was assembling and the table was being laid, but into the bedroom on the right. The Poles looked severe but were evidently curious.

"What can I do for you, sir?" lisped the little Pole.

"Look, gentlemen, I won't keep you long. There's money for you," he pulled out his notes. "Would you like three thousand? Take it and go your way."

The Pole gazed, wide-eyed, at Mitya, with a searching look.

"Three thousand?" He exchanged glances with Vrublevsky.

"Three, three! Listen, sir, I see you're a sensible man. Take three thousand and go to the devil, and Vrublevsky with you—d'you hear? But at once, this very minute, and forever. You understand that, forever. Here's the door—you go out of it. What have you got there, a topcoat, a fur coat? I'll bring it out to you. They'll get the horses out directly, and then—good-by, good sirs!"

Mitya awaited an answer with assurance. He had no doubts. An expression of extraordinary resolution passed over the Pole's face.

"And the money, sir?"

"The money, gentlemen? Five hundred rubles I'll give you this moment for the journey, and as a first installment, and two thousand five hundred tomorrow, in the town—I swear on my honor, I'll get it, I'll get it at any cost!" cried Mitya.

The Poles exchanged glances again. The short man's face looked more forbidding.

"Seven hundred, seven hundred, not five hundred, at once, this minute, cash down!" Mitya added, feeling something wrong. "What's the matter, gentlemen? Don't you trust me? I can't give you the whole three thousand straight off. If I give it, you may come back to her tomorrow—besides, I haven't the three thousand with me. I've got it at home in the town," faltered Mitya, his spirit sinking at every word he uttered. "Upon my word, the money's there, hidden."

In an instant an extraordinary sense of personal dignity showed itself in the little man's face.

"What next?" he asked ironically. "For shame!" and he spat on the floor. Pan Vrublevsky spat too.

"You do that, gentlemen," said Mitya, recognizing with despair that all was over, "because you hope to make more out of Grushenka? You're a couple of pimps, that's what you are?"

"This is a mortal insult!" The little Pole turned as red as a lobster, and he went out of the room, briskly, as though unwilling to hear another word. Vrublevsky swung out after him, and Mitya followed, confused and crestfallen. He was afraid of Grushenka, afraid that the Polish gentlemen would at once raise an outcry. And so indeed he did. The Pole walked into the room and threw himself in a theatrical attitude before Grushenka.

"Lady Agrippina, I have received a mortal insult!" he exclaimed. But Grushenka suddenly lost all patience, as though they had wounded her in the tenderest spot.

"Speak Russian! Speak Russian!" she cried. "Not another word of Polish! You used to talk Russian. You can't have forgotten it in five years." She was red with passion.

"Lady Agrippina . . ."

"My name's Agrafena—Grushenka—speak Russian or I won't listen!"

The Pole gasped with offended dignity, and quickly and pompously delivered himself in broken Russian:

"Lady Agrafena, I came here to forget the past and forgive it, to forget all that has happened till today——"

"Forgive? Come here to forgive me?" Grushenka cut him short, jumping up from her seat.

"Just so, lady, I'm not a coward. I'm magnanimous. But I was astounded when I saw your lovers. Sir Mitya offered me three thousand, in the other room, to depart. I spat in the sir's face."

"What? He offered you money for me?" cried Grushenka, hysterically. "Is it true, Mitya? How dare you? Am I for sale?"

"Sweet lady, my lady," yelled Mitya, "she's pure and shining, and I have never been her lover! That's a lie . . ."

"How dare you defend me to him?" shrieked Grushenka. "It wasn't virtue kept me pure, and it wasn't that I was afraid of Kuzma, but that I might hold up my head when I met him, and tell him he's a scoundrel. And did he actually refuse the money?"

"He took it! He took it!" cried Mitya. "Only he wanted to get the whole three thousand at once, and I could only give him seven hundred straight off."

"I see—he heard I had money and came here to marry me!"

"Lady Agrippina!" cried the little Pole. "I'm —a knight, I'm—a nobleman, and not a peon. I came here to make you my wife and I find you a different woman, perverse and shameless."

"Oh, go back where you came from! I'll tell them to turn you out and you'll be turned out," cried Grushenka, furious. "I've been a fool, to have been miserable these five years! And it wasn't for his sake, it was my anger made me miserable. And this isn't he at all! Was he like this? It might be his father! Where did you get your wig from? He was an eagle, but this is a gander. He used to laugh and sing to me. . . . And I've been crying for five years, damned fool, abject, shameless creature that I was!"

She sank back in her low chair and hid her face in her hands. At that instant the chorus of Mokroe girls began singing in the room on the left—a rollicking dance song.

"A regular Sodom!" Vrublevsky roared suddenly. "Landlord, send the shameless hussies away!"

The landlord, who had been for some time past inquisitively peeping in at the door, hearing shouts and guessing that his guests were quarreling, at once entered the room.

"What are you shouting for? D'you want to split your throat?" he said, addressing Vrublevsky, with surprising rudeness.

"Swine!" bellowed Pan Vrublevsky.

"Swine? And what sort of cards were you playing with just now? I gave you a pack and you hid it. You played with marked cards! I could send you to Siberia for playing with false cards, d'you know that, for it's just the same as false bank notes . . ."

And going up to the sofa he thrust his fingers between the sofa back and the cushion and pulled out an unopened pack of cards.

"Here's my pack unopened!"

He held it up and showed it to all in the room. "From where I stood I saw him slip my pack away, and put his in place of it—you're a cheat and not a gentleman!"

"And I twice saw the Pole change a card!" cried Kalganov.

"How shameful! How shameful!" exclaimed Grushenka, clasping her hands, and blushing for genuine shame. "Good Lord, he's come to that!"

"I thought so too!" said Mitya. But before he had uttered the words, Vrublevsky, with a contorted and infuriated face, shook his fist at Grushenka, shouting, "You low harlot!"

Mitya flew at him at once, clutched him in both hands, lifted him in the air, and in one instant had carried him into the room on the right, from which they had just come.

"I've thrown him on the floor, there," he announced, returning at once, gasping with excitement. "He's struggling, the scoundrel! But he won't come back, no fear of that."

He closed one half of the folding doors, and holding the other ajar called out to the little Pole:

"Most illustrious, will you be pleased to retire at once?"

"My dear Dmitri Fyodorovitch," said Trifon Borissovitch, "make them give you back the money you lost. It's as good as stolen from you."

"I don't want my fifty rubles back," Kalganov declared suddenly.

"I don't want my two hundred, either," cried Mitya, "I wouldn't take it for anything! Let him keep it as a consolation."

"Bravo, Mitya! You're tops, Mitya!" cried Grushenka, and there was a note of fierce anger in the exclamation.

The little Pole, crimson with fury, but still mindful of his dignity, was making for the door, but he stopped short and said suddenly, addressing Grushenka, "Lady, if you want to come with me, come. If not, good-by."

And swelling with indignation and importance he went to the door. This was a man of character: he had so good an opinion of himself that after all that had happened, he still expected that she would marry him. Mitya slammed the door after him.

"Lock it," said Kalganov. But the key clicked on the other side; they had locked it from within.

"That's wonderful!" exclaimed Grushenka relentlessly. "Serves them right!"

[Finally the most celebrated of all the Russian stories about Faro—for Pushkin was the Russian Shakespeare and The Queen of Spades was his most famous story. It was the theme of Tchaikovsky's opera, (in French) Pique Dame, *or "Spade Queen." [The life of Aleksandr Sergeevich Pushkin is recorded in numerous biographies and biographical sketches. With peculiar propriety it has been called Byronic, for Pushkin (1799-1837) and Byron (1788-1824) were contemporaries; their birth was similarly aristocratic; their lives were similarly romantic, unconventional, and dramatic. Pushkin was not himself a wild gambler as Dostoevski was, but he lived at a time when gambling was the order of the day for young men of family and he surely saw much of it.*

The Queen of Spades
by
ALEKSANDR SERGEEVICH PUSHKIN

I

THERE WAS a card party at the rooms of Naroumoff of the Horse Guards. The long winter night passed away imperceptibly, and it was five o'clock in the morning before the company sat down to supper. Those who had won ate with a good appetite; the others sat staring absently at their empty plates. When the champagne appeared, however, the conversation became more animated, and all took a part in it.

"And how did you fare, Sourin?" asked the host.

"Oh, I lost, as usual. I must confess that I am unlucky: I play *mirandole,* I always keep cool, I never allow anything to put me out, and yet I always lose!"

"And you did not once allow yourself to be tempted to back the red? Your firmness astonishes me."

"But what do you think of Hermann?" said one of the guests, pointing to a young engineer. "He has never had a card in his hand in his life, he has never in his life laid a wager, and yet he sits here till five o'clock in the morning watching our play."

"Play interests me very much," said Hermann, "but I am not in the position to sacrifice the necessary in the hope of winning the superfluous."

"Hermann is a German; he is economical—that is all!" observed Tomsky. "But if there is one person that I cannot understand, it is my grandmother, the Countess Anna Fedorovna."

"How so?" inquired the guests.

"I cannot understand," continued Tomsky, "how it is that my grandmother does not punt."

"What is there remarkable about an old lady of eighty not punting?" said Naroumoff.

"Then you do not know the reason why?"

"No, really; haven't the faintest idea."

"Oh! Then listen. You must know that, about sixty years ago, my grandmother went to Paris, where she created quite a sensation. People used to run after her to catch a glimpse of the 'Muscovite Venus.' Richelieu made love to her, and my grandmother maintains that he almost blew out his brains in consequence of her cruelty. At that time ladies used to play at Faro. On one occasion at the Court, she lost a very considerable sum to the Duke of Orleans. On returning home, my grandmother removed the patches from her face, took off her hoops, informed my grandfather of her loss at the gaming table, and ordered him to pay the money. My deceased grandfather, as far as I remember, was a sort of house-steward to my grandmother. He dreaded her like fire; but on hearing of such a heavy loss, he almost went out of his mind; he calculated the various sums she had lost, and pointed out to her that in six months she had spent half a million of francs, that neither their Moscow nor Saratoff estates were in Paris, and finally refused point-blank to pay the debt. My grandmother gave him a box on the ear and slept by herself as a sign of her displeasure. The next day she sent for her husband, hoping that this domestic punishment had produced an effect upon him, but she found him inflexible. For the first time in her life, she entered into reasonings and explanations with him, thinking to be able to convince him by pointing out to him that there are debts and debts, and that there is a great difference between a prince and a coachmaker. But it was all in vain. My grandfather still remained obdurate. But the matter did not rest there. My grandmother did not know what to do. She had shortly before become acquainted with a very remarkable man. You have heard of Count St. Germain, about whom so many marvelous stories are told. You know that he represented himself as the Wandering Jew, as the discoverer of the elixir of life, of the philosopher's stone, and so forth. Some laughed at him as a charlatan; but Casanova, in his *Memoirs,* says that he was a spy. But be that as it may, St. Germain, in spite of the mystery surrounding him, was a very fascinating person, and was much sought after in the best circles of society. Even to this day my grandmother retains an affectionate recollection of him, and becomes quite angry if anyone speaks disrespectfully of him. My grandmother knew that St. Germain had large sums of money at his disposal. She resolved to have recourse to him, and she wrote a letter to him asking him to come to her without delay. The queer old man immediately waited upon her and found her overwhelmed with grief. She described to him in the blackest colors the barbarity of her husband, and ended by declaring that her whole hope depended upon his friendship and amiability.

St. Germain reflected.

" 'I could advance you the sum you want,' said he, 'but I know that you would not rest easy until you had paid me back, and I should not like to bring fresh troubles upon you. But there is another way of getting out of your difficulty: you can win back your money.'

" 'But, my dear Count,' replied my grandmother, 'I tell you that I haven't any money left.'

" 'Money is not necessary,' replied St. Germain; 'be pleased to listen to me.'

"Then he revealed to her a secret, for which each of us would give a good deal . . ."

The young officers listened with increased attention. Tomsky lit his pipe, puffed away for a moment and then continued:

"That same evening my grandmother went to Versailles to the *jeu de la reine*. The Duke of Orleans kept the bank; my grandmother excused herself in an offhanded manner for not having yet paid her debt, by inventing some little story, and then began to play against him. She chose three cards and played them one after the other: all three won, and my grandmother recovered every farthing that she had lost."

"Mere chance!" said one of the guests.

"A fairy tale!" observed Hermann.

"Perhaps they were marked cards!" said a third.

"I do not think so," replied Tomsky gravely.

"What!" said Naroumoff, "you have a grandmother who knows how to hit upon three lucky cards in succession, and you have never yet succeeded in getting the secret of it out of her?"

"That's the deuce of it!" replied Tomsky. "She had four sons, one of whom was my father; all four were determined gamblers, and yet not to one of them did she ever reveal her secret, although it would not have been a bad thing either for them or for me. But this is what I heard from my uncle, Count Ivan Ilitch, and he assured me, on his honor, that it was true. The late Chaplitsky—the same who died in poverty after having squandered millions—once lost, in his youth, about three hundred thousand rubles—to Zoritch, if I remember rightly. He was in despair. My grandmother, who was always very severe upon the extravagance of young men, took pity, however, upon Chaplitsky. She gave him three cards, telling him to play them one after the other, at the same time exacting from him a solemn promise that he would never play at cards again as long as he lived. Chaplitsky then went to his victorious opponent, and they began a fresh game. On the first card he staked fifty thousand rubles and won; he doubled the stake and won again, till at last, by pursuing the same tactics, he won back more than he had lost. . . .

"But it is time to go to bed: it is a quarter to six already."

And indeed it was already beginning to dawn; the young men emptied their glasses and then took leave of each other.

II

THE OLD COUNTESS A—— was seated in her dressing room in front of her looking glass. Three waiting maids were around her. One held a small pot of rouge, another a box of hairpins, and the third a tall cap with bright red ribbons. The Countess had no longer the slightest pretensions to beauty, but she still preserved the habits of her youth, dressed in strict accordance with the fashion of seventy years before, and made as long and as careful a toilette as she would have done sixty years previously. Near the window, at an embroidery frame, sat a young lady, her ward.

"Good morning, Grandmamma," said a young officer, entering the room. "*Bonjour, Mademoiselle Lise*. Grandmamma, I want to ask you something."

"What is it, Paul?"

"I want you to let me introduce one of my friends to you, and to allow me to bring him to the ball on Friday."

"Bring him direct to the ball and introduce him to me there. Were you at B——'s yesterday?"

"Yes; everything went off very pleasantly, and dancing was kept up until five o'clock. How charming Eletskaia was!"

"But, my dear, what is there charming about her? Isn't she like her grandmother, the Princess Daria Petrovna? By the way, she must be very old, the Princess Daria Petrovna."

"How do you mean, old?" cried Tomsky thoughtlessly, "she died seven years ago."

The young lady raised her head and made a

sign to the young officer. He then remembered that the old Countess was never to be informed of the death of any of her contemporaries, and he bit his lips. But the old Countess heard the news with the greatest indifference.

"Dead!" said she, "and I did not know it. We were appointed maids of honor at the same time, and when we were presented to the Empress. . . ." And the Countess for the hundredth time related to her grandson one of her anecdotes.

"Come, Paul," said she, when she had finished her story, "help me to get up. Lizanka, where is my snuffbox?"

And the Countess with her three maids went behind a screen to finish her toilette. Tomsky was left alone with the young lady.

"Who is the gentleman you wish to introduce to the Countess?" asked Lizaveta Ivanovna in a whisper.

"Naroumoff. Do you know him?"

"No. Is he a soldier or a civilian?"

"A soldier."

"Is he in the Engineers?"

"No, in the Cavalry. What made you think that he was in the Engineers?"

The young lady smiled, but made no reply.

"Paul," cried the Countess from behind the screen, "send me some new novel, only pray don't let it be one of the present-day style."

"What do you mean, Grandmother?"

"That is, a novel in which the hero strangles neither his father nor his mother, and in which there are no drowned bodies. I have a great horror of drowned persons."

"There are no such novels nowadays. Would you like a Russian one?"

"Are there any Russian novels? Send me one, my dear, pray send me one!"

"Good-by, Grandmother; I am in a hurry. Good-by, Lizaveta Ivanovna. What made you think that Naroumoff was in the Engineers?"

And Tomsky left the boudoir.

Lizaveta Ivanovna was left alone; she laid aside her work and began to look out of the window. A few moments afterwards, at a corner house on the other side of the street, a young officer appeared. A deep blush covered her cheeks; she took up her work again and bent her head down over the frame. At the same moment the Countess returned, completely dressed.

"Order the carriage, Lizaveta," said she, "we will go out for a drive."

Lizaveta arose from the frame and began to arrange her work.

"What is the matter with you, my child, are you deaf?" cried the Countess. "Order the carriage to be got ready at once."

"I will do so this moment," replied the young lady, hastening into the anteroom.

A servant entered and gave the Countess some books from Prince Paul Alexandrovitch.

"Tell him that I am much obliged to him," said the Countess. "Lizaveta! Lizaveta! where are you running to?"

"I am going to dress."

"There is plenty of time, my dear. Sit down here. Open the first volume and read to me aloud."

Her companion took the book and read a few lines.

"Louder," said the Countess. "What is the matter with you, my child? Have you lost your voice? Wait—give me that footstool—a little nearer—that will do!"

Lizaveta read two more pages. The Countess yawned.

"Put the book down," said she, "what a lot of nonsense! Send it back to Prince Paul with my thanks. But where is the carriage?"

"The carriage is ready," said Lizaveta, looking out into the street.

"How is it that you are not dressed?" said the Countess. "I must always wait for you. It is intolerable, my dear!"

Lizaveta hastened to her room. She had not been there two minutes, before the Countess began to ring with all her might. The three waiting-maids came running in at one door and the valet at another.

"How is it that you cannot hear me when I ring for you?" said the Countess. "Tell Lizaveta Ivanovna that I am waiting for her."

Lizaveta returned with her hat and cloak on.

"At last you are here!" said the Countess. "But why such an elaborate toilette? Whom do you intend to captivate? What sort of weather is it? It seems rather windy."

"No, Your Ladyship, it is very calm," replied the valet.

"You never think of what you are talking about. Open the window. So it is: windy and bitterly cold. Unharness the horses. Lizaveta, we won't go out—there was no need for you to deck yourself like that."

"What a life is mine!" thought Lizaveta Ivanovna.

And, in truth, Lizaveta Ivanovna was a very unfortunate creature. "The bread of the stranger is bitter," says Dante, "and his staircase hard to climb." But who can know what the bitterness of dependence is so well as the poor companion of an old lady of quality? The Countess A—— had by no means a bad heart, but she was capricious, like a woman who had been spoiled by the world, as well as being avaricious and egotistical, like all old people who have seen their best days, and whose thoughts are with the past and not the present. She participated in all the vanities of the great world, went to balls, where she sat in a corner, painted and dressed in old-fashioned style, like a deformed but indispensable ornament of the ballroom; all the guests on entering approached her and made a profound bow, as if in accordance with a set ceremony, but after that nobody took any further notice of her. She received the whole town at her house, and observed the strictest etiquette, although she could no longer recognize the faces of people. Her numerous domestics, growing fat and old in her antechamber and servants' hall, did just as they liked, and vied with each other in robbing the aged Countess in the most barefaced manner. Lizaveta Ivanovna was the martyr of the household. She made tea, and was reproached with using too much sugar; she read novels aloud to the Countess, and the faults of the author were visited upon her head; she accompanied the Countess in her walks, and was held answerable for the weather or the state of the pavement. A salary was attached to the post, but she very rarely received it, although she was expected to dress like everybody else, that is to say, like very few indeed. In society she played the most pitiable role. Everybody knew her, and nobody paid her any attention. At balls she danced only when a partner was wanted, and ladies would only take hold of her arm when it was necessary to lead her out of the room to attend to their dresses. She was very self-conscious, and felt her position keenly, and she looked about her with impatience for a deliverer to come to her rescue; but the young men, calculating in their giddiness, honored her with but very little attention, although Lizaveta Ivanovna was a hundred times prettier than the barefaced and cold-hearted marriageable girls around whom they hovered. Many a time did she quietly slink away from the glittering but wearisome drawing room, to go and cry in her own poor little room, in which stood a screen, a chest of drawers, a looking glass and a painted bedstead, and where a tallow candle burned feebly in a copper candlestick.

One morning—this was about two days after the evening party described at the beginning of this story, and a week previous to the scene at which we have just assisted—Lizaveta Ivanovna was seated near the window at her embroidery frame, when, happening to look out into the street, she caught sight of a young Engineers officer, standing motionless with his eyes fixed upon her window. She lowered her head and went on again with her work. About five minutes afterward she looked out again—the young officer was still standing in the same place. Not being in the habit of coquetting with passing officers, she did not continue to gaze out into the street, but went on sewing for a couple of hours, without raising her head. Dinner was announced. She rose up and began to put her embroidery away, but glancing casually out of the window, she perceived the officer again. This seemed to her very strange. After dinner she went to the window with a certain feeling of uneasiness, but the officer was no longer there—and she thought no more about him.

A couple of days afterward, just as she was stepping into the carriage with the Countess, she saw him again. He was standing close behind the door, with his face half concealed by his fur collar, but his dark eyes sparkled beneath his cap. Lizaveta felt alarmed, though she knew not why, and she trembled as she seated herself in the carriage.

On returning home, she hastened to the window—the officer was standing in his accustomed place, with his eyes fixed upon her. She drew back, a prey to curiosity and agitated by a feeling which was quite new to her.

From that time forward not a day passed without the young officer's making his appearance under the window at the customary hour, and between him and her there was established a sort of mute acquaintance. Sitting in her place at work, she used to feel his approach; and raising her head, she would look at him longer and longer each day. The young man seemed to be very grateful to her: she saw with the sharp eye of youth how a sudden flush covered his pale cheeks each time that their glances met. After about a week she commenced to smile at him. . . .

When Tomsky asked permission of his grandmother, the Countess, to present one of his friends to her, the young girl's heart beat violently. But hearing that Naroumoff was not an Engineer, she regretted that by her thoughtless question she had betrayed her secret to the volatile Tomsky.

Hermann was the son of a German who had become a naturalized Russian, from whom he had inherited a small capital. Being firmly convinced of the necessity of preserving his independence, Hermann did not touch his private income, but lived on his pay, without allowing himself the slightest luxury. Moreover, he was reserved and ambitious, and his companions rarely had an opportunity of making merry at the expense of his extreme parsimony. He had strong passions and an ardent imagination, but his firmness of disposition preserved him from the ordinary errors of young men. Thus, though a gamester at heart, he never touched a card, for he considered his position did not allow him—as he said—"to risk the necessary in the hope of winning the superfluous," yet he would sit for nights together at the card table and follow with feverish anxiety the different turns of the game.

The story of the three cards had produced a powerful impression upon his imagination, and all night long he could think of nothing else. If, he thought to himself the following evening, as he walked along the streets of St. Petersburg, if the old Countess would but reveal her secret to me! If she would only tell me the names of the three winning cards. Why should I not try my fortune? I must get introduced to her and win her favor—become her lover. . . . But all that will take time, and she is eighty-seven years old: she might be dead in a week, in a couple of days even! But the story itself: can it really be true? No! Economy, temperance and industry: those are my three winning cards; by means of them I shall be able to double my capital—increase it sevenfold, and procure for myself ease and independence.

Musing in this manner, he walked on until he found himself in one of the principal streets of St. Petersburg, in front of a house of antiquated architecture. The street was blocked with equipages; carriages, one after the other, drew up in front of the brilliantly illuminated doorway. At one moment there stepped out onto the pavement the well-shaped little foot of some young beauty, at another the heavy boot of a cavalry officer, and then the silk stockings and shoes of a member of the diplomatic world. Furs and cloaks passed in rapid succession before the gigantic porter at the entrance.

Hermann stopped. "Whose house is this?" he asked of the watchman at the corner.

"The Countess A——'s," replied the watchman.

Hermann started. The strange story of the three cards again presented itself to his imagination. He began walking up and down before the house, thinking of its owner and her strange secret. Returning late to his modest lodging, he could not go to sleep for a long time, and when at last he did doze off, he could dream of nothing but cards, green tables, piles of banknotes and heaps of ducats. He played one card after the other, winning uninterruptedly, and then he gathered up the gold and filled his pockets with the notes. When he woke up late the next morning, he sighed over the loss of his imaginary wealth, and then sallying out into the town, he found himself once more in front of the Countess's residence. Some unknown power seemed to have attracted him thither. He stopped and looked up at the windows. At one of these he saw a head with luxuriant black hair, which was bent down probably over some book or an embroidery frame. The head was raised. Hermann saw a fresh complexion and a pair of dark eyes. That moment decided his fate.

III

Lizaveta Ivanovna had scarcely taken off her hat and cloak when the Countess sent for her and again ordered her to get the carriage ready. The vehicle drew up before the door, and they prepared to take their seats. Just at the moment when two footmen were assisting the old lady to enter the carriage, Lizaveta saw her Engineer standing close beside the wheel; he grasped her hand; alarm caused her to lose her presence of mind, and the young man disappeared—but not before he had left a letter between her fingers. She concealed it in her glove, and during the whole of the drive she neither saw nor heard anything. It was the custom of the Countess, when out for an airing in her carriage, to be constantly asking such questions as: "Who was that person that met us just now?" "What is the name of this bridge?" "What is written on that signboard?" On this occasion, however, Lizaveta returned such vague and absurd answers that the Countess became angry with her.

"What is the matter with you, my dear?" she exclaimed. "Have you taken leave of your senses, or what is it? Do you not hear me or understand what I say? Heaven be thanked, I am still in my right mind and speak plainly enough!"

Lizaveta Ivanovna did not hear her. On returning home she ran to her room, and drew the letter out of her glove; it was not sealed. Lizaveta read it. The letter contained a declaration of love; it was tender, respectful, and copied word for word from a German novel. But Lizaveta did not know anything of the German language, and she was quite delighted.

For all that, the letter caused her to feel exceedingly uneasy. For the first time in her life she was entering into secret and confidential relations with a young man. His boldness alarmed her. She reproached herself for her imprudent behavior and knew not what to do. Should she cease to sit at the window and, by assuming an appearance of indifference towards him, put a check upon the young officer's desire for further acquaintance with her? Should she send his letter back to him, or should she answer him in a cold and decided manner? There was nobody to whom she could turn in her perplexity, for she had neither female friend nor adviser. At length she resolved to reply to him.

She sat down at her little writing table, took pen and paper, and began to think. Several times she began her letter and then tore it up—the way she had expressed herself seemed to her either too inviting or too cold and decisive. At last she succeeded in writing a few lines with which she felt satisfied.

"I am convinced," she wrote, "that your intentions are honorable, and that you do not wish to offend me by any imprudent behavior, but our acquaintance must not begin in such a manner. I return you your letter, and I hope that I shall never have any cause to complain of this undeserved slight."

The next day, as soon as Hermann made his appearance, Lizaveta rose from her embroidery, went into the drawing room, opened the ventilator and threw the letter into the street, trusting that the young officer would have the perception to pick it up.

Hermann hastened forward, picked it up and then repaired to a confectioner's shop. Breaking the seal of the envelope, he found inside it his own letter and Lizaveta's reply. He had expected this, and he returned home, his mind deeply occupied with his intrigue.

Three days afterwards, a bright-eyed young girl from a milliner's establishment brought Lizaveta a letter. Lizaveta opened it with great uneasiness, fearing that it was a demand for money, when suddenly she recognized Hermann's handwriting.

"You have made a mistake, my dear," said she. "This letter is not for me."

"Oh, yes, it is for you," replied the girl, smiling very knowingly. "Have the goodness to read it."

Lizaveta glanced at the letter. Hermann requested an interview.

"It cannot be," she cried, alarmed at the audacious request, and the manner in which it was made. "This letter is certainly not for me."

And she tore it into fragments.

"If the letter was not for you, why have you torn it up?" said the girl. "I should have given it back to the person who sent it."

"Be good enough, my dear," said Lizaveta, disconcerted by this remark, "not to bring me any more letters for the future, and tell the person who sent you that he ought to be ashamed."

But Hermann was not the man to be thus put off. Every day Lizaveta received from him a letter, sent now in this way, now in that. They were no longer translated from the German. Hermann wrote them under the inspiration of passion, and spoke in his own language, and they bore full testimony to the inflexibility of his desire and the disordered condition of his uncontrollable imagination. Lizaveta no longer thought of sending them back to him; she became intoxicated with them and began to reply to them, and little by little her answers became longer and more affectionate. At last she threw out of the window to him the following letter:

"This evening there is going to be a ball at the Embassy. The Countess will be there. We shall remain until two o'clock. You have now an opportunity of seeing me alone. As soon as the Countess is gone, the servants will very probably go out, and there will be nobody left but the Swiss, but he usually goes to sleep in his lodge. Come about half past eleven. Walk straight upstairs. If you meet anybody in the anteroom, ask if the Countess is at home. You will be told 'No,' in which case there will be nothing left for you to do but go away again. But it is most probable that you will meet nobody. The maidservants will all be together in one room. On leaving the anteroom, turn to the left, and walk straight on until you reach the Countess's bedroom. In the bedroom, behind a screen, you will find two doors: the one on the right leads to a cabinet, which the Countess never enters; the one on the left leads to a corridor, at the end of which is a little winding staircase; this leads to my room."

Hermann was restless, like a tiger, as he waited for the appointed time to arrive. At ten o'clock in the evening he was already in front of the Countess's house. The weather was terrible; the wind blew with great violence; the sleety snow fell in large flakes; the lamps emitted a feeble light; the streets were deserted; from time to time a sledge, drawn by a sorry-looking hack, passed by, on the lookout for a belated passenger. Hermann was enveloped in a thick overcoat, and felt neither wind nor snow.

At last the Countess's carriage drew up. Hermann saw two footmen carry out in their arms the bent form of the old lady, wrapped in sable fur, and immediately behind her, clad in a warm mantle, and with her head ornamented with a wreath of fresh flowers, followed Lizaveta. The door was closed. The carriage rolled away heavily through the yielding snow. The porter shut the street door; the windows became dark.

Hermann began walking up and down near the deserted house; at length he stopped under a lamp and glanced at his watch: it was twenty minutes past eleven. He remained standing under the lamp, his eyes fixed upon the watch, impatiently waiting for the remaining minutes to pass. At half-past eleven precisely, Hermann ascended the steps of the house and made his way into the brightly illuminated vestibule. The porter was not there. Hermann hastily ascended the staircase, opened the door of the anteroom and saw a footman sitting asleep in an antique chair by the side of a lamp. With a light, firm step Hermann passed by him. The drawing room and dining room were in darkness, but a feeble reflection penetrated thither from the lamp in the anteroom.

Hermann reached the Countess's bedroom. Before a shrine, which was full of old images, a golden lamp was burning. Faded stuffed chairs and divans with soft cushions stood in melancholy symmetry around the room, the walls of which were hung with China silk. On one side of the room hung two portraits painted in Paris by Madame Lebrun. One of these represented a stout, red-faced man of about forty years of age in a bright-green uniform and with a star upon his breast; the other, a beautiful young woman, with an aquiline nose, forehead curls and a rose in her powdered hair. In the corners stood porcelain shepherds and shepherdesses, dining-room clocks from the workshop of the celebrated Lefroy, bandboxes, roulettes, fans and the various playthings for the amusement of ladies that were in vogue at the end of the last century, when Montgolfier's balloons and Mesmer's magnetism were the rage. Hermann stepped behind the screen. At the back of it stood a little iron bedstead; on the right was the door which led to the cabinet; on the left—the other which led to the corridor. He opened the latter, and saw the little winding staircase which led to the room of the poor companion. But he retraced his steps and entered the dark cabinet.

The time passed slowly. All was still. The clock in the drawing room struck twelve; the strokes echoed through the room one after the other, and everything was quiet again. Hermann stood leaning against the cold stove. He was calm; his heart beat regularly, like that of a man resolved upon a dangerous but inevitable undertaking. One o'clock in the morning struck—then two—and he heard the distant noise of carriage wheels. An involuntary agitation took possession of him. The carriage drew near and stopped. He heard the sound of the carriage steps being let down. All was bustle within the house. The servants were running hither and thither, there was a confusion of voices, and the rooms were lit up. Three antiquated chambermaids entered the bedroom, and they were shortly afterwards followed by the Countess who, more dead than alive, sank into a Voltaire armchair. Hermann peeped through a chink. Lizaveta Ivanovna passed close by him, and he heard her hurried steps as she hastened up the little spiral staircase. For a moment his heart was assailed by something like a pricking of conscience, but the emotion was only transitory, and his heart became petrified as before.

The Countess began to undress before her looking glass. Her rose-bedecked cap was taken off, and then her powdered wig was removed from off her white and closely cut hair. Hairpins fell in showers around her. Her yellow satin dress, brocaded with silver, fell down at her swollen feet.

Hermann was a witness of the repugnant mysteries of her toilette; at last the Countess was in her nightcap and dressing gown, and in this costume, more suitable to her age, she appeared less hideous and deformed.

Like all old people in general, the Countess suffered from sleeplessness. Having undressed, she seated herself at the window in the Voltaire armchair and dismissed her maids. The candles were taken away, and once more the room was left with only one lamp burning in it. The Countess sat there looking quite yellow, mumbling with her flaccid lips and swaying to and fro. Her dull eyes expressed complete vacancy of mind, and, looking at her, one would have thought that the rocking of her body was not a voluntary action of her own, but was produced by the action of some concealed galvanic mechanism.

Suddenly the deathlike face assumed an inexplicable expression. The lips ceased to tremble, the eyes became animated—before the Countess stood an unknown man.

"Do not be alarmed, for Heaven's sake, do not be alarmed!" said he in a low but distinct voice. "I have no intention of doing you any harm. I have only come to ask a favor of you."

The old woman looked at him in silence, as if she had not heard what he had said. Hermann thought that she was deaf, and, bending down toward her ear, he repeated what he had said. The aged Countess remained silent as before.

"You can insure the happiness of my life," continued Hermann, "and it will cost you nothing. I know that you can name three cards in order——"

Hermann stopped. The Countess appeared now to understand what he wanted; she seemed as if seeking for words to reply.

"It was a joke," she replied at last. "I assure you it was only a joke."

"There is no joking about the matter," replied Hermann angrily. "Remember Chaplitsky, whom you helped to win."

The Countess became visibly uneasy. Her features expressed strong emotion, but they quickly resumed their former immobility.

"Can you not name me these three winning cards?" continued Hermann.

The Countess remained silent; Hermann continued:

"For whom are you preserving your secret? For your grandsons? They are rich enough without it; they do not know the worth of money. Your cards would be of no use to a spendthrift. He who cannot preserve his paternal inheritance will die in want, even though he had a demon at his service. I am not a man of that sort; I know the value of money. Your three cards will not be thrown away upon me. Come!"

He paused and tremblingly awaited her reply. The Countess remained silent; Hermann fell upon his knees.

"If your heart has ever known the feeling of love," said he, "if you remember its rapture, if you have ever smiled at the cry of your newborn child, if any human feeling has ever entered into your breast, I entreat you by the feelings of a wife, a lover, a mother, by all that is most sacred in life, not to reject my prayer. Reveal to me your secret. Of what use is it to you? Maybe it is connected with some terrible sin, with the loss of eternal salvation, with some bargain with the devil. Reflect—you are old; you have not long to live—I am ready to take your sins upon my soul. Only reveal to me your secret. Remember that the happiness of a man is in your hands, that not only I, but my children and grandchildren, will bless your memory and reverence you as a saint. . . ."

The old Countess answered not a word.

Hermann rose to his feet.

"You old hag!" he exclaimed, grinding his teeth. "Then I will make you answer!"

With these words he drew a pistol from his pocket.

At the sight of the pistol, the Countess for the second time exhibited strong emotion. She shook her head and raised her hands as if to protect herself from the shot—then she fell backwards and remained motionless.

"Come, an end to this childish nonsense!" said Hermann, taking hold of her hand. "I ask you for the last time: Will you tell me the names of your three cards, or will you not?"

The Countess made no reply. Hermann perceived that she was dead.

IV

Lizaveta Ivanovna was sitting in her room, still in her ball dress, lost in deep thought. On returning home, she had hastily dismissed the chambermaid who very reluctantly came forward to assist her, saying that she would undress herself, and with a trembling heart had gone up to her own room, expecting to find Hermann there, but yet hoping not to find him. At the first glance she convinced herself that he was not there, and she thanked her fate for having prevented his keeping the appointment. She sat down without undressing and began to recall to mind all the circumstances which in so short a time had carried her so far. It was not three weeks since the time when she first saw the young officer from the window—and yet she was already in correspondence with him, and he had succeeded in inducing her to grant him a nocturnal interview! She knew his name only through his having written it at the bottom of some of his letters; she had never spoken to him, had never heard his voice, and had never heard him spoken of until that evening. But, strange to say, that very evening at the ball, Tomsky, being piqued with the young Princess Pauline N——, who, contrary to her usual custom, did not flirt with him, wished to revenge himself by assuming an air of indifference; he therefore engaged Lizaveta Ivanovna and danced an endless mazurka with her. During the whole of the time he kept teasing her about her partiality for Engineer officers; he assured her that he knew far more than she imagined, and some of his jests were so happily aimed that Lizaveta thought several times that her secret was known to him.

"From whom have you learned all this?" she asked, smiling.

"From a friend of a person very well known to you," replied Tomsky, "from a very distinguished man."

"And who is this distinguished man?"

"His name is Hermann."

Lizaveta made no reply; but her hands and feet lost all sense of feeling.

"This Hermann," continued Tomsky, "is a man of romantic personality. He has the profile of a Napoleon, and the soul of a Mephistopheles. I believe that he has at least three crimes upon his conscience. . . . How pale you have become!"

"I have a headache. But what did this Hermann—or whatever his name is—tell you?"

"Hermann is very much dissatisfied with his friend: he says that in his place he would act very differently. I even think that Hermann himself has designs upon you; at least, he listens very attentively to all that his friend has to say about you."

"And where has he seen me?"

"In church, perhaps; or on the parade—God alone knows where. It may have been in your room, while you were asleep, for there is nothing that he——"

Three ladies approaching him with the question, *"Oubli ou regret?"* interrupted the conversation which had become so tantalizingly interesting to Lizaveta.

The lady chosen by Tomsky was the Princess Pauline herself. She succeeded in effecting a reconciliation with him during the numerous turns of the dance, after which he conducted her to her chair. On returning to his place, Tomsky thought no more either of Hermann or Lizaveta. She longed to renew the interrupted conversation, but the mazurka came to an end, and shortly afterwards the old Countess took her departure.

Tomsky's words were nothing more than the customary small talk of the dance, but they sank deep into the soul of the young dreamer. The portrait sketched by Tomsky coincided with the picture she had formed with her own mind, and, thanks to the latest romances, the ordinary countenance of her admirer became invested with attributes capable of alarming her and fascinating her imagination at the same time. She was now sitting with her bare arms crossed and with her head, still adorned with flowers, sunk upon her uncovered bosom. Suddenly the door opened and Hermann entered. She shuddered.

"Where were you?" she asked in a terrified whisper.

"In the old Countess's bedroom," replied Hermann. "I have just left her. The Countess is dead."

"My God! What do you say?"

"And I am afraid," added Hermann, "that I am the cause of her death."

Lizaveta looked at him, and Tomsky's words found an echo in her soul: "This man has at least three crimes upon his conscience!" Hermann sat down by the window near her, and related all that had happened.

Lizaveta listened to him in terror. So all those passionate letters, those ardent desires, this bold obstinate pursuit—all this was not love! Money—that was what his soul yearned for! She could not satisfy his desire and make him happy! The poor girl had been nothing but the blind tool of a robber, of the murderer of her aged benefactress! . . . She wept bitter tears of agonized repentance. Hermann gazed at her in silence: his heart, too, was a prey to violent emotion, but neither the tears of the poor girl nor the wonderful charm of her beauty, enhanced by her grief, could produce any impression upon his hardened soul. He felt no pricking of conscience at the thought of the dead old woman. One thing only grieved him: the irreparable loss of the secret from which he had expected to obtain great wealth.

"You are a monster!" said Lizaveta at last.

"I did not wish for her death," replied Hermann. "My pistol was not loaded."

Both remained silent.

The day began to dawn. Lizaveta extinguished her candle; a pale light illumined her room. She wiped her tear-stained eyes and raised them towards Hermann. He was sitting near the window, with his arms crossed and with a fierce frown upon his forehead. In this attitude he bore a striking resemblance to the portrait of Napoleon. This resemblance even struck Lizaveta.

"How shall I get you out of the house?" said she at last. "I thought of conducting you down the secret staircase, but in that case it would be necessary to go through the Countess's bedroom, and I am afraid."

"Tell me how to find this secret staircase—I will go alone."

Lizaveta arose, took from her drawer a key, handed it to Hermann and gave him the necessary instructions. Hermann pressed her cold, powerless hand, kissed her bowed head and left the room.

He descended the winding staircase, and once more entered the Countess's bedroom. The dead old lady sat as if petrified; her face expressed profound tranquillity. Hermann stopped before her, and gazed long and earnestly at her, as if he wished to convince himself of the terrible reality; at last he entered the cabinet, felt behind the tapestry for the door, and then began to descend the dark staircase, filled with strange emotions. Down this very staircase, thought he, perhaps coming from the very same room, and at this very same hour sixty years ago, there may have glided, in an embroidered coat, with his hair dressed *à l'oiseau royal* and pressing to his heart his three-cornered hat, some young gallant who has long been moldering in the grave, but the heart of his aged mistress has only today ceased to beat. . . .

At the bottom of the staircase Hermann found a door, which he opened with a key, and then traversed a corridor which conducted him into the street.

V

THREE DAYS after the fatal night, at nine o'clock in the morning, Hermann repaired to the Convent of ——, where the last honors were to be paid to the mortal remains of the old Countess. Although feeling no remorse, he could not altogether stifle the voice of conscience, which said to him: "You are the murderer of the old woman!" In spite of his entertaining very little religious belief, he was exceedingly superstitious; and believing that the dead Countess might exercise an evil influence on his life, he resolved to be present at her obsequies in order to implore her pardon.

The church was full. It was with difficulty that Hermann made his way through the crowd of people. The coffin was placed upon a rich catafalque beneath a velvet baldachin. The deceased Countess lay within it, with her hands crossed upon her breast, with a lace cap upon her head and dressed in a white satin robe. Around the catafalque stood the members of her household; the servants in black *caftans,* with armorial ribbons upon their shoulders, and candles in their hands; the relatives—children, grandchildren, and great-grandchildren—in deep mourning.

Nobody wept; tears would have been *une affectation.* The Countess was so old that her death could have surprised nobody, and her relatives had long looked upon her as being out of the world. A famous preacher pronounced the funeral sermon. In simple and touching words he described the peaceful passing away of the righteous, who had passed long years in calm preparation for a Christian end. "The angel of death found her," said the orator, "engaged in pious meditation and waiting for the midnight bridegroom."

The service concluded amidst profound silence. The relatives went forward first to take farewell of the corpse. Then followed the numerous guests, who had come to render the last homage to her who for so many years had been a participator in their frivolous amusements. After these followed the members of the Countess's household. The last of these was an old woman of the same age as the deceased. Two young women led her forward by the hand. She had not strength enough to bow down to the ground—she merely shed a few tears and kissed the cold hand of her mistress.

Hermann now resolved to approach the coffin. He knelt down upon the cold stones and remained in that position for some minutes; at last he arose, as pale as the deceased Countess herself; he ascended the steps of the catafalque and bent over the corpse. At that moment it seemed to him that the dead woman darted a mocking look at him and winked with one eye. Hermann started back, took a false step and fell to the ground. Several persons hurried forward and raised him up. At the same moment Lizaveta Ivanovna was borne fainting into the porch of the church. This episode disturbed for some minutes the solemnity of the gloomy ceremony. Among the congregation arose a deep murmur, and a tall thin chamberlain, a near relative of the deceased, whispered in the ear of an Englishman who was standing near him that the young officer was a natural son of the Countess, to which the Englishman coldly replied, "Oh!"

During the whole of that day Hermann was strangely excited. Repairing to an out-of-the-way restaurant to dine, he drank a great deal of wine, contrary to his usual custom, in the hope of deadening his inward agitation. But the wine only served to excite his imagination still more. On returning home, he threw himself upon his bed without undressing and fell into a deep sleep.

When he woke up it was already night, and the moon was shining into the room. He looked at his watch: it was a quarter to three. Sleep had left him; he sat down upon his bed and thought of the funeral of the old Countess.

At that moment somebody in the street looked in at his window, and immediately passed on again. Hermann paid no attention to this incident. A few moments afterwards he heard the door of his anteroom open. Hermann thought that it was his orderly, drunk as usual, returning from some nocturnal expedition, but presently he heard footsteps that were unknown to him: somebody was walking softly over the floor in slippers. The door opened, and a woman dressed in white entered the room. Hermann mistook her for his old nurse, and wondered what could bring her there at that hour of the night. But the white woman glided rapidly across the room and stood before him—and Hermann recognized the Countess!

"I have come to you against my wish," she said in a firm voice, "but I have been ordered to grant your request. Three, seven, ace will win for you if played in succession, but only on these conditions: that you do not play more than one card in twenty-four hours, and that you never play again during the rest of your life. I forgive you my death, on condition that you marry my companion, Lizaveta Ivanovna."

With these words she turned round very quietly, walked with a shuffling gait towards the door and disappeared. Hermann heard the street door open and shut, and again he saw someone look in at him through the window.

For a long time Hermann could not recover himself. He then rose up and entered the next room. His orderly was lying asleep upon the floor, and he had much difficulty in waking him. The orderly was drunk as usual, and no information could be obtained from him. The street-door was locked. Hermann returned to his room, lit his candle, and wrote down all the details of his vision.

VI

Two FIXED IDEAS can no more exist together in the moral world than two bodies can occupy one and the same place in the physical world. "Three, seven, ace" soon drove out of Hermann's mind the thought of the dead Countess. "Three, seven, ace" were perpetually running through his head and continually being repeated by his lips. If he saw a young girl, he would say, "How slender she is! quite like the three of hearts." If anybody asked, "What is the time?" he would reply, "Five minutes to seven." Every stout man that he saw reminded him of the ace. "Three, seven, ace" haunted him in his sleep, and assumed all possible shapes. The threes bloomed before him in the forms of magnificent flowers, the sevens were represented by Gothic portals, and the aces became transformed into gigantic spiders. One thought alone occupied his whole mind—to make a profitable use of the secret which he had purchased so dearly. He thought of applying for a furlough so as to travel abroad. He wanted to go to Paris and tempt fortune in some of the public gambling houses that abounded there. Chance spared him all this trouble.

There was in Moscow a society of rich gamesters, presided over by the celebrated Chekalinsky, who had passed all his life at the card table and had amassed millions, accepting bills of exchange for his winnings and paying his losses in ready money. His long experience secured for him the confidence of his companions, and his open house, his famous cook, and his agreeable and fascinating manners gained for him the respect of the public. He came to St. Petersburg. The young men of the capital flocked to his rooms, forgetting balls for cards, and preferring the emotions of Faro to the seductions of flirting. Naroumoff conducted Hermann to Chekalinsky's residence.

They passed through a suite of magnificent rooms, filled with attentive domestics. The place was crowded. Generals and privy councilors were playing at Whist; young men were lolling carelessly upon the velvet-covered sofas, eating ices and smoking pipes. In the drawing room, at the head of a long table, around which were assembled about a score of players, sat the master of the house, keeping the bank. He was a man of about sixty years of age, of a very dignified appearance; his head was covered with silvery-white hair; his full, florid countenance expressed good nature, and his eyes twinkled with a perpetual smile. Naroumoff introduced Hermann to him. Chekalinsky shook him by the hand in a friendly manner, requested him not to stand on ceremony, and then went on dealing.

The game occupied some time. On the table lay more than thirty cards. Chekalinsky paused after each throw, in order to give the players time to arrange their cards and note down their losses, listened politely to their requests, and more politely still, put straight the corners of cards that some player's hand had chanced to bend. At last the game was finished. Chekalinsky shuffled the cards and prepared to deal again.

"Will you allow me to take a card?" said Hermann, stretching out his hand from behind a stout gentleman who was punting.

Chekalinsky smiled and bowed silently, as a sign of acquiescence. Naroumoff laughingly congratulated Hermann on his abjuration of that abstention from cards which he had practiced for so long a period, and wished him a lucky beginning.

"Stake!" said Hermann, writing some figures with chalk on the back of his card.

"How much?" asked the banker, contracting the muscles of his eyes. "Excuse me, I cannot see quite clearly."

"Forty-seven thousand rubles," replied Hermann.

At these words every head in the room turned

suddenly around, and all eyes were fixed upon Hermann.

He has taken leave of his senses! thought Naroumoff.

"Allow me to inform you," said Chekalinsky, with his eternal smile, "that you are playing very high; nobody here has ever staked more than two hundred and seventy-five rubles at once."

"Very well," replied Hermann, "but do you accept my card or not?"

Chekalinsky bowed in token of consent.

"I only wish to observe," said he, "that although I have the greatest confidence in my friends, I can only play against ready money. For my own part, I am quite convinced that your word is sufficient, but for the sake of the order of the game, and to facilitate the reckoning up, I must ask you to put the money on your card."

Hermann drew from his pocket a bank note and handed it to Chekalinsky, who, after examining it in a cursory manner, placed it on Hermann's card.

He began to deal. On the right a nine turned up, and on the left a three.

"I have won!" said Hermann, showing his card.

A murmur of astonishment arose among the players. Chekalinsky frowned, but the smile quickly returned to his face.

"Do you wish me to settle with you?" he said to Hermann.

"If you please," replied the latter.

Chekalinsky drew from his pocket a number of bank notes and paid at once. Hermann took up his money and left the table. Naroumoff could not recover from his astonishment. Hermann drank a glass of lemonade and returned home.

The next evening he again repaired to Chekalinsky's. The host was dealing. Hermann walked up to the table; the punters immediately made room for him. Chekalinsky greeted him with a gracious bow.

Hermann waited for the next deal, took a card and placed upon it his forty-seven thousand rubles, together with his winnings of the previous evening.

Chekalinsky began to deal. A jack turned up on the right, a seven on the left.

Hermann showed his seven.

There was a general exclamation. Chekalinsky was evidently ill at ease, but he counted out the ninety-four thousand rubles and handed them over to Hermann, who pocketed them in the coolest manner possible and immediately left the house.

The next evening Hermann appeared again at the table. Everyone was expecting him. The generals and privy councilors left their Whist in order to watch such extraordinary play. The young officers quitted their sofas, and even the servants crowded into the room. All pressed around Hermann. The other players left off punting, impatient to see how it would end. Hermann stood at the table and prepared to play alone against the pale, but still smiling, Chekalinsky. Each opened a pack of cards. Chekalinsky shuffled. Hermann took a card and covered it with a pile of bank notes. It was like a duel. Deep silence reigned around.

Chekalinsky began to deal; his hands trembled. On the right a queen turned up, and on the left an ace.

"Ace has won!" cried Hermann, showing his card.

"Your queen has lost," said Chekalinsky, politely.

Hermann started; instead of an ace, there lay before him the queen of spades! He could not believe his eyes, nor could he understand how he had made such a mistake.

At that moment it seemed to him that the queen of spades smiled ironically and winked her eye at him. He was struck by her remarkable resemblance. . . .

"The old Countess!" he exclaimed, seized with terror.

Chekalinsky gathered up his winnings. For some time Hermann remained perfectly motionless. When at last he left the table, there was a general commotion in the room.

"Splendidly punted!" said the players. Chekalinsky shuffled the cards afresh, and the game went on as usual.

Hermann went out of his mind, and is now confined in room Number 17 of the Oboukhoff Hospital. He never answers any questions, but he constantly mutters with unusual rapidity: "Three, seven, ace! Three, seven, queen!"

Lizaveta Ivanovna has married a very amiable young man, a son of the former steward of the old Countess. He is in the service of the State somewhere, and is in receipt of a good income. Lizaveta is also supporting a poor relative.

Tomsky has been promoted to the rank of captain, and has become the husband of the Princess Pauline.

THE GREAT AMERICAN GAME

Bret Harte saw all the gambling games of the Wild West. His characters were often Poker players, but when he wrote about a game he favored the "family" games of his times, Euchre and Seven-up or Old Sledge. The following story runs the gamut, in and out of the San Francisco gaming parlors with their prismed chandeliers lighting up gentlemen in white tie and tails and ladies in décolletage that would fit the fashions of today—but what his homelier heroes really liked was a quiet game of Euchre by lantern-light. *The name Euchre defies etymologists; the game is the purely American form of the ancient Triomphe games of Europe (see page 23). Euchre is simplicity itself; each player is dealt five cards and tries to win more than half the tricks.*

Uncle Jim and Uncle Billy

by BRET HARTE

THEY were partners. The avuncular title was bestowed on them by Cedar Camp, possibly in recognition of a certain matured good humor, quite distinct from the spasmodic exuberant spirits of its other members, and possibly from what, to its youthful sense, seemed their advanced ages—which must have been at least forty! They had also set habits even in their improvidence, lost incalculable and unpayable sums to each other over Euchre regularly every evening, and inspected their sluice-boxes punctually every Saturday for repairs—which they never made. They even got to resemble each other, after the fashion of old married couples, or, rather, as in matrimonial partnerships, were subject to the domination of the stronger character; although in their case it is to be feared that it was the feminine Uncle Billy—enthusiastic, imaginative, and loquacious—who swayed the masculine, steady-going, and practical Uncle Jim. They had lived in the camp since its foundation in 1849; there seemed to be no reason why they should not remain there until its inevitable evolution into a mining town. The younger members might leave through restless ambition or a desire for change or novelty; they were subject to no such trifling mutation. Yet Cedar Camp was surprised one day to hear that Uncle Billy was going away.

The rain was softly falling on the bark thatch of the cabin with a muffled murmur, like a sound heard through sleep. The southwest trades were warm even at that altitude, as the open door testified, although a fire of pine bark was flickering on the adobe hearth and striking out answering fires from the freshly scoured culinary utensils on the rude sideboard, which Uncle Jim had cleaned that morning with his usual serious persistency. Their best clothes, which were interchangeable and worn alternately by each other on festal occasions, hung on the walls, which were covered with a coarse sailcloth canvas instead of lath-and-plaster, and were diversified by pictures from illustrated papers and stains from the exterior weather. Two "bunks," like ships' berths—an upper and lower one—occupied the gable-end of this single apartment, and on beds of coarse sacking, filled with dry moss, were carefully rolled their respective blankets and pillows. They were the only articles not used in common, and whose individuality was respected.

Uncle Jim, who had been sitting before the fire, rose as the square bulk of his partner appeared at the doorway with an armful of wood for the evening stove. By that sign he knew it was nine o'clock: for the last six years Uncle Billy had regularly brought in the wood at that hour, and Uncle Jim had as regularly closed the door after him, and set out their single table, containing a greasy pack of cards taken from its drawer, a bottle of whisky, and two tin drinking cups. To this was added a ragged memorandum book and a stick of pencil. The two men drew their stools to the table.

"Hol' on a minit," said Uncle Billy.

His partner laid down the cards as Uncle Billy extracted from his pocket a pillbox, and, opening it, gravely took a pill. This was clearly an innovation on their regular proceedings, for Uncle Billy was always in perfect health.

"What's this for?" asked Uncle Jim half scornfully.

"Agin ager."

"You ain't got no ager," said Uncle Jim, with the assurance of intimate cognizance of his partner's physical condition.

"But it's a pow'ful preventive! Quinine! Saw this box at Riley's store, and laid out a quarter on it. We kin keep it here, comfortable, for evenings. It's mighty soothin' arter a man's done a hard day's work on the river-bar. Take one."

Uncle Jim gravely took a pill and swallowed it, and handed the box back to his partner.

"We'll leave it on the table, sociable like, in case any of the boys come in," said Uncle Billy, taking up the cards. "Well. How do we stand?"

Uncle Jim consulted the memorandum book. "You were owin' me sixty-two thousand dollars on the last game, and the limit's seventy-five thousand!"

"Je whillikins!" ejaculated Uncle Billy. "Let me see."

He examined the book, feebly attempted to challenge the additions, but with no effect on the total. "We oughter hev made the limit a hundred thousand," he said seriously; "seventy-five thousand is only triflin' in a game like ours. And you've set down my claim at Angel's?" he continued.

"I allowed you ten thousand dollars for that," said Uncle Jim, with equal gravity, "and it's a fancy price too."

The claim in question being an unprospected hillside ten miles distant, which Uncle Jim had never seen, and Uncle Billy had not visited for years, the statement was probably true; nevertheless, Uncle Billy retorted:

"Ye kin never tell how these things will pan out. Why, only this mornin' I was taking a turn round Shot Up Hill, that ye know is just rotten with quartz and gold, and I couldn't help thinkin' how much it was like my old claim at Angel's. I must take a day off to go on there and strike a pick in it, if only for luck."

Suddenly he paused and said, "Strange, ain't it, you should speak of it to-night? Now I call that queer!"

He laid down his cards and gazed mysteriously at his companion. Uncle Jim knew perfectly that Uncle Billy had regularly once a week for many years declared his final determination to go over to Angel's and prospect his claim, yet nevertheless he half responded to his partner's suggestion of mystery, and a look of fatuous wonder crept into his eyes. But he contented himself by saying cautiously, "You spoke of it first."

"That's the more sing'lar," said Uncle Billy confidently. "And I've been thinking about it, and kinder seeing myself thar all day. It's mighty queer!" He got up and began to rummage among some torn and coverless books in the corner. "Where's that 'Dream Book' gone to?"

"The Carson boys borrowed it," replied Uncle Jim. "Anyhow, yours wasn't no dream—only a kind o' vision, and the book don't take no stock in visions." Nevertheless, he watched his partner with some sympathy and added, "That reminds me that I had a dream the other night of being in 'Frisco at a small hotel, with heaps o' money, and all the time being sort o' scared and bewildered over it."

"No?" queried his partner eagerly yet reproachfully. "You never let on anything about it to *me!* It's mighty queer you havin' these strange feelin's, for I've had 'em myself. And only tonight, comin' up from the spring, I saw two crows hopping in the trail, and I says, 'If I see another, it's luck, sure!' And you'll think I'm lyin', but when I went to the woodpile just now there was the *third* one sittin' up on a log as plain as I see you. Tell 'e what folks ken laugh—but that's just what Jim Filgee saw the night before he made the big strike!"

They were both smiling, yet with an underlying credulity and seriousness as singularly pathetic as it seemed incongruous to their years and intelligence. Small wonder, however, that in their occupation and environment—living daily in an atmosphere of hope, expectation, and chance, looking forward each morning to the blind stroke of a pick that might bring fortune—they should see signs in nature and hear mystic voices in the trackless woods that surrounded them. Still less strange that they were peculiarly susceptible to the more recognized diversions of chance, and were gamblers on the turning of a card who trusted to the revelation of a shovelful of upturned earth.

It was quite natural, therefore, that they should return from their abstract form of divination to the table and their cards. But they were scarcely seated before they heard a crackling step in the brush outside, and the free latch of their door was lifted. A younger member of the camp entered. He uttered a peevish "Halloo!" which might have passed for a greeting, or might have been a slight protest at finding the door closed, drew the stool from which Uncle Jim had just risen before the fire, shook his wet clothes like a Newfoundland dog, and sat down. Yet he was by no means churlish nor coarse-looking, and this act was rather one of easy-going, selfish, youthful familiarity than of rudeness. The cabin of Uncles Billy and Jim was considered a public right or "common" of the camp. Conferences between individual miners were appointed there. "I'll meet you at Uncle Billy's" was a common tryst. Added to this was a tacit claim upon the partners' arbitrative powers, or the equal right to request them to step outside if the interviews were of a private nature. Yet there was never any objection on the part of the partners, and to-night there was not a shadow of resentment of this intrusion in the patient, good-humored, tolerant eyes of Uncles Jim and Billy as they gazed at their guest. Perhaps there was a slight gleam of relief in Uncle Jim's when he found that the guest was unaccompanied by any one, and that it was not a tryst. It would have been unpleasant for the two partners to have stayed out in the rain while their guests were exchanging private confidences in their cabin. While there might have been no limit to their good will, there might have been some to their capacity for exposure.

Uncle Jim drew a huge log from beside the hearth and sat on the driest end of it, while their guest occupied the stool. The young man, without turning away from his discontented, peevish brooding over the fire, vaguely reached backward for the whisky bottle and Uncle Billy's tin cup, to which he was assisted by the latter's hospitable hand. But on setting down the cup his eye caught sight of the pillbox.

"Wot's that?" he said, with gloomy scorn. "Rat poison?"

"Quinine pills—agin ager," said Uncle Jim. "The newest thing out. Keeps out damp like Injin-rubber! Take one to follow yer whisky. Me and Uncle Billy wouldn't think o' settin' down, quiet like, in the evening arter work, without 'em. Take one—ye'r' welcome! We keep 'em out here for the boys."

Accustomed as the partners were to adopt and wear each other's opinions before folks, as they did each other's clothing, Uncle Billy was, nevertheless, astonished and delighted at Uncle Jim's enthusiasm over *his* pills. The guest took one and swallowed it.

"Mighty bitter!" he said, glancing at his hosts with the quick Californian suspicion of some practical joke. But the honest faces of the partners reassured him.

"That bitterness ye taste," said Uncle Jim quickly, "is whar the thing's gettin' in its work. Sorter sickenin' the malaria—and kinder waterproofin' the insides all to onct and at the same lick! Don't yer see? Put another in yer vest pocket; you'll be cryin' for 'em like a child afore ye get home. Thar! Well, how's things agoin' on your claim, Dick? Boomin', eh?"

The guest raised his head and turned it sufficiently to fling his answer back over his shoulder at his hosts. "I don't know what *you'd* call 'boomin',' " he said gloomily; "I suppose you two men sitting here comfortably by the fire, without caring whether school keeps or not, would call two feet of backwater over one's claim 'boomin';" I reckon *you*'d consider a hundred and fifty feet of sluicing carried away, and drifting to thunder down the South Fork, something in the way of advertising to your old camp. I suppose *you*'d think it was an inducement to investors! I shouldn't wonder," he added still more gloomily, as a sudden dash of rain down the wide-throated chimney dropped in his tin cup—"and it would be just like you two chaps, sittin' there gormandizing over your quinine—if yer said this rain that's lasted three weeks was something to be proud of!"

It was the cheerful and the satisfying custom of the rest of the camp, for no reason whatever, to hold Uncle Jim and Uncle Billy responsible for its present location, it's vicissitudes, the weather, or any convulsion of nature; and it was equally the partners' habit, for no reason whatever, to accept these animadversions and apologize.

"It's a rain that's soft and mellowin'," said Uncle Billy gently, "and supplin' to the sinews and muscles. Did ye ever notice, Jim"—ostentatiously to his partner—"did ye ever notice that you get inter a kind o' sweaty lather workin' in it? Sorter openin' to the pores!"

"Fetches 'em every time," said Uncle Billy. "Better nor fancy soap."

Their guest laughed bitterly. "Well, I'm going to leave it to you. I reckon to cut the whole concern to-morrow, and 'lite' out for something new. It can't be worse than this."

The two partners looked grieved, albeit they were accustomed to these outbursts. Everybody who thought of going away from Cedar Camp used it first as a threat to these patient men, after the fashion of runaway nephews, or made an exemplary scene of their going.

"Better think twice afore ye go," said Uncle Billy.

"I've seen worse weather afore ye came," said Uncle Jim slowly. "Water all over the Bar; the mud so deep ye couldn't get to Angel's for a sack o' flour, and we had to grub on pine nuts and jackass-rabbits. And yet—we stuck by the camp, and here we are!"

The mild answer apparently goaded their guest to fury. He rose from his seat, threw back his long dripping hair from his handsome but querulous face, and scattered a few drops on the partners. "Yes, that's just it. That's what gets me! Here you stick, and here you are! And here you'll stick and rust until you starve or drown! Here you are—two men who ought to be out in the world, playing your part as grown men—stuck here like children 'playing house' in the woods; playing work in your wretched mudpie ditches, and content. Two men not so old that you mightn't be taking your part in the fun of the world, going to balls or theatres, or paying attention to girls, and yet old enough to have married and have your families around you, content to stay in this God-forsaken place; old bachelors, pigging together like poorhouse paupers. That's what gets me! Say you *like* it? Say you expect by hanging on to make a strike—and what does that amount to? What are *your* chances? How many of us have made, or are making, more than grub wages? Say you're willing to share and share alike as you do—have you got enough for two? Aren't you actually living off each other? Aren't you grinding each other down, choking each other's struggles, as you sink together deeper and deeper in the mud of this cussed camp? And while you're doing this, aren't you, by your age and position here, holding out hopes to others that you know cannot be fulfilled?"

Accustomed as they were to the half-querulous, half-humorous, but always extravagant, criticism of the others, there was something so new in this arraignment of themselves that the partners for a moment sat silent. There was a slight flush on Uncle Billy's cheek, there was a slight paleness on Uncle Jim's. He was the first to reply. But he did so with a certain dignity which neither his partner nor their guest had ever seen on his face before.

"As it's *our* fire that's warmed ye up like this, Dick Bullen," he said, slowly rising, with his hand resting on Uncle Billy's shoulder, "and as it's *our* whisky that's loosened your tongue, I reckon we must put up with what ye'r' saying, just as we've managed to put up with our own way o' living, and not quo'll with ye under our own roof."

The young fellow saw the change in Uncle Jim's face and quickly extended his hand, with an apologetic backward shake of his long hair. "Hang it all, old man," he said, with a laugh of mingled contrition and amusement, "you mustn't mind what I said just now. I've been so worried thinking of things about *myself,* and, maybe, a little about you, that I quite forgot I hadn't a call to preach to anybody—least of all to you. So we part friends, Uncle Jim, and you too, Uncle Billy, and you'll forget what I said. In fact, I don't know why I spoke at all—only I was passing your claim just now, and wondering how much longer your old sluice-boxes would hold out, and where in thunder you'd get others when they caved in! I reckon that sent me off. That's all, old chap!"

Uncle Billy's face broke into a beaming smile of relief, and it was *his* hand that first grasped his guest's; Uncle Jim quickly followed with as honest a pressure, but with eyes that did not seem to be looking at Bullen, though all trace of resentment had died out of them. He walked to the door with him, again shook hands, but remained looking out in the darkness some time after Dick Bullen's tangled hair and broad shoulders had disappeared.

Meantime, Uncle Billy had resumed his seat and was chuckling and reminiscent as he cleaned out his pipe.

"Kinder reminds me of Jo Sharp, when he was cleaned out at Poker by his own partners in his own cabin, comin' up here and bedevilin' *us* about it! What was it you lint him?"

But Uncle Jim did not reply; and Uncle Billy, taking up the cards, began to shuffle them, smiling vaguely, yet at the same time somewhat painfully. "Arter all, Dick was mighty cut up about what he said, and I felt kinder sorry for him. And, you know, I rather cotton to a man that speaks his mind. Sorter clears him out, you know, of all the slumgullion that's in him. It's just like washin' out a pan o' prospecting: you pour in the water, and keep slushing it round and round, and out comes first the mud and dirt, and then the gravel, and then the black sand, and then—it's all out, and there's a speck o' gold glistenin' at the bottom!"

"Then you think there *was* suthin' in what he said?" said Uncle Jim, facing about slowly.

An odd tone in his voice made Uncle Billy look up. "No," he said quickly, shying with the instinct of an easy pleasure-loving nature from a possible grave situation. "No, I don't think he ever got the color! But wot are ye moonin' about for? Ain't ye goin' to play? It's mor' 'n half past nine now."

Thus adjured, Uncle Jim moved up to the table and sat down, while Uncle Billy dealt the cards, turning up the jack or right bower—but *without* that exclamation of delight which always accompanied his good fortune, nor did Uncle Jim respond with the usual corresponding simulation of deep disgust. Such a circumstance had not occurred before in the history of their partnership. They both played in silence—a silence only interrupted by a larger splash of raindrops down the chimney.

"We orter put a couple of stones on the chimney-top, edgewise, like Jack Curtis does. It keeps out the rain without interferin' with the draft," said Uncle Billy musingly.

"What's the use if—"

"If what?" said Uncle Billy quietly.

"If we don't make it broader," said Uncle Jim half wearily.

They both stared at the chimney, but Uncle Jim's eye followed the wall around to the bunks. There were many discolorations on the canvas, and a picture of the Goddess of Liberty from an illustrated paper had broken out in a kind of damp, measly eruption. "I'll stick that funny handbill of the 'Washin' Soda' I got at the grocery store the other day right over the Liberty gal. It's a mighty perty woman washin' with short sleeves," said Uncle Billy. "That's the comfort of them picters, you kin always get somethin' new, and it adds thickness to the wall."

Uncle Jim went back to the cards in silence. After a moment he rose again, and hung his overcoat against the door.

"Wind's comin' in," he said briefly.

"Yes," said Uncle Billy cheerfully, "but it wouldn't seem nat'ral if there wasn't that crack in the door to let the sunlight in o'mornin's. Makes a kind o' sundial, you know. When the streak o' light's in that corner, I says 'six o'clock!' when it's across the chimney I say 'seven!' and so 't is!"

It certainly had grown chilly, and the wind was rising. The candle guttered and flickered; the embers on the hearth brightened occasionally, as if trying to dispel the gathering shadows, but always ineffectually. The game was frequently interrupted by the necessity of stirring the fire. After an interval of gloom, in which each partner successively drew the candle to his side to examine his cards, Uncle Jim said:

"Say?"

"Well!" responded Uncle Billy.

"Are you sure you saw that third crow on the wood-pile?"

"Sure as I see you now—and a darned sight plainer. Why?"

"Nothin', I was just thinkin'. Look here! How do we stand now?"

Uncle Billy was still losing. "Nevertheless," he said cheerfully, "I'm owin' you a matter of sixty thousand dollars."

Uncle Jim examined the book abstractedly. "Suppose," he said slowly, but without looking at his partner, "suppose, as it's gettin' late now, we play for my half share of the claim agin the limit—seventy thousand—to square up."

"Your half share!" repeated Uncle Billy, with amused incredulity.

"My half share of the claim—of this yer house, you know—one half of all that Dick Bullen calls our rotten starvation property," reiterated Uncle Jim, with a half smile.

Uncle Billy laughed. It was a novel idea; it was, of course, "all in the air," like the rest of their game, yet even then he had an odd feeling that he would have liked Dick Bullen to have known it. "Wade in, old pard," he said. "I'm on it."

Uncle Jim lit another candle to reinforce the fading light, and the deal fell to Uncle Billy. He turned up jack of clubs. He also turned a little redder as he took up his cards, looked at them, and glanced hastily at his partner. "It's no use playing," he said. "Look here!" He laid down his cards on the table. They were the ace, king and queen of clubs, and jack of spades, —or left bower—which, with the turned-up jack of clubs—or right bower—comprised *all* the winning cards!

"By jingo! If we'd been playin' four-handed, say you an' me agin some other ducks, we'd have made 'four' in that deal, and h'isted some money—eh?" and his eyes sparkled. Uncle Jim, also, had a slight tremulous light in his own.

"Oh no! I didn't see no three crows this afternoon," added Uncle Billy gleefully, as his partner, in turn, began to shuffle the cards with laborious and conscientious exactitude. Then dealing, he turned up a heart for trumps. Uncle Billy took up his cards one by one, but when he had finished his face had become as pale as it had been red before. "What's the matter?" said Uncle Jim quickly, his own face growing white.

Uncle Billy slowly and with breathless awe laid down his cards, face up on the table. It was exactly the same sequence *in hearts,* with the knave of diamonds added. He could again take every trick.

They stared at each other with vacant faces and a half-drawn smile of fear. They could hear the wind moaning in the trees beyond; there was a sudden rattling at the door. Uncle Billy started to his feet, but Uncle Jim caught his arm. *"Don't leave the cards!* It's only the wind; sit down," he said in a low awe-hushed voice. "It's your deal; you were two before, and two now, that makes your four; you've only one point to make to win the game. Go on."

They both poured out a cup of whisky, smiling vaguely, yet with a certain terror in their eyes. Their hands were cold; the cards slipped from Uncle Billy's benumbed fingers; when he had shuffled them he passed them to his partner to shuffle them also, but did not speak. When Uncle Jim had shuffled them methodically he handed them back fatefully to his partner. Uncle Billy dealt them with a trembling hand. He turned up a club. "If you are sure of these tricks you know you've won," said Uncle Jim in a voice that was scarcely audible. Uncle Billy did not reply, but tremulously laid down the ace and right and left bowers.

He had won!

A feeling of relief came over each, and they laughed hysterically and discordantly. Ridiculous and childish as their contest might have seemed to a looker-on, to each the tension had been as great as that of the greatest gambler, without the gambler's trained restraint, coolness, and composure. Uncle Billy nervously took up the cards again.

"Don't," said Uncle Jim gravely; "it's no use —the luck's gone now."

"Just one more deal," pleaded his partner.

Uncle Jim looked at the fire, Uncle Billy hastily dealt, and threw the two hands face up on the table. They were the ordinary average cards. He dealt again, with the same result. "I told you so," said Uncle Jim, without looking up.

It certainly seemed a tame performance after their wonderful hands, and after another trial Uncle Billy threw the cards aside and drew his stool before the fire. "Mighty queer, warn't it?" he said, with reminiscent awe. "Three times running. Do you know, I felt a kind o' creepy feelin' down my back all the time. Criky! what luck! None of the boys would believe it if we told 'em—least of all that Dick Bullen, who don't believe in luck, anyway. Wonder what he'd have said! and, Lord! how he'd have looked! Wall! What are you starin' so for?"

Uncle Jim had faced around, and was gazing at Uncle Billy's good-humored, simple face. "Nothin'!" he said briefly, and his eyes again sought the fire.

"Then don't look as if you was seein' suthin' —you give me the creeps," returned Uncle Billy a little petulantly. "Let's turn in, afore the fire goes out!"

The fateful cards were put back into the drawer, the table shoved against the wall. The operation of undressing was quickly got over, the clothes they wore being put on top of their blankets. Uncle Billy yawned, "I wonder what kind of a dream I'll have tonight—it oughter be suthin' to explain that luck." This was his "good night" to his partner. In a few moments he was sound asleep.

Not so Uncle Jim. He heard the wind gradually go down, and in the oppressive silence that followed could detect the deep breathing of his companion and the far-off yelp of a coyote. His eyesight becoming accustomed to the semidarkness, broken only by the scintillation of the dying embers of their fire, he could take in every detail of their sordid cabin and the rude environment in which they had lived so long. The dismal patches on the bark roof, the wretched makeshifts of each day, the dreary prolongation of discomfort, were all plain to him now, without the sanguine hope that had made them bearable. And when he shut his eyes upon them, it was only to travel in fancy down the steep mountain side that he had trodden so often to the dreary claim on the overflowed river, to the heaps of "tailings" that encumbered it, like empty shells of the hollow, profitless days spent there, which they were always waiting for the stroke of good fortune to clear away. He saw again the rotten "sluicing," through whose hopeless rifts and holes even their scant daily earnings had become scantier. At last he arose, and with infinite gentleness let himself down from his berth without disturbing his sleeping partner, and wrapping himself in his blanket, went to the door, which he noiselessly opened. From the position of a few stars that were glittering in the northern sky he knew that it was yet scarcely midnight; there were still long, restless hours before the day! In the feverish state into which he had gradually worked himself it seemed to him impossible to wait the coming of the dawn.

But he was mistaken. For even as he stood there all nature seemed to invade his humble cabin with its free and fragrant breath, and invest him with its great companionship. He felt again, in that breath, that strange sense of freedom, that mystic touch of partnership with the birds and beasts, the shrubs and trees, in this greater home before him. It was this vague communion that had kept him there, that still held these world-sick, weary workers in their rude cabins on the slopes around him; and he felt upon his brow that balm that had nightly lulled him and them to sleep and forgetfulness. He closed the door, turned away, crept as noiselessly as before into his bunk again, and presently fell into a profound slumber.

But when Uncle Billy awoke the next morning he saw it was late; for the sun, piercing the crack of the closed door, was sending a pencil of light across the cold hearth, like a match to rekindle its dead embers. His first thought was of his strange luck the night before, and of disappointment that he had not had the dream of divination that he had looked for. He sprang to the floor, but as he stood upright his glance fell on Uncle Jim's bunk. It was empty. Not only that, but his *blankets*—Uncle Jim's own particular blankets—*were gone!*

A sudden revelation of his partner's manner the night before struck him now with the cruelty of a blow; a sudden intelligence, perhaps the very divination he had sought, flashed upon him like lightning! He glanced wildly around the cabin. The table was drawn out from the wall a little ostentatiously, as if to catch his eye. On it was lying the stained chamois-skin purse in which they had kept the few grains of gold remaining from their last week's "clean up." The grains had been carefully divided, and half had been taken! But near it lay the little memorandum book, open, with the stick of pencil lying across it. A deep line was drawn across the page on which was recorded their imaginary extravagant gains and losses, even to the entry of Uncle Jim's half share of the claim which he had risked and lost! Underneath were hurriedly scrawled the words:—

"Settled by *your* luck, last night, old pard.
—JAMES FOSTER."

It was nearly a month before Cedar Camp was convinced that Uncle Billy and Uncle Jim had dissolved partnership. Pride had prevented Uncle Billy from revealing his suspicions of the truth, or of relating the events that preceded Uncle Jim's clandestine flight, and Dick Bullen had gone to Sacramento by stagecoach the same morning. He briefly gave out that his partner had been called to San Francisco on important business of their own, that indeed might necessitate his own removal there later. In this he was singularly assisted by a letter from the absent Jim, dated at San Francisco, begging him not to be anxious about his success, as he had hopes of presently entering into a profitable business, but with no further allusions to his precipitate departure, nor any suggestion of a reason for it. For two or three days Uncle Billy was staggered and bewildered; in his profound simplicity he wondered if his extraordinary good fortune that night had made him deaf to some explanation of his partner's, or, more terrible, if he had shown some "low" and incredible intimation of taking his partner's extravagant bet as *real* and binding. In this distress he wrote to Uncle Jim an appealing and apologetic letter, albeit somewhat incoherent and inaccurate, and bristling with misspelling, camp slang, and old partnership jibes. But to this elaborate epistle he received only Uncle Jim's repeated assurances of his own bright prospects, and his hopes that his old partner would be more fortunate, single-handed, on the old claim. For a whole week or two Uncle Billy sulked, but his invincible optimism and good humor got the better of him, and he thought only of his old partner's good fortune. He wrote him regularly, but always to one address—a box at the San Francisco post office, which to the simple-minded Uncle Billy suggested a certain official importance. To these letters Uncle Jim responded regularly but briefly.

From a certain intuitive pride in his partner and his affection, Uncle Billy did not show these letters openly to the camp, although he spoke freely of his former partner's promising future, and even read them short extracts. It is needless to say that the camp did not accept Uncle Billy's story with unsuspecting confidence. On the contrary, a hundred surmises, humorous or serious, but always extravagant, were afloat in Cedar Camp. The partners had quarreled over their clothes—Uncle Jim, who was taller than Uncle Billy, had refused to wear his partner's trousers. They had quarreled over cards—Uncle Jim had discovered that Uncle Billy was in possession of a "cold deck," or marked pack. They had quarreled over Uncle Billy's carelessness in grinding up half a box of "bilious pills" in the morning's coffee. A gloomily imaginative mule-driver had darkly suggested that, as no one had really seen Uncle Jim leave the camp, he was still there, and his bones would yet be found in one of the ditches; while a still more credulous miner averred that what he had thought was the cry of a screech-owl the night previous to Uncle Jim's disappearance, might have been the agonized utterance of that murdered man. It was highly characteristic of that camp—and, indeed, of others in California—that nobody, not even the ingenious theorists themselves, believed their story, and that no one took the slightest pains to verify or disprove it. Happily, Uncle Billy never knew it, and moved all unconsciously in this atmosphere of burlesque suspicion. And then a singular change took place in the attitude of the camp towards him and the disrupted partnership. Hitherto, for no reason whatever, all had agreed to put the blame upon Billy—possibly because he was present to receive it. As days passed, that slight reticence and dejection in his manner, which they had at first attributed to remorse and a guilty conscience, now began to tell as absurdly in his favor. Here was poor Uncle Billy toiling through the ditches, while his selfish partner was lolling in the lap of luxury in San Francisco! Uncle Billy's glowing accounts of Uncle Jim's success only contributed to the sympathy now fully given in his behalf and their execration of the absconding partner. It was proposed at Biggs's store that a letter expressing the indignation of the camp over his heartless conduct to his late partner, William Fall, should be forwarded to him. Condolences were offered to Uncle Billy, and uncouth attempts were made to cheer his loneliness. A procession of half a dozen men twice a week to his cabin, carrying their own whisky and winding up with a "stag dance" before the premises, was sufficient to lighten his eclipsed gayety and remind him of a happier past. "Surprise" working parties visited his claim with spasmodic essays towards helping him, and great good humor and hilarity prevailed. It was not an unusual thing for an honest miner to arise from an idle gathering in some cabin and excuse himself with the remark that he "reckoned he's put in an hour's work in Uncle Billy's tailings!" And yet, as before, it was very improbable if any of these reckless benefactors *really* believed in their own earnestness or in the gravity of the situation. Indeed, a kind of hopeful cynicism ran through their performances. "Like as not, Uncle Billy is still in 'cahoots' [*i.e.*, shares] with his old pard, and is just laughin' at us as he's sendin' him accounts of our tomfoolin'."

And so the winter passed and the rains, and the days of cloudless skies and chill starlit nights began. There were still freshets from the snow reservoirs piled high in the Sierran passes, and the Bar was flooded, but that passed too, and only the sunshine remained. Monotonous as the seasons were, there was a faint movement in the camp with the stirring of the sap in the pines and cedars. And then, one day, there was a strange excitement on the Bar. Men were seen running hither and thither, but mainly gathering in a crowd on Uncle Billy's claim, that still retained the old partners' names in "The Fall and Foster." To add to the excitement, there was the quickly repeated report of a revolver, to all appearance aimlessly exploded in the air by some one on the outskirts of the assemblage. As the crowd opened, Uncle Billy appeared, pale, hysterical, breathless, and staggering a little under the back-slapping and hand-shaking of the whole camp. For Uncle Billy had "struck it rich"—had just discovered a "pocket," roughly estimated to be worth fifteen thousand dollars!

Although in that supreme moment he missed the face of his old partner, he could not help seeing the unaffected delight and happiness shining in the eyes of all who surrounded him. It was characteristic of that sanguine but uncertain life that success and good fortune brought no jealousy nor envy to the unfortunate, but was rather a promise and prophecy of the fulfillment of their own hopes. The gold was there —Nature but yielded up her secret. There was no prescribed limit to her bounty. So strong was this conviction that a long-suffering but still hopeful miner, in the enthusiasm of the moment, stooped down and patted a large boulder with the apostrophic "Good old gal!"

Then followed a night of jubilee, a next morning of hurried consultation with a mining expert and speculator lured to the camp by the good tidings; and then the very next night—to the utter astonishment of Cedar Camp—Uncle Billy, with a draft for twenty thousand dollars in his pocket, started for San Francisco, and took leave of his claim and the camp forever!

When Uncle Billy landed at the wharves of San Francisco he was a little bewildered. The Golden Gate beyond was obliterated by the incoming sea fog, which had also roofed in the whole city, and lights already glittered along the gray streets that climbed the grayer sand hills. As a Western man, brought up by inland rivers, he was fascinated and thrilled by the tall-masted seagoing ships, and he felt a strange sense of the remoter mysterious ocean, which he had never seen. But he was impressed and startled by smartly dressed men and women, the passing of carriages, and a sudden conviction that he was strange and foreign to what he saw. It had been his cherished intention to call upon his old partner in his working clothes, and then clap down on the table before him a draft for ten thousand dollars as *his* share of their old claim. But in the face of these brilliant strangers a sudden and unexpected timidity came upon him. He had heard of a cheap popular hotel, much frequented by the returning goldminer, who entered its hospitable doors—which held an easy access to shops—and emerged in a few hours a gorgeous butterfly of fashion, leaving his old chrysalis behind him. Thence he inquired his way; hence he afterwards issued in garments glaringly new and ill fitting. But he had not sacrificed his beard, and there was still something fine and original in his handsome weak face that overcame the cheap convention of his clothes. Making his way to the post office, he was again discomfited by the great size of the building, and bewildered by the array of little square letterboxes behind glass which occupied one whole wall, and an equal number of opaque and locked wooden ones legibly numbered. His heart leaped; he remembered the number, and before him was a window with a clerk behind it. Uncle Billy leaned forward.

"Kin you tell me if the man that box 690 b'longs to is in?"

The clerk stared, made him repeat the question, and then turned away. But he returned almost instantly, with two or three grinning heads besides his own, apparently set behind his shoulders. Uncle Billy was again asked to repeat his question. He did so.

"Why don't you go and see if 690 is in his box?" said the first clerk, turning with affected asperity to one of the others.

The clerk went away, returned, and said with singular gravity, "He was there a moment ago, but he's gone out to stretch his legs. It's rather crampin' at first; and he can't stand it more than ten hours at a time, you know."

But simplicity has its limits. Uncle Billy had already guessed his real error in believing his partner was officially connected with the building; his cheek had flushed and then paled again. The pupils of his blue eyes had contracted into suggestive black points. "Ef you'll let me in at that winder, young fellers," he said, with equal gravity, "I'll show yer how I kin make *you* small enough to go in a box without crampin'! But I only wanted to know where Jim Foster *lived*."

At which the first clerk became perfunctory again, but civil. "A letter left in his box would get you that information," he said, "and here's paper and pencil to write it now."

Uncle Billy took the paper and began to write, "Just got here. Come and see me at—" He paused. A brilliant idea had struck him; he could impress both his old partner and the upstarts at the window; he would put in the name of the latest "swell" hotel in San Francisco, said to be a fairy dream of opulence. He added "The Oriental," and without folding the paper shoved it in the window.

"Don't you want an envelope?" asked the clerk.

"Put a stamp on the corner of it," responded Uncle Billy, laying down a coin, "and she'll go through." The clerk smiled, but affixed the stamp, and Uncle Billy turned away.

But it was a short-lived triumph. The disappointment at finding Uncle Jim's address conveyed no idea of his habitation seemed to remove him farther away, and lose his identity in the great city. Besides, he must now make good his own address, and seek rooms at the Oriental. He went thither. The furniture and decorations, even in these early days of hotel building in San Francisco, were extravagant and overstrained, and Uncle Billy felt lost and lonely in his strange surroundings. But he took a handsome suite of rooms, paid for them in advance on the spot, and then, half frightened, walked out of them to ramble vaguely through the city in the feverish hope of meeting his old partner. At night his inquietude increased; he could not face the long row of tables in the pillared dining room, filled with smartly dressed men and women; he evaded his bedroom, with its brocaded satin chairs and its gilt bedstead, and fled to his modest lodgings at the Good Cheer House, and appeased his hunger at its cheap restaurant, in the company of retired miners and freshly arrived Eastern emigrants. Two or three days passed thus in this quaint double existence. Three or four times a day he would enter the gorgeous Oriental with affected ease and carelessness, demand his key from the hotel clerk, ask for the letter that did not come, go to his room, gaze vaguely from his window on the passing crowd below for the partner he could not find, and then return to the Good Cheer House for rest and sustenance. On the fourth day he received a short note from Uncle Jim; it was couched in his usual sanguine but brief and businesslike style. He was very sorry, but important and profitable business took him out of town, but he trusted to return soon and welcome his old partner. He was also, for the first time, jocose, and hoped that Uncle Billy would not "see all the sights" before he, Uncle Jim, returned. Disappointing as this procrastination was to Uncle Billy, a gleam of hope irradiated it: the letter had bridged over that gulf which seemed to yawn between them at the post office. His old partner had accepted his visit to San Francisco without question, and had alluded to a renewal of their old intimacy. For Uncle Billy, with all his trustful simplicity, had been tortured by two harrowing doubts: one, whether Uncle Jim in his new-fledged smartness as a "city" man—such as he saw in the streets—would care for his rough companionship; the other, whether he, Uncle Billy, ought not to tell him at once of his changed fortune. But, like all weak, unreasoning men, he clung desperately to a detail—he could not forego his old idea of astounding Uncle Jim by giving him his share of the "strike" as his first intimation of it, and he doubted, with more reason perhaps, if Jim would see him after he had heard of his good fortune. For Uncle Billy had still a frightened recollection of Uncle Jim's sudden stroke for independence, and that rigid punctiliousness which had made him doggedly accept the responsibility of his extravagant stake at Euchre.

With a view of educating himself for Uncle Jim's company, he "saw the sights" of San Francisco—as an overgrown and somewhat stupid child might have seen them—with great curiosity, but little contamination or corruption. But I think he was chiefly pleased with watching the arrival of the Sacramento and Stockton steamers at the wharves, in the hope of discovering his old partner among the passengers on the gangplank. Here, with his old superstitious tendency and gambler's instinct, he would augur great success in his search that day if any of the passengers bore the least resemblance to Uncle Jim, if a man or woman stepped off first, or if he met a single person's questioning eye. Indeed, this got to be the real occupation of the day, which he would on no account have omitted, and to a certain extent revived each day in his mind the morning's work of their old partnership. He would say to himself, "It's time to go and look up Jim," and put off what he was pleased to think were his pleasures until this act of duty was accomplished.

In this singleness of purpose he made very few and no entangling acquaintances, nor did he impart to any one the secret of his fortune, loyally reserving it for his partner's first knowledge. To a man of his natural frankness and simplicity this was a great trial, and was, perhaps, a crucial test of his devotion. When he gave up his rooms at the Oriental—as not necessary after his partner's absence—he sent a letter, with his humble address, to the mysterious lock-box of his partner without fear of false shame. He would explain it all when they met. But he sometimes treated unlucky and returning miners to a dinner and a visit to the gallery of some theatre. Yet while he had an active sympathy with and understanding of the humblest, Uncle Billy, who for many years had done his own and his partner's washing, scrubbing, mending, and cooking, and saw no degradation in it, was somewhat inconsistently irritated by menial functions in men, and although he gave extravagantly to waiters, and threw a dollar to the crossing-sweeper, there was always a certain shy avoidance of them in his manner. Coming from the theatre one night Uncle Billy was, however, seriously concerned by one of these crossing-sweepers turning hastily before them and being knocked down by a passing carriage. The man rose and limped hurriedly away; but Uncle Billy was amazed and still more irritated to hear from his companion that this kind of menial occupation was often profitable, and that at some of the principal crossings the sweepers were already rich men.

But a few days later brought a more notable event to Uncle Billy. One afternoon in Montgomery Street he recognized in one of its smartly dressed frequenters a man who had a few years before been a member of Cedar Camp. Uncle Billy's childish delight at this meeting, which seemed to bridge over his old partner's absence, was, however, only half responded to by the ex-miner, and then somewhat satirically. In the fullness of his emotion, Uncle Billy confided to him that he was seeking his old partner, Jim Foster, and, reticent of his own good fortune, spoke glowingly of his partner's brilliant expectations, but deplored his inability to find him. And just now he was away on important business. "I reckon he's got back," said the man dryly. "I didn't know he had a lock-box at the post office, but I can give you his other address. He lives at the Presidio, at Washerwoman's Bay." He stopped and looked with a satirical smile at Uncle Billy. But the latter, familiar with Californian mining-camp nomenclature, saw nothing strange in it, and merely repeated his companion's words.

"You'll find him there! Good-by! So long! Sorry I'm in a hurry," said the ex-miner, and hurried away.

Uncle Billy was too delighted with the prospect of a speedy meeting with Uncle Jim to resent his former associate's supercilious haste, or even to wonder why Uncle Jim had not informed him that he had returned. It was not the first time that he had felt how wide was the gulf between himself and these others, and the thought drew him closer to his old partner, as well as his old idea, as it was now possible to surprise him with the draft. But as he was going to surprise him in his own boardinghouse—probably a handsome one—Uncle Billy reflected that he would do so in a certain style.

He accordingly went to a livery stable and ordered a landau and pair, with a Negro coachman. Seated in it, in his best and most ill-fitting clothes, he asked the coachman to take him to the Presidio, and leaned back in the cushions as they drove through the streets with such an expression of beaming gratification on his good-humored face that the passers-by smiled at the equipage and its extravagant occupant. To them it seemed the not unusual sight of the successful miner "on a spree." To the unsophisticated Uncle Billy their smiling seemed only a natural and kindly recognition of his happiness, and he nodded and smiled back to them with unsuspecting candor and innocent playfulness. "These yer 'Frisco fellers ain't *all* slouches, you bet," he added to himself half aloud, at the back of the grinning coachman.

Their way led through well-built streets to the outskirts, or rather to that portion of the city which seemed to have been overwhelmed by shifting sand dunes, from which half-submerged fences and even low houses barely marked the line of highway. The resistless trade winds which had marked this change blew keenly in his face and slightly chilled his ardor. At a turn in the road the sea came in sight, and sloping towards it the great Cemetery of Lone Mountain, with white shafts and marbles that glittered in the sunlight like the sails of ships waiting to be launched down that slope into the Eternal Ocean. Uncle Billy shuddered. What if it had been his fate to seek Uncle Jim there!

"Dar's yar Presidio!" said the Negro coachman a few moments later, pointing with his whip, "and dar's yar Wash'woman's Bay!"

Uncle Billy stared. A huge quadrangular fort of stone with a flag flying above its battlements stood at a little distance, pressed against the rocks, as if beating back the encroaching surges; between him and the fort but farther inland was a lagoon with a number of dilapidated, rudely patched cabins or cottages, like stranded driftwood around its shore. But there was no mansion, no block of houses, no street, not another habitation or dwelling to be seen!

Uncle Billy's first shock of astonishment was succeeded by a feeling of relief. He had secretly dreaded a meeting with his old partner in the "haunts of fashion"; whatever was the cause that made Uncle Jim seek this obscure retirement affected him but slightly; he even was thrilled with a vague memory of the old shiftless camp they had both abandoned. A certain instinct—he knew not why, or less still that it might be one of delicacy—made him alight before they reached the first house. Bidding the carriage wait, Uncle Billy entered, and was informed by a blowzy Irish laundress at a tub that Jim Foster, or "Arkansaw Jim," lived at the fourth shanty "beyant." He was at home, for "he'd shprained his fut." Uncle Billy hurried on, stopped before the door of a shanty scarcely less rude than their old cabin, and half timidly pushed it open. A growling voice from within, a figure that rose hurriedly, leaning on a stick, with an attempt to fly, but in the same moment sank back in a chair with an hysterical laugh—and Uncle Billy stood in the presence of his old partner! But as Uncle Billy darted forward, Uncle Jim rose again, and this time with outstretched hands. Uncle Billy caught them, and in one supreme pressure seemed to pour out and transfuse his whole simple soul into his partner's. There they swayed each other backwards and forwards and sideways by their still clasped hands, until Uncle Billy, with a glance at Uncle Jim's bandaged ankle, shoved him by sheer force down into his chair.

Uncle Jim was first to speak. "Caught, b'gosh! I mighter known you'd be as big a fool as me! Look you, Billy Fall, do you know what you've done? You've druv me out er the streets whar I was makin' an honest livin', by day, on three crossin's! Yes," he laughed forgivingly, "you druv me out er it, by day, jest because I reckoned that some time I might run into your darned fool face"—another laugh and a grasp of the hand—"and then, b'gosh! not content with ruinin' my business *by day,* when I took to it at night, *you* took to goin' out at nights too, and so put a stopper on me there! Shall I tell you what else you did? Well, by the holy poker! I owe this sprained foot to your darned foolishness and my own, for it was getting away from *you* one night after the theater that I got run into and run over!

"Ye see," he went on, unconscious of Uncle Billy's paling face, and with a naïveté, though perhaps not a delicacy, equal to Uncle Billy's own, "I had to play roots on you with that lock-box business and these letters, because I did not want you to know what I was up to, for you mightn't like it, and might think it was lowerin' to the old firm, don't yer see? I wouldn't hev gone into it, but I was played out, and I don't mind tellin' you *now,* old man, that when I wrote you that first chipper letter from the lock-box I hedn't eat anythin' for two days. But it's all right *now,*" with a laugh. "Then I got into this business—thinkin' it nothin'—jest the very last thing—and do you know, old pard, I couldn't tell anybody but *you*—and, in fact, I kept it jest to tell you—I've made nine hundred and fifty-six dollars! Yes, sir, *nine hundred and fifty-six dollars!* solid money, in Adams and Co.'s Bank, just out er my trade."

"Wot trade?" asked Uncle Billy.

Uncle Jim pointed to the corner, where stood a large, heavy crossing-sweeper's broom. "That trade."

"Certingly," said Uncle Billy, with a quick laugh.

"It's an outdoor trade," said Uncle Jim gravely, but with no suggestion of awkwardness or apology in his manner; "and thar ain't much difference between sweepin' a crossin' with a broom and raking over tailing with a rake, *only—wot ye get* with a broom *you have handed to ye,* and ye don't have to *pick it up and fish it out er* the wet rocks and sluice-gushin'; and it's a heap less tiring to the back."

"Certingly, you bet!" said Uncle Billy enthusiastically, yet with a certain nervous abstraction.

"I'm glad ye say so; for yer see I didn't know at first how you'd tumble to my doing it, until I'd made my pile. And ef I hadn't made it, I wouldn't hev set eyes on ye agin, old pard—never!"

"Do you mind my runnin' out a minit," said Uncle Billy, rising. "You see, I've got a friend waitin' for me outside—and I reckon—" he stammered—"I'll jest run out and send him off, so I kin talk comf'ble to ye."

"Ye ain't got anybody you're owin' money to," said Uncle Jim earnestly, "anybody follerin' you to get paid, eh? For I kin jest set down right here and write ye off a check on the bank!"

"No," said Uncle Billy. He slipped out of the door, and ran like a deer to the waiting carriage. Thrusting a twenty-dollar gold piece into the coachman's hand, he said hoarsely, "I ain't wantin' that kerridge just now; ye kin drive around and hev a private jamboree all by yourself the rest of the afternoon, and then come and wait for me at the top o' the hill yonder."

Thus quit of his gorgeous equipage, he hurried back to Uncle Jim, grasping his ten-thousand-dollar draft in his pocket. He was nervous, he was frightened, but he must get rid of the draft and his story, and have it over. But before he could speak he was unexpectedly stopped by Uncle Jim.

"Now, look yer, Billy boy!" said Uncle Jim; "I got suthin' to say to ye—and I might as well clear it off my mind at once, and then we can start fair agin. Now," he went on, with a half laugh, "wasn't it enough for *me* to go on pretendin' I was rich and doing a big business, and gettin' up that lock-box dodge so as ye couldn't find out whar I hung out and what I was doin'—wasn't it enough for *me* to go on with all this play-actin', but *you,* you long-legged or'nary cuss! must get up and go to lyin' and play-actin', too!"

"*Me* play-actin'? *Me* lyin'?" gasped Uncle Billy.

Uncle Jim leaned back in his chair and

laughed. "Do you think you could fool *me?* Do you think I didn't see through your little game o' going to that swell Oriental, jest as if ye'd made a big strike—and all the while ye wasn't sleepin' or eatin' there, but jest wrastlin' yer hash and having a roll down at the Good Cheer! Do you think I didn't spy on ye and find that out? Oh, you long-eared jackass-rabbit!"

He laughed until the tears came into his eyes, and Uncle Billy laughed too, albeit until the laugh on his face became quite fixed, and he was fain to bury his head in his handkerchief.

"And yet," said Uncle Jim, with a deep breath, "gosh! I was frighted—jest for a minit! I thought, mebbe, you *had* made a big strike—when I got your first letter—and I made up my mind what I'd do! And then I remembered you was jest that kind of an open sluice that couldn't keep anythin' to yourself, and you'd have been sure to have yelled it out to *me* the first thing. So I waited. And I found you out, you old sinner!" He reached forward and dug Uncle Billy in the ribs.

"What *would* you hev done?" said Uncle Billy, after an hysterical collapse.

Uncle Jim's face grew grave again. "I'd hev—I'd—hev cl'ared out! Out er 'Frisco! out er Californy! out er Ameriky! I couldn't have stud it! Don't think I would hev begrudged ye yer luck! No man would have been gladder than me." He leaned forward again, and laid his hand caressingly upon his partner's arm—"Don't think I'd hev wanted to take a penny of it—but I—thar! I *couldn't* hev stood up under it! To hev had *you,* you that I left behind, comin' down here rollin' in wealth and new partners and friends, and arrive upon me—and this shanty—and"—he threw towards the corner of the room a terrible gesture, none the less terrible that it was illogical and inconsequent to all that had gone before—"and—and—*that broom!*"

There was a dead silence in the room. With it Uncle Billy seemed to feel himself again transported to the homely cabin at Cedar Camp and that fateful night, with his partner's strange, determined face before him as then. He even fancied that he heard the roaring of the pines without, and did not know that it was the distant sea.

But after a minute Uncle Jim resumed:

"Of course you've made a little raise somehow, or you wouldn't be here?"

"Yes," said Uncle Billy eagerly. "Yes! I've got—" He stopped and stammered. "I've got—a—few hundreds."

"Oh, oh!" said Uncle Jim cheerfully. He paused, and then added earnestly, "I say! You ain't got left, over and above your d——d foolishness at the Oriental, as much as five hundred dollars?"

"I've got," said Uncle Billy, blushing a little over his first deliberate and affected lie, "I've got at least five hundred and seventy-two dollars. Yes," he added tentatively, gazing anxiously at his partner, "I've got at least that."

"Je whillikins!" said Uncle Jim, with a laugh. Then eagerly, "Look here, pard! Then we're on velvet! I've got *nine* hundred; put your *five* with that, and I know a little ranch that we can get for twelve hundred. That's what I've been savin' up fer—that's my little game! No more minin' for *me.* It's got a shanty twice as big as our old cabin, nigh on a hundred acres, and two mustangs. We can run it with two Chinamen and jest make it howl! Wot yer say—eh?" He extended his hand.

"I'm in," said Uncle Billy, radiantly grasping Uncle Jim's. But his smile faded, and his clear simple brow wrinkled in two lines.

Happily Uncle Jim did not notice it. "Now, then, old pard," he said brightly, "we'll have a gay old time tonight—one of our jamborees! I've got some whisky here and a deck o' cards, and we'll have a little game, you understand, but not for 'keeps' now! No, siree; we'll play for beans."

A sudden light illuminated Uncle Billy's face again, but he said, with a grim desperation, "Not tonight! I've got to go into town. That fren o' mine expects me to go to the theayter, don't ye see? But I'll be out to-morrow at sun-up, and we'll fix up this thing o' the ranch."

"Seems to me you're kinder stuck on this fren'," grunted Uncle Jim.

Uncle Billy's heart bounded at his partner's jealousy. "No—but I *must,* you know," he returned, with a faint laugh.

"I say—it ain't a *her,* is it?" said Uncle Jim.

Uncle Billy achieved a diabolical wink and a creditable blush at his lie.

"Billy?"

"Jim!"

And under cover of this festive gallantry Uncle Billy escaped. He ran through the gathering darkness, and toiled up the shifting sands to the top of the hill, where he found the carriage waiting.

"Wot," said Uncle Billy in a low confidential tone to the coachman, "wot do you 'Frisco fellers allow to be the best, biggest, and riskiest gamblin'-saloon here? Suthin' high-toned, you know?"

The Negro grinned. It was the usual case of the extravagant spendthrift miner, though perhaps he had expected a different question and order.

"Dey is de 'Polka,' de 'El Dorado,' and de 'Arcade' saloon, boss," he said, flicking his whip meditatively. "Most gents from de mines prefer de 'Polka,' for dey is dancing wid de gals frown in. But de real *prima facie* place for gents who go for buckin' agin de tiger and straight-out gamblin' is de 'Arcade.' "

"Drive there like thunder!" said Uncle Billy, leaping into the carriage.

True to his word, Uncle Billy was at his partner's shanty early the next morning. He looked a little tired, but happy, and had brought a draft with him for five hundred and seventy-five dollars, which he explained was the total of his capital. Uncle Jim was overjoyed. They would start for Napa that very day, and conclude the purchase of the ranch; Uncle Jim's sprained foot was a sufficient reason for his giving up his present vocation, which he could also sell at a small profit. His domestic arrangements were very simple; there was nothing to take with him—there was everything to leave behind. And that afternoon, at sunset, the two reunited partners were seated on the deck of the Napa boat as she swung into the stream.

Uncle Billy was gazing over the railing with a look of abstracted relief towards the Golden Gate, where the sinking sun seemed to be drawing towards him in the ocean a golden stream that was forever pouring from the Bay and the three-hilled city beside it. What Uncle Billy was thinking of, or what the picture suggested to him, did not transpire; for Uncle Jim, who, emboldened by his holiday, was luxuriating in an evening paper, suddenly uttered a long-drawn whistle, and moved closer to his abstracted partner. "Look yer," he said, pointing to a paragraph he had evidently just read, "just you listen to this, and see if we ain't lucky, you and me, to be jest wot we air—trustin' to our own hard work—and not thinkin' o' 'strikes' and 'fortins.' Jest unbutton yer ears, Billy, while I reel off this yer thing I've jest struck in the paper, and see what d—d fools some men kin make o' themselves. And that theer reporter wot wrote it—must hev seed it reely!"

Uncle Jim cleared his throat, and holding the paper close to his eyes read aloud slowly:

" 'A scene of excitement that recalled the palmy days of '49 was witnessed last night at the Arcade Saloon. A stranger, who might have belonged to that reckless epoch, and who bore every evidence of being a successful Pike County miner out on a "spree," appeared at one of the tables with a Negro coachman bearing two heavy bags of gold. Selecting a Faro-bank as his base of operations, he began to bet heavily and with apparent recklessness, until his play excited the breathless attention of every one. In a few moments he had won a sum variously estimated at from eighty to a hundred thousand dollars. A rumor went round the room that it was a concerted attempt to "break the bank" rather than the drunken freak of a Western miner, dazzled by some successful strike. To this theory the man's careless and indifferent bearing towards his extraordinary gains lent great credence. The attempt, if such it was, however, was unsuccessful. After winning ten times in succession the luck turned, and the unfortunate "bucker" was cleared out not only of his gains, but of his original investment, which may be placed roughly at twenty thousand dollars. This extraordinary play was witnessed by a crowd of excited players, who were less impressed by even the magnitude of the stakes than the perfect *sang-froid* and recklessness of the player, who, it is said, at the close of the game tossed a twenty-dollar gold piece to the banker and smilingly withdrew. The man was not recognized by any of the habitués of the place.'

"There!" said Uncle Jim, as he hurriedly slurred over the French substantive at the close, "did ye ever see such God-forsaken foolishness?"

Uncle Billy lifted his abstracted eyes from the current, still pouring its unreturning gold into the sinking sun, and said, with a deprecatory smile, "Never!"

Nor even in the days of prosperity that visited the Great Wheat Ranch of "Fall and Foster" did he ever tell his secret to his partner.

SEVEN-UP

¶Though All Fours, an ancient English game, has been one of the great American games throughout our history, it is doubtful if one American in ten thousand would recognize its name. Then mention that it is the game in which you play for high, low, jack, and the game, and nearly everyone will exclaim, "Oh, of course!" ¶Neither All Fours nor High-Low-Jack is the name of an actual game played in

the United States. Seven-Up or Old Sledge was the popular form of the game before the late nineteenth century; then Pitch or Setback and Cinch took over, in all their variations; and today only Pitch remains in any force. ¶*Somewhere along the line, Mark Twain either recorded or invented the following incident, written for a long-defunct Buffalo periodical in 1871.*

Science vs. Luck

by MARK TWAIN

AT THAT TIME, in Kentucky (said the Hon. Mr. K——), the law was very strict against what is termed "games of chance." About a dozen of the boys were detected playing "Seven-Up" or "Old Sledge" for money, and the grand jury found a true bill against them. Jim Sturgis was retained to defend them when the case came up, of course. The more he studied over the matter, and looked into the evidence, the plainer it was that he must lose a case at last—there was no getting around that painful fact. Those boys had certainly been betting money on a game of chance. Even public sympathy was roused in behalf of Sturgis. People said it was a pity to see him mar his successful career with a big prominent case like this, which must go against him.

But after several restless nights an inspired idea flashed upon Sturgis, and he sprang out of bed delighted. He thought he saw his way through. The next day he whispered around a little among his clients and a few friends, and then when the case came up in court he acknowledged the Seven-Up and the betting and, as his sole defense, had the astounding effrontery to put in the plea that Old Sledge was not a game of chance! There was the broadest sort of a smile all over the faces of that sophisticated audience. The judge smiled with the rest. But Sturgis maintained a countenance whose earnestness was even severe. The opposite counsel tried to ridicule him out of his position and did not succeed. The judge jested in a ponderous judicial way about the thing, but that did not move him. The matter was becoming grave. The judge lost a little of his patience and said the joke had gone far enough. Jim Sturgis said he knew of no joke in the matter—his clients could not be punished for indulging in what some people chose to consider a game of chance until it was *proven* that it was a game of chance. Judge and counsel said that would be an easy matter and forthwith called Deacons Job, Peters, Burke, and Johnson, and Dominies Wirt and Miggles, to testify; and they unanimously and with strong feeling put down the legal quibble of Sturgis by pronouncing that Old Sledge *was* a game of chance.

"What do you call it *now?*" said the judge.

"I call it a game of science!" retorted Sturgis, "and I'll prove it, too!"

They saw his little game.

He brought in a cloud of witnesses and produced an overwhelming mass of testimony to show that Old Sledge was not a game of chance but a game of science.

Instead of being the simplest case in the world, it had somehow turned out to be an excessively knotty one. The judge scratched his head over it a while and said there was no way of coming to a determination, because just as many men could be brought into court who would testify on one side as could be found to testify on the other. But he said he was willing to do the fair thing by all parties, and would act upon any suggestion Mr. Sturgis would make for the solution of the difficulty.

Mr. Sturgis was on his feet in a second.

"Impanel a jury of six of each, Luck *versus* Science. Give them candles and a couple of decks of cards. Send them into the jury room, and just abide by the result!"

There was no disputing the fairness of the proposition. The four deacons and the two dominees were sworn in as the "chance" jurymen, and six inveterate old Seven-Up professors were chosen to represent the "science" side of the issue. They retired to the jury room.

In about two hours Deacon Peters sent into the court to borrow three dollars from a friend. [Sensation.] In about two hours more Dominie Miggles sent into the court to borrow a "stake" from a friend. [Sensation.] During the next three or four hours the other dominie and the other deacons sent into court for small loans. And still the packed audience waited, for it was a prodigious occasion in Bull's Corners, and one in which every father of a family was necessarily interested.

The rest of the story can be told briefly. About daylight the jury came in, and Deacon Job, the foreman, read the following

VERDICT

WE, THE JURY in the case of the Commonwealth of Kentucky vs. John Wheeler *et al.*, have carefully considered the points of the case, and tested the merits of the several theories advanced, and do hereby unanimously decide that the game commonly known as Old Sledge or Seven-Up is eminently a game of science and not of chance. In demonstration whereof it is hereby and herein stated, iterated, reiterated, set forth, and made manifest that, during the entire night, the "chance" men never won a game or turned a jack, although both feats were common and frequent to the opposition; and furthermore, in support of this our verdict, we call attention to the significant fact that the "chance" men are all busted, and the "science" men have got the money. It is the deliberate opinion of this jury, that the "chance" theory concerning Seven-Up is a pernicious doctrine, and calculated to inflict untold suffering and pecuniary loss upon any community that takes stock in it.

"That is the way that Seven-Up came to be set apart and particularized in the statute books of Kentucky as being a game not of chance but of science, and therefore not punishable under the law," said Mr. K——. "That verdict is of record, and holds good to this day."

FIVE HUNDRED

Nothing is more capricious than the public taste in card games and nothing is more unpredictable than the success or failure of a particular game. With all kinds of scientific theories and elaborate campaigns men have tried time after time to popularize a game, and, with two exceptions, all have ingloriously failed. The two exceptions are: Richard Canfield did actually put over a form of Solitaire; and the United States Playing Card Company (1904) did actually make Five Hundred a nationally popular game.

Five Hundred, an elaboration of Euchre, was produced to combat Bridge, which then was rapidly displacing Euchre. Exactly why a playing-card manufacturer should want to combat Bridge is a mystery, for he could sell as many packs of cards for one game as for the other, and the United States Playing Card Co. never tried to make money for licensing its copyright on Five Hundred. The mystery will never be solved, for no present executive of the company ever happened to hear what the reason might have been.

Whatever the reason, Five Hundred quickly became and long (twenty years) remained the principal card game of women in all but the greatest metropolises; and even today, in the heyday of the Bridge and Rummy games, it is much played.

A Good Game for Three but Not for the Timorous

by GEOFFREY MOTT-SMITH

"OH, I couldn't go to the movies alone," said Aunt Matilda. "I wouldn't dare. I'm much too timorous."

Wilbur Jones looked at his wife, Dorothy, and sighed resignedly. They had been out every evening for a week, showing Aunt Matilda the hot spots. Was one quiet evening at home too much to ask?

But now that Aunt Matilda had put her foot down on their apologetic suggestion that she go to the movies by herself. . . .

"Why should we go out, anyway?" asked Aunt Matilda. "You two can listen to the radio, or play cards. I'll write some letters."

"We could *all* play cards," Dorothy said. "Suppose I call up Tillie and see if she'll make a fourth for Bridge."

"I'm sorry, I don't play Bridge," said Aunt Matilda, "but I'd really like to play something. What else is there you might teach me?"

"How about Five Hundred?"

"Yes, I think I could manage. I used to play Five Hundred when I was a girl. That's a nice game for three . . ."

Wilbur's spirits sank, after having been lifted by the prospect of a snappy game of Contract Bridge. He had played Five Hundred only a few times, and foresaw a boring session in which he and his wife would probably have to remind Aunt Matilda what the game was all about. But at least he could take the weight off his feet. . . .

Aunt Matilda cut the first deal. Mrs. Jones, at her left, started the bidding with a pass. Wilbur passed also. Aunt Matilda bid "six spades," and after she had picked up the widow and discarded, the hands were as follows:

Dorothy	*Wilbur*
♡ A J 8	♡ Q 10
◇ 9 7	◇ K J 10
♣ Q 9 8	♣ K 7
♠ 10 8	♠ A J 9

Aunt Matilda
♡ K
◇ A Q
♣ A J 10
♠ K Q 7
Joker

(Remember that the ♣ J is a trump—the left bower.)

The Three-Hand Game: The "500" deck has 33 cards, ace high, 7 low in each suit, plus a Joker, which is the highest trump, called *best bower*. Jack of trumps (*right bower*) is next, then *left bower* (jack of same color as trumps). Other suits rank A–K–Q–J–10–9–8–7. DEAL: 10 cards to each, 3–4–3, and 3 cards to Widow. BIDDING: Suits rank notrump–♡–◇–♣–♠. Each player gets one bid, dealer first. Each player must overcall previous bid, or pass.

WIDOW: Winning bidder picks up Widow, then discards any three cards, which remain hidden.

PLAY: Bidder leads to first trick, and players must follow suit if able. Winner of trick leads to next trick.

SCORING: Each plays for himself. First to reach 500 wins. If bidder fails to make his contract, the value of the contract is deducted from his score. If he wins all ten tricks, he scores 250, unless his actual contract was worth more than 250. An adversary scores 10 for each trick he wins. Most players use the Avondale Schedule for scoring:

TRICKS	6	7	8	9	10
♠	40	140	240	340	440
♣	60	160	260	360	460
◇	80	180	280	380	480
♡	100	200	300	400	500
NT	120	220	320	420	520

Aunt Matilda led the ♡ K and Dorothy won. Without any clue to what to lead, she returned the ◇ 9. Aunt Matilda cashed her two diamond tricks, then the ♣ A, and led the ♣ 10. Wilbur won with the ♣ K and led his third diamond. Aunt Matilda trumped with the ♠ 7 and led the ♠ Q. Wilbur made both his ♠ A and ♠ J, but Aunt Matilda made her bid.

Wilbur was pleasantly surprised by Aunt Matilda's management of the hand. He took the opportunity to say, "That was close figuring, Aunt Matilda. I probably would have bid more than six with five trumps and two side aces, myself."

"Not exactly," murmured Aunt Matilda, "you see, I picked up the joker and the ace of clubs in the widow."

"You *what?* Did you make that bid on four trumps, not including the joker and right bower and ace? You must have got a peek at the widow!"

"Well, it seemed to me," said Aunt Matilda placidly, "that it must have something, after both of you had passed."

Dorothy dealt for the next hand. Wilbur picked up a strong heart suit, fortified with two bowers and some side cards. It looked good for at least seven tricks, so, bearing in mind the widow he boldly bid "eight hearts."

"My, my," said Aunt Matilda, "that makes it rather expensive for me. Eight no trumps."

"I DOUBLE!" shouted Wilbur.

"You can't," said Dorothy. "This isn't bridge—I pass. It's all yours, Aunt Matilda."

The hands after the discard:

Dorothy	*Wilbur*
♡ 10 7	♡ K Q J 9 8
◇ K 9 8 7	◇ A J
♣ K J	♣ Q
♠ J 8	♠ K Q

Aunt Matilda
♡ A
◇ —
♣ A 10 9 8 7
♠ A 10 9
Joker

Aunt Matilda commenced with the ace and another club. Dorothy dutifully led a heart, and Aunt Matilda was back in with the ♡ A. She ran down the string of clubs, then took her ♠ A. Next she led the joker, saying "Play spades."

"Hold on!" cried Wilbur. "Can you do that?"

"Oh, yes, at notrump I can call for any suit I want."

Seething, Wilbur flung down his last spade, and Aunt Matilda took the last two tricks with the ♠ 10 and ♠ 9.

"Gracious me, I made nine tricks. I didn't bid enough."

That was too much for Wilbur. Quite rudely he burst out, "Seems to me you did plenty of bidding. I suppose you picked up the joker and your two aces in the kitty this time too?"

"No," said Aunt Matilda, unperturbed, "I found only the ace of spades. I had that nice club suit and the joker to start with. But you're quite right. Cousin William always did say I was an overbidder."

It was now Wilbur's turn to deal. His eyes bulged as he picked up four aces, two queens and a king. He ruminated whether to bid six or seven no trumps. He was interrupted by hearing Aunt Matilda say firmly, "Seven diamonds!"

Great heavens, said Wilbur to himself, does the old girl expect to find four cards in the widow, all jokers?

But worse was to come. Dorothy took thought, and then said, "Eight clubs!"

"What do you people think you are doing?" raved Wilbur. "Well, I'm not going to be talked out of this hand simply because I can't double you. Eight notrump!"

The widow was a disappointment. After the discard:

Dorothy		*Wilbur*
♡ 10		♡ A 9
◇ —		◇ A
♣ J 10 9 8 7		♣ A K Q
♠ K J 10		♠ A Q 9 8
Joker		
	Aunt Matilda	
	♡ K Q J 7	
	◇ K Q J 10 7	
	♣ —	
	♠ 7	

Wilbur commenced with the ace and queen of spades. His wife won the second trick. When she put back a club, Wilbur congratulated himself that his diamond ace was still unattacked. Another lead set up the spades, and Mrs. Jones again returned a club. Wilbur cashed the long spade, and followed with the remaining three aces. But the loss of two spades, a heart, and a trick to the joker set him two tricks.

"So I get fixed on that swell hand," fumed Wilbur, "just because I couldn't get a single picture out of the widow."

"Weren't you rather optimistic?" murmured Aunt Matilda. "You could be pretty sure there was nothing in the widow when we were both bidding."

"How do I know what you were bidding on? You might be bidding on a couple of jacks and a lot of optimism again."

"Ooo, but I never overbid first hand. And I'm sure Dorothy would have made her bid too. I had seven sure tricks and so did Dorothy. Was there a diamond in the widow? There was? Bother!—I would have made eight. I really ought to have bid it, but it seemed unfair for me to be piggish when I've been holding all the cards. . . ."

What Wilbur said to himself at this point has never been revealed, but when Aunt Matilda reached 500 a couple of deals later by overcalling his nine hearts with ten clubs, he was heard to mutter something about "belong in the movies—doubling for Clyde Beatty . . ."

CRIBBAGE

[Cribbage has the best literary background and the least satisfactorily literature of all English card games. A noted poet, Sir John Suckling, is credited with the invention of the game and there is no more reason to doubt the story than to believe it; in any case, Suckling could only have built on an old English game that was already more than a hundred years old. What has been written about Cribbage will not exceed in interest the rules and history one may find in any current volume of Hoyle. The only amusing bit of Cribbage literature we know is the following brief excerpt from Mark Twain's "£1,000,000 Bank Note." There isn't much Cribbage in it, but we like it anyway, even if the dinner party of fourteen seems to wind up with at least fifteen guests and maybe more.

from "The £1,000,000 Bank Note"

by MARK TWAIN

IT WAS a lovely dinner-party of fourteen. The Duke and Duchess of Shoreditch, and their daughter the Lady Anne-Grace-Eleanor-Celeste-and-so-forth-and-so-forth-de-Bohun, the Earl and Countess of Newgate, Viscount Cheapside, Lord and Lady Blatherskite, some untitled people of both sexes, the minister* and his wife and daughter, and his daughter's visiting friend, an English girl of twenty-two, named Portia Langham, whom I fell in love with in two minutes, and she with me—I could see it without glasses.

The usual thing happened, the thing that is always happening under that vicious and aggravating English system—the matter of precedence couldn't be settled, and so there was no dinner. Englishmen always eat dinner before they go out to dinner, because they *know* the risks they are running; but nobody ever warns the stranger, and so he walks placidly into the trap. Of course, nobody was hurt this time, because we had all been to dinner, none of us being novices excepting Hastings, and he having been informed by the minister at the time that he invited him that in deference to the English custom he had not provided any dinner. Everybody took a lady and processioned down to the dining room, because it is usual to go through the motions; but there the dispute began. The Duke of Shoreditch wanted to take precedence and sit at the head of the table, holding that he outranked a minister who represented merely a nation and not a monarch; but I stood for my rights, and refused to yield. In the gossip column I ranked all dukes not royal, and said so, and claimed precedence of this one. It couldn't be settled, of course, struggle as we might and did, he finally (and injudiciously) trying to play

* The United States Minister: this was before the diplomats exchanged between the United States and England had ambassadorial rank.

birth and antiquity, and I "seeing" his Conqueror and "raising" him with Adam, whose direct posterity I was, as shown by my name, while *he* was of a collateral branch, as shown by *his*, and by his recent Norman origin; so we all processioned back to the drawing-room again and had a perpendicular lunch—plate of sardines and a strawberry, and you group yourself and stand up and eat it. Here the religion of precedence is not so strenuous; the two persons of highest rank chuck up a shilling, the one that wins has first go at his strawberry, and the loser gets the shilling. The next two chuck up, then the next two, and so on. After refreshment, tables were brought, and we all played Cribbage, sixpence a game. The English never play any game for amusement. If they can't make something—or lose something, they don't care which—they won't play.

We had a lovely time; certainly two of us had, Miss Langham and I. I was so bewitched with her that I couldn't count my hands if they went above a double sequence; and when I struck home I never discovered it, and started up the outside row again, and would have lost the game every time, only the girl did the same, she being in just my condition, you see; and consequently neither of us ever got out, or cared to wonder why we didn't; we only just knew we were happy, and didn't wish to know anything else, and didn't want to be interrupted. And I told her—I did, indeed—told her I loved her; and she—well, she blushed till her hair turned red, but she liked it; she said she did. Oh, there was never such an evening! Every time I pegged I put on a postscript; every time she pegged she acknowledged receipt of it, counting the hands the same. Why, I couldn't even say "Two for his heels" without adding, *"My,* how sweet you do look!" and she would say, "Fifteen two, fifteen four, fifteen six, and a pair are eight, and eight are sixteen—*do* you think so?"—peeping out aslant from under her lashes, you know, so sweet and cunning. Oh, it was just *too*-too!

PINOCHLE

¶*[Pinochle has produced as ingenious problems as Whist or Bridge, though not nearly so many of them. The best are from the three-hand game Auction Pinochle. In a book* Auction Pinnochle *(sic), published in 1913, the author, A. P. George, was remarkably accurate in his Pinochle analysis even though the game was then very new. We give here the "curiosities" from his book.*

The Highest Possible Bidding Hand

♠ A A 10 10 K K Q Q J J
♡ A
◇ A J J
♣ A

WITH a melding strength of 480, this hand is good for not less than 203 points in tricks, and is a safe bid at 680. Assuming that the Widow should consist of ◇ A 10 10, and one of the opponents should hold ◇ 9 9 only, the bidder would make 238 in tricks, a total score of 718.

[This is a traditional hand and 99+ per cent of all Pinochle players will tell you that 718 is the highest possible total score. They are wrong. It is the highest possible score with spades trumps, and so may be the most lucrative score when spades count double, but the highest possible total score is made on this hand:

♠ A Q Q
◇ A A 10 10 K K Q Q J J
♣ A
♡ A

The meld remains 480. The three cards laid away are ♠ A 10 10. One opponent holds ♠ K K alone, and one of his kings will fall under the bidder's ace. The opponents will win one trick composed of king, queen, and jack, leaving the bidder 241 points for a total score of 721.]

A Trick Hand

LEFT	RIGHT
♠ J J 9 9	♠ A A 10 10
◇ A 10 K Q J 9	◇ ——
♣ J J 9 9	♣ A A 10 10
♡ A	♡ A Q Q J J 9 9

BIDDER
♠ K K Q Q
◇ A 10 K Q J 9
♣ K K Q Q
♡ K

WIDOW: ♡ 10 10 K

Bidder, with 360 to meld, bids 400. He lays away the entire widow, giving him 24 points. He needs only 16 points more and cannot make them. His right-hand opponent leads hearts at every opportunity and his left-hand opponent overtrumps everything but the ace of diamonds. The bidder can at best take a queen of hearts on his ace of trumps, giving him 14 points at most.

❡*P. Hal Sims is best remembered for his remarkable Bridge record—and, incidentally, his colorful personality—but he was good at every game. From his book Pinochle Pointers we take two problems applying to the original game of two-hand Pinochle, played with a 48-card pack —a game at which, incidentally, Hal Sims excelled. In these problems, the preliminary play is ended; it is assumed that each player knows the location of every card; and it is obligatory to trump when unable to follow suit and to win a trump lead if able.*

Example 1

PLAYER A
♠ J
♡ 10 Q J
♢ K K
♣ 9

PLAYER B
♠ A 9
♡ A K
♢ A A
♣ A

Spades are trumps. Player B leads. How should he play?

ANSWER

Player B takes both aces of diamonds and the ace of clubs, then leads ♠ 9 and must win the remaining tricks.

Example 2

PLAYER A
♠ ——
♡ A 10
♢ A 10
♣ 10 Q J

PLAYER B
♠ A
♡ A
♢ A 9
♣ A A K

Spades are trumps. Player B leads. What should he lead? What should Player A play?

ANSWER

Player B leads the ace of spades. Player A discards a club. By this play he scores fewer points in cards but must get last trick with the ace of diamonds, adding 10 to his score.

SOLITAIRE

The literature of Solitaire or Patience games is extensive but is almost wholly composed of the rules of play. True, there was a prize-winning short story Solitaire, *by Fleta Springer Campbell, but there was no card-playing in it; the title was an allusion to the gambler in the pioneer Wild West days who sat down to play Solitaire with his gun on the table beside him in case he caught himself cheating. We content ourselves with two recent essays on the subject.*

from The Complete Book of Solitaire and Patience Games

by ALBERT MOREHEAD *and* GEOFFREY MOTT-SMITH

It is natural to suppose that Solitaire games preceded card games for two or more players. We can easily imagine how Solitaire grew out of the rites of dealing and selection, the pictorial layouts, of fortunetelling; and divination is the first known use of the tarots.

Alas! This is conjecture. The historical record, none too certain in respect to games and sports generally, is particularly wanting as to Solitaire.

The ultimate origin of playing cards is a matter of scholarly dispute. But it is agreed that they were introduced to northern Europe, probably from Italy, during the thirteenth or fourteenth century. We even know the principal rules of a game played at that time, Tarocchi or Tarok. (It survives to this day in central Europe.) But not until the nineteenth century, it seems, did anyone trouble to record the rules of a Solitaire game for posterity.

A news letter dated 1816 reports that Napoleon Bonaparte, in exile at St. Helena, occupies his time in "playing Patience." This is the earliest reference to Patience as a game unearthed by the Oxford English Dictionary. It is evident that "Patience" was no neologism, but on the contrary, was in such familiar usage as to require no elucidation.*

There is more than one reference to the playing of Patience in Tolstoy's *War and Peace,* one in a scene supposed to have taken place in 1808. We believe that Tolstoy was most careful in historical allusions; this reference can the more

* Certainly this is so if one credits the allusion in Shakespeare's *Antony and Cleopatra* (page 12).

readily be accepted as not anachronistic since Tolstoy was himself a passionate devotee of Solitaire.

There are probably much earlier references in French literature. The earliest English books on Patience appear to have drawn on French sources; the very names of the games are almost all French—La Belle Lucie, Les Quatre Coins, L'Horloge, La Nivernaise, La Loi Salique, Le Carré Napoleon, etc.

II

WHETHER Napoleon invented any of the games bearing his name, or even whether he played them, we do not know. Perhaps they were older games, renamed for the First Consul by his admirers. During his brilliant military campaigns in Italy and Austria, thousands of commercial products changed to the brand name "Napoleon." Alternatively, it is possible that the Napoleon Solitaires were invented during the extraordinarily fecund period of the Revolution (from 1789 to about 1800). This was the heyday of experiments and innovations in playing cards. It was at this time that the ace (taken to symbolize the lowest social class) began to be regularly placed above the king (the nobility). Old designs gave way to new symbols of the Revolution. At some gambling casinos the faces of the cards changed daily, and the "house rule" as to the ranking of the cards changed three times in a week.

Many new games, and new variants of old games, were invented during this period. It is natural to suppose that the Solitaire family also effloresced. But again history failed to supply a chronicler.

There is no reference to Solitaire, much less the description of a particular Patience, in the books on which we rely for the early history of card games—such as Charles Cotton's *The Compleat Gamester* (1674), Abbé Bellecour's *Académie des jeux* (1768), Bohn's *Handbook of Games* (1850).

III

THE FIRST compendium of Solitaire games in English was, we believe, Lady Adelaide Cadogan's *Illustrated Games of Patience,* about 1870. This pioneer work ran through many editions and even today is occasionally reprinted. In England, it has made the name "Cadogan" to some degree a common noun, meaning any book on Solitaire, much as any book on card games in general is called a "Hoyle."

Spurred no doubt by Lady Cadogan's example, two other ladies hastened to repair the hiatus in games literature, Mrs. E. D. Cheney with *Patience* and Annie B. Henshaw with *Amusements for Invalids* (Boston, 1870). Soon the publishers of handbooks on chess, Whist, croquet, badminton and the like added Solitaire to their lists. In 1883 Dick & Fitzgerald of New York issued their first series of *Dick's Games of Patience,* following with a second series in 1898. These excellently printed and illustrated volumes greatly extended the list of recorded Solitaires.

By the end of the century, there was no dearth of books on Solitaire. Among others who made notable contributions were "Cavendish" (Henry Jones), "Professor Hoffmann" (Angelo Lewis), Basil Dalton, and Ernest Bergholt.

IV

SOLITAIRE is traditionally a game for invalids, shut-ins, recluses. By a quirk of fate (or man), those who have the greatest use for playing cards are denied them. American prisons and asylums class playing cards as lethal weapons—because they are edged! The inmates must forgo cards, or use the substitutes sometimes provided—thick tiles bearing the impress of playing-card designs. The more elaborate Solitaires, we are told, are attempted only by "lifers."

At least one shut-in has surmounted the difficulties. The late Bill Beers was an inmate of a mental asylum. He invented not only a great many worthwhile chess problems but also the excellent Patience which we herein list as Cribbage Solitaire III. We suggest "Bill Beers" as an appropriate variant name.

The following passage occurs in Somerset Maugham's *The Gentleman in the Parlour:*

"I reproached myself as I set out the cards. Considering the shortness of life and the infinite number of important things there are to do during its course, it can only be the proof of a flippant disposition that one should waste one's time in such a pursuit . . . But I knew seventeen varieties of Patience. I tried the Spider and never by any chance got it out. . . ."

One wonders whether this self-reproach was sincere. It is not "proof of a flippant disposition" to take recreation. We are reminded of a man in real life, a statesman who bore no inconsiderable burden of responsibility; at moments of crisis, when he could but wait the outcome of events, he was wont to relax with Solitaire. Oddly enough, he too was a devotee of Spider. His name was Franklin Delano Roosevelt.

The catharsis of Patience has been recognized

by many novelists. We have mentioned Tolstoy, who himself had an addiction to Patience bordering on superstition. At times of perplexity, he played cards to decide his course (though he has confessed that when he disliked the answer he shuffled the cards and dealt anew). In Dostoevsky's *The Brothers Karamazov* the character Grushenka resorts to Solitaire to weather an almost unbearable period of suspense. (The game is called "Fools," which may be a Russian equivalent of the English pejorative "Idiot's Delight.")

V

ANOTHER name that has become almost a common noun is "Canfield."

Mr. Canfield was the proprietor of a fashionable gambling salon at Saratoga in the Gay Nineties. His proposition was: You purchase a deck for fifty dollars and play a game of the Solitaire Canfield; I will pay you five dollars for every card in your foundation piles when the game is over. According to R. F. Foster, the player's average expectation is between five and six cards, so that Mr. Canfield stood to win about twenty-five dollars per game. Despite this inordinate "house percentage," his proposition was accepted by thousands, and the cult of Canfield spread all over the country. Mr. Canfield is supposed to have garnered a fortune, but he later stated that his Solitaire room was less lucrative than the roulette wheel. Two housemen operating the wheel could handle a score of customers, whereas for every Solitaire punter he had to hire a houseman to watch the player for fraud.

The game actually played at Canfield's Casino is that described herein as "Canfield." But the name has been very widely misapplied to another game, Klondike, which is by far the most-played Solitaire today.

However, the time has come when we may well cease insisting that Canfield is a misnomer for Klondike. "Canfield" has become almost a generic name for Patience itself.

During WPA days, a subsidized citizen submitted to our editorial eye a manuscript entitled "Chances of Winning at Solitaire." The attack on this knotty problem was purely empirical; the industrious author had played over 5,000 games and recorded the results of each. Internal evidence indicated that the 5,000 trials were all upon the same Solitaire—but what Solitaire was nowhere divulged. Inquiry elicited the fact that the author thought "Solitaire" to be the name of a specific game—the only one known to him. When we asked its rules, he complied with a description of Klondike.

This incident is but one of many that have convinced us (a) Klondike is the only Solitaire known to thousands of benighted persons; (b) all but a few bibliophiles like ourselves call it Canfield or simply Solitaire.

How Klondike came to be selected as the popular favorite is an inexplicable mystery. One would think *a priori* that it is among the least likely candidates for supremacy. One would expect the mantle to fall on a Solitaire that can be won frequently, or that gives great scope for skill, or that requires little time to play. Klondike fails in all three respects. The player's chance of winning is surely not greater than 1 in 30; the few choices that arise must be settled by guesswork; a game takes more than the average time for one-deck Solitaires.

from "The New York Times"

YOU CAN'T LOSE IF YOU CHEAT

WHEN President Eisenhower, back from Denver to Gettysburg, told some Bridge-playing visitors "I've become a Solitaire man," he allied himself with an even bigger majority than he had in 1952. Card players often argue about which game is America's favorite—Bridge, Poker, Gin Rummy, Canasta—but invariably they overlook the one that holds first place by a wide margin. It's Solitaire, which nearly 75% of all Americans play at one time or another.

Solitaire is not only the most popular card game, it is the oldest card game. More than a thousand years ago, when playing cards were a newfangled Chinese invention, Chinese and Korean priests would deal out the cards in patterns not unlike today's Solitaire layouts. The fall of the cards revealed the wishes of the gods. Fortunetelling came next, and fortunetellers introduced playing cards into Europe (late in the 13th century).

The name Solitaire, though it is used throughout the United States, is not quite proper. The original Solitaire was not a card game but a puzzle, played with pegs and a small wooden board, and according to one untrustworthy legend it was invented by a prisoner in the Bastille during the French Revolution. The game that Americans call Solitaire is called Patience in England.

Whatever you call it, Solitaire is the traditional pastime of convalescents, invalids, prisoners, and other shut-ins. Napoleon at St.

Helena and Gen. Jonathan Wainwright in a Japanese prison camp played Solitaire "interminably." Franklin D. Roosevelt was another Solitaire-playing president.

Leo Tolstoy was a Solitaire addict, but his purpose was the ancient Chinese one. When faced with a difficult problem he would play a game of Solitaire and let the cards decide (but if he didn't like their decision, he cheated). To J. P. Morgan, Solitaire was something to do while thinking. During the 1907 panic a group of bankers went scurrying to him for guidance. He let them wait while he sat alone in his study and with great deliberation played out a game of Solitaire. Then he emerged and announced his decision: He would buy stocks to support the market.

J. P. Morgan's game was Miss Milligan, a two-deck Solitaire. It takes twenty minutes to play, which gave him plenty of time to think.

CHRISTMAS REVELRY AT THE PATIENCE CLUB

From *Punch*, 1936; reproduced by permission of *Punch*

SIDELIGHTS ON CARD PLAYING

[There isn't much to be said about kibitzers that Lee Hazen doesn't say in the following article, published in Cosmopolitan *in 1948; and when you read it you will understand why Hazen, one of the highest-ranking of the Bridge champions, is ranked just as high for witty remarks.*

Kibitzers Do Not Live Long

by LEE HAZEN

UNHONORED and unsung, a famous name will soon observe its twentieth anniversary. No celebration is likely to mark this anniversary. The name is one nobody loves.

The birth date of this unenviable name, so far as the American public is concerned, was February, 1929. The occasion was a play that opened on Broadway—a hit, by the classic definition, for it ran 120 performances. Also, it elevated to movie stardom a young actor named Edward G. Robinson. In the title role, Mr. Robinson told various cardplayers what they ought to do and what they should have done. The play was called "The Kibitzer."

The American language opened its arms wide and took the new word in. "Spectator" and "onlooker" had been drab appellations for the card-table buttinsky; "kibitzer" fitted him to a T. Now nearly everyone knows what a kibitzer is, though most people mispronounce it (KIBitzer is right, not kiBITzer).

Whatever you call him—and it won't be good—the kibitzer is a traditional object of derision, of scorn, of anger, of anything but respect. He is about as popular as the baseball umpire, if not less so. Jokes about him are legion, and he is the butt of them all.

Item. A Chicago court solemnly issued an injunction restraining a particularly obnoxious kibitzer from watching Pinochle games.

Item. Four Bridge players at the New York Bridge Whist Club, noting that their kibitzer had dozed off, turned out all the lights and began to bid and slap down their cards loudly, so that the kibitzer, awaking suddenly, cried out in panic, "I've gone blind!"

Item. At the same club, where kibitzers always

Drawing *by* HOFF

Reprinted from *Esquire*, March 1934; © 1934 by Esquire, Inc.

substitute for players who must temporarily leave the room, an overkibitzed foursome found occasion to excuse themselves one by one. Finally four kibitzers were left to work on one another while the players, having set up a table in another room, peacefully continued their game —alone.

Item. For seven hours a kibitzer had watched a Bridge game in Philadelphia. One player—call him Jones—was losing; the others were winning. As the last rubber began, Jones proposed a side bet, and the kibitzer agreed. The rubber was played; Jones won it and, by virtue of his side bet, recouped his losses and was a bit ahead. So was everyone else. The players all collected. The kibitzer was the only loser.

Obviously, card players consider the kibitzer the lowest form of animal life, and psychologists might tell you there is some reason for this. Here, in very brief, is the long-haired explanation: Man has an instinctive craving for struggle, for war and conquest. When fear deters him from the real struggle, he turns to a mock struggle, a game, where he can enjoy winning but won't be seriously hurt if he loses. Now, the kibitzer lacks even the courage for the mock struggle, and must appease his instinct vicariously by watching others and sharing their triumphs and their defeats. Anyone who has observed gambling games knows that a loser seldom wants to leave, even when all his money is gone. He will stick around for hours to watch the game go on. There are those who insist, though statistics do not support them, that kibitzers do not live long; no doubt the wish is father to the thought.

Being rooted in human psychology, the kibitzer is a universal sect, and as such takes his characteristics from the country and time in which he lives. While "kibitzer" is a fairly new word to us, the Germans have for generations called him *Kiebitz,* whence our name.

This name arose when German card games, played mostly in taverns and coffeehouses, were rough-and-tumble affairs marked by loud arguments and much card-slapping. The *Kiebitz,* or pewit (no cracks about nitwits, please), is a bird noted both for its curiosity and for the way it protects its delicious eggs (it flaps its wings in the faces of searchers, thus annoying them greatly).

A German caricaturist popularized the name. He portrayed a sleeping fat man whose mouth was open and down whose big red nose a fly was crawling; caption: *Kibitzer, keep your mouth shut!* This picture proved so successful that it was lithographed for quantity sale to taverns and coffeehouses.

The kibitzer first made his appearance in literature in an Italian manuscript of 1250 A.D., but the word for him then was "beggar." The author reported that the spectators at dice games outnumbered the players.

The American kibitzer, to do him justice, is much maligned. Under the influence of the Anglo-Saxon reserve, he is generally quite well behaved. Only when the urge becomes irresistible does he open his mouth. But somehow his good behavior has not added to his popularity.

Rules for kibitzers' deportment have been set down by an expert at the art—Captain Irving Woolfe, a retired businessman and World War I ace, who for some years has attended all the big Bridge tournaments to sit, silent and motionless, and watch. "Ike's" rules are: Don't say anything; if asked a question, answer it briefly and without expressing an opinion; never change facial expression; watch the hand of only one player; don't touch a player, or his chair, and don't sit too close. Captain Ike is as much a fixture at Bridge tournaments as is One-eyed Connolly at World Series, and he is one of the few kibitzers who have ever appeared as heroes in kibitzer stories. Thus:

A hand had been played, not wisely and not well, and one of the contestants turned to Ike, who was watching closely.

"How do you think he should have played it?" the contestant asked.

"Under an assumed name," replied Ike gently.

But seldom is the kibitzer permitted to talk back, even in the legends. Man apparently has an instinctive aversion to kibitzers, no matter how they act, and no matter how much—or how little—they know about the game. People are embarrassed by an expert kibitzer; his very glance seems critical. They are scornful of the kibitizing tyro. They are worried if they have a kibitzer they don't know, and you can't always judge by appearances.

There is a classic story, told of all games, about the faultless kibitzer who watched with keen interest for six hours and never opened his mouth. At this point a bitter argument arose among the players, and finally they agreed to leave the decision to the kibitzer. He shook his head sadly. "Sorry," he said. "I don't know the game."

Most feared by the expert Bridge players is the kibitzer who gasps, asks questions, or whispers to other kibitzers, while the play is in progress.

Sometimes no damage is done. At the height of his tournament fame, Ely Culbertson used to be followed about from table to table by a devoted gallery. Their murmurs of approbation provided a pleasing background for the master. On one hand, Ely and his partner somehow managed to land in a slam contract missing the two highest trumps. An opponent led out these two cards, then exclaimed ruefully, "I don't know why I didn't double."

A Culbertson kibitzer piped up disdainfully, "It's a good thing for you that you didn't. Mr. Culbertson redoubles like a flash!"

At other times the kibitzer's remark is a dead giveaway. Today the galleries follow Charles Goren, who has the outstanding tournament record. On an occasion when Goren had made a somewhat unusual lead, a woman spectator gasped and said, "But Mr. Goren——"

"Please, madam," Goren cautioned her pleasantly.

"I'm sorry," she said. Then, turning to her husband, she emitted a stage whisper that was heard all over the room: "I can't understand it. His book says *never* to lead a singleton against no-trump."

Among the most coveted trophies for which

the Bridge stars compete is the Harold S. Vanderbilt cup. Engraved on this cup are the names of all the great players of bridge; *not* engraved on it is the name of a kibitzer who once won the tournament, practically single-handed, for Howard Schenken and his team-mates.

Schenken, whose name is on the cup five times, was playing a hand at one no-trump. The play was completed and scored as down one—50 points for Schenken's opponents. Here the kibitzer spoke up: "Excuse me, Mr. Schenken, but didn't you make that bid?"

Now, Howard Schenken is noted for his politeness to everyone; that is, to almost everyone. There is one natural exception—kibitzers. His answer was sardonic: "When you contract for seven tricks and take only six, you are down one." But the kibitzer was undiscouraged; kibitzers always are. He reviewed the play trick by trick. The review proved that the kibitzer was right. The hand was rescored; instead of losing 50 points, Schenken's side scored 90 points (40 is the trick-score; 50 points bonus, always scored in tournaments, for making the contract). This made a net difference of 140 points, and the Schenken team finally won by 130; so if it hadn't been for the kibitzer they would have lost by 10 points.

The sad conclusion to all this is that Howard Schenken still despises kibitzers.

The sport of kibitzer-baiting is popular because no one ever has any sympathy for the victim. Occasionally a rare opportunity arises. For example, there was the celebrated case at the Mayfair Bridge Club, in New York.

A player found himself at a contract of five diamonds, redoubled and vulnerable. He lost the first two tricks, but then spread his hand and claimed the rest, which would give him his contract. His opponents were convinced and would have thrown in their cards—when there was an objection. And who objected? Who but the ubiquitous kibitzer? "He can't make it," proclaimed the kibitzer—"not if . . ." The kibitzer had figured out a complicated line of play that everyone else had overlooked.

A committee was called to sit as a jury upon this crime. In a burst of inspiration, these jurymen saw their duty plain, and they did it. They awarded the declarer 950 points, the score for making five diamonds. They awarded his opponents 400 points, the score for defeating the contract one trick, redoubled and vulnerable. And they fined the kibitzer 1,350 points for being so smart. Everyone applauded. Even the other kibitzers. There is no honor among kibitzers.

But the kibitzer's history is not without its flashes of glory. The most famous man ever known to the world of games, Edmond Hoyle, was only a kibitzer, according to his contemporaries. (They didn't use the word "kibitzer," then, of course; Mr. Hoyle died in 1769.) But while Mr. Hoyle only watched, and didn't play, he was the man they went to for advice; he wrote a book on games that was the biggest best seller of his century and has been a best seller ever since; and we still say "according to Hoyle."

Nor have kibitzers always been aimless and gainless. In the honky-tonk gambling houses of the Old West, when men were men and the big game was Faro, kibitzing could be a profitable vocation.

In those days, there were hangers-on who sat around the Faro game and waited for "sleepers." A sleeper was a bet that someone placed and then forgot about it. If the bet won, and nobody else took it, the kibitzer grabbed it. But, of course, he wasn't called a kibitzer then, either. They said he was "cadging sleepers"—a throwback to thirteenth-century Italy, for "cadge" means "beg."

Anyone who wants to go in for kibitzer-baiting can best turn to the most popular American card game, which is, you may learn with surprise, Solitaire. There's no better sport than sitting in a railroad car with some intelligent-looking but simple soul beside you, while you play a game of Solitaire on your lap, making up the rules as you go along! Your companion will go crazy trying to figure it out.

Which is a reminder that the most scientific sort of surveys have been lavished on finding out how many people play Bridge (30 million), how many play Gin Rummy (9 million), how many play Pinochle (12 million), how many play Solitaire (45 million, of whom 44 million cheat). But nobody has bothered to find out how many people kibitz.

The best guess is that it conforms to the death rate in Podunk, as reported by the Oldest Resident—"one per person."

Nevertheless, *somebody* has to say a good word for the kibitzer. As sole witness for the defense, we call upon Klondike Pete, the old prospector.

"I was all alone and stranded in the North Canadian wilds," says Pete, "and it was midwinter. I was snowed in; my dogs had stampeded; my sled was wrecked; my provisions were low; my fuel was gone; I was out of ammunition; the wolves were howling. There wasn't a human being within fifty miles. Things seemed hopeless.

"But was I worried? Certainly not! I just took out my old pack of cards and began a game of Solitaire.

"I hadn't been playing a minute when I felt a finger tapping my shoulder. I looked up. There was a well-fed, fur-clad man standing behind me.

" 'Why,' he asked, 'don't you play that red seven on the black eight?' "

On Nomenclature

WE GLEANED an important bit of Americana recently from one of the midtown Bridge emporiums. Strolling in on a busman's holiday, we found a high-power rubber game in progress among the big shots of the club. A gallery of kibitzers three deep was massed about the table. Presently came a bidding orgy that precipitated a violent dispute. Nearby kibitzers joined the players in assessing praise and blame. When opinion seemed to be veering toward united censure of one player, a voice was heard from the outskirts of the crowd, raised in championship of the culprit.

Immediately the speaker was treated to a glare from players and kibitzers alike. The moment of dead silence was broken by one of the players:

"Keep quiet, please! You're merely a tsitser!"

Evidently this reproof epitomized the general view, for discussion was immediately resumed, the dissenting voice being genteelly ignored.

Feeling that there was something here we did not wholly comprehend, we drew the proprietor aside and requested a definition of "tsitser." And this is what we learned:

A *kibitzer* is one who has asked and received permission to watch. He may participate in discussion with the players.

A *dorbitzer* is one who has asked and received permission of the kibitzers to join them. He may speak to the latter but not to the players.

A *tsitser* is one who has asked permission of nobody. His rights are strictly limited to hovering in the background and expressing his sentiments by exclaiming "Ts! ts! ts!"

—*from* THE BRIDGE WORLD

On Terminology

THE four men at the card table were being bothered by an irritating kibitzer. When the troublesome talker stepped into the next room to mix a drink, one of the players suggested, "This next hand let's make up a game nobody ever heard of—he won't know what the hell we're playing and maybe that will shut him up."

When the kibitzer returned, the dealer tore the top two cards in half and gave them to the man on his right; he tore the corners off the next three cards and placed them before the next player, face up; he tore the next five cards in quarters, gave fifteen pieces to the third man, four to himself and put the last piece in the center of the table.

Looking intently at four small pieces of card in his hand, the dealer said, "I have a mingle, so I think I'll bet a dollar."

The second man stared at the pasteboards scattered before him. "I have a snazzle," he announced, "so I'll raise you a dollar."

The third man folded without betting and the fourth, after due deliberation, said, "I've a farfle, so I'll just raise you two dollars."

The kibitzer shook his head slowly from side to side. "You're crazy," he said, "you're never going to beat a mingle and a snazzle with a lousy farfle."

—*from* PLAYBOY Magazine

Cartoon by H. T. Webster;
courtesy The New York *Herald Tribune*

[Editors' only note to this article: We aren't superstitious either, but—

I'm Not Superstitious . . . But

by RICHARD L. FREY

OF COURSE *I'm* not superstitious and neither are *you. We* are much too intelligent to believe any such folderol as that meeting a black cat, or walking under a ladder, can have the slightest effect on the distribution of the aces and kings in an inanimate set of pasteboards. *But* . . .

Everybody knows that Lady Luck is a whimsical creature. Nobody knows for sure what accounts for the way she hands out her smiles or her kicks in the teeth. But one thing we *can* tell, she's superstitious herself. Dealing with such an illogical and unpredictable character, why should we fly in the face of her convictions? After all, we certainly have to be polite to a lady.

The odd thing is, most superstitions have a grain of logic. Not always as much as motivated the charming Mary Clement—whose beauty, sense of humor, and skill at Contract Bridge were equally admired—when she made her famous remark to a long-necked and keen-eyed adversary: "I wish you wouldn't look into my hand. I happen to be superstitious."

Nevertheless, there are sound reasons why the late P. Hal Sims refused to have a kibitzer's foot on his chair, why David Bruce was superstitious about letting anyone stand behind him, and even why the Poker player gets up and walks around his chair three times for luck. Certainly when the formal Bridge laws take luck into account, that's official recognition of superstition with a vengeance.

I admit there's no accounting for such silly superstitions (it's okay, I have my fingers crossed) as a lucky suit of clothes, or a lucky necktie. At the beginning of a winning streak I enjoyed in tournament play some years ago, I happened to wear a particular tie on two successive days. I have a habit of unconsciously crumpling the end of my tie while I'm thinking. Though I carefully saved that tie exclusively for wear during tournaments, by the end of the year my lucky tie was frayed indeed. My fingers got so used to feeling that comforting frayed spot, that it was truly disturbing and bad for my game not to find it there when my wife finally insisted that I throw that "horrible worn-out tie" away.

She won, of course. After all, I'm not superstitious, am I? How could I insist on continuing to wear "that old rag" in the face of probable wifely amusement?

Coincidence is the source of most superstitions. One Tuesday evening a player trudges through a heavy rain to his Bridge game, plays and loses. It doesn't seem to faze him; sometimes one loses, sometimes one wins. The following Tuesday he goes back to the same game, undaunted. He loses again, and this time heavily.

"That's even more than you lost last week," remarks one of his adversaries in a sympathetic way.

"Yeah, you did take a beating last Tuesday, didn't you?" puts in another fellow player.

Our hero sighs and looks out the window at the driving rain.

The next week he makes another Tuesday evening Bridge date. This time he hopes it won't rain. But that night he stubbornly dons his rubbers to take one more crack at his jinx. Even before the game begins he is fearful this won't be his lucky night. Perhaps that little difference in his confidence affects his game just enough so that he does not play very well. For whatever reason, he loses again. Now he begins to wonder. He isn't superstitious—but are rainy Tuesdays just bad luck for him?

Next Tuesday dawns with a drizzle. Anxiously, he consults the weather forecast: "Rain, continuing tonight and tomorrow." He reaches for the telephone.

"Joe," he announces, "get somebody else to sit in for tonight, will you? I'm going to the movies."

Joe is amazed. "Since when would you rather go to the movies than play Bridge?"

"Well—" lamely—"rainy Tuesdays are just hard luck for me."

You see what happens? Somebody has to lose that night, and the fellow who inherits the place deep in the minus column begins to wonder. Soon there are a lot of players who are fearful of playing on stormy Tuesdays.

What about the winners? Well, either they believe that rainy Tuesdays are lucky for them or they don't take stock in that particular superstition. Maybe they believe, instead, that they have to step on all the cracks in the sidewalk—or avoid stepping on them—on the way to the game. It doesn't matter what the superstition is, if someone even half believes it, it can shake his confidence enough to affect his play.

There are explanations, if not sound reasons, for most taboos. The three-on-a-match idea, so the legend goes, was originally a sales-promotion scheme for match manufacturers. It grew up during World War I, and it is not too farfetched to believe that by the time the third man put his cigarette to a match a watchful sniper could spot the light, aim at it, and fire. Walking under a ladder? Well, ladders are unsteady, and usually the people standing on them are working with tools, or pails of paint, or other things which have been known to fall on passers-by.

The sense behind a card-player's superstitions may be harder to find but it is usually there. Hal Sims, though he lived to have people watch him play, never failed to feel a foot resting on his chair—and woe betide the owner of that foot. Burnstine disliked having kibitzers of all kinds, but a standing one was absolutely taboo. These idiosyncrasies are classed as superstitions, but they began as efforts to avoid disturbances of that utter concentration on the game which is so essential to successful play.

Bruce's ban on a standing spectator is actually as reasonable as Mary Clement's "superstition" against having her opponents try to peek at her cards. A sitting kibitzer looks at only one hand. But a standee can move around. Naturally, he doesn't want to watch a bust hand if he can watch the player whose cards offer some excitement. So he moves around with the aces and kings—thereby tipping off the hands to a player who understands simple psychology.

On the face of it, nothing seems more illogical than that a player can change his luck by getting up and walking three times around his own chair. It is ridiculous to suggest that this mere act can have any effect whatever upon the cards which will be dealt to him during or after his brief promenade. However, two things do happen which may affect his game. In getting up out of his chair, stretching, and taking even this little bit of exercise, a player will stimulate his circulation—enough, perhaps, to wake him up and start him thinking more clearly. And if he has real faith, or even a slight hope that his bow to superstition may improve his luck—if taking his little walk shakes off the psychology of defeat—his play is bound to improve. The quality of the cards isn't the only factor in card games, so this alone may be enough to start him winning—and to confirm him in what will be a lifelong superstition.

The very laws of Contract Bridge give official recognition to superstitions at which we scoff. At the beginning of each rubber the players cut cards to see which shall be partners and who shall deal first. That is part of the mechanics of the game. However, the player with the highest card also "has the right to choose his seat and the pack with which he will deal."

Assuming that neither deck is marked and each has its full complement of aces and kings, and assuming further that all the chairs are comfortable, each is in a good light, and none is in a draft, you might wonder why in the world the dignified framers of the Bridge laws would bother with such an inconsequential triviality.

Just watch any of these same sober solons in a bridge game. You will see the one who draws the highest card carefully ask what was the color of the deck dealt by the players who won the last rubber. If necessary, he will ungallantly unseat even a lady opponent from the chair upon which perched the victory. He will do this as diligently as a football captain will study the direction of the prevailing wind; or as carefully as a fisherman will inquire what fish are running, what bait they are taking, and where they are likely to be found. Sam Fry once suggested that the Bridge clubs post a statement on the bulletin board each day, announcing whether the cards are running North-South or East-West. Or alternating.

Yes, the trouble is that some days they alternate. You have to be quick to note the turn of he tide. The red deck, which has been "hot" for hours, may suddenly and unaccountably cool off. Oh, for a method of knowing when and where the blue begins . . . to favor its dealers with the aces and kings. Theatrical genius George S. Kaufman, in an introduction to a Bridge book by Charles Goren, announced that science was working on this matter. "For the present I can only say," he said, "that some highly promising results have been obtained with rabbits, but as yet I can only hint at the possibilities."

That book was published in 1942, and George hasn't mentioned the matter since. Maybe the problem *has* been solved, and George is just keeping the solution secret. Maybe that's why he wins all the time.

No one who observes the vagaries of luck as intimately as a frequent card-player can remain completely free of superstition. The very deck with which the game is played is rife with it. Some of this superstition derives from fortune-telling. The ace of spades is the card of death. The queen of spades is a card of ill omen. The nine of diamonds is called "The Curse of Scotland" for as many as six different reasons, all connected with Scottish misfortunes—ranging from the battle of Flodden to the unhappy fate of Mary, Queen of Scots.

There's no sense to it. Waldemar von Zedtwitz believes he is lucky at contracts played with diamonds as trumps; several of his finest hands happened to be played at diamond contracts. In a close choice, Sam Stayman always plays the four of hearts, because that won him two national championships. But he shudders when his partner plays the same card, because that way he lost two championships. It may seem funny to you—but he isn't taking any chances.

Many players think it brings bad luck if someone wishes them good luck before a game; equally they dislike to be called "lucky," or to have attention called to the score when they are winning. Some will try to counter the dire effects of this merely by knocking wood (it takes a superstition to offset a superstition); others will go so far as to quit the game.

Probably we are all a little like the atheist who said: "I do not believe in God. But since so many others do, perhaps they are right, and I am wrong. It can do me no harm to say a few prayers."

Maybe you are bold enough to break a chain letter, ignoring the warning that it will bring bad luck. But can you do so without a single qualm that perhaps it may? And if you do, will you never wonder whether any slight misfortune which follows may be a consequence? The fact is, we remember circumstances attendant upon extreme good fortune or ill fortune. If they recur, we are likely to take them as good or evil omens, as the case may be. We may even deliberately try to recreate them, as John McGraw did when he hired a wagon to carry a load of empty barrels where his Giants could see them on the way to dress for a ball game. Empty barrels are supposed to produce hits, and it was McGraw's business to see that his players got those hits. If a wagonload of empty barrels might do it, why should a successful manager leave it to chance to furnish the barrels?

However, *I* am not superstitious. Not a bit of it. Will I play next Tuesday? I'd be delighted. But have a fifth player handy. I wouldn't want you to be stuck in case it rains and I go to the movies.

[Edmond Hoyle's secret system for remembering the cards is worth reprinting just as it appeared in 1743.

from A Short Treatise on Whist

by EDMOND HOYLE, *Gent.*

CHAP. XIX

An ARTIFICIAL MEMORY, *or an easy Method of assisting the* MEMORY *of those that play at the Game of* WHIST./To which are added, *Several* CASES *not hitherto published.*

I.

PLACE of every Suit in your Hand, the worst of it to the left-hand and the best (in Order) to the right, and the Trumps in the like Order, always to the left of all the other Suits.

II.

If in the Course of Play you find you have the best Card remaining of any Suit, put the same to the left of your Trumps.

III.

And if you find you have the second best Card of any Suit to remember, place it on the right of your Trumps.

IV.

And if you have the third best Card of any Suit to remember, place a small Card of that Suit between the Trumps and that third best, to the right of the Trumps.

V.

To remember your Partner's first Lead, place a small Card of that Suit led in the midst of your Trumps, and if you have but one Trump, on the left of it.

VI.

When you deal, put the Trump turned up to the right of all your Trumps, and part with it as late as you can, that your Partner may know you have that Trump left, and so play accordingly.

VII.

To find where, or in what Suit your Adversaries revoke.

Suppose the two Suits on your right-hand to represent your Adversaries in the Order they sit, as to your right and left-hand:

When you suspect either of them to have made a Revoke in any Suit, clap a small Card of that Suit amongst the Cards representing that Adversary, by which means you record not only that there may have been a Revoke, but also which of them made it, and in what Suit.

If the Suit that represents the Adversary that made the Revoke, happens to be the Suit he revoked in, change that Suit for another, and as above, put a small Card of the Suit revoked in, in the middle of that exchanged Suit, and if you have not a Card of that Suit, reverse a Card of any Suit you have (except Diamonds) and place it there.

VIII.

As you have a way to remember your Partner's first Lead, you may also record in what Suit either of your Adversaries made their first Lead, by putting the Suit in which they made that Lead, in the Place which in your Hand represents that Adversary, as either of your right or left-hand; and if other Suits were already placed to represent them, then exchange them for the Suits in which each of them makes his first Lead.

The foregoing Method is to be taken when you find it more necessary to record the Adversary's first Lead, than to endeavour to find out a Revoke.

POEMS ABOUT CARD GAMES

¶There is a frightening mass of poetry (if you can call it that) about card games, but most of it is doggerel of too low order to reprint—in fact, it was not worth printing, or even reading, in the first place. ¶Through this cloud of ineptitude shine certain conspicuous lights. We have assembled some outstanding ones. Most of them fall in the "light verse" category, but we will start with one that might stand as the theme of this book or any book. Mr. Ware, who lived 1841-1911, wrote his poem about Whist, but it applies to almost any card game.

Whist

by EUGENE F. WARE

HOUR after hour the cards were fairly shuffled
And fairly dealt, but still I got no hand.
The morning came, and with a mind unruffled
I only said, "I do not understand."

Life is a game of cards. From unseen sources
The pack is shuffled and the hands are dealt.
Blind are our efforts to control the forces
That, though unseen, are no less strongly felt.

I may not like the way the cards are shuffled,
But yet I like the game and want to play;
And through the long, long night will I, unruffled,
Play what I get, until the break of day.

¶It is not surprising that the following is the most famous piece of English poetry dealing with a card game, for it is the only case in which a major poet describes a card game in a major poem. The poet was Alexander Pope; the poem, The Rape of the Lock; *the game, Ombre.* *¶Pope wrote* The Rape of the Lock *mostly in 1712. Its story is based all on a true incident of the London season: An admirer of the heroine (in the poem called Belinda) catches her unawares and snips off a lock of her hair for a keepsake; she is indignant and demands its return. Around this simple incident Pope wrote a satire on fashionable life in the court of Queen Anne. The poem has been generally considered Pope's masterpiece and the finest satire of its kind in English poetry.* *¶In the course of the poem Belinda plays a game of Ombre with two gentlemen of the court; the game occupies most of the third (of five) cantos. Ombre (see page 22) was then the favored three-hand card game of the fashionable London world, and its four-hand form, Quadrille, the favored four-hand game. Though not really difficult, Ombre was absurdly complex in rules and terminology. Instead of explaining it here we will make notes upon the numbered lines of the poem, which follows.*

from The Rape of the Lock
by ALEXANDER POPE

CANTO III

CLOSE by those meads, for ever crown'd with flow'rs,
Where Thames with pride surveys his rising tow'rs,
There stands a structure of majestic frame,
Which from the neighb'ring Hampton takes its name;
Here Britain's statesmen oft the fall foredoom 5
Of foreign Tyrants, and of Nymphs at home;
Here thou, great ANNA! whom three realms obey,
Dost sometimes counsel take—and sometimes Tea.
Hither the Heroes and the Nymphs resort,
To taste awhile the pleasures of a Court; 10
In various talk th' instructive hours they past,
Who gave the ball, or paid the visit last;
One speaks the glory of the British Queen,
And one describes a charming Indian screen;
A third interprets motions, looks, and eyes; 15
At ev'ry word a reputation dies.
Snuff, or the fan, supply each pause of chat,
With singing, laughing, ogling, *and all that.*
Meanwhile, declining from the noon of day,
The sun obliquely shoots his burning ray; 20
The hungry judges soon the sentence sign,
And wretches hang that jury-men may dine;
The merchant from th' Exchange returns in peace,
And the long labours of the Toilet cease.
Belinda now, whom thirst of fame invites, 25
Burns to encounter two advent'rous Knights,
At Ombre singly to decide their doom;
And swells her breast with conquests yet to come.

Line 5: Hampton Court Palace, on the Thames about 15 miles from (what was then) London, was a country residence of English sovereigns from Henry VIII to George I.
Line 7: ANNA is Queen Anne, under whom (in 1707) the "three realms" of England, Scotland and Wales had first been fully united to constitute Great Britain.
Lines 25-27: Belinda invites the two gentlemen to play a game of Ombre with her.

Straight the three bands prepare in arms to join,
Each band the number of the sacred Nine. 30
Soon as she spreads her hand, th' aërial guard
Descend, and sit on each important card:
First Ariel perch'd upon a Matadore,
Then each according to the rank they bore;
For Sylphs, yet mindful of their ancient race, 35
Are, as when women, wond'rous fond of place.
Behold, four Kings, in majesty rever'd,
With hoary whiskers and a forky beard;
And four fair Queens whose hands sustain a flow'r,
Th' expressive emblem of their softer pow'r; 40
Four Knaves in garbs succinct, a trusty band;
Caps on their heads, and halberts in their hand;
And party-colour'd troops, a shining train,
Draw forth to combat on the velvet plain.
The skilful Nymph reviews her force with care: 45
Let Spades be trumps! she said, and trumps they were.
Now move to war her sable Matadores,
In show like leaders of the swarthy Moors.
Spadillio first, unconquerable Lord!
Led off two captive trumps, and swept the board. 50
As many more Manillio forc'd to yield,
And march'd a victor from the verdant field.
Him Basto follow'd, but his fate more hard
Gain'd but one trump and one Plebeian card.
With his broad sabre next, a chief in years, 55
The hoary Majesty of Spades appears,
Puts forth one manly leg, to sight reveal'd,
The rest, his many-colour'd robe conceal'd.
The rebel Knave, who dares his prince engage,
Proves the just victim of his royal rage. 60
Ev'n mighty Pam, that Kings and Queens o'erthrew,
And mow'd down armies in the fights of Lu,
Sad chance of war! now destitute of aid,
Falls undistinguish'd by the victor Spade!

Line 30: Nine cards are dealt to each player, from a pack of 40 cards (K, Q, J, 7, 6, 5, 4, 3, 2, A of each suit).
Lines 31-44: The pack is described. The Sylphs, airy supernatural beings, are imagined by Pope to control all the events of the poem. The Matadores (line 33) are the three highest trumps in Ombre, as explained below.
Lines 45-46: Belinda is eldest hand (first to receive cards in the deal) and as such can name the trump and become the bidder (ombre) unless another player wishes to outbid her, which in this case no one does. She names spades. The other two players now become temporary partners in an effort to defeat her.
Line 47: Belinda leads first, not because she is ombre but because eldest hand always leads first. With spades trumps, the matadores are all sable, or black.
Line 49: Spadillio, or spadille, is the ace of spades, always the highest trump, whatever the trump suit. Both opponents follow suit.
Line 51: Manillio, or manille, is the second-highest trump. It is always the card of the trump suit that would otherwise be lowest—in this case, the deuce of spades. Both opponents follow suit again.
Line 53: Basto is the ace of clubs, always the third-highest trump regardless of the suit chosen. Now only one opposing trump falls; the other opponent is out of trumps and discards.
Lines 55-56: Having led her three matadores, Belinda leads the king of spades, the fourth-highest trump. Her luck was good, to hold all four top trumps; her play was doubtful, to lead them all out. With spades trumps, there are eleven trumps in all. Belinda has drawn ten of them, leaving herself trumpless and an opponent (the Baron) with the queen of spades, the only trump left.
Lines 59-64: On Belinda's fourth trump lead, the jack of clubs is discarded. This card, called Pam, was the highest card in the game of Loo but was merely another card in Ombre. Loo is still played in England, while Ombre is long forgotten.

Thus far both armies to Belinda yield; 65
Now to the Baron fate inclines the field.
His warlike Amazon her host invades,
Th' imperial consort of the crown of Spades.
The Club's black Tyrant first her victim dy'd,
Spite of his haughty mien, and barb'rous pride: 70
What boots the regal circle on his head,
His giant limbs, in state unwieldy spread;
That long behind he trails his pompous robe,
And, of all monarchs, only grasps the globe?
The Baron now his Diamonds pours apace! 75
Th' embroider'd King who shows but half his face,
And his refulgent Queen, with pow'rs combin'd
Of broken troops, an easy conquest find.
Clubs, Diamonds, Hearts, in wild disorder seen,
With throngs promiscuous strew the level green. 80
Thus when dispers'd a routed army runs,
Of Asia's troops, and Afric's sable sons,
With like confusion different nations fly,
Of various habit, and of various dye;
The pierc'd battalions disunited fall, 85
In heaps on heaps; one fate o'erwhelms them all.
The Knave of Diamonds tries his wily arts,
And wins (oh shameful chance!) the Queen of Hearts.
At this, the blood the Virgin's cheek forsook,
A livid paleness spreads o'er all her look; 90
She sees, and trembles at th' approaching ill,
Just in the jaws of ruin, and Codille.
And now (as oft in some distemper'd State)
On one nice Trick depends the gen'ral fate:
An Ace of Hearts steps forth: the King unseen 95
Lurk'd in her hand, and mourn'd his captive Queen:
He springs to vengeance with an eager pace,
And falls like thunder on the prostrate Ace.
The Nymph exulting fills with shouts the sky;
The walls, the woods, and long canals reply. 100

Line 65: Belinda has won the first four tricks. To make her contract she must win five of the nine tricks; or she can win with only four tricks if her opponents' tricks are divided 3-2 between them. If one opponent matches her four tricks she is beaten and must pay each opponent a double stake. Her opponents' strategy, therefore, must now be to win all the remaining tricks and let the likelier of their hands win four of them.
Lines 66-89: The Baron gets the lead with his high trump and does not falter until he has won four tricks in all, thus: Belinda leads the king of clubs; it is the highest club but it dies (*line 69*) because the Baron is void of clubs and trumps it with the spade queen, "consort of the spade king" (*line 68*). The Baron holds the K-Q-J of diamonds and leads them in order (*lines 76, 77, 87*); they must win because they are the highest diamonds and no trumps are left. Belinda and the third player follow suit or discard helplessly (*lines 79-80*).
Line 94: Now if either the Baron or his partner can win the last trick, Belinda is beaten (*beast* in 18th-century England, *bête* of course in France and, to this day, in Germany).
Lines 95-96: The Baron's last lead is the ace of hearts; but in Ombre this card ranked under all the face cards and Belinda had saved the king, the highest heart. So Belinda wins five tricks and the game, and . . .
Line 99: She gloats.

Next to Pope's Rape of the Lock, *the most famous of all poems about card games is Bret Harte's humorous contribution from his own Western precincts, when the railroads were a-building with a profusion of Chinese laborers recently imported. The game is Euchre.*

Plain Language from Truthful James

by BRET HARTE

TABLE MOUNTAIN, 1870

WHICH I wish to remark,
And my language is plain,
That for ways that are dark
And for tricks that are vain,
The heathen Chinee is peculiar,
Which the same I would rise to explain.

Ah Sin was his name;
And I shall not deny,
In regard to the same,
What that name might imply;
But his smile it was pensive and childlike,
As I frequent remarked to Bill Nye.

It was August the third,
And quite soft was the skies;
Which it might be inferred
That Ah Sin was likewise;
Yet he played it that day upon William
And me in a way I despise.

Which we had a small game,
And Ah Sin took a hand:
It was Euchre. The same
He did not understand;
But he smiled as he sat by the table,
With the smile that was childlike and bland.

Yet the cards they were stocked
In a way that I grieve,
And my feelings were shocked
At the state of Nye's sleeve,
Which was stuffed full of aces and bowers,
And the same with intent to deceive.

But the hands that were played
By that heathen Chinee,
And the points that he made,
Were quite frightful to see,—
Till at last he put down a right bower,
Which was the same Nye had dealt unto me.

Then I looked up at Nye,
And he gazed upon me;
And he rose with a sigh,
And said, "Can this be?
We are ruined by Chinese cheap labor!—"
And he went for that heathen Chinee.

In the scene that ensued
I did not take a hand,
But the floor it was strewed
Like the leaves on the strand
With the cards that Ah Sin had been hiding,
In the game "he did not understand."

In his sleeves, which were long,
He had twenty-four jacks*—
Which was coming it strong,
Yet I state but the facts;
And we found on his nails, which were taper,
What is frequent in tapers,—that's wax.

Which is why I remark
And my language is plain,
That for ways that are dark
And for tricks that are vain,
The heathen Chinee is peculiar,—
Which the same I am free to maintain.

* This word has puzzled the editors of nearly all anthologies; and, leaping to conclusions, they have changed it to read "twenty-four packs." But *jacks* was intended and is correct. In Euchre the jack of trumps is the *right bower* or highest trump; the jack of the other suit of the same color is the *left bower*, or second-highest trump. Cardsharpers use wax on their fingers to pick up a card without having to grasp it.

[Dr. Maurice Lewi, who died at the age of ninety-nine as we were writing this, was the most revered member of the Bridge-playing fraternity—which might surprise many of his fellow physicians, who knew him only as an equally revered member of the medical fraternity. That Dr. Lewi's son inherited some of the father's delicious wit is proved by the following spoof of Bridge and chess problems. It is a sad note that Bill Lewi died an untimely death, a young man.

A Game Philosopher *by* GRANT LEWI

That man is merely fortune's midge—
I ponder sagely, more or less—
When doing problems based on Bridge
And Chess.

As in the cannon's flaming mouth
One knows he fights a futile fight,
So the antagonists of South
And White.

The best defense of West and East
Must end with a disastrous guess,
But South is right on every least
Finesse.

And somber is Black's constant fate—
Despite the best that he can do
White always has a brilliant mate
In two.

I like to think myself a White,
Unconquerable in my attack,
But equally as well I might
Be Black.

And though as South I long to see
My foe by coup and squeeze oppressed,
I greatly fear that I may be
A West.

I pray that I may someday see
The answer to a gamester's dream
—White-South in action. That would be
A team!

Oh happy huntsmen, bound to win
Beneath good fortune's favored flag,
For you the game is always in
The bag.

[W. B. France, one of the outstanding light lyricists of our day, draws from a Duplicate Bridge game a moral similar to that drawn by Eugene F. Ware in the poem on page 296.

Bridge Tournament *by* W. B. FRANCE

THEY move to the tables in murmuring pairs
Rehashing the hand that was recently theirs,
Deploring the points their opponents had scored
To keep them from getting a top on the board.
Their bidding was proper, it seemed at the time—
Until they discovered its fruit was a lime;
And now they are chattering, chewing the fat:
You shoulda done this, and I shoulda done that,
We shoulda, we shouldna done this or done that.

And now they know better, and here's a new hand;
They tackle it boldly; their bidding is grand;
But somehow or other—it happens that way—
An African plopped in the woodpile of play,
And now they move on, with: You shoulda led clubs,
We shouldn'ta played our opponents for dubs,
I shoulda finessed it right offa the bat,
You shoulda done this and I shoulda done that,
We shoulda, we shouldna done this or done that.

Ah, Life, with your duplicates never the same
As circumstance varies the play of the game,
If hindsight were foresight, if stern could be prow,
If tails wagged the dogs and tomorrow were now—
How wise we could be, and how free of mistakes!
We all could be winning and getting the breaks,
Instead of reviewing the moments whereat
We shoulda done this or we shoulda done that,
We shoulda, we shouldna done this or done that!

[Ethel Jacobson has long enjoyed a foremost position among American writers of light verse. Her topics have an inexhaustible range, but Bridge players will never believe Ethel (or anyone else) could be as good on any topic as Ethel is on Bridge.

Why I Gave Up Bridge

by ETHEL JACOBSON

SOUTH

According to Culbertson,
I ought to pass.
This only counts to 1½ honor-tricks.
And we're vulnerable.
He'd pass.
But I'll say two spades.
Who's bidding this hand, anyway—
Culbertson, or me?

EAST

If you'd taken that finesse
The other way,
We would have made it.
You see, you should always lead
Up to the queen.
Then whoever who has the king can take it.
Or no, you lead the queen up to the ace;
Then you catch the king
If it's on the other side,
And you only make their jack good.
Or vice versa.
A simple rule to remember is:
Always finesse through the king.
If you'd taken it the other way, now . . .

N.NE BY W

Yes, I led a heart.
That's all I have left.
What, I've already trumped them
Three times?
Ha ha, if that isn't the best joke
On me!

UNCHARTED TERRITORY

Heavens, why didn't you take me out?
I only *inkled* a notrump!
I had a wonderful helping hand
But no suit—
Three little diamonds
And two little hearts,
But fine clubs if you only had the tops.
And I wasn't afraid of spades.
Because after they took their tricks
My nine would be established.
You should have taken me out.
I only *inkled*—
Why, partner, what are you tearing up those cards for?

[If it's part of the American scene, Edgar Guest has written about it. The kibitzer, alas, is part of the American scene—and Mr. Guest makes appropriate comment.

To the Kibitzer

by EDGAR A. GUEST

Withhold the inquest when the hand is played;
Come not to me with all your counsel good;
You who behind my chair, unasked, have stood,
Speak not to me of blunders I have made.

I am a peaceful, law-abiding man,
Long-suffering, patient, placid, meek and mild;
I am as gentle as a little child.
The stain of murder never marked my clan.

But when the cards are dealt and I have bid,
Air not your wisdom after I am through.
I know myself what I have failed to do;
I know the faulty reckoning I did.

Sit at the table; watch us if you will;
But understand your counsel comes too late.
Advice unsought-for often leads to hate.
Silence is golden! Would you live—keep still!

[Ogden Nash is the great name of light verse in the twentieth century; and having it on his own authority that the following bit is all he has written about card-playing we include it perforce, per se, ipso facto, and also because we like it. We trust we have written and will long continue to write the very books to which Mr. Nash takes exception here.

Your Lead, Partner, I Hope We've Read the Same Book

by OGDEN NASH

When I was just a youngster,
Hardly bigger than a midge,
I used to join my family
In a game of Auction Bridge.
We were patient with reneging,
For the light was gas or oil,
And our arguments were settled
By a reference to Hoyle.
Auction Bridge was clover;
Then the experts took it over.
You could no longer bid by the seat of your pants,
The experts substituted skill for chance.

The experts captured Auction
With their lessons and their books,
And the casual week-end player
Got a lot of nasty looks.
The experts captured Auction
And dissected it, and then
Somebody thought up Contract,
And we played for fun again.
It was pleasant, lose or win,
But the experts muscled in,
And you couldn't deal cards in your own abode
Without having memorized the latest code.

We turned to simpler pastimes
With our neighbors and our kin;
Oklahoma or Canasta,
Or a modest hand of Gin.
We were quietly diverted
Before and after meals,
Till the experts scented suckers
And came yapping at our heels.
Behold a conquered province;
I'm a worm, and they are robins.
On the grandchildren's table what books are displayed?
Better Slapjack, and *How to Win at Old Maid.*

In a frantic final effort
To frivol expert-free,
I've invented Amaturo
For just my friends and me.
The deck has seven morkels
Of eleven guzzards each,
The game runs counterclockwise,
With an extra kleg for dreech,
But if you're caught with a gruice,
The score reverts to deuce.
I'll bet that before my cuff links are on the bureau
Some expert will have written *A Guide to Amaturo.*

* * *

A Thought

"Cards . . .
With all the tricks
That idleness has yet contrived
To fill the void of an unfurnished brain
To palliate dullness
And give time a shove."

WILLIAM COWPER, 1786

[François Villon, laureate of the Parisian underworld, wrote about card games in the fifteenth century—but he wrote in the jargon of his environs and no one today can comprehend its meaning. Villon was the master of the ballade, whose rigid and intricate rhyming scheme has intrigued many writers of card-game verse. The next selections are two modern examples.

Three Ballades of Bridge

I. OF DESPAIR

My bidding methods merit praise.
I play with caution and with skill.
I know the many clever ways
To make the cards obey my will.
From me no brilliant coup, no frill
Of masterful technique is hid.
But all the good it does is nil.
I simply never get a bid.

O mournful nights, ill-fated days,
And afternoons so drear and chill!
You come and go, and yet I gaze
On no ace-king, no jack or jill.
As mournful as a whippoorwill,
As plaintive as a katydid,
I want to cry, in accents shrill,
"I simply never get a bid!"

Alas, that skill so seldom pays!
How rough a path, how steep a hill
Must we traverse who know each phase
Of play, yet always foot the bill.
Can this go on and on, until
My bones into the tomb are slid
While solemn dirges echo still,
"He simply never got a bid"?

Envoy

Blind goddess, heed my codicil:
An honor-trick or two amid
My cards would give me such a thrill!
I simply never get a bid.

II. OF HOPE

I'LL have the finest in the land,
The longest bed, the softest chair,
A cellar stocked with contraband
And servants running here and there,
Hispano-Suiza cars to bear
My weary bones o'er street and fen,
And yachts to sail on Nostrum Mare,
When I begin to win again.

All winter in the tropic sand
And surf I'll sport, till solar glare
Directs me north to Newfoundland
Or Maine—it doesn't matter where.
Apparel I will choose with care:
The finest suits, say nine or ten,
And shoes and shirts and underwear,
When I begin to win again.

And then won't nights be sweet and grand,
Won't days be lovely, bright and fair,
When I can spend with lavish hand
And have enough and more to spare!
I'll be composed and debonair,
I'll be the happiest of men,
I'll sing, I'll shout, I'll float on air
When I begin to win again.

Envoy

But you, opponents! you beware!
My wrath you'll feel, as, if and when
The Lord decides to grant my prayer
And I begin to win again.

—*from* THE BRIDGE WORLD

III. THE BALLAD OF THE INDIFFERENT BRIDGE PLAYER

by EDGAR A. GUEST

I AM not much at the game;
Careless the things that I do.
Those whose approval I claim,
When I attempt it, are few.
Bridge players look in dismay
After a hand I have played;
Always they icily say:
"Why did you lead me a spade?"

I, who am gentle and tame,
Am scorned by a merciless crew;
I bear the brunt and the blame
Whenever they mutter, "Down two!"
No matter what card I may play,
No matter the game's not my trade,
Always they sneeringly say:
"Why did you lead me a spade?"

Matron, young maiden or dame,
Brown eyes or gray eyes or blue,
Angrily treats me the same,
Recalling the cards that I threw.
Be it December or May,
Ever she starts this tirade
With a look that's intended to slay:
"Why did you lead me a spade?"

Envoy

Prince, when my soul flies away
And my form in the cold ground is laid,
Let me rest where nobody will say:
"Why did you lead me a spade?"

[The first international Bridge match was played in 1930. When the American team arrived at Southampton, British reporters asked its captain, Ely Culbertson, what he thought of English players. "Lousy," said Ely. They asked him who was the world's greatest player. "I am," said Ely. This did not endear Mr. Culbertson to British pressmen, including the famous (in crossword puzzles, very famous) editor of Punch.

Mr. Ely Culbertson
A Petulant Poem
by EVOE (E. V. KNOX)

in *PUNCH*

(Written after reading for the fortieth time that this great Transatlantic expert described the play of the British team in a recent Bridge Armageddon as "lousy.")

THE weather is hot and I am tired
And the world is full of war,
And a moratorium, long required
By the dithering nations, seems desired
As much as it was before;

I am ready to read of goods and gold
And to read of an Ascot gown,
But I don't see why I should still be told
How ELY CULBERTSON came to scold
The people of London town.

If I turn once more to the Press and find
What ELY CULBERTSON said,
I shall surely feel that the master-mind
Of American Bridge would aid mankind
If he went and boiled his head.

If he boiled his head and stewed his face
In a bowl of Indian tea,
If he always trumped his partner's ace
This earth would not be a sorrier place,
So far as I can see.

I may be captious—indeed, I am—
But I should not greatly care
If every time that he made Grand Slam
Mr. ELY CULBERTSON rubbed some jam
Into the roots of his hair.

I will not weep when the sun's last light
Fades over the western ridge,
I will not moan to the winds of night:
"Mr. ELY CULBERTSON may be right,
And ours was a lousy Bridge."

I will cry, "The morrow may be serene,
There are nobler worlds beyond,
And the rose would flower and the hills be seen
If ELY CULBERTSON, painted green,
Were drowned in the village pond."

[Phyllis McGinley's admirers stretch far farther than the pages of this book. Poker players should be proud that she sees their game as a sonnet.

Dealer's Choice
by PHYLLIS MCGINLEY

MRS. MCGREGOR likes her hand, regards
The sweetening pot with pleasure. This is Poker
Where stud brings never less than seven cards
And deuces are as puissant as the joker.
The Campbells have no luck tonight and, pouting,
Blond Mrs. Campbell borders close on tears.
Four aces lose. The host, from pantry shouting,
Sorts out requests for ginger ales and beers.

The gentlemen grow ever so faintly ribald,
While ladies ante out of turn and blush.
The glasses empty. All the nuts are nibbled.
Llewellyn Hatfield shows a royal flush.
And Mrs. Campbell, teeming with emotion,
Deals forth another round of Spit-in-the-Ocean.

CARD-SHARPERS

In 1950 the American Academy of Political and Social Sciences devoted an issue of its publication, The Annals, *to gambling in the United States; and both of the editors of this volume were asked to and did contribute articles. One of the editors, to whom was assigned the subject "The Professional Gambler," included in his article the following examination of those who cheat at card games.*

THE CHEAT

IN THE CODE of the Western world the dishonorable is far more reprehensible than the dishonest, and cheating at cards is the most dishonorable of all offenses. Especially to those subjectively interested, it carries a greater stigma than the seduction of a friend's wife, the misappropriation of property held in trust, or even a show of cowardice when faced with honorable battle. To the exposed cardsharper is meted out a life sentence of ostracism, and seldom is the sentence reprieved.

Among the conventionally respectable classes this might be expected; less easy to explain is almost the identical attitude among classes whose other standards range from unconventional to amoral. No valid conclusions can be drawn from the attitudes of violent criminals, for in their society, as in the most primitive, the penalty for any violation is likely to be death. When Arnold Rothstein was murdered, one theory held that he had been caught cheating in a game, another that he had welshed on a gambling loss, and there were other theories having nothing to do with gambling; we might as readily accept any one of these theories as any other. But in less violent criminal groups, cheating one's fellows at cards is one of the few acts for which self-interest is not adequate justification.

There were, for example, two minor criminals named Maurice and "the Greek" who shared a furnished room. One night Maurice made eighty dollars—untold wealth by their standards—and unwisely boasted about it to the Greek. Whether Maurice was a heavy sleeper or the Greek had the foresight to drug him, the fact remains that when Maurice awoke the next morning the Greek and the eighty dollars were gone. Maurice cursed his bad luck and reproached himself for stupidity, but did not seem to condemn the

Greek. This same Maurice displayed righteous indignation when another member of his group was exposed as having cheated Maurice and others in a card game. Though obviously cheating at cards is recognized in Maurice's society as a proper means of livelihood, cheating within the fraternity is barred, perhaps as cannibalism but more likely as a vestige of conventional ethics.

No less anomalous, perhaps, is a kindred case from more refined circles. Some twenty years ago, a golf club in New Jersey conducted weekly Bridge tournaments at which two of the regular players were a real estate man and a college student. The tournaments were played for prizes of no great intrinsic value, and there was little betting on the result, so the reward of victory was no more than transient glory and self-satisfaction. Nevertheless the college student found this sufficient incentive to falsify some scores. He was caught, and never again was he permitted to play in that or any other tournament or Bridge game among players who knew him. The real estate man was tried for falsifying some legal documents to his own financial advantage. He was convicted and served a short term in prison; and upon his release he resumed his place in the regular weekly Bridge tournaments.

Despite the severity of the penalty, there are some hundreds of thousands of persons who do, or are willing to, cheat in card games; the extent of their activity depending on the degree of their skill and their own appraisal of the danger of detection. Furthermore, this estimate of the number who cheat would be many times greater if the word "cheat" were not given a very restrictive definition here.

DEFINITION OF CHEATING

A SHARP distinction is drawn, among serious card players, between cheating and unethical conduct. Cheating is manipulation of the cards, marking the cards, or collusion with another player to victimize a third. Unethical conduct is, broadly, intentional breach of the rules or proprieties of play, with a view to giving oneself an advantage over the opponent.

Cheating is universally condemned; unethical conduct is viewed with a range of emotions of which the most harsh is disapprobation, ranging through toleration to outright condonement. Yet the respective offenses have the same motivation, and conscience would call them equivalent. The probable explanation for the difference in attitude is a practical one. Against the usual forms of unethical conduct, one has a defense; he can verify the actual score against an opponent who habitually makes "mistakes" or "oversights" therein, and he can hold his hand up against an opponent who peeks. The offense can be counteracted and the amenities still observed. Against cheating as defined here, the only defense is overt accusation, which is always unpleasant.

The proposed definition of cheating is invariable in the realm of cardplaying, and applies generally to other games. In dice games a player is cheating if he introduces loaded or improperly marked dice, or if he attempts to slide or otherwise control the dice so that they will fall to his advantage; he is not cheating, but is merely oversharp, if he willfully misreads the faces of the dice or deliberately misconstrues the terms of a bet. A backgammon player is cheating if he palms a stone to remove it prematurely from the board; but he is merely unethical if he attempts an illegal move, one his opponent can see and demand that he retract. A roulette or similar gambling wheel is dishonest if the operator can control its stopping point, and the operator of such a wheel is a cheater; he is merely unduly greedy if he tries to shortchange the winner of a bet.

THE CARDSHARPER

A CARDSHARPER is a person who derives his livelihood, or an essential part of it, by cheating in card games. (The term is not used among the gambling fraternity, to whom a professional player is a "mechanic" if he is skillful at manipulating the cards, and merely a "hustler" if he is not.) The essential ingredients of the cardsharper are that his principal activity is winning money in gambling games and that his method of winning is, by our definition, cheating. Therefore, he is by law a criminal, guilty of obtaining money under false pretenses.

All gamblers are predatory, and professional ones are relatively ruthless. The cardsharper, who is more akin to the confidence man than to any form of true gambler, is totally ruthless. His object is to separate victim from money, and he seldom cares how much the victim suffers in the process.

Like any other professional criminal, the cardsharper usually develops by tutelage and example. This requires association with other cardsharpers and leads to some degree of fellowship with them and of group consciousness.

Many cardsharpers, however, begin on their own. They may first be motivated by simple greed. A player in a regular card game sees and covets the money of the others. He finds he cannot win it, or at least cannot win enough of it, by straightforward methods, so he learns to cheat. Having exhausted the possibilities of winning from his original group, or having been detected and banished, he moves out among strangers, seeking games in which to exploit his skill, and eventually he becomes a member of the fraternity.

Then there are those who become addicted to engrossing games of skill. They cannot bear to be doing anything else when they might be playing the game. Sometimes their addiction causes them to lose their jobs. Sometimes they begin so young that they never get around to honest employment. In any case, they have no other means of livelihood and must win to live. The only way to assure winning is to cheat, and they become cheats. Such cases are analogous to that of the drug addict who turns to crime or prostitution to maintain the availability of the drug.

There are the conjurers, who train themselves as performers but as such are not successful—at least not successful enough. The personality that did not quite make a stage presence may be quite adequate in a card game; the dexterity that could not quite deceive a large audience may suffice in a small group who have no particular reason to be suspicious anyway.

CONFIDENCE MEN

FINALLY, there are the confidence men who have devised or adopted a scheme involving a card game. To effectuate the scheme they must perfect their cheating technique, at least enough to master the tricks requisite to their plan.

It is the confidence men that are usually thought of when the term "cardsharper" is used. It is to them that the signs in the smoking lounges of transatlantic liners, BEWARE OF CARDSHARPERS, refer. Admittedly they are far more dangerous than the player who merely cheats to give himself a slight but continuing advantage; the confidence man purposes to take hundreds and even thousands from a person who thought he was risking at most a few dollars. But in most cases the card game is only incidental to the routine of the confidence men. They build up to a planned situation in which the victim, in one coup, will lose all his money; after this climax they seek to end the game immediately and to part from the victim as soon as possible. The cardsharper as we define him here has a different object. He wishes to prolong the game and remain in it. The money he wins must seem to come to him from nothing more than good luck in the normal course of play.

There is another notable difference. When confidence men employ a card game to further their ends, their scheme still depends upon the proverbial *sine qua non* of their profession, "You can't cheat an honest man." Our true cardsharper, on the other hand, wishes to play only with honest men, they being least likely to be suspicious and also least likely to be aware of the several methods of cheating.

Examine typical cardplaying routines employed by confidence men. First there is Three-Card Monte, so simple and so time-honored that it is no less than wonderful that it can still find victims. The dealer pitches his stand like any huckster selling patent medicine or other merchandise, and manipulates three cards until they come to rest face down on his board. One of the three cards is a queen, and the dealer, proclaiming that "the hand is quicker than the eye," offers to bet bystanders that they cannot locate the queen. (Those familiar with the shell game, played with three walnut shells and a pea, will recognize this as the same game.) A good dealer can make money honestly at this game; his hand is indeed quicker than the eye, and the odds are two to one that the onlooker cannot pick the queen at random while the dealer may reasonably offer him only even money. The dealer's object, however, is to make far more money than a stranger would be willing to bet so casually.

To this end, a confederate of the dealer's selects a likely-looking victim and converses with him while both make small bets against the dealer, winning some, losing some. At a propitious moment the confederate "crimps" the queen—gives it a telltale crease in a corner. He and the victim then bet heavily that they can pick the queen. The dealer lays out the cards, the crimped one is turned, and it is not the queen; in the course of his manipulations the dealer has removed the crimp from the queen and put a crimp in one of the other cards.

Here one may see the working of the formula. The victim could not be cheated if he were an honest man; he loses because he is trying to cheat the dealer.

Three-Card Monte, as aforesaid, is simple, time-honored, and so picayune that it can hardly be associated with the true confidence man, that appellation being somewhat of an honorific in the underworld.

The cardsharpers against whom the transatlantic liners give warning employ more refined approaches. A group of them, perfect gentlemen by their manners, engage in a friendly game with their rich victim; the stakes are moderate (it being remembered that "moderate" is a relative term); a climactic betting situation is arranged, the victim pays by check, after everyone talks it over the check is destroyed and burned, and the game reverts to its more sensible stakes. The destroying of the check allays the suspicion of the victim, who discovers much later that it was not his check that was destroyed, but one switched with it, and that his own check has been cashed. There are various ways of leading up to the climax, and in many of them it is unnecessary to appeal to the victim's larcenous spirit, so the confidence men are truly "cheating an honest man"; nevertheless, the key is the fake destruction of the check and not the card game itself.

The games best suited to the cardsharper's art are Poker; nearly any two-hand game, and especially a game such as Gin Rummy; and the games of structure used primarily as gambling games, for example Black Jack and Red Dog. The game least suited to cheating is Bridge, and accordingly it is least popular with the cardsharpers. The greatest godsend to cardsharpers in many years was the emergence of Gin Rummy as a favorite game among those who like to play for high stakes; previously many of the present crop of Gin Rummy players had been Bridge players.

METHODS OF CHEATING AT CARDS

THE aristocracy of the cardsharping profession are prestidigitators as skilled at their art as is a performing magician at his. Years of all but incessant practice go into making such an artist. Against him the honest cardplayer is helpless even if he is aware of the techniques of cheating and on his guard against them. There are, however, a multitude of less refined cheating practices, requiring less art, and more or less difficult for the trained eye to detect.

The advantage of using marked cards in many games is obvious. This method of cheating requires little skill or practice—nothing more than a way of introducing the cards into the game. It is possible to mark honest cards by crimping them, or with matching ink applied during the game; but this is dangerous unless the other players are quite ingenuous. Markings so applied are quite apparent to anyone who is on the lookout for them.

Next in simplicity is the process of holding out one or more cards from the pack. Consider a game of Poker, in which five cards are dealt to each player. On an early occasion the sharper discards only four of his cards, secreting one. On each deal thereafter he discards the regular five cards but always has one card in addition. By being able to select as his Poker hand any five of six cards, whereas the other players have only five cards each, he almost doubles his chance of having the best hand; and it hardly matters whether the card held out is a high one or a low one. The card held out can always be dropped under the table when there is danger of detection, and there is no proof of which player is responsible for its being there—or, indeed, that it did not fall there accidentally. (It is worthy of passing mention that one cannot employ the holdout method among the most expert players; each, when dealing, can tell if the pack is even one card short, solely by the weight of the pack.)

Collusion among two or more players is another simple manner of cheating. By a system of prearranged signals they communicate to one another their holdings, their intentions, and their desires, and in many games this enables them to play to great advantage.

From these simpler techniques the repertory of the cardsharper ranges upward to feats that are most impressive. Cards can be dealt from the bottom or middle of the pack, and "second dealers" can withhold the top card while dealing the second, saving the top card until they come to the player to whom they wish it dealt. The pack in play can be removed from the table and another—a "cold" or prearranged deck—substituted for it. Once the cards have been cut, the dealer can switch them back to their original sequence, in which he has arranged them by skillful shuffling. The classic work describing these techniques is entitled *The Expert at the Card Table* (1902), written by E. S. Andrews under the pseudonym S. W. Erdnase; more modern books by Michael MacDougall, John Scarne and Sidney Radner give considerable space to cheating methods.

EQUIPMENT FOR CHEATING

THERE IS much equipment for cheating on the open market. Marked cards that cannot readily be distinguished from the honest cards put out by reputable playing-card manufacturers; inks and mechanical tools for marking one's own cards; the most elaborate machinery to be concealed within one's clothes for the purpose of holding out cards—dozens of firms do a thriving business in such equipment. One such firm, probably the largest, does an annual business of nearly half a million dollars. In some cases the merchandise is sold under the guise of conjurers' goods, but many of the catalogues make no effort to conceal the intended use of what they offer for sale. It is true that much of the equipment is as useful to a conjurer for doing card tricks as to a cardsharper for cheating in games.

It is widely held among the cardsharpers that the mechanical equipment sold by the gamblers' supply houses is bought only by "amateurs." This is substantially true. By an amateur they mean someone who has other means of livelihood; who wants to assure his winnings in the one or two games in which he plays regularly, but does not follow the cardsharping profession to the extent of moving around in search of new games. The fully professional cardsharper would be loath to risk the consequences of detection with a holdup device attached to his clothes or with marking tools or inks in his pockets. Furthermore, say the professionals, they do not need such props.

As already remarked, the honest player is helpless against the cardsharper of sufficient skill. Michael MacDougall, also mentioned above as a writer, is a detective specializing in the investigation and exposure of dishonest gambling practices; a former magician, he is among the most skillful practitioners at all cheating methods with cards. He can, for example, take an honestly shuffled and cut pack of cards and deal a hand of Bridge in which all the high cards fall to himself and his partner. He does this by "flashing" each card before it is dealt, and giving it to an opponent if it is a low card or saving it (by "second-dealing," described above) for himself or his partner if it is a high card. He "flashes" the card by holding it slightly apart—not more than a thirty-second of an inch—from the rest of the pack and catching a glimpse only of its corner. The unpracticed eye could not identify the card at this angle if given unlimited time; MacDougall must do it in a minor fraction of a second. It is an impressive and nearly incredible display, described here only as an extreme example of what can be done when the qualified magician wishes to turn to cardsharping.

HABITS AND HABITATS OF CARDSHARPERS

IT IS IMPOSSIBLE to make any supportable estimate of the numbers of cardsharpers active in the United States. For one thing, much depends upon definition. Is anyone who customarily employs any cheating practice (as cheating was defined above) to be considered a cardsharper? If so, it is not untenable to hold that there are at least half a million of them. There are statistics as to the number of Americans who play card games (more than sixty million), and the consensus of those who have observed the proportion of honest to dishonest players would support the estimate of one in a hundred. To the layman this may not seem a shocking proportion; to the student of games it is appallingly high, and he is reluctant to accept it.

A cardsharper who went to Miami in the winter of 1948-49 estimated that there were four thousand cardsharpers (persons capable of cheating and intending to cheat, though not necessarily professionals) in Miami looking for high-stake Gin Rummy games. More often than not, two of them would find themselves playing each other, each thinking he had enticed the other into the game. Of course, Gin Rummy represents the cardsharper's Mecca; Miami in season is the happy hunting grounds; and any cardsharper would be expected to gravitate toward Miami. The estimated figure, even if true, is not necessarily significant.

The total figure of five hundred thousand was arrived at by questioning professional cardplayers, some honest percentage players, and others who are cheaters and so cardsharpers by our definition, as to what they encounter as they travel about looking for games. With unexpected uniformity they replied that in each group making up a game (about fifteen or twenty persons) they would encounter one who attempted to cheat with more or less skill. More reliable estimates place the proportion of Americans that do not play for stakes to those that do at five to one.

Concentrations of cardplayers playing games for money may be observed in three places: the Bridge clubs of New York, the Poker houses of Gardena (a suburb of Los Angeles), California, and the gambling houses of Nevada. The New York Bridge clubs have a minor problem in this respect, for Bridge attracts few cardsharpers. The Gardena Poker clubs have a considerable problem, and so employ observers so experienced that a cardsharper must be very skillful to escape detection for very long. The Nevada gambling houses likewise employ skilled observers.

Only forty or fifty times in twenty years has cheating been detected in the New York Bridge clubs, and this should be expected. The Gardena Poker houses, which cater to a total patronage of some fifteen thousand persons, of whom fifteen or twenty per cent play regularly, detect and eject about two would-be cheaters each week, one hundred or so in the course of a year. Officially they deny that anyone who cheats ever plays throughout more than one session; but privately they admit that there are probably some twenty cheaters among their regular players, these twenty being so skillful that they can continue indefinitely to escape detection. The Nevada gambling houses report (even privately) a much better record, and say that not once a week in the entire state is a patron refused admittance because he cheats; but card games are a very inconsequential form of gambling in Nevada, where the big money goes on horse races and dice games, and those who play cards are killing time rather than gambling. Since the honest players who really want to gamble would not be at the card tables, the pickings are slim for the cardsharper.

The cardsharper's habitat, therefore, is a gaming place far less public than those described above. His game is in a private club or private house. He seldom abandons the game because he is exposed; rather, the game breaks up because the other players drop out, one by one, when they lose consistently, and in any game in which one player is regularly winning, the others must lose in the long run. It is when the game breaks up that the cardsharper moves along to other games.

—ALBERT MOREHEAD

¶*The pioneer classic on cheating is Girolamo Cardano's* Liber de Ludo Aleae (BOOK ON GAMES OF CHANCE), *written sometime after 1542 and before 1570. It is also a pioneer classic on the theory of probabilities as applied to games. Cardano was one of the great Italian physicians of his century. He had the necessary combination of the gambling urge, mathematical aptitude, intellectual curiosity, and facility with the pen. He wrote in Latin, but in 1953 Princeton University Press brought out his biography, by Dr. Oystein Ore, and a translation of his book, by Sydney Henry Gould. Both are important to students of the history of games and in large part to those who want to read and understand but not study.* ¶*In the middle sixteenth century, when Cardano wrote, the multiplicity of games already defied exhaustive study. "If I should speak of them all," he says, "it would be an endless task." Some of the games he knew—Primero, Trappola, Bassett, Flux, Tarocchi, Triumph—are mentioned in the article by "Cavendish" on old card games* (*page 19*). ¶*Cardano was one of the first men to write of the rational exercise of skill in card games; but, inevitably imbued with the spirit of card play in those times, he had to give his major attention to cheating devices.*

from Book on Games of Chance

by GIROLAMO CARDANO

ON FRAUDS IN GAMES OF THIS KIND

CARDS have this in common with dice, that what is desired may be got by fraud: the most contemptible kind is that which is backed up by the sword; a second kind has to do with recognition of the cards—in its worst form it consists of using marked cards, and in another form it is more excusable, namely, when the cards are put in a special order and it is necessary to remember this order. Such players are accustomed, when they know where the desired card is, to keep it on the bottom and to deal out others, which chance alone would not call for, until they get the suppressed card for themselves. But the other players in the first-mentioned class carry out very dangerous frauds which are worthy of death, as in fact the latter is also, but it is more concealed. Those, however, who know merely by close attention what cards they are to expect are not usually called cheats, but are reckoned to be prudent men.

As for those who use marked cards, some mark them at the bottom, some at the top, and some at the sides. The first kind are marked quite close to the bottom and may be either rough or smooth or hard; the second are marked with color and with slight imprints with a knife; while on the edges cards can be marked with a figure, a rough spot, with interwoven knots or humps, or with grooves hollowed out with a file. Some players examine the appearance of a card by means of mirrors placed in their rings. I omit the devices of kibitzers—the organum, the consensus, and the like.*

Certainly, in view of the small amount of pleasure provided by gambling and the rarity with which it favors our wishes, there are so many difficulties in it, and so many possibilities

* The "organ" was a loose floor board under the table on which one player rested his foot, receiving signals from an accomplice who moved the board slightly, usually by pulling a string from another room. The "consensus" is an unknown device; the word itself means complicity or collusion.—O.O.

of loss, that really there is nothing better than not to play at all. There are also some who smear the cards with soap so that they may slide easily and slip past one another. This was the trick practiced upon me by the well-known Thomas Lezius of Venice,* patrician, when in my youth I was addicted to gambling.

Now, in general, gambling is nothing but fraud and number and luck. Against fraud the one remedy is to beware of men of deceitful mind; for, just as a good man cannot be a cheat, so a cheat cannot be a good man. When you suspect fraud, play for small stakes, have spectators, shuffle the cards instead of merely collecting them, and if another collects them without shuffling, he is acting fraudulently. Have your own cards, and if others send out to buy cards, let them buy from men you can trust. Examine them inside and out and edgewise; touch the corners; if they are rough, or too smooth, or hard, or uneven, do not play; but before you can recognize what is wrong, your opponents will perhaps ruin you. Finally, let no one examine the cards in private. In Primaria (which is also called Primero), it is customary to uncover the cards from the back and from above as little as possible so that the kibitzers cannot see anything; a great part of the art appears to consist in this, and players boast about their skill in this respect.

Considerable perplexity arises on the following point. Since prestidigitators are capable of such admirable feats, why is it that they are usually unlucky at cards? It would seem reasonable that, just as they are able to deceive us with balls, pots, and coins, they should also be able to do it with cards and so invariably come out winners. But the condemned Spaniard was ordered (in fact, the prohibition, they say, was on pain of death) not to play, seeing that he could at will produce four cards that make chorus† either by deceiving the eye or by making the exchange by quickness of hand; for we must assign to either of these a prodigious art of prestidigitation. But Franciscus Sorna of Naples could change cards so quickly that nothing more wonderful could be imagined.

ON LUCK IN PLAY

In these matters luck seems to play a very great role, so that some meet with unexpected success while others fail in what they might expect; so that the above reasoning about the mean does not apply. For this mean is composed of extremes, not as in lawsuits, and valuations, and the like. For it is agreed by all that one man may be more fortunate than another, or even than himself at another time of life, not only in games but also in business, and with one man more than another and on one day more than another.

If anyone should throw with an outcome tending more in one direction than it should and less in another, or else it is always just equal to what it should be, then, in the case of a fair game there will be a reason and a basis for it, and it is not the play of chance; but if there are diverse results at every placing of the wagers, then some other factor is present to a greater or less extent; there is no rational knowledge of luck to be found in this, though it is necessarily luck.

However, astrologers make claims for themselves; yet I have never seen an astrologer who was lucky at gambling, nor were those lucky who took their advice. The reason is as follows: although, as in all matters of chance, it happens that they occasionally make the right forecast, nevertheless, if they have guessed right (for when they do not guess right, they must lose) then immediately afterward they go very badly wrong, since they become venturesome and lose more from one mistake than they win from forecasting correctly four times in a row. For the path into error is always steeper, and the loss is greater than the gain.

And I have seen others who make their decision with the help of geomancy;* but this is an unstable vanity and dangerous unless very moderate use is made of its deceptive help. As for the fact that some of them do make forecasts, this is to be explained on the ground that others make still more frequent mistakes. For since there is necessarily some inequality in this respect, one man will be right more often and another less. These statements appear likely to our reason.

Yet I have decided to submit to the judgment of my readers what happened to me in the year of 1526 in the company of Thomas Lezius, the patrician of Venice, leaving it to each reader to form his own opinion. I had just duly resigned from the office of rector of the scholars in the University of Padua on the third of August, and now I was journeying with Hieronymus Rivola, a scholar from Bergamo, on a certain night of

* Thomas Lezius was probably one of Cardano's gambling companions during the time he lived in the the town of Sacco.—O.O.

† Chorus: four of a kind.—O.O.

* A method of divination, or fortunetelling, based on the pattern assumed by a handful of earth flung down at random—a precursor of the Rorschach test.

the same month toward Venice. We were playing a game (called Bassette) and I won all the money he had. Then he asked me to play with him on credit, if I am not mistaken, up to two or three aurei,* and I won again. Then, finally, he wanted to carry it on endlessly, but I refused. He promised to pay what he owed me within three days; but he did not come.

Then he chanced to meet me and said that he would come to pay the money on Saturday (which was the day of the Nativity of the Virgin) and promised to take me to a beautiful prostitute. At that time I was just completing my twenty-fifth year, but I was impotent. Nevertheless, I accepted the condition; there was not a word about the game. He came on the day agreed; and in that year the festival of the Blessed Virgin was on Saturday. He took me to the home of Thomas Lezius; there was no Thais there, but a bearded man with a young servant. No money was paid but we played with marked cards. I lost to him all the money which he owed me, and he reckoned it as part of his debts just as though he had given it to me. I lost about twenty-five aurei or even a few more which I had, and played on, giving my clothes and my rings as security.

I returned home in sadness (as was natural), especially since there was no hope of getting money from home because uprisings and plots were raging at Milan. And so (and now I tell the truth, there being no reason why I should lie) I contrived for myself a certain art; I do not now remember what it was, since thirty-eight years have passed, but I think it took its rise in geomancy, by which I kept in mind on up to twenty-four plays all the numbers whereby I should win and all those whereby I should lose; by chance the former were far more numerous than the latter, even in the proportion (if I am not mistaken) of seven to one; and I do not recall now in what order these were against me.

But when I saw that I could not safely hold more numbers in my memory, I admonished my young servant, whose name was Jacob, that when he saw I had won back my clothes and my money he was to call me. I threatened that if he did not do it I would beat him severely. He promised and we went. As the game went on I won and lost in all the plays just as I had foreseen and after the third play I realized that there was no trickery or deceit about it. They laid down money freely and I accepted the wagers, but he was delighted by the example of the previous day and also on account of the marked cards (as I have said).

Thus his thoughts were inflamed by his youthful ardor; but the result was otherwise, for, on those plays in which I saw (as it were, without any real foreknowledge) that I would win, I did not reject any amount of money and made large bets on my own, and in the other cases, where I knew he would win, I refused if he was the first to wager, and wagered very meagerly myself: thus the result was that within twenty plays I regained my clothes, my rings, and money and also what he had added besides. As for the clothes, the rings, and a collar for the boy, I sent them home piecemeal. Out of the total number there remained four deals; I played and won, and also came out victor in a few deals which were not contained in the number.

Now I think it worthy of consideration that this fortune of mine seems to have been something greater than mere chance, since we see in it a beginning, increase, and a certain continuance so that certain remarkable things happen, as for instance that two aces occurred twice when defeat could not otherwise be brought about, and other things of this sort. We would also see a decline and then very often a change, and then great calamity or great good fortune, and other things in the same way. In view of all this I should think we ought to decide that there is something in this, although we do not know the law which connects the parts. It is as though you were fated in advance to be enriched or despoiled; especially seeing that from this there can follow something more important, as it happened to the man who, on leaving a game after losing all his money, injured the image of the Blessed Virgin with his fist. He was arrested and condemned to be hanged.

But whether the cause of that luck, be it in the conjunction of the stars or in the construction of a certain order of the universe, can affect the cards, which are considered bad or good only according to the conventions of men (since they signify nothing of themselves), is so worthy of doubt that it is easier to find a cause of this fact without that purpose than with it; without it the matter can well be reduced to chance, as in the constitution of the clouds, the scattering of beans, and the like.

ON CARD GAMES IN WHICH THERE IS OCCASION FOR TRAINED SKILL

SINCE HERE we exercise judgment in an unknown matter, it follows that the memory of

* The aureus was a gold coin that today would be worth about $8 in gold, about $35 in purchasing power.

those cards which we have deposited or covered or left should be of some importance, and in certain games it is of the greatest importance, as in Trappola, the Venetian game. In this game the threes, fours, fives, and sixes are removed. In the four suits there are sixteen of these, so that thirty-six cards are left. They are dealt out, five at a time and then four; in the case of two players eighteen cards are dealt and the same number left in a pile; if the first player is satisfied with his cards, he retains them, and if the second player is dissatisfied with his, he exchanges them and receives the nine top cards on the pile; and if these please him, then he himself keeps them, but if not, he exchanges them again with the second pile.

So you see how much depends on memory, judgment, skill in avoiding deception with due regard for safety. Many players, then, although they remember well, do not avoid the stratagems of their adversary carefully enough, or do not play with foresight, or too timidly, or as though they were angry.

Therefore when I had settled in the town of Sacco I was delighted by this game in a wonderful way; from it I saw the beginning of all good fortune. For by careful attention I brought it about that I was always mindful of all the cards which I had discarded.

When I had reduced the memory of these cards to the knowledge of one word, I learned to include in this fashion in a single word many other things as well; and thence by practising this invention a whole text and all that was contained in it. And after that passages were found and derived from authors, which led to extemporaneous declaiming.

But I return to the play of cards; seeing that this kind of game was most artificial, since it would depend on a fixed procedure and forced arrangements, I omitted all exercise of that kind of divination for many reasons. First of all, I betook myself to Padua and thence to Sacco and so I had no further opportunity for the game; for that type of chance does not have any place where skill is mixed into the game. Secondly, I was afraid that it might ruin me through being overconfident. Moreover, I said that, if it is deceptive because of the demon, it is thereby contrary to law, but if it depends on chance, then it is foolish to trust it. Also I shrank from a game which was condemned by the law. Moreover, I thought it foolish to wish to contend so absurdly when I could play under more profitable or safer conditions.

ON THE DIFFERENCE BETWEEN PLAY WITH CARDS AND PLAY WITH DICE

CARD GAMES differ from dice games even when these require skill, because play with dice depends more on judgment of future events; mostly, to be sure, on the success of one's opponent but also on one's own success, while play with cards requires only judgment of one's present holdings and of one's opponent's. To conjecture about the present is more the part of a prudent man skilled in human wisdom; but to conjecture about the future, although it is another kind of guessing, not as to what will be, but what we may rightly count on, is nevertheless the part rather of a divine man, or of an insane one, for the melancholy are given to prophesy. For in play with dice you have no certain sign, but everything depends entirely on pure chance, if the die is honest. Whatever there may be in it beyond unfounded conjecture and the arguments given above should be put down to blind chance.

But in cards, apart from the recognition of cards from the back there are a thousand other natural and worthy ways of recognizing them which are at the disposal of a prudent man. In this connection the game of chess surpasses all others in subtlety. It is subjected little or not at all to the arbitrariness of chance. Similarly, exercise with weapons surpasses everything else in usefulness, play with balls surpasses in healthfulness, Trappola in charm, Primero in beauty of invention and variety, Sanctius by the greatness of the stakes, Fritillus in attentive competition with little fatigue, Tarocchi in the passing of time, Cricones in dignity, and Triumph[us] in prudence and imitation of human life. So it is more fitting for the wise man to play at cards than at dice and at Triumph[us] rather than at other games; so it is agreed (but it is not in use) that this is a sort of midway game played with open cards, very close to the game of chess. It has an end when nothing further can be done and every game makes its own end. It is played with nine cards (for this is a satisfactory number) and is the mean between the great and the small; when the cards are placed on the table one begins to play, as one is accustomed to do with hidden cards. Since this is a most ingenious game, I am very much surprised that it has been neglected by so many nations.

DO THOSE WHO TEACH ALSO PLAY WELL?

PERHAPS SOMEONE will quite rightly ask whether the same people who know these rules also play well or not. For it seems to be a different thing to know and to execute, and many who play very well are very unlucky. The same question arises in other discussions. Is a learned physician also a skilled one? In those matters which give time for reflection, the same man is both learned and successful, as in mathematics, jurisprudence, and also medicine, for very rarely does the sick man admit no delay.

But in those matters in which no time is given and guile prevails, it is one thing to know and another to exercise one's knowledge successfully, as in gambling, war, dueling, and commerce. For although acumen depends on both knowledge and practice, still practice and experience can do more than knowledge. Also a certain physical acquaintance is of greater value in those matters where there is need of special knowledge, as in the appraisal of gems, paintings, and the recognition of counterfeit or genuine money.

So there are three elements in the case, not all of equal importance, namely, physical nature, acumen, and quickness. So it was right for Hannibal to make fun of the philosopher who had never seen a battle line and was discoursing on war. Thus it is with all games which depend on the arbitrariness of fortune, either entirely, or together with skill, when they are played rapidly and time is not given for careful thought. Since physical games, depending on agility of hand or sharpness of eye, are subject to training, it is not surprising that to know is one thing and to exercise one's knowledge, and exercise it rightly, is another. In certain matters, as in military affairs, knowledge joined to practice is of great value, but not practice joined to knowledge; for what is the principal thing in each matter ought to have precedence and be the greater.

¶ *There can never have been a more entertaining man than the late Frank Crowninshield, gentleman of the old school, littérateur and editor, and patron of Bridge; nor a more entertaining book of Bridge anecdotes than one (*THE BRIDGE FIEND*) that he wrote in 1908 under the name Arthur Loring Bruce. In one chapter he discussed cheating and unethical conduct at the then new game of Bridge. The reader may find the atmosphere rather rarefied, for in no other atmosphere did Mr. Crowninshield move.*

¶ *From Mr. Crowninshield's chapter one can see the great weakness of cheating, especially in a game such as Bridge where luck can go only so far. The young man who fleeced Mr. Schwab on the ship had to win every rubber and in addition had to ring in some really extraordinary hands. The hand that Mr. Schwab redoubled several times was too unusual to be true. It will be noted that no one figured out just how this young man was stacking the deck but he managed to win with something like twenty-three straight rubbers and it is just too much to credit that to luck. Mr. Schwab paid, even though he was advised not to. The more power to him. He could not prove he had been cheated and there was one chance in a billion that the game had been honest. It behooved Mr. Schwab as a gentleman to pay his loss on that possibility.*

¶ *The "Mississippi Heart Hand" appears in each incident recounted by Mr. Crowninshield. It was the ideal sharper's hand in the days of Bridge (before Auction or Contract), for there was no legal limit on doubles and redoubles and by geometric progression a single trick could soon become worth thousands of dollars. But the Whist sharpers used the hand too; compare James Hogg's story on page 35.*

from The Bridge Fiend

by ARTHUR LORING BRUCE

CHEATING AT BRIDGE

I SHALL BEGIN this chapter by quoting what I think the most extraordinary bit of impudence and rascality which it has ever been my fortune to hear of at the Bridge table. This occurred a few years ago at a pigeon club in Monte Carlo.

Four gentlemen, all well known along the Riviera, were playing Bridge for fairly large stakes. The game was composed of Lord E., an Englishman, Prince G., a Greek, and two Frenchmen. Lord E. owed the table—from previous rubbers—about five hundred francs.

The prince dealt and declared "no trumps." The score was one game all and love all on the third game. The Greek's hand consisted of: The queen and jack of hearts; eight clubs to the ace, king, queen; the lone ace of diamonds; and the ace and a small spade.

Lord E.—being the leader and holding ten hearts to the ace, king—doubled. The dealer declared himself satisfied and E. led his ace of hearts. Dummy had no hearts. E.'s partner played a low heart and G., the dealer, followed with the jack.

E., seeing that the queen must fall on the next round, exultantly played his king. When it got to the prince's turn to follow, he hesitated for some time and finally played a small spade. As nobody had followed suit and as somebody must have the queen of hearts, E. looked at his partner and asked him if he had no hearts, to which he replied, "No hearts." The leader looked at the prince, and then at his partner and said: "Partner, please examine, carefully, every card in your hand and tell me if you have a heart." His partner then repeated that he was void of hearts.

Lord E. turned to the prince and said: "I must ask you to follow suit on this trick. I insist on your playing the queen of hearts."

The Greek nonchalantly replied, in French: "I think I know the rules of this game as well as you do. If I revoke I am certainly bound to pay the penalty. As a matter of fact, you have no business to interest yourself with my play, other than to demand from me the usual penalties in case I infract any of the rules."

Lord E. still insisted that the prince must play his queen of hearts. The prince remarked that Lord E. owed the table five hundred francs from previous rubbers and that if he was dissatisfied with the game he could pay his indebtedness and stop playing. E. thereupon promptly pulled out some notes, paid his debt and rose to leave the table.

A tremendous discussion then took place. In this dispute, dummy, of course, was not supposed to take any part, but, being a gentleman of honor, and learning that Prince G. had actually held the queen of hearts, he told him that he feared he would thereafter have to forego the pleasure of playing with him and pointedly left the room, together with Lord E. and the Frenchman who had been playing third hand.

Prince G. was, from that time on, pointed out as a suspiciously slippery card player all along the Riviera.

Here was a case where it was perfectly evident that a man could save a considerable sum of money—roughly, thirty dollars, at ten-cent points—by revoking. By resorting to this ruse, he was sure of one trick in hearts, eight in clubs, the ace of spades, and the ace of diamonds—or five by cards. Three of these tricks he would have to lose as a penalty for his revoke; but, according to the rules, his side would go to 28—the revoking side can never go game—whereas, by following to the second round of hearts, he was certain to lose four by cards, the game, and the rubber.

Strange as it may seem, I have often heard Prince G.'s conduct condoned by men of unquestionably good character.

"Why is this," they have argued, "any worse than hiding an unintentional revoke and trying to deceive the adversaries by throwing down the guilty card at the end of the hand in an idle and careless way and hurriedly quitting the trick?"

Here is a famous anecdote of Lord de Ros who, some years ago, in the days of straight Whist, was a redoubtable player in England. Notwithstanding his skill, he simply could not play fair and had a distressing habit of slipping an ace on the bottom of the pack—after the cut. In this way he was always sure of the ace of trumps when it was his turn to deal. He was finally detected in the fraud and left London precipitatedly for the Continent, where, after a few years, he died. A well-known wag in London suggested, as a suitable epitaph for the unfortunate nobleman, the following lines:

HERE LIES LORD DE ROS—
IN CONFIDENT EXPECTATION
OF THE LAST TRUMP.*

A growing body of converts to the game of Bridge are the professional gamblers. Time was when a roving, talented and sociable pair of gamblers needed only a marked pack of cards and a knowledge of the mysteries of Poker to make a handsome living on a transatlantic liner or a Chicago "limited"; but we have changed all that, and no considerable or self-respecting gambler can now afford to be without a thorough mastery of the intricacies of Bridge.

A recent proof of this, which came under my own observation, is worth relating here, as the swindle was perpetrated with so much daring and deceived one of the cleverest and astutest Americans of our day.

A year ago last June Mr. Charles M. Schwab sailed for Europe on the *Kronprinzessin Cecilie*. On the second day out a certain Mr. A., a dapper, suave and plausible young man, introduced himself as the son of a very old—and deceased—friend of Mr. Schwab's. Mr. Schwab, who is a pattern of good nature, was, of course, delighted to make his acquaintance and was also exceedingly polite to Mr. B., the traveling companion of his new-found friend. B.—how singular is the net of Destiny!—turned out to be related to another of Mr. Schwab's friends.

Mr. A. yawned and deplored the fact that there was, apparently, no Bridge on board and mildly suggested a quiet little game of Double Dummy before luncheon—an invitation which Mr. Schwab smilingly accepted. The points were

* A slight but not serious misquotation.

to be fifty cents, a trifling sum for so rich a man as Mr. A. pretended to be.

Now, the best part of this narrative is that it is actually true. Mr. Schwab is said to be the best Double-Dummy player in America—with the possible exception of Mr. Elwell. He has played the game a great deal and is letter perfect, not only in the chances of making or leaving, but also in the art of combining his two hands.

I watched the game, from the "sidelines," for three successive mornings, and I should say that Mr. Schwab was a ten per cent better player than his suave opponent. Not to make this story too long, I shall simply state that Mr. Schwab lost nineteen straight rubbers. How the marvel was accomplished it would be difficult to say, but I could not fail to notice that Mr. B. was usually close beside his friend.

Occasionally, however, B. would leave the smoking-room, under some pretext or other, for a minute or two and return to his post beside Mr. A. with some hopeful little remark about the state of the weather, the proximity of a school of porpoises, or the likelihood of a good "run."

Was B. in the possession of a few extra packs of cards? Did he arrange them deftly for A.? Were the cards marked? Was A. a conjurer? These are questions which I am utterly unable to answer, but I believe that Mr. Schwab would have gone on with the game, in blind ignorance of the deception which was being played upon him, but for one preposterous error of judgment on the part of the son of his late lamented friend.

Success had apparently gone to A.'s head like wine, and he was evidently convinced that he could perpetrate any outrage upon the good-natured steel king. Mr. Schwab had dealt and made it a heart, with the five top honors in hearts and the four top honors in diamonds and clubs, and no spades. A. had doubled and Mr. Schwab had naturally redoubled. The farce went on until Mr. Schwab, in mild amazement, cried "enough."

Naturally, as my readers have long ago guessed, Mr. A. held the eight low hearts and the five top spades, so that, by pounding away at his spades, he was bound to make two by cards. This was a little too much even for Mr. Schwab's good nature, and the game broke up in a strained and awkward silence.

I was so curious to discover the methods of this sharper that I challenged him to two rubbers—at much lower points—and rather expected that he would let me win, as the stakes were hardly worth his while, but I never won a game in the two rubbers which I played with him, nor did, after, Mr. K. or Mr. N., two "added starters" in the race to get experience. A. actually won, in four mornings, twenty-seven rubbers and about two thousand three hundred dollars in cash.

Some of the passengers—one of them testified that these same gentlemen had crossed with him about a month before in the same easterly direction—urged Mr. Schwab not to pay A. a dollar until he had very carefully looked him up, but I believe that, after a little consideration of the matter, Mr. Schwab paid A. all that A. had stolen from him.

Here is another very interesting example of the wiles of a professional gambler. The yarn is an even more picturesque one than that of which the unfortunate Mr. Schwab was the hero on the *Cecilie*.

On this particular occasion the shorn lamb who was not protected from the winds of misery was Mr. H. D. Condie, the St. Louis merchant, who is a sound and careful player and who has played the game for eight years, both in this country and abroad. I shall tell the story as Mr. Condie narrated it to me.

He was coming down from Mackinac to Chicago on the steamer Northland and was approached by a polite young man—they are usually young and always polite—who asked him if he would make up a four at Bridge. Mr. Condie, not being in the humor for it, declined. The next morning, after breakfast, he asked him again, and this time Mr. Condie accepted, agreeing, however, to play only two rubbers.

They thereupon went to the stateroom of the stranger's "fat and jolly" friend, where they found two men awaiting them. Five-cent points were agreed upon, and the first rubber went against Mr. Condie by a close margin. On the second rubber he was twenty-four to sixteen and one game in.

It was Mr. Condie's deal, and he was sitting West. His opponent to the left touched his arm just as the cards were being cut, and drew his attention to a passing boat alongside of them. Without suspecting any fraud, he cut the pack which was presented to him, and dealt the cards. He was very soon staggered to see what a powerful hand he had dealt himself. His cards were: The six highest diamonds, the three highest clubs; the three highest spades and the lone king of hearts.

He promptly declared a diamond and was,

after a little hesitation, doubled by the leader, who, in turn, was promptly redoubled by Mr. Condie. At this point, third hand exposed the eight of diamonds and asked, in a whisper, if Mr. Condie knew that that suit, meaning diamonds, was trumps?

The dealer scanned his hand and saw that he had the six high trumps, and figured that, as third hand had one trump, the leader could not have more than six. The dealer complained, however, of the exposure, and told third hand that he did not care to see his cards and presumed that the leader did not either.

The leader, instead of going on with the doubling, offered to bet Mr. Condie fifty dollars even that he would beat him to the odd trick. The bet was accepted, and the leader led the ace of hearts, capturing the dealer's lone king. As it afterward turned out, the leader's hand consisted of the six low diamonds and seven hearts to the ace, queen, jack, ten; no spades, and no clubs. Dummy went down with six spades to the jack, ten; one low heart, and six low clubs.

As a matter of course, the leader had only to go on leading his hearts in order to win the odd trick and the fifty dollars. I suppose that, as Mr. Condie's attention was called to the passing boat through the porthole, a prepared pack had been deftly subsituted. Imagine the horror and chagrin in the camp of the enemy if Mr. Condie, being twenty-four and suspecting that all was not well in Denmark, had declared spades and scored up a small slam, the game, and the rubber. One cannot help hoping to live until such a golden chance to confuse the wicked is offered one. As it was, Mr. Condie sadly paid his bet, and, with an increased respect for the wisdom of others, proceeded on his weary way to his stateroom.

There is a special ban and blight that rests upon a man who cheats at cards. It is the one unforgivable sin. A man may beat his wife or refuse to support his children but, if he peeks at Bridge, he is lost to the end of eternity. In England a man may owe his tailor or his cheesemonger or his bootmaker, but he is everlastingly ostracized if he owes money at cards.

Perhaps the most famous scandal connected with cheating at Whist in all of English history is the celebrated case of Lord de Ros, which I have already mentioned. At the time of the furore, following the exposure, Lord Hertford was asked what he would do if he saw a man cheating at cards.

"Bet on him, of course," was his lordship's reply.

Lord de Ros' "system" was only available once in four deals—when he dealt! At such a crisis he would palm an ace and slip it on the bottom of the pack. He somehow marked all the other aces with his fingernails so that he could note, while dealing, to whom they fell. After the exposure of the fraud there was at White's Club a vulgar "outsider" whom de Ros had snubbed on one or two occasions. He remarked to one of de Ros' friends, in a very insulting tone, that he felt rather sorry for poor old de Ros, and would certainly leave his card on him, but he was afraid that de Ros would mark it.

"I think you can safely take the risk," said his lordship's friend. "I am certain that he would not think your card a high enough honor."

This bon mot is, I think, usually attributed to Lord Alvanley.

Another one, almost as good, is also apropos of poor de Ros. One evening he won enough from Lord G. at a single sitting of Whist to build a small house in the country. Lord G., when the house was shown to him, was asked how he would like to live in it. "Not at all," was the reply. "I should not deem it safe. It is, after all, only a house of cards."

There is, in a Chicago club, a very large game —usually fifty-cent stakes. At an afternoon session, Mr. T., who was playing third hand, took such a desperate, but successful, finesse, that his fourth-hand adversary uttered a little whistle of suspicion and surprise. T.'s partner offered to bet the whistling gentleman one hundred dollars that T. had a sound and sufficient reason for taking the finesse. The bet was taken, and Mr. T. was at once appealed to for his reasons.

"Why," turning to fourth hand, "my dear man," he murmured, "I saw every card in your hand."

There seems to be no end to the stories one hears of cheating at Bridge. We used to believe that these tales were all malicious inventions, but, of late, the scandals have increased at such a rate that we are inclined to think that there must be a pinch of truth in them somewhere.

For instance: In a well-known card club in New York there was, until quite recently, a gentleman who had a morbid love of cutting low for partners and for the first deal. This little passion of his cost him his position in New York society and, incidentally, his membership in the aforementioned club.

It fell out in this wise. He—Mr. X. we shall call him—found that by putting an ace on the top of a pack and covering it with four cards, the ace would become, very naturally, the fifth card from the top. By then riffling the pack on the table and choosing the fifth card in the spiral, or fan, he was certain to get an ace and, presumably, the deal. The frequency with which this polished gentleman cut the first deal finally became the matter of heated gossip and discussion in his club and, one winter's evening, it was proposed to watch him very carefully and take action against him if the suspicions of the gossips were proved true. The three gentlemen composing the house committee asked Mr. X. to make up a rubber at fairly high points. Three times, within the next hour or so, did Mr. X. reach over, after a completed rubber, and pick up a pack of cards, only to shuffle them, look, every now and again, at the bottom cards, cut them, place a few cards on top and otherwise manipulate them, and *mirabile dictu,* three times did he cut an ace or a deuce. When the seance was over the three gentlemen retired to the hall and held a short consultation. All three of them were convinced that Mr. X. had prepared the packs before cutting, but none of them wanted the unpleasant honor of bringing charges against him.

In the course of two or three days Mr. X. reappeared at his club and was handed the following sealed note by the doorman:

The house committee has reason to believe that the governors of this club would accept your resignation if you were to hand it in before their next regular meeting.

The next day his resignation was in the hands of the governors. Mr. X. has always been considered a good enough fellow, and his business reputation has been of the highest, but in such a trifling and petty thing as five-cent Bridge he simply could not run straight.

Another scandal now going the rounds is that of Mr. and Mrs. T., the young married couple in Philadelphia who played such first-rate Bridge, who were so pleasant to play with, and who won such a very considerable amount of money at the game in the politest circles of Philadelphia society. That they have lately come such a fearful cropper is due to Mrs. A., a lady who teaches Bridge in the Quaker City.

It seems that the T.'s always insisted on playing together. Their reason for refusing to be pitted against each other at the Bridge table was the reason given by so many married couples. As they both liked to play for money it was absurd for them to gamble against one another, as they had a common purse for their gains and losses at Bridge, etc.

Now, before proceeding with this recital, I must pause to advise married couples always to play at different tables if it can be conveniently arranged. I know that it seems absurd to suppose that ladies and gentlemen might be suspected of having private signals at the card table, but it is just as well to give the gossips, malicious or otherwise, no ground for their suspicions.

Mr. and Mrs. T., up to this year, had had a very lucky career at Bridge and had become famous for their skill and daring at the game. When Mrs. A., a prominent Bridge teacher in Philadelphia, heard on all sides that the T.'s were the best players in the city, she became a little nettled as she was sure that she and another lady, a pupil of hers, could defeat them at every point of the game.

A match was accordingly arranged at the house of the young married couple. Mrs. A., who was comfortably ahead of the game as a result of her successful winter of teaching, suggested twenty-cent points and the match was soon under way at these stakes. After two or three rubbers it occurred to Mrs. A. that the T.'s had mastered their game almost too perfectly. They seemed invariably to open the right suit; they always left the make when dummy seemed to demand it; whenever they doubled a make they invariably floated gracefully to victory. Mrs. A.'s eyes were beginning to open and her little store of cash to vanish.

With the score eighteen all Mrs. T. dealt, hesitated for an instant only, and left the make to dummy, who declared hearts, with seven hearts and five honors. When the hand had been played out and when the dealer had scored up a small slam, Mrs. A. observed acidly to Mrs. T.:

"How was it that, having six diamonds in your hand with the four top honors, you happened to pass it to your husband?"

"Oh," said Mrs. T., "I always somehow hate to make it a diamond."

A little later, with the score love all, Mr. T. dealt himself three aces and a guarded king. Notwithstanding this compulsory no-trumper he left it to his wife, who declared hearts, with seven hearts and four honors. This was a little too much for Mrs. A. She had not seen a trace of a signal between the T.'s, but rage and suspicion had gotten the best of her. After the hand she rose majestically from the table and said that she must refuse to go on with the rubber. On being questioned as to her reason for this she simply observed: "I don't like your makes" and, with her partner, she calmly and sedately left the house after settling for every rubber but the last.

That evening she confided the adventure to a feminine friend, under a strict promise of secrecy, and the next morning it was all over Philadelphia. On the following evening it was discussed in all the clubs and suburbs, and finally reached a New York society journal, where it was printed with the usual circumlocution and vivid coloring peculiar to periodicals of this class.

The next move was a suit brought by the T.'s against Mrs. A. for defamation of character, and a threatened countersuit against the T.'s for obtaining money under false pretenses. A short while ago the whole pother was smoothed over by a written apology from Mrs. A., but the T.'s now find it very difficult to scare up a rubber in Philadelphia. Indeed, the sympathy of most people is with Mrs. A. as, perhaps, it should be, in view of the two startling makes that were left to dummy by Mr. and Mrs. T.

Of course, if two perfect Bridge players play much together, their game, to the onlookers, seems almost like necromancy. It is extraordinary what subtle mysteries their brains seem to divine. Of this there can be no question, but it takes a little more than skill to pick up a hand with six diamonds to four top honors and leave the make to dummy, who has, incredible as it may seem, seven hearts and five honors. Skill will do many wonderful things, but it won't see through the backs of average playing cards.

Before leaving the matter of moral obliquity at Bridge I should like to ask my readers to settle for me a little question of this kind. As everybody knows, it is a great advantage to cut the first deal in a rubber and the lowest card cut will insure that particular cutter the deal. Now, it has been discovered, beyond the shadow of a doubt, that when a new pack of cards is riffled for the cut on a cloth bridge table, those cards in the fan, or spiral, the backs of which are most exposed to view, are, more often than not, the high cards, while those with the least part of their backs exposed are the low. This apparently inexplicable phenomenon is due, I am told, to the greater amount of paint on the high cards. Now, by choosing the least exposed cards in the fan we can often secure the deal. I have seen it work eight times out of ten and I dare say that seven out of ten would be a fair average for the success of the experiment. Query: Is it right for a player to select his card in this way? I know dozens of honest men who do it, regardless of whether the other players at the table know the trick or not. Is it ethical to practice this seemingly harmless artifice?

¶*Anyone who knocks around in card-playing circles as much as Ely Culbertson did must eventually encounter the cheating gentry. In his autobiography, which we have quoted before (pages 81, 222), Culbertson describes some of his experiences:*

from The Strange Lives of One Man

by ELY CULBERTSON

CARDSHARPS AND GAMBLERS

IN LOS ANGELES I had [1926] my first success. To my surprise, the Culbertson name was already known. I stayed at the Biltmore Hotel and arranged for a little studio. Within two weeks, twenty people had signed up, at one hundred dollars each, for a course of ten lessons. A few were from the motion-picture colony, but the majority were from the social sets of Los Angeles and Pasadena. These two worlds were rigidly closed to each other; from my class of Hollywood pupils in Beverly Hills to my class of society people in Pasadena I had to travel as great a distance, figuratively speaking, as from Los Angeles to New York. But they were uniformly kind and hospitable to me. After all, I was only a Bridge teacher, practically a stranger; and yet they opened their homes to me, invited me to their parties, and schemed to get me more pupils.

After my classes, I would drop in at a Bridge club to play five-cent auction. However, after a couple of weeks, I began to experience a strange feeling about the game. I have a very keen "ear" for the inner rhythm of the flow of cards in any card game. Here I felt that there was something strange—a faint new beat. I started to "listen" intently, and to watch. I became convinced that there was a cardsharp in that game. Soon I spotted the man.

There is a rhythm in the distribution of cards, a rhythm in good and bad breaks, and even a rhythm in the manner in which those breaks occur. A run of big cards is not a contradiction of this rhythm. But if dirty work is afoot, the way this run is repeated and the circumstances under which these big cards come out, hour after hour, will sound false to the finely attuned ear of a real card player.

There are three common ways of cheating at cards, other than simple palming. The first is with signals, usually practiced by naïve couples who must have that cute carriage for the baby.

A long puff on a cigarette will demand a lead in spades, and two short puffs (usually very panicky) will warn partner not to bid any more of that awful suit; or there will be a mysterious series of separations and joinings of fingers, as if the poor player suffered from rheumatic pains. In London I was once the victim of the smartest signals I have ever seen. They consisted of precise timing during bidding and play, based on the number of seconds of silence which elapsed before a bid or a play was made. The length of each period of silence indicated strength or weakness in a particular suit. Even here, however, a few rubbers sufficed to convince me that signals were being used, because I could hear the cheaters silently counting the seconds. After listening to one such silent count, I got up, continuing loudly, "eight, nine, etc. . . . that knocks me out, gentlemen. Good-by."

The second method of cheating is by stacking the deck in such a way that the cheat or his partner receives all or most of the high cards. The principal way in which the sharper tries to protect himself against the cut, which might destroy his prearranged deck, is by crimping (bending) a card so that an unwary opponent will cut at the prepared place.

I remember once sitting in a Paris café when a stranger invited me to play a few games of Écarté. We started by playing for drinks and soon were playing for money. Soon he was hard at work stacking the deck for the guileless American. For some time I admired his fine craftsmanship in making a crimp so delicate that one could barely see it. Not to disappoint him, I took particular pains to cut the deck exactly where the good chap wanted it. When it came to my turn to deal, I pretended to stack the deck. My crimp, however, was so enormous that it formed a large tunnel between the crimped and straight halves of the deck. My *tricheur* looked at me quizzically and, bending over, delicately cut the deck in such a manner that the last crimped card was left on top, which meant of course he would get all the cards I had apparently prepared for myself. I pretended to be very indignant. Slamming my fist on the table, I exclaimed, "That is a dirty trick! When you make a tiny, almost invisible crimp, I cut the deck just the way you want it. But when I make a crimp big enough for an elephant to crawl through, you double-cross me. You're a cheat!"

The third way of cheating is called "seconds." Beforehand, the card sharp delicately marks the backs of the important cards with fingernails, sharp points, crimps, or indelible ink.* I used to play in Paris with Père Constant, a prosperous retired cardsharp who had the habit of sticking his index finger in his lower vest pocket. In the days when he was active, he had kept in his left pocket a tiny sponge soaked with indelible red ink. In his right vest pocket, he kept another tiny sponge with blue ink. With this equipment he was able to mark any new deck of cards during actual play. And although at the time I played with him the old warhorse no longer practiced his craft, the habit persisted, and whenever he saw an ace or a king, his index finger would irresistibly plunge into his vest pocket.

I doubt that one in a hundred cardsharps is a good dealer of seconds. This extremely difficult feat is the property of the aristocrats of crookdom. By practicing for years on a schedule as rigorous as that of a great violinist, a man can make his fingers so supple that when he sees an ace or a king due to go to an adversary, he can deal him the card just below the ace or king, and keep the high card for himself or his partner. When one of these virtuosi deals, his fingers are truly quicker than the eye.

My man in the club was a dealer of "seconds." He was also an enthusiastic lover of Bridge, and took a liking to me. He showed his kindness by showering me—to my embarrassment—with a veritable downpour of aces and kings whenever I was his partner. I repaid him with the blackest of ingratitude; I had a talk with two friends of mine who were members of the club. They were very much surprised; in fact, they didn't believe me. The man was a retired businessman, widely known in Minneapolis, and a good sport. I explained to them how it was done, and they agreed to stand a "death watch." After a week they told me that I must have had delusions, for they had not seen the slightest thing. In fact, during that week the man had been losing! And then I knew that their "death watch" had been so alert that the clever sharp had got a whiff of suspicion and had cautiously desisted. But I stopped playing. I was a hard-working Bridge teacher and I feared that my good friend might cease to like me and begin to shower me with deuces and treys. A couple of years later I learned that he had finally been unmasked, after having collected a tidy little fortune.

* The true artist, of whom there are only a few in the world, need not mark them in any way. He "flashes" a corner of the card and in a fraction of a second decides whether or not to deal it.

There is another class of players who seek to make a living by playing cards, and especially Bridge. These experts do not cheat. There have been only two or three exceptions; and it is a tribute to the strength of character of expert players that, although their very bread and butter depend on their winnings, they are as a rule among the most ethical players in the country. There is no objection whatever to any Bridge player's collecting a monetary tribute for his superior skill. Winners and losers there will always be, and the better man is entitled to his reward. Nor is there any objection to any man's or woman's adding reasonably to his income through superiority in play. There are thousands of very nice people who are regular winners, and love it. But no one knows better than I the danger of moral disintegration threatening those who try, however honestly, to make a living at cards. In clubs I see many youngsters who should be sweating at some decent job but who are trying to hustle a few easy dollars. I have spoken earnestly to many of them for their own good; but only two or three gave up this dangerous line of least resistance. I have told these boys repeatedly that in Bridge as in anything else, there is no easy way. I have cited dozens of examples of men with unusual minds and splendid educations who are now wrecks because they thought they could indefinitely, parasitically, prey upon society in Bridge and other games. I have told them that in my entire life I have seen only one notable exception of a professional player surviving—and that was only because he quit. The notable exception is I.

Within three months I had a good following in Los Angeles and began to spread out to Pasadena and Santa Barbara. Jo came to join me and we moved over to the California Bridge Club, which I had organized with Roy Sargent. She did most of the teaching, while I concentrated on business promotion and continued my work on matches against Gordon Tevis and his wife, Catherine. We became good friends, and one day at the Biltmore Hotel Gordon introduced me to Rex Le Roy, an old Western gambler who might have stepped out of a page of Bret Harte.

He was a gentleman to his fingertips, the old type of professional gambler whose word was as good as gold, who played hard but straight, and who never did a crooked thing in his life. Near Pasadena, Le Roy operated an ornate casino which was one of the sights of the coast, and although his large income was derived from roulette, dice, and Poker, he himself was devoted to Auction Bridge. Gordon Tevis told me that the smart guys up and down the coast considered Le Roy the best player in America. He was anxious to play me a match—there was no one else who would take him on.

We lost no time discussing terms.

"How about you taking Tevis, Culbertson, and I'll get a partner?"

"I'd like to play with Tevis," I said, "but I have my own partner."

"Oh, that's swell," Le Roy beamed. "How about next Thursday, here at my apartment in the Biltmore? We'll have a nice little friendly game—say fifty cents a point a player."

To Le Roy, who dealt in tens of thousands daily at the race track and his casino, this was really a nominal stake. To me, it was a fortune. I had no backers, and I had just enough money to last one game. I did not fear his skill, for I had never known of any professional "practical" gambler who could conceivably be ranked among the first fifty Auction players. I decided to take the chance against his being lucky, even though it might mean that all my advance payments for Bridge lessons would go into the pot.

I said, "I'd like to play next Thursday, but I'll have to ask Mrs. Culbertson if she is free."

"Mrs. Culbertson!" Le Roy was amazed. "I thought you said you had a partner."

"She's my partner."

"Now look here," he said with a kind smile, "I'd like to beat you, but I don't play against women or children."

"I'm willing to pay for the fun," I said. "In fact, Le Roy, I don't want to hurt your feelings, but I'm sure a course of lessons from Mrs. Culbertson would benefit any Bridge player, even you."

Le Roy snorted. "No woman Bridge player can be anything but a delicious joke. She may be a good teacher, but I want a man's game. Besides, I never play for more than one-tenth of a cent a point against ladies."

"Well, Le Roy, I'll tell you what I'll do. Mrs. Culbertson will play for one-tenth of a cent, and I'll accommodate you for ninety-nine and nine-tenths of a cent a point. Let's try one evening, and if you think she's too soft, I'll get a real player."

And so it was agreed. The next Thursday, before the game, we had a magnificent dinner as Le Roy's guests. Gordon Tevis, our only kibitzer, was there. During dinner, Jo and I observed with curiosity a small, mouselike man of indeterminate habiliments and demeanor.

"Who's that man?" I whispered to Gordon.

"He's Le Roy's partner."

"What's his business?"

"He's a dealer."

Shivers ran up my spine. "My God! A dealer of seconds?"

This time in a hoarse whisper, Gordon said, "No. He's a dealer at Le Roy's gambling joint."

"Is he a good player?"

"Lousy! I hear he's an old Whist player, and doesn't like Auction. But his boss wants him to play, so what can he do?"

When, after a few hands, I had taken the measure of Mr. Otto Schneider, I realized for the first time in what extreme contempt Le Roy held us. Rex himself was a very fine card player; but, like so many old Whist players, he looked upon bidding as an annoying and windy introduction to the play of the hand, which to him was the main bout.

The match was a slaughter for Le Roy and his dealer. It lasted into the early hours of the morning and we won the enormous sum of four thousand dollars.

Le Roy never uttered a word of reproach to Otto. To us he admitted that he had underestimated us and asked for a return match.

"I'd like to play you another match at double the stakes, if you will let me send to San Francisco for my old partner. I warn you that we played together for years and never were beaten."

To make sure that we understood, he described the big clean-ups he and his partner had made in Bridge among bookmakers and gamblers. Despite his warning we accepted the challenge. Jo was to play for one-fifth of a cent and I for a dollar ninety-nine and four-fifths cents a point—the largest stake I ever played for in my life.

The days before the match were filled with agitation and cogitation. The problem I had to solve was whether the first match had been a cruel come-on, or if Le Roy was just what he seemed to be—a fine, kindly, straightforward Western gambler, with his own peculiar but strict code of ethics. In a sense, I was taking an awful risk, for the match was to take place in his own casino, and should he or his partner start to deal crookedly, we would be helpless. But I decided that to an old-fashioned gambler like Le Roy the presence of a woman in the game would make any crooked work unthinkable. Confronted with some of our more modern gamblers, especially in New York, I would have had no such illusions. But with Le Roy our main fear was that we might get one of the diabolically uncanny runs of bad cards that would wipe us out before the tide could turn.

On the evening of the match Jo and I gave a dinner at Marsel's for Le Roy and all our pupils. Afterward we went to the gambling house. By Le Roy's order, all the gambling devices stopped running as our party entered. He announced that this was solely a Bridge match and that he did not want to tempt any of our guests to lose money on the wheel.

Le Roy then introduced us to his famous partner, who had just arrived from San Francisco. He turned out to be a small, wiry, hard-faced and steely-eyed individual, looking every frown a gangster. In fact, he *was* a gangster, widely known from San Francisco to Chicago. When poor Jo saw him, she visibly blanched, and there was a strained hush among our pupils. I could see that they were awed and were losing confidence in us. I could hardly blame them. Jo was slender, and during serious matches looked very much like a young, frightened girl. I was then a flyweight. I have never cultivated a poker face, considering that sort of thing childish. During a game, patches of color show on my cheeks, my hands are restless, my hair gets rumpled, and my eyes shine with excitement. Facing these two grim gamblers, we probably looked like children.

Our pupils' fears did not last long. Le Roy's partner was greatly superior to his predecessor, but both he and Le Roy lacked science, imagination, and change of pace. Their game had crystallized long ago, and since then nothing had been added or taken away. Against them, Jo and I fenced lightly with approach bids, tentative doubles, trap passes, and surprise leads. The gamblers were overcautious, and marveled at our tightrope-walking bids; in vain did they wait for us to break our necks. To the dismay of the loyal croupiers, waiters, and bouncers in the casino, and to the delight of our pupils, the two gamblers performed like big bulls ferociously charging light-footed toreadors and always missing by inches.

The game stopped at five in the morning. We had won over six thousand dollars. Both Le Roy and his partner rose from the table and stretched languidly. It had been a long session. They had had a very good time, but Rex had to suppress a yawn. To them a few thousand here or there meant nothing and they had enjoyed playing with the "kids." To us, it was everything.

Le Roy was true to his tradition of courtesy and gallant manners as he stood before the door of our club, where he had taken us in his car.

"Mrs. Culbertson," he said, "I apologize for thinking that women are not as good players as men. You and your husband have not only given me the licking of my life, but you yourself are the finest Bridge player I have ever seen."

I suppressed a snicker. For I remembered that once I too had had to apologize to Jo.

William E. McKenney was one of the most controversial figures in card annals. McKenney devoted the better part of his life to building up the American Contract Bridge League. He nursed it, coddled it, and spent most of his own earnings paying its postage and printing bills and office overhead. But somewhere along the line he got the idea that he owned it, and that was a mistake. By the time McKenney's blood, sweat and tears had built the League up to 9,000-odd members these members came to the inevitable conclusion that they didn't care to be bossed any more. After twenty-two years of czardom (1927-1948), McKenney was voted out of office. It was no doubt a necessary thing and developments have supported it (today the A.C.B.L. membership exceeds 70,000), but if a Bridge Hall of Fame ever comes along, Bill McKenney deserves one of the prominent niches. Among other things, McKenney ranked with Sidney Lenz among the best amateur magicians the card-playing world has produced. Armed with this special knowledge, for years he was a leader in measures to keep dishonest players out of clubs and tournaments.

You Can't Cheat a Bridge Player (*and get away with it*)

by WILLIAM E. MCKENNEY

CONTRACT BRIDGE is the cardsharper's Mecca. It is the game of millionaire yachtsmen and indolent society matrons. It is the game in which a British duke reputedly lost £20,000 in a single game.

All the accomplished crooked dealers in the world have one by one gravitated toward Contract Bridge, toward the high-stake games which are played regularly in the fashionable clubs or the luxurious homes of the rich. Yet having achieved their goal, having been accepted into such games, they have promptly and without exception gone down to inglorious defeat. Some were exposed and disgraced, some were arrested and jailed, but most of them just went broke.

By myriad ingenious methods, the result of hours of patient study and years of untiring practice, the cardsharper has endeavored to separate the Bridge player from his money. All his attempts, even the most elaborately planned and most brilliantly executed of them, have failed. Why?

POKER IS AN IDEAL GAME FOR CHEATING

TRADITIONALLY, cardsharpers have operated in big-money Poker games. In days gone by, they found rich rewards on the Mississippi River steamboats and on transatlantic luxury liners. Today, river traffic is no more, transatlantic passengers have learned to be cautious, and the sharper can exist only by gaining access to games in private homes and clubs.

Poker is the ideal game for cheating. Practically every trick of the trade yields a measurable advantage, and the opportunity for profit is great enough to be commensurate with the risk. The principal stratagems are:

The cold deck: In many Poker games, a player may (and a good gambler *will*) bet everything he has on a single hand. Introducing a prearranged deck is a bid for one-shot bets. After a single deal, the deck will be shuffled up and will no longer be prearranged. But in that single deal, the sharper can break the game.

Holding out cards: In Poker, the best combination of cards found in a player's five-card hand wins the pot. With six or seven cards to choose from, instead of five, a player would have a tremendous mathematical advantage. The cheater palms one or two cards, and always chooses a combination from the five cards he is dealt *plus* the one or two cards he is holding out. In Poker the entire deck is not dealt out, some of the cards being retained by the dealer, so that there is no automatic check on whether there are always exactly fifty-two cards.

Whipsawing: In Poker, collusion between two crooked players usually takes the form of "whipsawing." One of the crooks signals to his confederate the information that he has a winning hand. The confederate raises, the crook raises back, and any innocent player who has a good hand must meet all these raises to stay in the pot. Whipsawing increases the size of the pot, with little danger of detection. In Poker, a man may throw his hand away without showing it, and the other players need never find out that the confederate's hand did not justify his betting. Furthermore, in Poker, bluffing is an accepted stratagem and can cover a multitude of sinful bets.

Crooked dealing: In Poker, the placing of just a few cards, even two or three of them, may be decisive. Crooked dealing, stacking the deck, or any other method of arranging the fall of the cards may give the crook a chance for a clean-up all in one pot, instead of winning bit by bit throughout the game.

Marking the cards: In Poker, if a player always knows when he has the winning hand, and when his hand is beaten by another player's hand, he will never make a losing bet. He can never be bluffed. In any game, if you always win and never lose, your profits will be considerable. It is easy to use marked cards in Poker, because there are only a few cards in the hand of each player to read (in Stud Poker, it is necessary to ready only one card).

WHY CHEATING À LA POKER FAILS AT BRIDGE

WHEN YOU ANALYZE the devious ways of the cardsharper, and then try to apply any such system of cheating to the game of Bridge, it soon becomes obvious that nearly everything stated as an advantage in a Poker game becomes a disadvantage in a Bridge game.

Take, for example, the most beautiful, the most artistic expedient known to the crook; dealing in such a way that the cards will fall just where he wants them.

At Bridge, the crook shuffles and deals only once in four times. True, it is a tremendous advantage to be always sure of holding a couple of aces, but when this happens only once in four hands, the advantage is immediately reduced by three-quarters. In Bridge it is impossible to clean up on one hand and get out of the game.

There are also the vagaries of distribution to contend with. The sharper may give himself an ace, only to find that an opponent is void of that suit and can trump it; he may give himself a king, and never win a trick with it because an opponent holds the ace-queen of the same suit and traps it in a finesse.

Take the other Poker methods one by one, and see how futile they are when applied to a Bridge game.

Holding out becomes impossible, because the full fifty-two cards have to be dealt every time.

Introducing a cold deck may work, but it is only one hand in a series of fifty or more. The cardsharper cannot very well introduce more than one cold deck, because his clothes would bulge and he would be conspicuous.

Whipsawing has its counterpart in Bridge in a deliberate attempt to play badly so that your partner will be a loser. Sadly for the crooked gentry, whipsawing in Bridge is so inconvenient that one may as well not attempt it. In the first place, it requires the connivance of three out of the four players. Bridge is a partnership game. If you deliberately make mistakes so that your partner will lose, you necessarily lose with him. How can the crook dare approach so many prospective confederates?

To complete the list of disadvantages, whipsawing in Bridge is very easily detected. If the other players in the game consistently play well when they are opposed to one player, and play badly when they are with him, he must soon begin to suspect something rotten.

Now, when you take the final method of cheating, which is the use of marked cards or the preparation of signals between partners so that they may know what each other holds, you find that it suffers from both of the two big disadvantages.

Signals are both highly effective and very easy to detect. Contract Bridge is a game of probabilities, or deduction, and of analysis. There is an accepted right way, and a recognized wrong way, to bid and play. If a player, flying in the face of accepted practices, consistently employs bids, leads and plays which mathematically prove to be unsound, and if he consistently profits from such violations of the code, the people with whom he is playing will begin to murmur. This will soon be followed by suspicion, and once his antagonists are suspicious, it does not matter whether they can prove anything or not. They will not play with the suspected crook, and that's all there is to it. He cannot win money from people who will not play with him.

But that is not the reason the cardsharpers went broke when they tried to crash the big-money Bridge games. The reason they went broke is closely connected with the reason why they cannot profitably use marked cards.

Expert Bridge players are so good at card-reading that they usually have a pretty good idea where every important card is. They don't need marked cards to know this. Once the expert has learned from deduction where the cards are, he knows just as much as the crook knows, marked cards and all. From this point on, nothing will count except analysis; and unless the crook is an expert player himself, which he seldom is, he will be hopelessly outdistanced.

THE CASE OF MR. X.

"SCANDAL SHEETS," when the gossip market is dull, like to fall back on stories of how idle housewives go to Bridge clubs and there have their pin money taken away from them by cheating players. It is true that there are many Bridge studios and clubs and that many idle housewives do like to kill a few hours playing Contract Bridge there, but it is a pretty safe bet that at such clubs the houswives are playing only against people just as honest as they. From time to time the petty crooks did make a stab at these club games, where though the stakes are small they can pick up three or four dollars from an afternoon's exertions; but most of the crooks gave it up as a bad job.

There was, for example, Mr. X. He was not such an accomplished sharper, but he had what he thought was a sound plan of campaign. His wants were simple. If he could get just a few dollars to pay his room rent, and to feed and clothe him, he would be satisfied. He played a fairly good game of Bridge himself, about as well as the suckers he intended to play with, so that whatever good cards he could deal himself would represent a clear advantage. He knew several Bridge clubs at which he could find the type of game he wanted, and he planned to shift around from one to the other so that his constant success would not become conspicuous.

Mr. X. employed the technique known as "casing and crimping." Whenever it was his turn to shuffle the cards, he would gather the cards to him in such a way as to alternate the high ones and the low ones. Thus, in a series of perhaps twenty cards, the order would be an ace, then a deuce, then another ace, then perhaps a three, and so forth. If an opponent deals the cards off the top of the deck in that order, the crook and his partner would get all the high cards and the two opponents all the low cards.

Having prepared the order of the top cards of the deck, Mr. X. would shuffle the cards in such a way as never to disturb this group of cards at the top. He would then dent one card a little bit (known as a *crimp*) to influence the cut of the deck at the proper point. The stage would now be all set for the unwitting dealer to hand Mr. X. and his partner a slam hand.

This is the simplest, and therefore the most widely used method of manipulating the cards in a Bridge game.

Mr. X. did not, as so many cardsharpers do, wreck his chances of success by greediness. Nevertheless he reckoned without the law of averages, and cold mathematics finally overtook him, overwhelmed him, and sent him beaten back to where he came from.

In a game of skill like Contract Bridge one may bank pretty heavily upon the law of averages. That is, he may expect the luck of the deal to even up, so that he will hold good hands just about as often as he holds bad hands. If he plays well, he will win more on his good hands than he loses on his bad hands. Mr. X., of course, was going the law of averages one better. He counted on breaking even in the three deals in which he did not handle the cards, and winning in the one deal in which he could prearrange the deck.

This was perfectly sound except that Mr. X. did not give proper consideration to the danger of losing streaks. Suddenly he collided with one of those disastrous losing streaks. Rubber after rubber, day after day, *all three* of the honest deals went against him. With a three-to-one edge to fight, Mr. X. had to lose.

Now, of course, with enough time and patience —and capital—Mr. X. would have come out all right anyway. He could have put up with his losses until luck broke the other way. The difficulty was that Mr. X. needed those few dollars of winnings every day to meet his living expenses.

Clearly, he told himself, he would have to arrange to stack the deck more than once in four deals, to give himself a still greater advantage than he had reckoned on before. In order to do this he had to find a way to shuffle the cards when it was really someone else's turn to shuffle. In a Bridge game, shuffling is considered work. No one objects to letting someone else work for him. Habit, however, causes a Bridge player's hands to reach out for the cards when it is his turn to shuffle, and player after player in these games would reach—and find his hands knocking against those of Mr. X., who was also reaching. It could be laughed off the first few times, but then the inevitable question arose: Why was Mr. X. so anxious to shuffle? The next step was to observe the results when Mr. X. did shuffle, and almost invariably the result was a good score for Mr. X. In quick succession came the voicing of suspicion to the club proprietor, consultation with the proprietors of other clubs, careful study of Mr. X.'s actions while he shuffled, and finally a polite but inexorable notification to Mr. X. that he should refrain from presenting himself at any Bridge club after that, for he would not be permitted to play.

It is easy to trace the weakness which broke down Mr. X.'s clever plan. It is easy to say that a more intelligent crook could have played on indefinitely without being caught. But always there is some slip, some overlooked factor which catches up with the cardsharper and wrecks any plan of which he is capable, no matter how thoughtfully it was conceived.

There is also human nature. All men condition their desires upon what they already have. A cheater who has several thousand dollars wants to clean up in high-stake games. Only a petty crook who is broke would, like Mr. X., be content with the coffee money he can win in low-stake housewives' games. Being broke, he has not enough capital to weather a protracted losing streak and is consequently driven to the boldness which eventually causes his detection.

WHY THE EXPERTS DON'T CHEAT

UP IN the higher brackets of Contract Bridge, where the stakes range from 1 cent per point up to 4 cents or 5 cents, there is no such thing as an out-and-out sucker. Even rich people do not play in such games unless they know something about Contract Bridge. Thus, the crook who tries to crash such a game will lose his cheating advantage by being outplayed, unless he is also an expert player himself.

This gives rise to one obvious question: How can one know that the expert players are honest?

It takes a pretty good Bridge player to know from his own experience how nearly impossible it is to cheat advanced players without their finding it out, but for the layman the reasons can be expressed in a few words.

Expert players remember, sometimes for years, every card in every hand they play. They particularly notice the very good hands, which result in easy game or slam contracts. Having all these hands in mind, they could hardly fail eventually to notice the coincidence of a single player's holding consistently good cards when he deals or when he shuffles, and not otherwise. Being thoroughly cognizant at all times of the correctness of bids and plays, they know constant winning is due to skill or to luck, and if someone wins constantly because of unusual luck, the need for a satisfactory answer must immediately occur to them. Once the experts start watching any crook, his days are numbered.

In other words, you cannot fool the experts. Once or twice a truly superb Bridge player has tried it, and has gotten away with it—for a while. But only for a while.

That is why it is easy to answer any doubts in the mind of the average player as to whether the experts are honest or crooked. They are all honest. In fact, they lean over backwards to avoid suspicion. They know that they could not get away with cheating for a very long period, and anyone smart enough to be an expert Bridge player is usually smart enough not to sacrifice the rest of his life for a brief period of false prosperity.

THE CASE OF THE BOGUS COUNT

ABOVE ALL, you can't fool anybody that plays high-stake Bridge into thinking you can win without being a good player, and they know who is a good player and who isn't. Not only do they have the evidence of their own judgment, they have the test of championship tournaments in which duplicate Bridge is played and the luck of the deal is eliminated. They expect the tournament champions to be good players, but a man who can't make his way in tournaments can't be expected to win consistently in money games against better players, and if he does win the suspicion is automatic.

One clever foreign sharper had that proved to him in a fairly recent game. A real aristocrat of the cheating profession, he could even deal seconds and bottom cards, which represents the ultimate in dealing skill. An educated and thoroughly presentable man, he posed as the "Count of So and So"—and he acted like one. He soon found himself welcome at a number of society Bridge games where the stakes were high enough to permit him to build up a sizable fortune.

Being a clever and a plausible talker, the Count was able to give good explanations of all the seemingly unsound plays he made, and his society antagonists, who were good but not in the top rank, believed him to be a fine player and assumed his success to be a combination of luck and skill.

The Count's professional activities came to a halt only when he accidentally found himself in a game with a fine player who did not have a wide enough reputation to cause the Count to be on guard. The expert was first amused by some of the Count's fake explanations, but his amusement made him just curious enough to inquire of his hostess how successful the Count was in Bridge games. When he learned that the Count nearly always won, he issued a discreet warning. The hostess and her friends investigated, and the Count was in no position to stand investigation. Almost before he knew it he was out on his ear.

That is why the crooks have tried their hand at Contract Bridge only long enough to admit defeat and turn their backs on the game forever. Anyone who is really clever with a deck of cards can do better getting a job as a magician, going from table to table in night clubs, performing card tricks, getting small salaries from the proprietors and, occasionally, one-dollar tips from delighted patrons.

And that is why Mr. and Mrs. Average Player can sit down in almost any Bridge game and be fairly sure there aren't any crooks around. It wouldn't be worth while for the crooks.

Percival Wilde wrote a whole series of stories about a young man, a disciple of a reformed cardsharper who went about making the world safe for suckers. We selected this one, but they are all good. They are collected in a book called ROGUES IN CLOVER.

The Adventure of the Fallen Angels

by PERCIVAL WILDE

THE atmosphere in the little room was electric. The explosion, one sensed rather than felt, would soon come.

From outside, far below in the street, came the occasional clatter of a belated taxicab. From above came the steady, unwinking glare of high-powered lights. The clock on the mantel, and the overflowing ashtrays, indicated the hour of two in the morning. Yet the men seated about the Bridge table in the Himalaya Club, cutting in and out at the end of each rubber, played with a concentration that was apparently regardless of everything else.

Straker, so he asserted afterwards, had been on the verge of an apoplectic stroke since midnight. Billings clutched his cards in a nervous hand, and impatiently awaited the moment when the accusation would be made. Chisholm, who could watch the ticker spell out fluctuations which meant tens of thousands to him without turning a hair, bit the ends of his straggly mustache from time to time, and hoped that his exterior did not betray his excitement.

Like the others, Chisholm had absolute confidence in Anthony P. Claghorn—"Tony" Claghorn to his intimates—who, by his own admission, was an expert on everything having to do with games of chance; but, as the minutes stretched into hours, and as Claghorn, with not a wrinkle in his lofty brow, confined himself to smoking the best cigars that the Himalaya Club—and his hosts—provided, and refrained from uttering a word, Chisholm's worries multiplied.

He could not assert that Tony had been an inattentive spectator. At nine, promptly, the game had begun. At nine, promptly, Tony had pulled up the most comfortable chair, and had anchored in it. At half-hourly intervals or thereabouts, rubbers had ended, and the six players cutting to determine the four to play next, had changed seats. At half-hourly intervals or thereabouts Tony, without moving, had called for a fresh cigar.

At ten Chisholm had glanced at Tony questioningly. Tony had replied with an innocent stare. At intervals from then on to midnight, Straker, Billings, Hotchkiss, and Bell had glanced questioningly at the silent young man. He had given them glance for glance—but no satisfaction. Yet during the preceding afternoon Tony had discoursed eloquently upon the ease with which he would solve the mystery.

To be sure, it had been a mystery of Tony's own creating. Roy Terriss, the suspect, had not been looked upon as such until Tony, by a few well-chosen words, had called the attention of his clubmates to the fact that Roy was a remarkably consistent winner. Before that time it had been admitted that Roy was generally successful at Bridge; that he enjoyed playing in an expensive game; and that the game was rarely, if ever, expensive for him. It was Tony who pointed out that Roy's gains, during a winter's play, probably amounted well up into five figures; and it was Tony who, without making direct accusations, had raised his eyebrows significantly at moments when that simple act was not altogether beneficial to Roy's reputation.

Having created the mystery, he had been invited to solve it. With becoming modesty he had accepted the task, and, after sitting solemnly through one five-hour session, had expressed a desire to sit through another. This wish granted, he had declared his intention of being present on yet a third occasion. The results had been painful to his friends, who, expecting they hardly knew what, had thrown caution to the winds, and had been divested of large sums by Terriss, who knowing nothing at all of what was afoot, had played calmly, coldly, and with deadly precision.

Chisholm, indeed, had explained his own mistakes to Tony that very afternoon. "I'm a conservative player," he had asserted earnestly. "I follow the book. I know the rules, and I don't try to improve on them. I don't overbid, and, if the other fellow overbids, I'm a sharp at doubling. But when I'm expecting the whole game to blow up any minute, I can't put my mind on it, and I don't play like myself."

"Even at twenty-five cents a point?"

"What does twenty-five cents a point matter when I'm waiting for you to start the fireworks? Take that hand last night: it was good for three odd. I bid up to five. That wasn't like me, was it? Then Terriss doubled—that's what any sane, level-headed player would have done, holding his cards; and, instead of shutting up and taking my medicine like a little man, what did I do but redouble! Claghorn, I put it to you: was that the act of a normal man? Was that the kind of play you'd look for from me? Then the finesses didn't hold, and I got set for eight hundred points."

Tony smiled reminiscently. "That was a most instructive hand," he commented. "Now, if you had doubled his four instead of going up yourself—"

Chisholm cut him short with a growl.

"Look here," he pointed out succinctly, "we didn't get you into this to give us Bridge lessons, you know. If we wanted lessons, we could get them for about a tenth of what his performance is costing us. You said there was something queer about the game. We're waiting to be shown, that's all."

At two o'clock, ten hours later, Chisholm was still waiting.

Billings, neat and dapper, a stickler for etiquette, had, upon this third evening, to his everlasting embarrassment, been detected in a revoke. He had paid the penalty promptly—graciously; had, indeed, insisted upon its being exacted. But the look which he had given Tony had explained more eloquently than could any number of words how he had come to be guilty. And Hotchkiss, fumbling his cards nervously, had failed to cover an honor with an honor—with results which bulked large when the score was added.

And at two o'clock, Billings and Hotchkiss, as well as Straker, Bell, and Chisholm, were waiting—waiting.

The great moment, the long anticipated moment, came when it was least expected. At two-fifteen the men had adjourned hopelessly. Chisholm was balancing the score; his confederates had already opened their checkbooks; Terriss, with folded arms, was waiting to learn the exact amount of his gains.

It was then that Tony flicked the ash from the tip of his cigar, and spoke. "Mr. Terriss is again the only winner," he murmured, as if to himself. "I wonder what he would say if I mentioned that the cards with which he has been winning are marked."

In an instant Terriss was on his feet.

"What did you say, Claghorn?" he thundered. "What did you say?"

Tony stood his ground stoutly. "I made the statement," he declared, "that you have been winning with marked cards." He took up the two packs that had been used in the Bridge game, and balanced them in his hands. "I still make that statement."

"You—!" shouted Terriss, and dashed at him.

Chisholm thrust his bulk between.

"Take it easy, Terriss," he suggested, "we all know what's been going on. Mr. Claghorn has been looking into things for us."

Terriss gazed around the circle of faces.

"What's this? A conspiracy?" he demanded.

Chisholm shook his head. "Terriss, you know us better than that. Bell, Hotchkiss, Straker, Billings—they've all got reputations to lose, not to mention me. We've asked Mr. Claghorn to investigate. That's all."

"And how is Mr. Claghorn qualified to pass upon such matters? What right has Mr. Claghorn to make accusations against me?"

A chorus answered him. Straker, it appeared, had been present upon a certain occasion when Tony had unmasked one Schwartz. Billings, who had been another witness of that feat, contributed details of the manner in which Tony had exposed a sharper at Palm Beach. Chisholm, a third witness, had half a dozen stories at his finger tips.

Tony Claghorn's career, it was evident from their testimony, had been one long succession of triumphs. His wake was dotted with discomfited cheats, prestidigitators, and imposters. Once put upon the scent, he had never failed to bring down his man.

With appropriate modesty Tony bowed his head while his friends detailed his triumphs. To be sure, the credit for each victory was wholly due to one Bill Parmelee, an unassuming countryman whose acquaintance Tony had made one summer; and Tony, not once, but a dozen times, had explained how his own contribution to the various episodes which had since become famous was of the slightest. But Tony's explanations must have lacked the convincing note, for his friends did not hesitate to trumpet his praises to the four corners of the earth.

That they should forget the quiet young man who had played the leading rôle was not unnatural; Parmelee, farmer and reformed gambler, cared nothing for advertising, and chose to remain out of sight. Almost mechanically his laurels descended upon Claghorn, who, despite his protestations, found the eminence thus forced upon him far from unpleasant.

When Terriss's monotonous success at Bridge had come to Tony's attention, he had attempted to interest Parmelee in the matter. He had failed. Parmelee, Cincinnatus of gamblers, cared more for his blooded cattle than for fresh laurels. And he had not agreed entirely with Claghorn's conclusions.

"Tony, because a man's a winner, it doesn't follow that he's a cheat," he had pointed out.

"No, but in this case—"

"In any case," Parmelee had interrupted, "you must remember that for every dollar won by dishonest gambling, a thousand are probably won by honest play."

"You don't really believe that!"

"I don't know whether I do or not. But that's what I like to think."

Tony's enthusiasm had been damped, but not extinguished. After revolving the subject in his mind overnight, he had decided that he himself was entirely competent, and that Bill's confidence in human nature was, to say the very least, exaggerated. Wherefore, Tony had gallantly launched himself into the breach.

He smiled at Terriss across the table. Success was his, and its taste was sweet.

"Marked cards, Mr. Terriss," he repeated, "marked cards."

Terriss glanced at the set faces about him, and his assurance decreased visibly.

"I suppose," he faltered, "that it will be quite useless for me to say that I didn't know the cards were marked."

"Quite useless," said Tony.

"I won fairly and squarely, I played the game according to the rules."

"What's the good of arguing?" inquired Straker icily.

Terriss gazed about helplessly. "No; there's no good in arguing if you're all against me," he assented. "What do you expect me to do?"

"Make good."

"How?"

"Give back what you won."

Terriss snorted. "I'll be damned if I do," he declared.

"If you don't," said Chisholm, "you will forfeit your membership in this club."

"And if I do," challenged Terriss, "will I hold on to it? Am I the kind of man whom you want to remain? What's the difference whether I give back my winnings or not—except to me? I've been caught cheating, haven't I? That makes me an undesirable member by itself, doesn't it? Of course, I say that I played honestly: that's what you'd expect me to say. But, even if I gave back my winnings, you won't believe me."

"It's the correct thing to do, Terriss," said Straker quietly.

"What does the correct thing matter to a man who has been caught cheating? No; if I'm to be hanged, I'd rather be hanged as a wolf than as a lamb." He took up the score, and surveyed the totals. "Gentlemen, you owe me money. Write your checks."

"What?" gasped Chisholm.

"You've lost. Pay me."

"What about the marked cards?"

"Well, what about them? If there are marked cards, you may have profited by them yourself. Try and prove you didn't."

"I lost!" spluttered Chisholm, nearly speechless.

"What of that? If the cards hadn't been marked you might have lost still more. And that applies to all of us." With supreme self-confidence he beamed upon the players. "Pay me," he invited; "pay me, or I'll bring suit against every man jack of you. You see, I no longer have a reputation to lose, and it won't hurt me to go to court. But if you fellows think you will enjoy the publicity, if you look forward to seeing your names decorating the front pages of the newspapers, just try getting out of your debts."

Helplessly the conspirators turned to Tony. "What do you advise?" they asked as one man.

Tony shrugged his shoulders. "This is out of my department," he said modestly.

Straker glanced about keenly. "You know," he said brightly, "Terriss may be bluffing."

Terriss grinned. "If that's what you think, why don't you call his bluff?"

There was a pause. Then Billings seized his pen and dashed off a check.

"Here you are," he said ungraciously, "I have a wife and two daughters. I can't afford to get mixed up in a scandal."

"Quite so," said Terriss. "I thought you'd see the point after I'd explained it to you."

One by one the men wrote checks, and passed them to the lone winner. He pocketed them carefully, rose, surveyed the conspirators. "Gentlemen," he murmured, "I am about to leave you, to return to my poor but honest domicile. And I have one last request to make of you: don't tell anybody what happened in this room tonight; don't breathe a word of it to your closest friend."

Straker laughed aloud. "Won't we?" he cackled. "Oh, won't we? I'll make it my business to see that every man in this club knows just what took place in twenty-four hours."

Terriss smiled ominously. "In that event, Straker," he warned, "don't pretend you're surprised when I bring suit for criminal libel."

"What?"

"Against each and every one of you." At the threshold he paused. "I can't stop you from blackening my reputation among yourselves; you seem to have done that pretty thoroughly, anyhow. But let me hear that any one of you has dared to say a word against me outside of this room, and I'll hit back! By George, I will! I'll hit back, and I'll hit back hard! Marked cards! Who brought them into the game? Who profited by them? Who didn't profit by them?" A mocking smile hovered upon his lips as he opened the door. "Gentlemen, think it over! Before you do anything, think it over—and then don't do it!"

The latch clicked, and he was gone.

It was Billings who first broke an agonized silence. "Another such victory," he soliloquized, "and we'll all be broke. What do we do next, Claghorn?"

But that worthy, pausing only to light a fresh cigar, had prudently retreated to the threshold.

"What do we do next, Claghorn?" Hotchkiss echoed.

Tony shrugged his shoulders. "This is out of my department," he said modestly.

Long, long after he had left, gently closing the door behind him, the conspirators sat round the table, comparing notes, exchanging advice, and sympathizing with each other's misfortunes. But that, however interesting in itself, has nothing to do with this story.

II

THERE ARE always several ways of looking at a matter. A disinterested judge, for example, might hesitate to characterize the episode which we have recounted as a triumph for Mr. Anthony P. Claghorn. But Claghorn himself spoke of it as a triumph without question. He had set out to expose a sharper; he had succeeded. That the operation had been monstrously costly to his friends was not so important as the fact that it had attained its object. Tony, indeed, did not use stronger terms than "triumph" only because stronger terms did not occur to him.

To his pretty wife he related his exploit with gusto. She understood nothing of cards, but Tony wanted admiration, and her admiration was better than none. But the approbation which mattered most was that of Bill Parmelee, and to that Tony looked forward eagerly. Half a dozen times Tony had been a mystified spectator while Bill, moving along curious lines, had laid the foundations of one of his many victories. It had been Tony's part to observe, to wonder, and to applaud at the conclusion of each carefully planned campaign.

Now, Tony felt modestly, the rôles were reversed. Without help from his friend, acting entirely upon his own initiative he—Tony—had brought his attack to a successful conclusion. It would be Bill's turn to listen while Tony condescended to explain. In the anticipation it was all very pleasant, and Tony lost no time in scurrying to the little town in which Parmelee had immured himself.

"I was satisfied that something was wrong," Tony began magisterially, "oh, long ago; ever so long ago."

"In spite of what I said?" Bill inquired.

"What did you say?" asked Tony tolerantly.

"I tried to convince you that a man can be a winner without being a cheat."

"Oh, yes; I remember that."

"I said that for every dollar won by dishonest gambling, a thousand are probably won by honest play."

"I remember that also," Tony admitted, and lighted a cigar, "but your faith in human nature is—shall we say—exaggerated? In this case the suspect—I'd rather not tell you his name—broke down and admitted everything."

"Well! Well!" said Bill. "Go on with your story."

"I investigated the case carefully. I used a process of elimination. The game was Bridge. Certain methods of cheating were, therefore, useless."

"Quite correct."

"A holdout, for example, would be of no value," said Tony, and went on to explain the nature of a holdout to the man who had initiated him into its mysteries. "By a holdout," he volunteered graciously, "I mean a device which can be used for the purpose of keeping one or more cards in concealment until the player wants them in his own hand."

Not a vestige of a smile was visible on

Bill's placid countenance. "I have heard there were such devices," he murmured.

"Quite so; but as I have explained to you, the suspect—whom I prefer not to call by name—could not possibly have used one. It would have meant introducing a fifty-third card into a complete deck, and that would have been detected at once. You see, if Ter—the suspect had introduced a fifth ace into his hand it would inevitably have duplicated an ace in some other hand. Whenever all the cards are dealt out, a holdout becomes worthless."

Bill stared at the carpet intently. "Not altogether worthless," he qualified.

"Altogether worthless," Tony insisted.

"A holdout might be used on the deal itself," murmured Bill, as if to himself. "The—ahem!—suspect might put all four aces and all four kings as well into a holdout, offer the pack to be cut without them, and pass them into his own hand on the deal."

"What?" gasped Tony.

Bill continued unemotionally. "Of course, that would be pretty raw. Nobody but a beginner would try to get away with anything like that. A really sharp player, playing Bridge, would pass the top cards into his partner's hand. His partner, you see, wouldn't have to be a confederate: give him more than his share of aces and kings, and he'd go a no-trumper, wouldn't he? In all innocence he'd make the correct bid. It would be quite enough for the sharper, sitting across the table, to give him the cards warranting it."

"By George!" ejaculated Tony. "I never thought of that!"

"There are still other ways in which a holdout might be used without duplicating any one of the fifty-two cards in the deck, but it's not necessary to discuss them. Go on, Tony."

It was with a sensation that the wind had been taken out of his sails that the young man continued. "Rightly or wrongly, I decided that the suspect was not using a holdout. You don't think he was, Bill?" he interjected anxiously.

"No."

"I continued with my process of elimination. There are many cheating devices. In Bridge most of them are useless. But one cheating device is useful in every card game." He paused, to aim a long forefinger at his friend. "I refer, of course, to marked cards."

"Ah-ha!"

"I examined the cards carefully. They were not marked. But I risked everything on a bold bluff," chortled Tony, "and it worked. I made one heap of all my winnings," he misquoted, "and I risked it all on one pitch—on one pitch—I forget how it goes on."

"Cut out the poetry and tell me what happened."

"I picked the psychological instant. I've always been good at that—picking the psychological instant—and I boldy accused Ter—the suspect of using marked cards. I knew well enough he wasn't using them. Here"—and Tony produced the cards themselves from capacious pockets—"here they are—unmarked. But I understand human nature, and I felt sure that if I accused a cheat of cheating he would—ahem!—collapse. Whether or not I happened to mention the exact method he was using did not matter; the accusation would be enough."

"Did it work?"

"To perfection. Ter—the suspect was silent, and silence is confession."

Bill smiled. "Is it?" he queried. "If so, a sleeping man is guilty of anything and everything."

"The suspect knew the game was up."

"Perhaps he felt you were carrying too many guns for him. What was the use of pleading innocence when you—and your friends—were convinced he was guilty?"

"I made it a point to treat—ahem!—the suspect with scrupulous fairness."

"Why not call him by his name? Roy Terriss?"

"How did you know?" gasped Tony.

"That's neither here nor there. Go on."

But Tony was too astonished to continue. "How did you know?" he demanded. "How on earth did you know?"

Bill shook his head. "We'll skip that for the time being. Finish your story."

Tony gazed at his friend with some bewilderment. He had looked forward to this moment of triumph. In the realization it was not so satisfactory as in prospect. He passed a shaky hand over his brow. "Perhaps you can finish the story yourself, Bill?"

"Perhaps I can. Terriss admitted nothing. Terriss denied nothing. He refused to give back the money he had won. That took nerve, and I admire him for it. He knew he had no chance of vindicating himself. He decided to wait for a better opportunity."

Tony nodded reluctantly. "Most of that's quite correct," he admitted grudgingly.

"You accused Terriss of playing with marked cards. He replied that if the cards were marked he hadn't benefited by it. And he added what was, after all, a logical conclusion: that the marks might have been of value to your friends."

"Absurd on the face of it," commented Tony, "the cards aren't marked."

"Not so absurd as you think," qualified Bill, and his face set in stern lines. "The cards *are* marked."

III

SOMETIMES the word "surprise" is too feeble fully to express a state of mind. Indeed, to picture Tony's reaction to his friend's simple announcement in reasonably accurate terms, it would be necessary to overhaul, refurbish, and expand the English dictionary.

Tony gazed at Bill with eyes that popped out of his head, opened his mouth two or three times, wetted his lips, and spluttered, "Wh-what did you say?"

"I said," repeated Bill, "that these cards are marked."

"But they can't be!" exploded Tony. "Don't you see? That was the whole beauty of my bluff—that the cards were what they should be, and that I made him believe they were something else."

Bill smiled grimly. "Sometimes a bluff isn't a bluff. Sometimes a man shoots in the dark and hits the bull's-eye. Sometimes a well-meaning blunderer like you, Tony, tells the truth when he leasts suspects it."

"But it's impossible! I've examined those cards with a magnifying glass! I've gone over them not once, but a dozen times! I haven't found a thing!"

"Tony, you didn't know what to look for." Bill spread half a dozen cards on a convenient table. "In the first place, the cards are of an uncommon pattern. You notice the two little angels in the center? They're what is known as 'Angel-Backs!' "

"They're the cards that the club supplies."

"I don't doubt that."

"For the last eight months no other cards have been used at the Himalaya."

"Then how about these?" Bill spread half a dozen cards from the second pack on the table.

Tony gave the cards, decorated with a conventional geometrical design, only a glance. "Oh, those? Those are poorer-class cards which the club laid in when it began to run short of the better ones."

"The Angel-Backs being the better class?"

"Of course. You can see that in a minute."

Bill half-closed his eyes reminiscently.

"When I made my living as a gambler—when I was just beginning to learn the ropes—Angel-Backs were fairly common. They were good cards. They were high-priced, but they were worth it. They gradually dropped out of use; cheaper cards took their place. Today people don't care about quality; it is price that matters. In fact, this pack of Angel-Backs is the first that I have seen in some years. I was under the impression that they were no longer being manufactured."

Tony could not restrain his impatience.

"Come back to the subject, Bill," he begged. "You said the cards were marked. Which pack? And how are they marked?"

"The Angel-Backs, of course. Look at the angels closely."

"I see nothing."

Bill smiled. "This angel, for example, must have gone walking in the mud. His right foot is not as clean as it might be."

"What of that?"

"This other angel evidently put one hand into the mud. You'll notice it's dirty. This third angel knelt in it: there's some on one of his knees. And this fourth angel must have been doing somersaults; you'll notice his complexion has become decidedly swarthy."

"By George!" ejaculated Tony.

"Go through the pack," invited Bill, "and you'll find that there isn't an angel in it who wouldn't be the better for a bath. And you'll find —it's a pure coincidence, doubtless—that the kings have marks on their right shoulders, the queens marks on their left shoulders, the jacks marks at the waistline, and so on through the lot. The angels are small—and the marks are still smaller—but they're very evident when you're looking for them."

Without a word Tony whipped out a magnifying glass, and bent over the cards. "You're right!" he said excitedly; "you're right. And that proves my case beyond a doubt."

"What do you mean?"

"Terriss was using marked cards. My guess hit the nail on the head. Terriss marked the cards while the game was under way."

"Marked them as delicately as this? As accurately? Tony, don't you believe it!"

"But cards can be marked during the progress of a game."

"Yes—with a prick, or with a spot of color. But to mark cards like this? To select a minute speck on the back of each, and dot it as neatly as these are dotted? That takes time, skill, and privacy. The man who marked those cards did it in his room."

"You mean Terriss brought the marked pack with him, and substituted it for one we were using?"

"Not likely."

"Why not? It could have been done."

"It's most improbable. You'll notice that every card in the pack is marked—not the high cards alone."

"What of that?"

"What would be the object—in Bridge? Really fine players place the cards as far down as the sevens and eights. But who ever heard of taking a finesse against a three-spot? Or a four? Or a five?* Why should any sane man take the trouble—and the risk—to mark them?"

Tony corrugated his brow. "Perhaps," he hazarded, "perhaps the man who marked the cards was keen on doing a thorough job. Having begun, he didn't know when to stop."

Bill shook his head decisively. "It won't do, Tony. It won't do at all. An amateur might have done that—you might have done that at a first attempt—but the man we are looking for is a professional, or I know nothing about gambling and gamblers. Look at the beauty of the work! See how perfectly his shading matches the color of the backs! And, remember, if he marked the twos and threes there was a good reason."

Tony shrugged his shoulders. "Reason or no reason, I can't see that it's of any particular importance."

But Bill was already studying a timetable. "The next train for town leaves in forty minutes," he mentioned. "I'm going to pack my bag."

Tony gazed at him with surprise.

"Going to town because the twos and threes are marked? Really, I think you're exaggerating their importance."

* It is impossible to finesse against a three or a four. There are many cases in which a finesse has been taken against a five—and the finesse was marked, even though the cards were not. For example:

	NORTH 10 9 2	
WEST 8 7		EAST Q J 5 3
	SOUTH A K 6 4	

West leads the 8, North covers with the 9, East plays the jack and South the king. Later North leads the 10, East plays the queen, South takes the ace, and West's 7 drops. On a lead of the 2 from the North hand, South now has an indicated finesse against East's 5.

"It would be difficult to do that," said Bill. He rose and glanced keenly at his friend. "In the first place, they prove that Roy Terriss is innocent."

"How so?"

"I have been given to understand that he plays no other game than Bridge."

"Yes; that's so."

"Well, the man who marked these cards didn't expect to play Bridge at all. That's my second point, Tony. The man who marked the cards didn't neglect the little ones for the soundest reason in the world."

"And what's that?" asked Tony scornfully.

Bill opened his valise, and began to jam articles of clothing into it. He glanced at his friend and smiled, opened his mouth to speak, closed it, and smiled again. "Tony, hasn't it struck you yet?" he demanded at length. "The man who marked these cards expected to play Poker!"

IV

UPON every other occasion that Parmelee had accompanied him to town, Tony had been filled with happy anticipation. It had meant, invariably, that the manhunt was on in earnest; that a pursuit which would end only with the exposure of the guilty individual was under way. In the past Tony—a privileged spectator, knowing enough to whet his curiosity to the utmost, but never knowing quite as much as he wanted to—had enjoyed a long succession of happy thrills.

Not once, but half a dozen times, had he observed Parmelee picking up a scent like a well-trained bloodhound, disentangling it from others, following it to a surprising conclusion. Tony had watched, wondered, admired; here was drama, hot off the griddle, served in the most appetizing fashion, and the clubman, whose chief entertainment in earlier days had been provided by the headlines of the sensational newspapers, had come to learn that a thrill at first hand was worth a dozen relayed through print. It had all been most enjoyable—yet Tony, upon this particular occasion, was conscious of no pleasurable feelings.

He gazed gloomily out of the window and gave himself up to unhappy reflections. The cards had been marked; Terriss was not the guilty man. Both facts, Tony was compelled to admit, were crystal clear. It followed, as night follows day, that the criminal must be one of his own particular cronies: Chisholm, Billings, Hotchkiss, Bell, or Straker. Tony reviewed the list to the accompaniment of the click of the wheels. Manhunting, he admitted, was a sport which eclipsed all other sports; but somehow it lost its zest when the prospective victim was one of his own friends.

After half an hour's gloomy meditation he turned to the quiet countryman at his side. "Bill," he ventured tentatively, "I take it that when you reach town you will want to go to the Himalaya Club."

"You take it correctly."

"It's not necessary, you know."

"Why not?"

"Well, really, I haven't asked you to investigate anything."

"That's all right, old fellow," Bill responded heartily; "I haven't waited to be asked."

Tony's voice carried a gentle tinge of reproof. "Don't you think," he enquired tactfully, "that you should wait until you are asked?"

Bill laughed. "Meaning, I suppose, that I'm butting in—"

"I wouldn't say that."

"No; but it's what you are thinking." He glanced shrewdly at Claghorn. "Tony, old fellow, you shot in the dark, and you brought down the wrong man. You have branded Roy Terriss a crooked gambler—a cheat, a thief—a man unfit to be received in decent society. Do you want him to rest under that cloud?"

"No, no, indeed," began Tony vociferously, "that's not what I mean at all——"

"Of course not," Bill chimed in; "you're too fair and square to tolerate anything like that. You want Terriss cleared—cleared triumphantly —only—" and Bill smiled shrewdly—"only you're rather scared that I'm going to fix the blame on one of your very best friends. Isn't that so?"

Tony nodded.

Bill grinned. "That's what might happen, no doubt. I'm not denying it. If I merely wanted to bag a man, and didn't care how I did it, I think I could convict any one of your friends—or you yourself, for that matter."

"Convict me?" gasped Tony.

"It could be done. How did you come by those marked cards?"

"Why, why, I took them from the table."

"How did they get there? How do I know you didn't mark them yourself? How do I know that you and your friends weren't banded together to rob Terriss?"

It was Tony's turn to grin. "Well, we lost."

"To Terriss, perhaps. But the night before the same crowd won pretty heavily from somebody else—what?"

"How did you know that?"

"It doesn't matter," said Bill; "I know it—that's enough. I'm simply trying to show you how easy it would be to find a victim if I were after no more than that. You and your friends have touched pitch, Tony, and you can't touch pitch without being defiled."

Tony's brain whirled. "You mean, then," he sputtered, "you mean that the guilty man is Chisholm—or Billings—or Straker—or Bell—or Hotchkiss—or—or me?"

Bill laughed. "If it will comfort you—and I think it will—I'll let you into a secret, and tell you that I don't suspect any of them—or you, I mean," he corrected gravely.

Tony felt a crushing weight rising buoyantly, easily, happily. "Do you mean that?" he cried.

"We're looking for a professional cheat," said Bill. "Remember that. Hold fast to that. It's the only thing, Tony, between you yourself and the deep sea. You've been worrying about your friends so much that you've completely overlooked what a suspicious character somebody else is."

"Who?" begged Tony.

"Tony Claghorn," said Bill—he smiled at his friend's consternation—"Tony Claghorn has been running around with me so much that he has acquired a first-hand knowledge of cheating devices. How do you know he hasn't used that knowledge? How do you know he hasn't tried to convert theory into practice? It would be profitable—very profitable—and he might get away with it. No, Tony," said Bill, "Roy Terriss is safe. It's Tony Claghorn we have to look after now. And if I'm going to town it's because I think I see a chance to save his skin."

Tony was so completely dumbfounded that he was silent for the rest of the trip.

V

It was between hours at the Himalaya Club when the two men walked in. The regulars, who ate their lunch in the raftered dining hall every day, had departed, and the even more regulars, who experimented with games of chance in its card room from late afternoon until early morning, had not yet arrived.

"We'd better go away and come back later," said Tony.

"Why not wait here?" suggested Bill. He seated himself at a table. "Tony, how would you like to play some cold hands?"

Tony gazed at his friend with a suspicious eye. "What stake?" he inquired.

"Why any stake at all?" countered Bill. "We'll play for nothing—and the fun of it."

Tony assented doubtfully. Ordinarily filled with implicit trust in his friends, his adventure on the train had sadly shaken his equilibrium. He—Tony—was under suspicion. Any move of Bill's might therefore be dangerous to him. In some vague, incomprehensible manner disaster threatened—with the most innocent exterior.

With noticeable lack of enthusiasm he seated himself at the table and rang for cards.

Bill glanced at the box and did not open it. "I don't care for these cards," he announced. "Can't we have some Angel-Backs?"

"I'll see, sir," said the man.

Tony's suspicions redoubled. "What's the matter with the cards?" he inquired.

"I like to play with cards of better quality," the countryman alleged. His eyes shone as the waiter returned with a pack of the required pattern.

He broke the seal, opened the box, and riffled the cards thoughtfully.

"Do you like these better?" Tony asked.

"Much better. Very much better." He dealt the cards, face down, with amazing speed. "King of hearts. Two of diamonds. Eight of hearts. Ace of spades. Three of clubs. Seven of spades. Ten of hearts. Seven of clubs. Five of hearts. Seven of hearts."

"What's this?" demanded Tony. "Legerdemain?"

Bill shrugged his shoulders. "Call it what you like. But if you will look at your cards you will find that you have a four-flush in hearts. You will fill on the draw. The card on top of the pack is another heart."

"And you?" gasped Tony.

"Triplets; nothing but triplets," smiled Bill; "three sevens."

"And they'll be four of a kind on the draw?"

"That would be too raw, old fellow. Now, a full house will be enough. That will beat your flush."

Tony broke into a roar of laughter. "I see it!" he cried. "Of course I see it!"

"What do you see?"

"You stacked the cards!"

"That's pretty evident."

"And they weren't hard to stack because you substituted the marked pack—the pack I brought up to the country—for the new pack the waiter handed you!"

"Is that so?" challenged Bill.

"These cards are marked!"

"Admitted."

"They must be the same pack, unless—unless——"

"Well, say it."

"Unless," faltered Tony, with cold sweat breaking out suddenly on his brow, "unless every pack of Angel-Backs in the club is marked!"

Bill smiled. "That's what I'm trying to find out," he granted.

"They may all be—shall we say?—Fallen Angels."

Without a word Tony rang for the waiter. "We want another pack—two more packs—of Angel-Backs," he snapped.

The waiter shook his head. "Sorry, sir, I can't do it."

"Why not?"

"We're running very short of the Angel-Backs, and the members prefer them to the other cards. They're better quality. The steward instructed me not to give out more than one pack to a party."

Tony extracted a bank note from his pocket. "I want two packs of Angel-Backs," he repeated. "Do you understand?"

"I'll do what I can," said the waiter. He was back in a few minutes with a single pack. "I couldn't get you two," he apologized. "There's not a gross left, sir. I'm breaking orders as it is, sir."

In silence Tony passed the unopened box to his friend. "Open it, Bill."

Parmelee put his hands behind his back. "Open it yourself. You might accuse me of substituting another pack."

Without a word Tony broke the seal, inverted the box, and allowed the cards to cascade upon the table.

"Well?" Bill inquired.

"Marked—marked; every blamed one of them!"

"Fallen Angels!" murmured Parmelee. "Fallen Angels! Tony, don't you think we might have a chat with the steward?"

Tony clenched his fists. "If he's the man who marked them I'll see that he's out of a job in ten minutes!"

"Why so excitable?" soothed Bill. "What would the steward have to gain by trickery? He isn't the man we want, you can depend upon that."

He listened quietly while his explosive friend summoned the steward, and explained the state of affairs to that worthy. The man examined the cards, paled, bit his lips. "Really, sir," he stammered, "this is most surprising—most surprising——"

"It is!" asseverated Tony.

"I wouldn't believe it if I didn't see it with my own eyes. It's monstrous—incredible!"

"How do you explain it?"

"I—I don't."

"How do we know that you're not the guilty man?"

"Oh, sir, I've been in the employ of this club for twenty-eight years! It would be late in life for me to turn round and become a common cheat. Really, sir, you don't think that I could be capable of such a thing?"

Bill broke into the conversation. "How many more packs of Angel-Backs have you?"

"Less than a gross."

"Why didn't you order more?"

"I did. The jobber couldn't fill my orders."

"Oh!" Bill half closed his eyes. "When did you first buy Angel-Backs?"

"About a year ago, sir. Shall I tell you about it?"

"I wish you would."

"A sample pack was sent us by a mail-order house. The International Supply Company, they called themselves."

"What was their address?"

"A post-office box at Times Square Station, New York City, sir."

"Go on."

"Samples are sent to us frequently, but this sample was unusually good."

"Angel-Backs—I should think so!"

"Not only that, but the cards were remarkably cheap; so cheap, in fact, that the club could sell them at the same price as inferior cards and still make money."

"Didn't that make you suspicious?"

"The International Supply Company explained that the pattern was about to be discontinued, and that they had a large quantity on hand. If we would take them all, they would make us a special price, sir. I didn't make the purchase on my own responsibility. I referred the matter to the House Committee. They told me to go ahead."

"What else?"

"That's all, sir. The members liked the cards, as I explained they would. We used nothing else for many months. Then the Angel-Backs began to run short. I tried to buy more."

"Your letters to the International Supply Company were returned unclaimed?"

"Yes, sir. They had gone out of business."

Bill smiled. "The scent becomes more interesting as we follow it." He turned to his friend. "Tony, what's the next move?"

"To examine the rest of the cards, of course."

Bill's eye twinkled, but he nodded soberly. "Suppose you do that, Tony. There are over a hundred packs left, so it will take time. But be thorough about it: go through every pack, and tabulate your results in writing."

VI

After his volcanic friend had departed Bill motioned the steward to a chair at his side. "I have a good many questions to ask you," he began, "but Mr. Claghorn is safely out of the way for at least an hour. He will examine every pack of Angel-Backs in the storeroom, and he will find every card marked." The steward waited for him to continue. "In the first place, the membership of this club changes rapidly, doesn't it?"

"What do you mean, sir?"

"New members are elected—old members resign, or become inactive."

"More frequently than I like. Yes, sir."

"At a rough guess, how many members, very active a year ago, are inactive today?"

"Twenty, perhaps," said the steward.

"Write their names on a piece of paper." The man did so.

"Play for high stakes is common here?" pursued Bill.

"It is a rule, sir."

"But not all of the twenty played Poker."

"No, sir."

"Scratch out the names of those who played other games. That leaves how many?"

"An even dozen, sir."

"Now let us take another angle. There have been big winners in the club during the past year?"

"Yes, sir. At least eight or ten."

"How many of them did their winning at Poker?"

"Five or six."

"Write down their names. Compare the two lists. How many of the big winners—at Poker—do you find among the inactive members?"

"Only one, sir."

"That's easy to explain, isn't it? A big winner doesn't become inactive. A big winner sticks to the game just as long as he continues winning."

"Naturally, sir."

"Yet one man who was a big winner—at Poker—didn't wait for his luck to change. He stopped coming to the club."

The steward nodded. "That always puzzled me, sir. He played Poker, and he had the reputation of being the strongest player that ever sat down to a table in these rooms. He played nearly every night for six months——"

"And then?"

"I never could understand it, sir, but he simply stopped coming."

Bill looked keenly at the other. "Was this man—by some curious coincidence—elected to membership just about a year ago?"

The steward nodded with dawning comprehension. "He was, sir. Mr. Ashley Kendrick was proposed one week after I had purchased the Angel-Backs. The Membership Committee has always been notoriously lax; it's easy to get into the Himalaya. Mr. Kendrick was elected five days after his name had been posted."

"He played Poker?"

"Yes, sir."

"With the Angel-Backs?"

"Yes, sir."

"And he won?"

"Invariably, sir."

"Then, six months later, when the cards began to run short, he stopped coming?"

"Oh, no, sir."

"What do you mean?"

"He stopped coming; that part's correct, sir. But at the time we hadn't begun to run short of Angel-Backs."

Bill whistled. "This gets more interesting as we go along!"

"We were using nothing but Angel-Backs at that time; the supply was very plentiful. Mr. Kendrick simply failed to show up one evening—that was all."

"You had his address?"

"Yes, sir, but it was an address which won't help. His address was right here—in care the Himalaya Club."

"No forwarding address, I suppose?"

"None needed, sir. From the moment he joined until the last evening he spent here Mr. Kendrick never received a letter."

It was at this juncture that Tony Claghorn thrust his exuberant self into the picture. "Bill," he announced, "I've examined the Angel-Backs."

"All of them? So soon?"

"It wasn't necessary to look at more than a card or two from each pack. They're all marked."

He had expected his announcement to produce a sensation. He was disappointed.

"Yes; I expected to hear that," said Bill calmly. "In the meantime, I've been busy."

Tony swallowed his chagrin. "With what result?" he demanded.

"Tony, I've run up a blind alley. I've found out something, but it doesn't help—not a darn bit. I'm stumped. I found the trail getting hotter and hotter, and I followed it. I fetched up against a blank wall."

"If you had allowed me to help you," Tony declared, "that wouldn't have happened."

"Perhaps not. Perhaps not."

"It's not too late now," invited Tony.

Bill grinned ruefully. "All right, Tony. Show me how to lay my hands on a fellow named Ashley Kendrick."

"Ashley Kendrick? Ashley Kendrick? Why, he hasn't been in here for months."

"I know that already."

"I can't tell you how to reach him, but I can put you in touch with his best friend."

"Also a member of this club?"

"He used to be," said Tony. "He's a chap by the name of Venner; a nice chap, but the unluckiest there ever was."

Bill glanced at the steward. "Is his name on your list of inactives?"

"Yes, sir."

"But not on the list of winners?"

"No, sir. As Mr. Claghorn says, Mr. Venner was—unfortunate."

Bill sucked in his breath sharply. "I wonder . . . I wonder . . . if by any chance his misfortunes began about the time that the Angel-Backs started to run short."

The steward started. "Come to think of it, they did, sir."

Bill leaped to his feet and flung his arms above his head with excitement unusual for him. "What a fool I was! What a dunderhead! What a numbskull! I should have seen it at once! I should have guessed it right off! Why, it's as plain as the nose on a man's face!"

Tony neither understood nor shared his enthusiasm. "I don't see what you're driving at."

"Don't you see how Venner explains everything?"

Tony fixed a look of mild reproach upon him. "Bill," he cautioned, "don't let me hear you say a word against Venner! He's as fine a fellow as there ever was—even if his luck turned—and I don't see how he explains anything."

By a superhuman effort Bill composed his face, and seated himself again. "Sorry, Tony. Perhaps I was too enthusiastic. But tell me about Venner; tell me all about him."

Tony stood on his dignity. "I don't see what Venner has to do with this case."

"All right, you don't see," said Bill, controlling his impatience with difficulty, "but tell me what I want to know, anyhow."

Tony had acknowledged his friend's authority

too long to shake it off easily. "If you insist——"

"I do."

"Then I'll tell you; though I warn you in advance that it won't help you at all." He bent a searching look on the steward. "This must go no further," he warned. "This is to remain a secret among the three of us."

"I shan't say a word, sir. But if you'd prefer to have me go away . . ."

Magnanimously Tony shook his head.

"Inasmuch as I suspected you, you have a right to listen." He turned to Parmelee. "Bill," he began, "Venner joined the club something less than a year ago—a fine fellow—a gentleman, every inch of him."

"Go on."

"He played Poker. I played with him myself any number of times. He rarely played for high stakes—that is, in the beginning. He played a fair game—broke a little better than even. Then, to his misfortune, he met Kendrick.

"Of course, I needn't tell you about Kendrick, one of the best Poker players I ever saw; a man who could almost read your mind; who always played in the biggest game, and kicked because it wasn't bigger. Venner met Kendrick, and was fascinated by him. He gave up playing himself to watch Kendrick play: he said he had never seen anything so wonderful. And Kendrick used to like it; Kendrick always saved a chair near him for Venner.

"The two came to be close friends. You'd never see one without the other. Kendrick seemed to like teaching Venner; and Venner's eyes never left Kendrick. And when the game broke up they'd go away together. Kendrick used to live here in the club. For a time, I believe, Venner shared Kendrick's rooms.

"Then, one night Kendrick didn't show up, and Venner acted as if he had lost the best friend he had in the world. He hovered round the table at which Kendrick used to play; he kept his eyes on the door as if Kendrick might come through it any minute; he asked every man he met if he had seen Kendrick.

"For a week Venner watched. He told more than one of us that he suspected Kendrick had met with foul play. Then he gave him up for lost."

Parmelee's eyes were fixed on vacancy.

"It was then that Venner took Kendrick's place in the game—the big game?"

"Yes, it was an asinine thing to do, but Venner thought he had learnt enough from Kendrick to fill his boots. He did—for a night or so. He won—won heavily—and then his luck turned. He'd win one evening. He'd lose twice as much the next. He'd win a thousand—and lose three. He'd win two thousand—and lose five.

"I urged him to stop. I urged him any number of times, but he always explained that out of ordinary courtesy he couldn't. He had won from the other fellows. He had to do the fair thing by giving them a chance for revenge."

Tony paused and nodded gravely.

"That's what Venner did: a chivalrous, gentlemanly, insane performance. Don't you think so?"

Bill turned to the steward. "What do you think?" he inquired.

"After twenty-eight years in the employ of this club I have learnt that there are times when it is wiser not to think."

Bill nodded. "I can understand how you lasted twenty-eight years." He turned to Tony. "Finish your story."

Tony lowered his voice. "I'm coming to the part I want kept secret. Venner lost. Venner lost every cent he had. Venner had to stop coming to the club. He was posted for nonpayment of dues."

"Where is he now? And what is he doing?"

"Never tell a soul, will you? Venner's down and out. He's had to take a job as a waiter in a cheap restaurant, and I have to ruin my digestion by having a meal there every once in so often."

Parmelee grinned and cast a grateful glance at his friend. "Tony, you've helped! You have no idea how you've helped!" He rose and deliberately winked at the steward. "Are you good at riddles?"

"What's the riddle, sir?"

"This is a hard one. See if you can guess it." Gravely he propounded: "If a farmer, twenty-five years old, lives in Connecticut, goes to New York on the midday train, spends the afternoon at the Himalaya Club and then, because he has a cast-iron digestion, has his dinner at a cheap restaurant, what—what is the waiter's name?"

"Venner, sir," said the steward promptly.

"Go to the head of the class," said Bill.

VII

WHILE Parmelee and his much-mystified friend proceed to a frowzy, second-class eating place on lower Eighth Avenue, there to be served by one Venner, there to corral the said Venner in an untidy, private dining-room, there to tempt the said Venner with promises of immunity and gradually increasing amount of currency until his silent tongue becomes exceedingly loquacious, let us turn back the pages of time two years to the very beginning of an exceedingly strange story.

The day was unbearably hot and sultry. Layers of heated air, writhing and twisting like heavy oil in their ascent, floated lazily upwards from the broiling streets. The asphalt itself was soft and gummy; choking dust, the accumulation of a rainless week, lay in ambush to take suffering humanity by the throat; and in innumerable windows sickly geraniums drooped and wilted under the merciless rays of the sun.

A thermometer, hung at street level, would have indicated a temperature well into the nineties. The same thermometer, carried up five flights of stairs in any one of the nearby tenements would gradually have registered higher and higher figures, until, under the metallic roof, assailed from above by the burning glare of the sun, and from below by the outpour of scorching air, it would actually have indicated a temperature in excess of one hundred. Yet the man who bent over a little table in the inferno known as a hall bedroom, in the topmost story of one of the most dilapidated buildings in the section, was too intent upon his labors to notice such minor matters as the weather.

His single window was closed, its inside covered with soap, so that no observer across the street might peer through it. His door was locked—not merely locked, but barricaded by pieces of furniture which had been moved against it. And, despite the heat, for not a breath of air traveled through the room, a kettle, placed on a portable oil stove, boiled briskly at the man's elbow.

On the table before which he sat, paper cartons—dozens and scores of them—were stacked in orderly fashion until they reached the ceiling. At his right-hand was a saucer containing a reddish liquid with an alcoholic odor. At his left-hand was a second saucer containing a bluish liquid. Half a dozen minute camel's-hair brushes were carefully ranged before him. And, as if the weather and the stove and the tightly closed openings had not made the room hot enough, a high-powered electric light was suspended from a cord, casting a blinding glare upon the man's hands, and upon the objects which were engrossing his attention.

He rose, removed a carton from the huge pile, and, holding it dexterously, allowed the steam from the boiling kettle to hiss upon the paper seal. The carton flew open. With delicate care he set it upon the floor and emptied it of its contents: an even gross of individually sealed small paper boxes. Each seal in turn was held for an instant in the jet of escaping steam; each gave way almost instantly.

The man placed the open boxes on one side, seated himself again, and, wiping his hands carefully so that no moisture from them might make a mark, shook one of the boxes, and removed from it a new pack of playing cards. He spread them out on the table, took up one of his brushes, dipped it in the colored liquid, and, with the expertness gained by long practice, placed a microscopic dot on the back of each card.

Had an observer been present he would have noted that the color applied matched the back of the card perfectly; stranger yet, he would have noted that after the minute spot of moisture had dried the closest scrutiny would have been required to show that the card had been tampered with. While moist, the tiny speck of liquid was visible; when dry, it blended with the surrounding color so excellently that no person unacquainted with the secret would have been able to discover a mark.

During his manipulations the man had been careful not to disturb the order of the cards: factory-packed playing cards are always arranged in the same manner. He examined six or eight cards closely, satisfied himself that the marks which he had made were indistinguishable, leveled the pack, and returned it to its box. For a second time he held the seal in the jet of steam. Then he closed the flap, pressed the seal so that it adhered again, and laid the box to one side.

A dozen cartons under the table represented the labor of several weeks. Working at the greatest speed which he would permit himself, his output did not exceed ten packs an hour—and each carton contained a gross of packs—and the huge pile before him numbered at least several hundred cartons. Had he paused to calculate he might well have been terrified at the result: ten packs an hour; eighty to a hundred a day; at the very best, not more than five gross a week. And nearly a year would elapse before he might reach the completion of his gigantic task.

Presumably, the man had made his calculations before commencing; had estimated the expenditure of time, and had decided that it was worth his while, for he paused not an instant upon finishing one pack before beginning on another. He worked rapidly yet carefully, with a concentration which might have been explained only had a slave-driver, with a whip, been standing behind him. Practice had brought him surprising skill. There was no waste motion; no misdirected energy. Little by little the pile of unfinished work diminished; little by little the pile of finished work grew.

At seven o'clock, or thereabouts, he extinguished the oil stove, drew a clean white sheet over the mountain of cartons, washed, and made himself presentable, and went out, padlocking the door of his room behind him. Other tenants of the building, gathered at the entrance for a breath of air, nodded to him as he strode by them. "Good evening, Mr. Kendrick," they chorused.

"Good evening," said Kendrick, and went on his way—to a lunch room round the corner.

"What's he do for a living?" inquired one of the neighbors.

"He's a literary man," said one better informed.

"A which?"

"A literary man. He writes novels and books and stories. Locks himself in his room from morning till night, and writes—just writes. He told me so himself. Keeps regular hours, just like a working man, too."

"That ain't work—just writing," commented a listener, and broke off to inquire, "Have you ever read anything he's wrote?"

"Not yet. He says there'll be nothing of his published for a year. But he's going to let me know when something comes out."

Let us dive headlong for the end of that year. The pile of unfinished work had shrunk—finally vanished. The little room was filled with neatly stacked cartons, which one might have examined and sworn had never been opened. And the International Supply Company—alias Kendrick—having offered samples of superior quality playing cards at ruinous prices to three clubs, equally notorious for the size of the games played under their roofs, and for the ease with which a stranger might secure membership, had arranged to sell the entire quantity to the Himalaya.

The following day a horse-drawn truck, specially hired for the occasion, and personally driven by the International Supply Company—alias Kendrick—delivered several hundred gross of marked cards to the Himalaya Club.

Within a week Mr. Ashley Kendrick was proposed for membership in that notorious organization.

He was elected five days later.

Within less than a month he was voted the best Poker player who had ever seated himself at one of the Himalaya's card tables, and his former neighbors, who had looked forward to reading his books, novels, and stories, waited a while—and then forgot him.

VIII

A GAMBLER'S PARADISE: a place where the play is continuous, where the stakes are high, where the players are liberal, and where every card is marked. It was in such an unbelievably blissful spot that Kendrick now found himself. For a whole year he had worked and planned; for a whole year he had lived economically on his savings; if he was at length to be rewarded, he felt that he deserved it.

Yet he did not make the mistake of playing too well. An infallible player discourages his opponents, whereas an occasional loss is not expensive, and greatly heartens the victim. Kendrick, who knew every card in the pack, who could read his opponents' hands as readily as if they had been exposed, who could tell every time whether or not it was worth while to draw, could have won far more than he actually permitted himself to. Hardly an evening went by without Kendrick's sustaining at least one sensational loss; hardly a session without his going down to defeat on at least one well-advertised hand. But never did the gambler rise from his seat poorer than when he had settled himself into it; never did the end of a session make it necessary for Kendrick to produce his checkbook.

He limited himself strictly to a maximum winning, and his self-control was such that he never exceeded the fixed amount. Yet the maximum was a liberal maximum, for at the end of ten days he had recouped himself for the expenditure of the preceding year, and at the end of three months his bank account had begun to assume formidable proportions.

At the end of four months he increased his maximum liberally, and doubled his bank account, and at the end of five months he began to fling off all restraint. He began to play Poker of a brand unheard of even at the Himalaya, where fine players abounded. He had put by a gigantic nest-egg; and it was his program to win as much as possible against the day when the Angel-Backs would begin to run short.

It was at this juncture that Venner, so he confessed to Parmelee, projected himself into the situation.

Venner, a shiftless ne'er-do-well of pleasing personality, had dissipated a modest inheritance, and was fast nearing the end of his slender resources. He played Poker tolerably; upon occasion he had not hesitated to cheat, and, in the hope of extending his dishonest operations enough to make a killing, he had purchased half a dozen packs of cards at the club, and had taken them home with him with the laudable intention of marking them. Once marked, he would find opportunities to substitute them for the club's cards.

He had marked two or three packs before he made the astounding discovery that the cards were already marked. He could not believe the evidence of his eyes. Feverishly he broke open the sealed boxes, to find that some pioneer in knavery had been before him. More cards, covertly examined at the Himalaya itself, confirmed the amazing truth.

Venner had intended to indulge in cheating on a small scale. His discovery of the existence of a swindle of such gigantic dimensions left him simply thunderstruck. For an instant he reflected that, knowing the secret, he too, could win as he pleased. But upon second thought it occurred to him that there would be quite as much gain, and far less risk, were he to make a cat's-paw of the daring sharper who was doubtless at work this instant.

For months Kendrick had been a sensational winner. Within twenty-four hours after penetrating his secret Venner confronted him.

"You can't prove anything," Kendrick said.

"I know it," said Venner.

"I'm the most surprised man in the world to learn that the cards are marked," Kendrick alleged.

"Then you won't object if I pass the word on to the other members, and see that other cards are used?"

Kendrick's eyes narrowed. Venner was easy for him to see through. "What's the alternative?" he demanded.

"Divvy up with me," murmured Venner. "Pay me half of whatever you win, and I'll be silent as the grave."

He paused. "If you don't, I'll expose you. I'll say that you confessed everything——"

"Nobody will believe it."

"If that's what you think turn down my offer."

Kendrick was in an unpleasant position, and was fully aware of it. The solution—the solution that flashed upon him at once—was to pretend to accept Venner's terms, and to disappear forever from the scene. But the weak point was painfully obvious: Venner, out of spite, might set the authorities upon his trail. It would be better, Kendrick decided instantaneously, to wait until Venner, too, was thoroughly besmirched; to make Venner an accomplice who dared not open his mouth without imperiling his own freedom. And then, also, even if he had to divide his future winnings, a great deal of money might be amassed in a short time—say, two or three weeks.

He shook Venner's hand heartily.

"You're a man after my own heart," he said. "I accept your proposition."

Then began the short but interesting period during which Venner, according to Tony's description, sat at Kendrick's side and ostensibly studied his game, but during which Venner, according to his own confession, followed the play with an eagle eye to make sure that his partner in crime did not win more than he would admit, and thus defraud him of his share.

After a few days Venner invited himself to live in Kendrick's rooms; he could keep a closer watch on him in that manner, and for two brief but happy weeks Venner's income was exceedingly large. He treated himself to a new outfit of clothing, and began to sport small but costly scarf pins. He even looked at automobiles; his improved circumstances would warrant him in purchasing one.

Then, upon the evening of the day that Venner, after convening himself in executive session, had voted that Kendrick should henceforth pay him three-quarters and not merely half of his winnings, the astute gambler disappeared. Venner was worried; honestly believed that his partner had met with foul play. At the end of a week a letter, mailed en route to Mexico City, told Venner the truth. Kendrick had disappeared for good. He had won enough to support him in comfort the rest of his life. He did not propose to share his winnings, even with so likeable a chap as Venner. Nevertheless, he gave Venner his blessing, and mentioned that he admired Venner's collection of scarf pins, which he had taken to Mexico with him.

At once Venner found himself in straitened circumstances. His income had vanished; his expenditure continued. But the Angel-Backs promised relief.

He took Kendrick's place in the big game, and won heavily for two nights. On the third night, to his unutterable horror, cards of a strange pattern were used, and Venner, compelled to play honest poker against men who qualified as experts, lost more than he had won the two preceding sessions.

On the fourth night the Angel-Backs returned, and Venner did well. But on the fifth and sixth nights other cards were supplied and the results were harrowing.

What followed partook of the nature of a nightmare. Venner had run into debt; willing or unwilling, he was compelled to play. And he was suddenly confronted with a situation far more dangerous than any that had ever faced Kendrick: the Angel-Backs were running short, other cards were being substituted, and, if Venner invariably won with the Angel-Backs and lost upon all other occasions, it would not be long before some astute observer called attention to the circumstance.

He used to lie awake at night, summoning up hideous pictures, visioning the possibilities. It occurred to him that he might purchase more Angel-Backs, mark them and introduce them into the play. He found that cards of that pattern were not obtainable at any price. Even had they been obtainable, he could not bring them to the table without inviting suspicious comment.

He thought of marking the cards which the club had substituted for the Angel-Backs; but he realized that the sleight-of-hand necessary to exchange them for the pack in use was far beyond him. In his petty cheating in the past he had occasionally indulged in the form of dishonesty known as ringing in a cold pack. That was possible, playing for moderate stakes, with no spectators. It was impossible, save for some sharper far more expert than he, in a big game closely watched by twenty or more men.

For a ghastly week Venner endured the tortures of the damned. Like Kendrick, he found it well to limit his winnings when the gods were good to him, and when chance brought a deck of marked cards to the table. But, unlike Kendrick, he was compelled too often to play with strange cards—and he found it quite impossible to limit his losings.

For all his sins in the past the cheat paid a thousand times over during that week. To put in an appearance each night, smiling and jovial, while his soul writhed in torment; to forego pot after pot when the Angel-Backs offered it to him, because to win too much might create suspicion; to lose upon other nights, and lose heavily—disastrously—because he dared not change his style of play; no wonder the man cracked under the strain.

He began to play wildly, recklessly. His opponents, shrewd students of psychology, sensed the change in the wind. In two consecutive sessions they stripped him.

Courtesy prohibits a man from taking another's last cigarette, but it does not prohibit a man from taking another's last dollar. His opponents showed him no mercy. When Venner left the Himalaya Club for the last time, he had borrowed as much as his friends would lend, he owned nothing, and his pockets were empty.

This, coming by driblets in the beginning, coming faster and faster as the man's emotions mastered him in the end, was the story that Parmelee and Claghorn heard from the lips of one Venner, a waiter in a frowzy, second-class eating-place on lower Eighth Avenue.

IX

It was not until half an hour after they had left the restaurant, on their walk uptown, that Bill opened his mouth. Tony, completely floored, for once in his life, had marched at his side in silence.

"We started, didn't we," said Bill, "to find out whether or not Roy Terriss cheated at Bridge? It's funny over what a long trail it has led us! Terriss—the Angel-Backs—the Himalaya—Kendrick—Venner——"

"Don't mention that man's name to me!" interrupted Tony.

"Why not?"

"When I think of what I've been doing to my digestion on his account: eating in that miserable restaurant at least once a week because I sympathized with him! Ugh!"

"Venner is a whole lot worse off, isn't he? You have been a guest of the restaurant; he is a waiter in it."

"Serves him right!"

"Perhaps. Perhaps. Something—call it what you will—has a great way of getting even with the man who doesn't play fair. Venner is paying—Venner is paying heavily. If you're a real man, Tony, you might go on eating a meal in that restaurant once in a while."

"Why?"

"Some day you may be able to set Venner on the right path, and that would be your way of paying whatever you owe. How about it, Tony?"

"Er—I'll think about it."

Bill nodded his approval. "Pay! Pay! Pay! You can't get out of it!"

"No? How about Kendrick?"

"He'll be no exception. Think of the year's slavery he endured before he could bring off his coup! Think what he could have done—where he could have been today—had he applied the same energy to any honest pursuit!"

"He's living in luxury, in Mexico."

"Yes, for six months, perhaps."

"He won enough to support him for the rest of his life."

"Lots of gamblers have done that, but somehow the money doesn't last. Money made that way never lasts. Like the angels—the fallen angels—it has wings! An honest man can call on the law to protect his property. Kendrick can't. The moment the others find that out—in Mexico—what chance will he have?" Bill shook his head vigorously. "No, of the two, I think Venner is the lucky one. He's alive, and I'll bet two to one this minute that Kendrick isn't. He worked too hard for his money to give it up alive; and in Mexico life is cheap—very cheap."

"Maybe," said Tony; "maybe." He thought hard for a minute. Then he turned to his friend. "From the very beginning I've never understood why you've been so keenly interested in this affair. What was it? Love of adventure?"

"Not after six years of drifting about the country, old fellow."

"Then what was it?"

Bill permitted himself the luxury of a smile. "As I told you this morning—it seems so long ago, doesn't it?—it was nothing but a friendly desire to save your reputation."

"My reputation," repeated Tony incredulously.

"That was all. You see, after you had exposed Terriss, it occurred to him that you were a pupil of mine, and he came straight to headquarters with his troubles."

"He went to you?" gasped Tony.

"That is the thought I am trying to convey," Bill assented. "Terriss was innocent. You know that now. He knew it then, and he convinced me like a shot. He wanted to be vindicated, but that wasn't all; he was dead sure that if the cards were marked you had marked them yourself, and he wanted to see you—you and your friends —behind the bars! He is a clever man, a mighty quick-thinking man, and I'm pretty sure that if I hadn't taken the case he'd have turned the tables on you before now!"

Tony's face became purple. "But I'm innocent! You know I'm innocent!"

"Sometimes it's very hard to prove, Tony. Terriss was innocent, but he couldn't make you see it."

Tony swallowed hard. "My friends and I owe Terriss a handsome apology."

"You do!"

"I shall see that it is forthcoming. And, by the way, whatever fee you charge Terriss will be paid by me."

"Fair enough."

"Your expenses, too. Whatever they were. I will reimburse you."

Bill smiled. "Well, you heard me promise Venner a hundred dollars if he'd tell his story."

"I'll pay that."

"When you make out your check to Venner, make a mistake and slip in an extra nought before the decimal point."

"Why on earth should I do that?" protested Tony.

"No reason at all," said Bill, "except that I'm sentimental. For a hundred dollars—a contemptible hundred dollars—Venner turned his soul inside out. I'm going to improve his self-respect by convincing him that his soul is worth at least a thousand."

Tony nodded. "I get your point. The check will read a thousand. And now, your fee."

"That will come high."

"I expect that."

"Terriss expected it too, the quick-thinking devil! He insisted on your friends paying up because he wanted plenty of ready money on hand to satisfy me."

Tony smiled. His finances had taken a turn for the better since he had followed his friend's example and had become merely a spectator, and not a participant, in games of chance. His bank account had become plethoric, and the knowledge was pleasant.

"Bill," he said, "you can't frighten me. Name what you want."

"It will come hard."

"If it does, it's worth it."

"All right, Tony, here goes." Bill stretched out his hand. "Pay me fifty-two Angel-Backs—fifty-two marked cards—fifty-two Fallen Angels. I'm going to nail them to the walls of my bedroom as a souvenir!"

CARD TRICKS

¶The hustler, typical denizen of the nonviolent underworld, who would rather live by his wits poorly than by honest labor well, has seldom been faithfully portrayed in American literature. A noteworthy exception is Nelson Algren's novel THE MAN WITH THE GOLDEN ARM, *set on the south side of Chicago. ¶In the scene that we reprint, the hero, Frankie, and his satellite, the Sparrow, are temporarily in jail but, to their joint delight, are cellmates. Frankie is a professional dealer in gambling-house Poker games and a typical wise guy besides. The Sparrow is his satellite and disciple (though neither word is in the hustler's lexicon). ¶Even so brief an excerpt demands a glossary. Regrettably the author did not supply one, but we will do our best and hope Chicago has no peculiar semantic system. ¶*BAG*—the box for the house take; the kitty.* PUNK*—any youth; no baser connotation.* WISE GUY*—a hustler, not a smart alec. All the world is divided into two classes, wise guys and chumps.* CUE*—a billiard cue, used in pool, or pocket billiards;* FIFTEEN FISH*—there are fifteen balls in most pool games, and of course the ideal is to pocket them all;* SIX-NO-COUNT*—a handicapping agreement whereby the superior player must pocket at least six balls in a row for any to count, a run of five or fewer counting zero.* A SECOND OFF THE BOTTOM*—see page 322. Mr. Algren may have slipped here; seconds are dealt from the top but it is hard to imagine a reason for dealing a second from the bottom.* GOLDEN ARM*—simply one that makes money, whether in dealing cards or in casting dice.* SLOT*—the dealer's position in any gambling game.* PASS, RIDING*—a pass is a winning throw at Craps; money is riding when the bet consists of the original stake plus all winnings.* LITTLE JOE *is a cast of 4,* PHOEBE *is 5,* BIG DICK *is 10,* EIGHTER FROM DECATUR *is obviously 8 and the Decatur, inserted for rhyme, is a town in Texas, county seat of Wise County.* THE HARD WAY *signifies a pair, as 6 made with 3-3 rather than 4-2 or 5-1.* SCRATCH SHEET*—a bookmaker's bulletin telling what horses are entered or have been withdrawn from the day's races.* PATCH*—the big-city neighborhood to which the person speaking is native.* WARPITUDE*—a self-defining portmanteau word, surely original with Mr. Algren, that could well be adopted into the English language. ¶We will end here, trusting that the bowling terms used later in the story by Mr. Algren are clear.*

from

The Man with the Golden Arm

by NELSON ALGREN

FRANKIE could never acknowledge that he squinted a bit. "If anythin' was wrong with my peepers the army wouldn't of took me," he argued. "The hand is quicker than the eye—'n I got a very naked eye." Yet he sometimes failed to see a thing directly beneath that same very naked eye. "Where's the bag?" he would ask. "Under your nose, Dealer," someone would point out. "Well, there's suppose to be six bucks in it," he'd explain as if that, somehow, were why he hadn't seen it right away.

He squinted a bit now, in the cell's dim light, with the ever-present deck in his hand. "I can control twenty-one cards," he boasted to Sparrow. "If you don't believe me put your money where your mouth is. I'll deal six hands 'n call every one in the dark. Name your hand. You want three kings? Okay, here we go, you get what you ask for. But watch out, punk—that hand beside you is flushin' 'n that bird with nothin' but an ace showin' is gonna cop with three concealed bullets." And that's how it would be whether he was showing off in a cell or in the back booth of Antek Witwicki's tug and Maul Bar.

"I give a man a square shake till he tries a fast one or talks back to me," he warned the punk. To hear him tell it Frankie Machine was pretty mean. "When I go after a wise guy I don't care who he is, how much he's holdin'—when you see me start pitchin' 'em in, then you know the wise guy is gettin' boxed." Sparrow nodded. He was the only hustler on Division Street who still believed there was anything tough about Frankie Machine. The times he had seen Frankie back down just didn't count for Sparrow.

"What you got to realize in dealin' Stud is that it's just like drill in the army—'n the dealer's the drill sergeant. Everybody got to be in step 'n stay on their toes 'n there can't be no back talk or you got no harmony left—I'm good with a cue because that's in the wrist too. Used to get fifteen fish for an exhibition of six-no-count. No, they never put my picture on the wall but I lived off the stick three months all the same when the heat was on 'n that's more 'n a lot of hustlers can say."

It was more than Frankie could say too. He would have starved in those three months if it hadn't been for Sophie's pay checks. And although Sparrow was seldom allowed to forget, for long, what a mean job that of an army drill sergeant was, Frankie's report was still hearsay; he'd put in thirty-six months without so much as earning a pfc's stripe. Somehow the army had never quite realized what a machine he was with a deck.

(There were those who still thought he was called Machine because his name was Majcinek. But the real sports, the all-night boys, had called him Automatic Majcinek for years; till Louie Fomorowski had shortened that handle for him. Now, whether in the dealer's slot, at the polls or on a police blotter, he was simply Frankie Machine.)

The bottom card squeaked as he dealt to Sparrow on the gray cell floor, and it irritated him that he couldn't get a second off the bottom without hitting the card above. Though he never had sufficient nerve to deal from the bottom while in the dealer's slot he liked to feel he had the knack as a symbol of his skill.

For he had the touch, and a golden arm. "Hold me up, Arm," he would plead, trying for a fifth pass with the first four still riding, kiss his rosary once for help with the faders sweating it out and zing—there it was, Little Joe or Phoebe, Big Dick or Eighter from Decatur, double trey the hard way and dice be nice—when you get a hunch bet a bunch—bet a dollar and then holler—make me five to keep me alive—it don't mean a thing if it don't cross that string—tell 'em where you got it and how easy it was.

When it grew too dark to read the spots on the cards Frankie pulled a tattered and wadded scratch sheet off his lap. "Took me ten years to learn this little honey—watch the lunch hooks now." Sparrow watched the long, sure fingers begin to weave swiftly and delicately. "Fifty operations in less than a minute," Frankie boasted—and there it was, a regular Sinatra jazzbow with collar attached out of nothing but yesterday's scratch sheet. "If it was just silk you could put it on now," Sparrow said with awe. "Why couldn't you just turn 'em out all day, Dealer? Everybody in the patch'd buy one—there's a fortune in it."

"I ain't no businessman," Frankie explained, "I'm a hustler—now give me five odd numbers between one'n ten that add up to thirty-two."

Sparrow pretended to figure very hard, tracing meaningless numerals with his forefinger in the cell's grayish dust until it was time for Frankie to show him how. Somehow Sparrow never seemed certain which were the odd and which the even numbers. "Mat'matics is on my offbalanced side," he allowed. "I make them dirty offslips."

Yet he was as accurate as an adding machine in anticipating combinations in any alley crap game; he distinguished clearly between odd and even then—sometimes before they turned up. "Playin' the field is one thing, solvin' riddles is another," it seemed to Sparrow, and he saw nothing unusual in the distinction. "It's what they couldn't figure in the draft, neither," he recalled. "I was either too smart or too goofy but they couldn't tell which. It was why I had to get rejected for moral warpitude."

Frankie was making a vertical row of three ones and a parallel row of two ones. Adding the first row, he got a total of three and, adding the second, a total of two; by the proximity of the two totals he had a total of thirty-two.

"There's somethin' wrong somewheres, Frankie," Sparrow complained, sounding distressed. "You got my big eyes rollin' the lights goin' on in my head—but if I just knew some good old long division I could put the finger on what's wrong."

"Nothin' wrong at all, Sparrow. Strictly on the legit—just the new way of doin' things we have these days. Like the new way of makin' ten extra bucks for you out of every hundred you got in the bank. This I wouldn't show to nobody only you. Only me'n the bankers know this one 'n they're sweatin' it out that the people'll find out 'n have 'em all broke in a week. Swear you won't tell?

"Saint take me away if I tell."

"No good. Swear a Hebe one."

"I don't know no Hebe one, Dealer."

No oath was necessary. He would have died before betraying the smallest of Frankie's professional secrets. "Of course," Frankie warned him now, "in order to get away with this one you got to give up your interest—you willin' to give up your interest?"

The question worried Sparrow. "Is it a Hebe bank 'r a Polak one, Frankie?"

"What's the diff?"

"If it's a Hebe one maybe I got a uncle workin' there, he'll just sneak me a fistful when the president ain't peekin'."

"You got no uncle in this one," Frankie decided firmly. "In fact you got no uncle nowheres. You ain't even got a mother."

"Maybe I got somebody in the old country, Frankie." Hopefully.

"There ain't none left in the old country so quit stallin'—you gonna take a chance or not? You can't make this tenner 'n keep your interest too."

"Okay, Frankie, I'll chance it."

"It's just this simple, buddy-O." He began tearing tiny squares off the hand-fabricated jazz bow, each square representing ten dollars, until he was ready to make a hypothetical deposit of ten squares—thus with an account of one hundred dollars he pretended to withdraw that amount, then replaced it beginning with the last square he had withdrawn, in the old burlesque routine, so that by the time he had replaced the hundred he still retained one square in his hand. "And there's your daily-double money 'n you still got your hundred in the bank," he announced triumphantly. "You can do it all day, they can't stop you as long as the sign outside says the bank is open for business. It's on the legit so they got to let you—that's the new way of doin' things we got these days."

Sparrow removed his glasses, blew on them, put them back on and goggled dizzily, first at Frankie and then down at the make-believe money. It was hard to tell, when the punk goggled like that, whether he really didn't understand or was just putting on the goof act to please Frankie. "Somethin' wrong again," he complained, seemingly unable to put a finger on the trouble at all. Before he had time to gather his shocked wits Frankie had another sure-fire miracle working for him.

"Here's how you always pick up a couple bucks in a bowlin' alley, Solly. You're bowlin' 'n you get a perfect split railroad—the seven 'n the ten pins. A guy offers you twenty to one you can't pick it up. 'I never seen it done my whole life,' he'll tell you, 'Wilman couldn't pick it up.' He'll even show you a record book where it says it ain't been done in years. You tell him, 'Put up 'r shut up.' So he puts up a double saw 'n you just stroll down the alley 'n pick 'em up with the lunch hooks. That's all. Strictly on the legit."

"Is that in a Hebe bowlin' alley 'r a Polak one?"

"I done it on a guy on Milwaukee so I guess it's a Polak one."

Sparrow could see through that one right there. "That's out. I'd get my little head cracked for sure. Then I'd be offbalanced on bot' sides."

"That'd even you up then. You'd be just right."

For no seeming reason Sparrow suddenly pointed an accusing finger at Frankie. "Who's the ugliest man in this jail?" he demanded to know and answered himself just as suddenly. "Me."

Then sat down to brood upon that reply as though it had been offered by another. "What do I care how I look anyhow?" he assuaged the insult he had so abruptly dealt himself. "What counts is I know how to get along with people."

"If you could get along with anybody you wouldn't be in trouble up to your ears all the time," Frankie reminded him gently. "You wouldn't be one conviction away from Mr. Schnackenberg's habitual act."

"I'm t'ree convictions away from Mr. Schnackenberg," the punk assured Frankie, "so long as I don't catch no two alike." Then confessed his off balanced state with a certain plaintive moodiness: "I can get in more trouble in two days of not tryin' than most people can get into in a lifetime of tryin' real hard—why is that, Frankie?"

"I don't know," Frankie sympathized, "it's just that some cats swing like that, I guess."

Whatever Frankie meant by that, Sparrow skipped it to supply his own explanation. "It's 'cause I really like trouble, Frankie, that's my trouble. If it wasn't for trouble I'd be dead of the dirty monotony around this crummy neighborhood. When you're as ugly as I am you got to keep things movin' so's people don't get the time to make fun of you. That's how you keep from feelin' bad."

Yet he poked more fun at his own peaked and eager image, the double-lensed glasses and the pipestem neck, the anxious, chinless face, than did all others together. He was too quick to take the sting out of others' jibes by putting them on his own tongue first—his anticipation of insult was usually unfounded, the others had not been thinking of Sparrow's ugliness at all. Others were long used to him, he alone could not get used to himself. All he could do was to smile his shrewd, demented little grin and just be glad he was Solly Saltskin instead of Blind Pig or Drunkie John.

Sitting tailor-fashion on the cement floor, he blinked up at the whitewashed walls as they were lit by the first half glow of the nightlights along the tier; blew the jailhouse dust off his glasses and brought his cap around till the peak was over his eyes to express his feeling that he wouldn't be going anywhere before morning.

"I'll bet you don't have a cap on." Frankie was off again on his endless challenging of the punk; Sparrow fumbled a moment to be certain that he had, yet declined the challenge. "I'll bet you don't have shoes on, I'll bet you aren't smoking a cigarette. I'll bet I can get on a streetcar without a transfer, say nothin' to the conductor, pay him nothin' 'n walk right on in. I can't tell you the answer to all those, I don't want to expose myself."

"I won't expose you 'n don't you expose me," Sparrow offered, standing up to shake hands on that equivocal pact. And having shaken, began diverting himself by swinging, hand over hand, from the great beam directly overhead. "Look at me!" he demanded. "The Tarzan of the City!"

Frankie hauled him down by his spindling shanks.

"It's just the new way of walkin'," Sparrow explained, "we got all kinds of new ways to do things since you come back, Frankie."

"They'll get you in trouble the same as the old ways," Frankie assured the punk glumly.

¶*Stephen Leacock enjoyed his* Bridge *or* Poker *game as much as the next man, and occasionally said so in print, but apparently he did* not *like to be shown card tricks.*

The Card Trick

by STEPHEN LEACOCK

In which is shown how the drawing-room juggler may be permanently cured of his card trick.

The drawing-room juggler, having slyly got hold of the pack of cards at the end of the game of Whist, says:

"Ever see any card tricks? Here's rather a good one; pick a card."

"Thank you, I don't want a card."

"No, but just pick one, any one you like, and I'll tell which one you pick."

"You'll tell who?"

"No, no; I mean, I'll know which it is, don't you see? Go on now, pick a card."

"Any one I like?"

"Yes."

"Any color at all?"

"Yes, yes."

"Any suit?"

"Oh, yes; do go on."

"Well, let me see, I'll—pick—the—ace of spades."

"Great Caesar! I mean you are to pull a card out of the pack."

"Oh, to pull it out of the pack! Now I understand. Hand me the pack. All right—I've got it."

"Have you picked one?"

"Yes, it's the three of hearts. Did you know it?"

"Hang it! Don't tell me like that. You spoil the thing. Here, try again. Pick a card."

"All right, I've got it."

"Put it back in the pack. Thanks. (Shuffle, shuffle, shuffle—flip)—There, is that it?" (triumphantly).

"I don't know. I lost sight of it."

"Lost sight of it! Confound it, you have to look at it and see what it is."

"Oh, you want me to look at the front of it!"

"Why, of course! Now then, pick a card."

"All right. I've picked it. Go ahead." (Shuffle, shuffle, shuffle—flip.)

"Say, confound you, did you put that card back in the pack?"

"Why, no. I kept it."

"Holy Moses! Listen. Pick—a—card—just one—look at it—see what it is—then put it back—do you understand?"

"Oh, perfectly. Only I don't see how you are ever going to do it. You must be awfully clever."

(Shuffle, shuffle, shuffle—flip.)

"There you are; that's your card, now, isn't it?" (This is the supreme moment.)

"NO. THAT IS NOT MY CARD."

(This is a flat lie, but Heaven will pardon you for it.)

"Not that card! ! ! ! Say—just hold on a second. Here, now, watch what you're at this time. I can do this cursed thing, mind you, every time. I've done it on father, on mother, and on every one that's ever come round our place. Pick a card. (Shuffle, shuffle, shuffle—flip, bang.) There, that's your card."

"NO. I AM SORRY. THAT IS NOT MY CARD. But won't you try it again? Please do. Perhaps you are a little excited—I'm afraid I was rather stupid. Won't you go and sit quietly by yourself on the back veranda for half an hour and then try? You have to go home? Oh, I'm so sorry. It must be such an awfully clever little trick. Good night!"

How to Plan, How to Build Card Houses

by GEOFFREY MOTT-SMITH

BREATHES there a man with soul so dead that no child waits his avuncular tread, herald of frolics afloor; who never a palace of cards has made, nor ever a castle in Spain essayed, with turrets and towers galore? If such there breathe, go, mark him well, the world his shameful secret tell, an outcast forever more.

Thus would have spoken the bard, had it been his misfortune to meet such a misbegotten wight.

Yet, his strictures are perhaps too harsh. Accident of circumstance may have deprived the benighted soul, in his own childhood, of contact with the unwritten lore of card architecture. For unwritten it is: search the pages of the Hoyles, the encyclopedias, the juvenilia, and nowhere do you find recorded the classic equations developed in this recondite branch of engineering.

Games Digest rushes to the breach. Here, for the first time [1938] in history (so far as our researches reveal), is set down the fundamental facts as to *the engineering and architecture of card houses.*

THE CONSTRUCTION GANG

COMMENCING with first essentials, we have the boss of the construction gang. He had better be an adult with a steady hand. The gang itself must include one or more persons of age seven to fourteen, of either sex. The larger the gang, the better, up to the point where discipline as to the apportionment of duties can no longer be maintained.

The several members of the construction corps may well specialize in various phases of construction: One may deal in *beams,* another in *risers,* another in *ceilings,* and little Phoebe, aged five, may be appeased as *passer of materials* to the masons. Arches and gables had better be handled by the boss.

THE CARPET

MUCH of the success of the construction depends upon a suitable choice of substructure. Of course the houses should be built on the floor, never on a table or other raised structure if juveniles are present. Bare floor is almost never suitable; best is a rough-surfaced carpet. By that we mean a carpet with a good plane surface, such as linoleum or straw, but with the surface worn or roughened. Totally useless is a rug with a thick pile, or a lumpy rag carpet.

THE CARDS

AVOID *new* playing cards of any description. The suitability of cards increases with their age. They cannot be made into stable arches at all unless somewhat worn, and even the ceilings will slide if the lacquer is unbroken.

Avoid cards advertised as indestructible. The

truer the claim, the worse for our purpose. Use cheap paper cards, the cheaper the better.

Playing cards are made in two standard widths. The narrower are now more generally used in table games, but both styles can be used in making houses. If you have some cards of both sizes, use the narrower for arches and for risers, and use the wider as far as practicable for ceilings.

The number of decks required depends, of course, on how large a structure you plan to build. Scarcely anything can be done with less than two decks. Magnificent castles can be managed with four.

ARCHES AND GABLES

TURNING now to some of the fundamental units of construction, we note two basic types of arches. Each is made up of two cards, canted against each other like a tent. (See Figures 1 and 2.) What we shall call *the arch* stands on the shorter edges of the cards, so that the longer edges are vertical. *The gable* stands on the longer edges and thus does not reach so high as the arch.

Arches and gables cannot be superposed unless the edges of the cards are worn enough to offer some real friction. Single units of either type can be erected even with slippery cards, when reinforced by *beams*.

A *beam* is a card standing upright across the open side of an arch or gable and leaning against its two members. (See Figures 1 and 2.) If care is taken to see that the beam contacts both sides of the arch, the latter is greatly strengthened by it. Whenever practicable put a beam on each side of an arch.

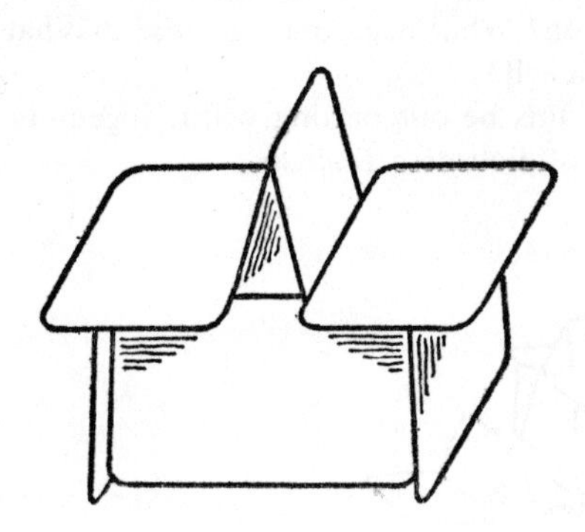

Figure 1. The pagoda

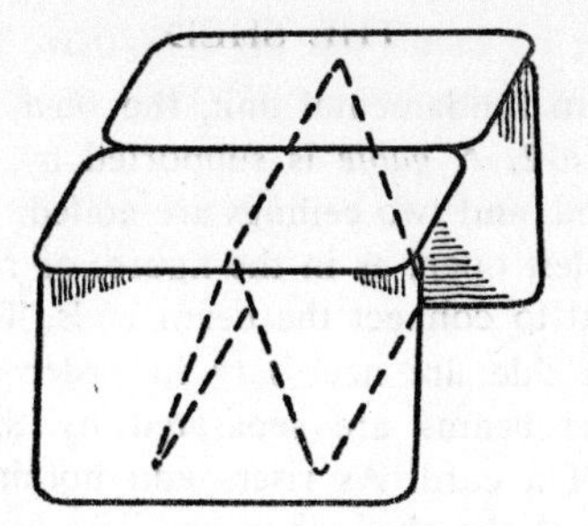

Figure 2. The shed

THE PAGODA

THE most stable of all complex structures is the *pagoda,* illustrated in Figure 1. It is consequently the unit most used to make a tall structure.

To make a pagoda, start with an *arch* and place *beams* on both sides of it. (The beams rest on their longer edges. We shall not in this article deal with beams placed the other way.) Then add two *risers,* resting across the beam-ends. The arch is thus enclosed in a rectangular box.

Now place two *ceilings* on the box like a lid, enclosing the peak of the arch between them. These ceilings should be slid onto the risers from the outside, until they fit snugly against the arch and so hold it from collapsing.

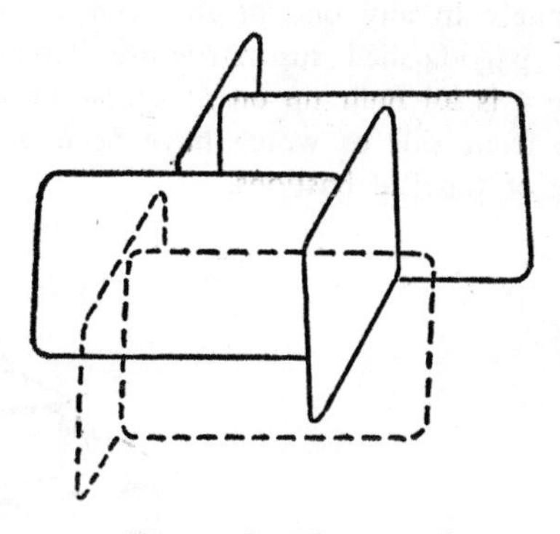

Figure 3. The corral

Remarkably tall structures can be compounded of pagodas alone. If two pagodas are built side by side, in either orientation, and if connecting ceilings are laid between them, this connection will support a third pagoda. By commencing with six or nine pagodas as a base, a pyramid can be built up to four or six stories. (In the days of our youth we once built an Aztec pyramid *eleven* stories high.)

This plan of construction is used in the rear of the castle shown in Figure 4. Three pagodas support two, and the two are surmounted by one.

THE SHED

A SECOND fundamental unit, the *shed,* is shown in Figure 2. A *gable* is supported by beams at either end, and two ceilings are added. The sides may be left open, as in the figure, or risers may be added to connect the beam ends. Two risers on each side are necessary in order to reach, since the beams are separated by the longer length of a card. As risers add nothing to the strength of the shed, they are best omitted unless they tie in with other structures at each end of the shed.

In Figure 4 a single shed is shown, standing on top of the corral base and in front of the pagodas.

THE CORRAL

IT IS sometimes desired to make a broad base, in support of a superstructure, and free of irregularities such as the peaks in pagoda construction. A series of sheds might seem to answer the purpose, but does not, for the reason that the ceiling cannot be made level.

An ideally simple plan for such a base is the *corral,* depicted in Figure 3. Commence with four risers, interlocked so as to support each other as shown by the solid lines. The dotted lines indicate how the corral can be extended indefinitely in any one of the four directions.

The pagoda-shed superstructure depicted in Figure 4 is all built up on an extensive corral, to the front side of which have been added a couple of fanciful bastions.

MINOR UNITS

THE THREE units described suffice for the compounding of very elaborate castles. There are at least two other units of general utility. The *chimney* is built around an arch, with beams and risers set on their shorter edges. The *bridge* is a series of two or more arches or gables set side by side and connected by ceilings.

STYLE

WE HAVE encountered some iconoclasts who deny the right of taste in the architectural styles of card castles. The *summum bonum* of a card house, they say, is to be as high as possible. The requirements of good taste must give way before the urgencies of engineering.

The elevated readers of *Games Digest* will scarcely be won to this depraved view. The card engineer who cannot dissociate Doric simplicity from Byzantine ornament had better turn to building post offices or some other pursuit within his impoverished talents.

Figure 4 was constructed not solely to illustrate the various units, but also to elucidate a common offense against propriety. The general plan of this castle is well conceived. The corral fits harmoniously with the pyramid of pagodas. But the shed is a rank intruder. What is its function? What need does it satisfy? What story does it tell?

Let this be our parting word: ingenuity without fastidiousness is chaos.

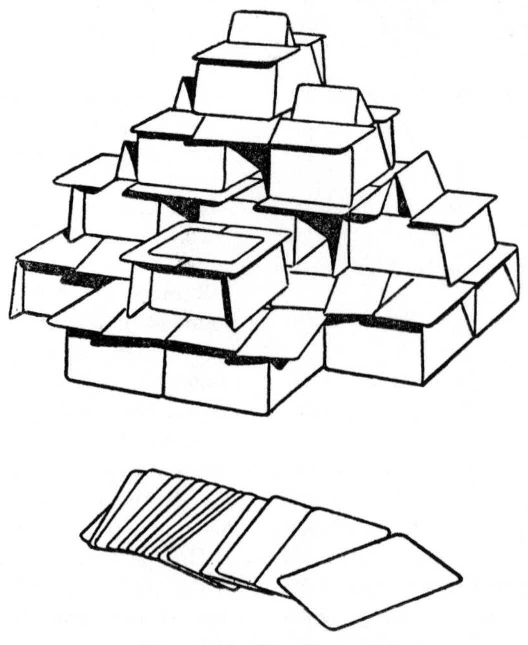

Figure 4. The Pyramid

Afterword

BY CHARLES H. GOREN

MOST *of my contacts with Howard Dietz have been somewhat indirect, mainly through some of his engaging lyrics. But we got a little closer when Helen Sobel did her book* All The Tricks. *Howard and I were each asked to do a Foreword, which we did in oriental style, at the conclusion of the book. His followed mine; but in* The Fireside Book of Cards *Jacoby and Morehead evidently considered it protocol to reverse the order, and we have every reason to anticipate that we will enjoy the relationship just as well and that the union will be blessed with all the success of our first effort.*

One of my earliest physical contacts with Dietz was more direct and took place at curfew time at the Stork Club in New York. My pinpointing of the time may be a little loose, but it was close enough to 4:00 A.M. *so that in all justice some curfew measure should have been invoked. My companion—an English army officer whose enthusiasm for things in general and bridge in particular had not been dampened by the rigorous campaign with General Montgomery in North Africa—suggested that Dietz and his bride entertain us for a rubber of bridge.*

The idea had much greater merit as a social venture than as a study in investments, and at daylight we walked up Broadway from Greenwich Village with our tails between our legs.

I am grateful to Jacoby and Morehead for teaming up and providing me with an opportunity to renew acquaintance with several old friends within the covers of their splendid book. Outstanding among them is Somerset Maugham, the most distinguished man of letters in our generation. Time can never erase the thrill I experienced in finding my name on the same jacket with Mr. Maugham's when he wrote the Foreword to my Standard Book of Bidding *in 1944. We celebrated the occasion with a dinner and bridge in his New York apartment, and though he was a most extravagant host, my unintentional contribution at the gaming table turned the venture into a profitable operation for him, as he won every rubber that night. It is significant too that this evening appears to have fashioned his subsequent design for living.*

As I turn the pages of this volume I come across another character who has meant much to me in a personal way—George S. Kaufman, who ranks as a Life Master among playwrights. He wrote the Foreword to my first important book, and a more encouraging toast has rarely been heard. It was in all sin-

cerity that I wrote to him: "George, I wish you had done the book and I had written the Foreword." George, of course, is an old hand at the bon mot. Though it was a score of years ago, it seems almost yesterday that he delivered this choice morsel: It was at the Regency Club, where George had dropped in as a rubber was in progress. At the point of entry the dealer bid one spade. It is recorded that Sam Fry overcalled with two diamonds, was doubled and set 800 points. The rubber continued laboriously, and at the end of another half hour the dealer again opened with one spade. Fry's overcall of two diamonds was greeted with a resounding double. George reached for his hat and bid goodbye to the players. "This," he announced firmly, "is where I came in."

It is tempting to browse through the Table of Contents for a visit with more of my old friends—and I am doing so on my own time—but right now I have a moment for only one more call, and it is gratifying to observe that special vitality has been injected into the book by inclusion of the delightful, durable Sidney Lenz, from whom I learned most of what I know about play.

Index

About the Editors

OSWALD JACOBY *has long been recognized as the most versatile and brilliant of card-players and writers on card games. He is on all lists of the all-time greats in Contract Bridge and Poker and is also the principal authority on Canasta and Gin Rummy. His books on Poker, Canasta, and Gin Rummy have been not only the largest-selling but also the standard classics in their fields. He writes a daily article on Bridge and other games, distributed by NEA Syndicate, which appears in hundreds of newspapers. By profession, however, Mr. Jacoby is an actuary (insurance mathematician). He lives in Dallas, Texas.*

ALBERT MOREHEAD *has been called "the modern Hoyle." He has written or edited more than sixty books on the rules and procedure of card games. He is Bridge editor of* The New York Times *and editor of* The Official Rules of Card Games. *Like Mr. Jacoby, Mr. Morehead is primarily in a profession unconnected with games. He is a lexicographer, or editor of dictionaries and encyclopedias. He is southern (Georgian) born but lives in New York City.*